SEVENTEENTH CENTURY TOKENS OF THE BRITISH ISLES

SEVENTEENTH CENTURY TOKENS
OF THE
BRITISH ISLES
AND THEIR VALUES

Michael Dickinson

Based on Williamson, with revisions, additions and valuations

SPINK
LONDON

TO ANGELA

For her forbearance, encouragement
and application to those household chores
which I would have had to share
were it not for writing this book

First published 1986
Reprinted 2004
Spink & Son Ltd
69 Southampton Row
Bloomsbury
London WC1B 4ET

Typeset by Deltatype, Ellesmere Port
Printed in Great Britain by
Cromwell Press
Trowbridge
Wiltshire

ISBN 0 900 652 780

Contents

Illustrations

Preface to the Reprint

Almost eighteen years have passed since the above Preface was written. For over half of that time this catalogue has been out of print, and recent sales of second-hand copies at amounts well in excess of £100 have emphasized the high level of interest in the series.

Philip Skingley of the Book Department at Spink indicated a willingness to address this situation, and I have thought long and hard about the pros and cons of whether to undertake a full or partial revision, or to sanction a straightforward reprint of the work.

I am currently busy with two large numismatic projects. One is my collaboration with Robert Thompson in the completion of the final parts of the catalogue of the Norweb Collection of tokens, to be published in the *Sylloge of Coins of the British Isles* series: these will cover the City of London, the County of Middlesex, uncertain pieces and forgeries. The other project, an individual effort, is the preparation for publication by Spink of *Token Coinage of the British Isles: a Concise Guide with Valuations* (the title not yet confirmed). This will be a revised, revamped and greatly extended version of the Seaby catalogue *British Tokens and their Values,* last published in 1984. The seventeenth-century section will comprise a listing of known major types issued by local authorities in towns and cities with a selection of traders' tokens from each county. The *British Tokens and their Values* feature of providing totals of issuers for every issuing locality in their respective counties will be retained and will incorporate up-to-date published information.

For a variety of reasons - my existing commitments, the fact that there are several dozen major new types of seventeenth-century tokens awaiting first publication in the forthcoming Norweb sylloges, and my feeling that, ultimately, a comprehensive new standard work on the series would be preferable - you, the reader, have a reprint rather than a new edition in your hands. This work will, however, remain current for the foreseeable future and, used in conjunction with occasional listings of examples for sale in Spink's own *Numismatic Circular* and my forthcoming *Token Coinage of the British Isles,* should provide a reasonably full picture of the series and current values.

Michael Dickinson
January 2004

Preface

This book is the first in nearly a hundred years to provide in one work a catalogue of the token coinage of the British Isles in the seventeenth century. Its purpose is twofold: to provide as full a listing as possible of these interesting coins, and to give a guide to their market value.

I have based the catalogue on the existing standard reference work on the series edited by George C. Williamson, *Trade Tokens Issued in the Seventeenth Century*, published between 1889 and 1891, itself a revision of William Boyne's similarly titled original of 1858.

Williamson's numbering system has been retained throughout, subsequently-discovered tokens being added into a suitable position within each section with a number followed by A, or B, etc. I suspect that there may be disappointment in some quarters that I have not taken the opportunity to renumber the series completely. After much consideration, however, I concluded that, because this book is a priced catalogue as much as a reference work, the least unsatisfactory option was to stick basically to Williamson's enumeration as it is for all areas still the most widely used.

I have tried to add all major new varieties and incorporate corrected descriptions that have appeared in numismatic and other publications and British coin auction catalogues in the last 95 years. I claim to have referred to all the *major* references on tokens for different areas of the British Isles which have been printed in that time, and many of the less important ones too. No doubt a few of these more recently published specimens have been missed, but I have also added a good number of entirely unpublished pieces of which London alone has close to 250. Williamson listed over 12,700 different examples; here the total reaches around 14,000, this figure excluding many minor varieties. Boyne's estimate (1858) that the entire issue of the time did not exceed 20,000 varieties still looks reasonable today.

Limitation of space has made impossible a rendering of the full reading of each token, let alone the inclusion of biographical and other details of the issuers; however, I trust that the references provided separately at the head of each county or section, in addition to the Bibliography, will easily lead those interested to further published information.

Some of Williamson's listed varieties have been omitted as research has since shown that they were either wrongly attributed, or do not exist, often because of misreadings. Some tokens appear more than once in Williamson, under different counties, and I have tried to eliminate the wrong or most doubtful attributions. One example that comes to mind is the halfpenny of Mary Earle of 'Rysley'. In Williamson it is claimed for Risley in both Derbyshire and Lancashire, but nearly 30 years ago strong evidence was put forward for it belonging to Riseley in Bedfordshire.

Valuations have been given not only for the commoner pieces but for rare ones too. Many seventeenth-century tokens – certainly a majority in the case of some areas – do not come on to the market from one generation to another. These and other extremely rare specimens have been left unpriced individually, although a minimum general value for them has been given at the beginning of each section. The prices are those that a collector can expect to pay from a knowledgeable dealer; they are a close guide to B. A. Seaby Ltd's selling prices at the time of going to press.

Apart from the valuation aspect, this work in many respects represents the completion of a project first begun by Peter Seaby with the late Monica Bussell, and published in B. A. Seaby Ltd's *Coin and Medal Bulletin* starting in July 1960. Unfortunately only three English counties, Buckinghamshire, Essex and Hertfordshire, plus the principality of Wales, were ever completed. About eight years ago, when Peter Seaby suggested that I might like to bring his original idea to fruition in book form, I accepted the challenge without much thought as to the great amount of work involved in producing something of a reasonable standard. I very much hope that you, the reader, will feel that my efforts have been worthwhile.

Finally, let me exhort any new student of the series to search out and publish new information, especially regarding issuers of tokens. There is much interesting material in parish registers, hearth tax returns, wills, and other local archives waiting to be uncovered.

Acknowledgements

My special thanks are due to John Wetton, who generously lent me his own extensive listings of unpublished London and Southwark pieces, and several scarce books and pamphlets not in the libraries of B. A. Seaby Ltd or the British Numismatic Society. I am grateful to Eileen Judson for strongly criticizing my first attempt at the relative pricing of the tokens of Essex! This persuaded me to research more carefully the frequency of the appearance on the market of every county's tokens since about 1890.

I am indebted to many collectors and dealers who have helped to make the catalogue section more complete and less inaccurate. In particular Garry Atkins, Edward Baldwin, Nigel Clark, Ernest Danson, the late Harold Good, Philip Greenall, Bob Lyall, Peter Mitchell, the late V. J. Newbury, Peter Preston-Morley, Brian Reeds, Fr. Gerard Rice, John Rose, C. M. Rowe, Robert Sharman, Jock Shaw, Roger Shuttlewood, Derek Smith, the late Bill Townsend, E. A. Watkin, Vincent West, Derek White, J. Wilton and David Young, among several others, have taken much time and trouble to furnish me with details of some unpublished tokens, or other snippets of information. Messrs Shuttlewood and Clark also kindly lent me some of their own tokens for illustration in the plates and on the jacket.

This book has also benefited from the study of copies of 'Williamson' annotated by well-known collectors of the past: William Gilbert, Ralph Nott, and Frank Macfadyen. I have to thank Peter Seaby for making this information available to me, along with his own notes made over many years; he also read through the introductory text and made some useful suggestions. I have been able to make use of other very useful material supplied to him some time ago by collectors other than those mentioned above, especially Dr T. Agnew, M. J. Harris, H. F. V. Johnstone, E. J. Laker, the Hon. R. Henry Norweb and Mrs E. M. Norweb, D. A. Pickrill and W. A. Seaby.

The illustrations of the Arms of the Livery Companies of London have been specially drawn by Jock Shaw. They are a near-complete record of those which appear on tokens; 54 different coat-of-arms are represented, with much greater accuracy than Boyne's original drawings, and several of them were not shown by Boyne.

About half of the tokens illustrated in the plates are in the Heberden Coin Room at the Ashmolean Museum, Oxford. I am extremely grateful to Nicholas Mayhew for allowing me to select specimens from the collection for illustration. Frank Purvey took the photographs of these tokens and those for the book jacket; his expertise in this field is widely known. Other illustrations are from various sources.

Finally, I record with pleasure the help I have received from Peter Clayton throughout the final stages of production of this work. For example, it was his idea for me to give a separate bibliography for each section. Without his attention to other important details and his considerable experience in numismatic publishing, the catalogue would have been much the poorer.

Michael Dickinson

'Tokens are essentially democratic; they were issued by the people, and it is of the people that they speak. They record, with few exceptions, the names of no monarchs; they speak of no wars or events of great Parliamentary importance; they were not issued by Governments or Cabinets, nor by Peers or Members of Parliament, but by the unknown and small traders of well-nigh every village and town in the country, and by officials . . . in boroughs, villages, and districts, as well as in larger towns, parishes, and hundreds.'

George C. Williamson (1889)

Introduction

The historical background

The chief reason for the extensive issues of token-coinage in the seventeenth century was the chronic shortage of official coins in denominations small enough to facilitate the everyday transactions for which money was increasingly required. Their success was long-lasting: they were issued over a period of around a quarter of a century throughout England and Wales from about the time of Charles I's execution, and for a similar, nearly contemporary, time span in Ireland. That they were tolerated for such a time was due to the absence of any real will on the part of governments – both Republican and Royalist – to remedy the situation.

Although the first dozen years of their issue were those of the unsettled Commonwealth period of our history, the lack of long-term stable government was not the only reason for inaction by the authorities. There was also a continuing unwillingness to issue official coinage of intrinsic value in metals other than gold or silver. Today we are content to use a currency which is really only a token coinage, as the coins intrinsically are worth much less than their face value; but until the early nineteenth century coins were expected to have their full value in metal, and herein lay the problem.

In England and Wales the silver penny had formed the basis of coinage from the late eighth century onwards. With occasional lapses – notably around the middle of the sixteenth century – metallic standards were kept high, sterling silver (.925 fineness) being the norm. From Saxon times to the reign of Edward I the need for smaller denominations of coinage was, for the most part, met by the cutting up of pennies into halves or quarters (hence fourth thing, or farthing).

In 1279 a large issue of round halfpenny and farthing coins was begun by Edward I and, although the halfpenny continued to be struck in limited quantities right up to the time of the Commonwealth, the number in circulation was seldom sufficient. Mintage of the farthing was always small, at least judging from surviving specimens; after the middle of the fifteenth century very few were struck and none at all are known after the reign of Edward VI (1547–53).

The gradual rise in the price of silver, due to its increasing use for purposes other than coinage, and adherence to the traditional principle of coinage having virtually its full intrinsic value, compounded the problem. Alfred the Great's pennies of the late ninth century weigh 24 grains or 1 *penny*weight; in 1350 those of Edward III are just over 20 grains; by 1601, the coins are of under 8 grains (0.52 gram) each. Farthings of only 2 grains or so each would obviously be too tiny to be practical; those of the preceding reigns had anyway been inconveniently small and were easily lost. Some attempt was made in Elizabeth I's reign (1558–1603) to alleviate the situation by the issue of three-halfpence and three-farthing coins which, together with one halfpenny's or one farthing's worth of goods, respectively, could be given as change for twopence or a penny.

Of course, the solution to the problem was the coinage of denominations smaller than one penny on larger-sized flans and in base metal, and the first regally issued legal tender halfpennies and farthings appeared at last in 1672. We know now that the public began to accept base metal as currency four hundred years before this, however.

Despite the fact that among poorer folk coinage was little used or needed, unofficial money started to circulate as long ago as the thirteenth century. Continental imitations in base silver of English pennies, generally known as 'easterlings', were imported in increasing numbers. Many of the poorer quality and smaller coins doubtless saw service as halfpennies; all were officially recognized as such in 1299 for a few months until prohibited the following year. Jettons or reckoning-counters began to be used here about the same time for arithmetical purposes. English-manufactured in the main till the late fourteenth century, they were also imported on a big scale from France, the Low Countries and, from about 1550 to the early seventeenth century, from Nuremberg; it is very likely that many of them would have been accepted as small change from time to time.

Thus, while bartering for goods and services was commonplace, the need for low-value coinage grew steadily. Late in the fourteenth century Scotland began issuing debased silver coinage, much of which found its way into England; about the same time also, small *soldini* of Venice were being imported too. Both these types of coin were mentioned in a Commons petition to Henry IV in 1402 as being used by the populace through necessity.

As far as is known, English tokens *per se* first appeared in the thirteenth century. From that time until the period covered by this book they were made almost exclusively of lead or other lead-based alloys. The earliest pieces were issued by ecclesiastical sources, and would have had a small local circulation. From perhaps the middle of the fourteenth century onwards they were made for commerical purposes, especially in London, but unfortunately for us today those that survive give very few clues as to who issued them. Most of the medieval ones only have designs on them, though some have initials as well. Later examples occasionally have crude motifs, but often only initials; a few, mostly of the earlier seventeenth century, bear dates. Between about 1540 and 1560 prices generally doubled, and in doing so further increased the amount of 'leaden money' in circulation as farthings and halfpence. Even leather is believed to have been utilised. Many complaints were made that tradespeople were causing great losses to the poor by the use of tokens, which could only be exchanged for commodities from the issuers.

Important developments began to take place in Elizabeth's reign. An idea was put forward in 1574 for a coinage of halfpence and farthings in base silver, which were to weigh 12 and 6 grains respectively; later, pattern 'pledges' for a coinage in copper were struck, some dated 1601. These projects came to nothing because of the Queen's disapproval, but the city authorities in Bristol – then England's second most important city – had over 100,000 copper farthing tokens struck on square or nearly square blanks between about 1577 and 1583. Moreover, these were authorised by the Queen herself to circulate within the city and for ten miles around it and, as such, apart from sceats issued in Northumbria and York in the ninth century, are the earliest copper pieces to have been used with the assent of an English monarch. They are the true forerunners of the unauthorised seventeenth-century series (see Gloucestershire, nos. 21 to 22A).

At this point mention must be made briefly of the situation in other parts of these islands. Scotland had its own separate coinage until 1707, but its rulers did not have the same aversion to base metals as in England. Billon (base silver) issues featured throughout the fifteenth, sixteenth and early seventeenth century. The first regal copper coins were struck at Edinburgh about 1466, over 200 years in advance of England. Low-denomination copper coinage was issued in adequate quantities in the seventeenth century and this explains the total absence of trade tokens, with one uncertain exception, in the period covered by this book. Judging by the paucity of tokens in the far north of England, Scottish coppers were welcomed here too.

Ireland also had its own coinage, closely based on England's. Regal copper coins also first appeared here in the 1460s, farthings and half-farthings being struck, and Elizabeth I ordered copper pennies and halfpennies for Ireland in 1601–2, despite refusing a similar issue for England. Coinage for Ireland was generally spasmodic at best, even allowing for the extreme shortage of small denominations throughout much of the sixteenth century, and foreign silver and gold coins were in use to a considerable extent. The Isle of Man had to make do with English, Irish and other foreign coins, particularly Dutch ducatons (with forgeries of same) and their fractions. In the Channel Islands, adequate French money was in circulation.

James I (1603–25) was well aware of the advantages of copper coinage. As James VI of Scotland (from 1567) he had issued *turners* there in 1597. These were based on the French *double tournois*, many of which were used as farthings in the south of England in the early seventeenth century. In 1613 he granted to Lord Harington, a favourite of his, a patent for the coinage of copper farthings. This licence passed, after Harington's death, to others also well-connected; it was renewed by Charles I and continued until the issue of coins was suspended by Parliament in 1644, by which time nearly 100 million are believed to have been struck. These farthings were intended to circulate throughout England, Wales and Ireland in order to prevent permanently the use of private lead tokens. But they were greatly disliked by the public as they were of virtually no intrinsic value, which meant that vast profits were made from their issue by the Crown and patentees; on their suppression Parliament passed a resolution that they should be redeemed from money raised on the patentees' estates.

Considerable efforts were made to foist these coins on the public, many of the issues being sold at a rate of 21 shillings' worth of farthings for 20 shillings of silver, and this led to the practice of some employers buying large quantities and paying their workpeople only in these farthings, although this abuse was later curtailed. While the last types of Charles I, the 'rose' farthings, average about 13 grains in weight, most of the earlier issues were of only 9 grains or so; the original Harington pieces of James I did not exceed about 7½ grains each and occasionally weighed only 3 grains. (Compare these figures with the 90 grains average for the regal copper farthings of Charles II in the 1670s.) Counterfeiting became rife especially during the reign of Charles I because of the large profit to be made by so doing; in 1634 and afterwards this led to the frequent refusal by the patentees to accept their earlier coins back with the excuse that *all* were false – genuine pieces included. Although traders, and the poor in particular, lost money because of this, their final suppression was also a nuisance. More serious was the severe lack of silver coinage, due to hoarding in the Civil War (1642–9).

During the first half of the seventeenth century the aim of eradicating unofficial lead tokens was not fully achieved, and from 1644 they began appearing in quantity, especially in London. There exist a number of patterns for farthings in Charles I's reign. One of these, dated 1644, is of 22.5 mm diameter and shows that serious thought was being given to the prospect of a copper coinage of intrinsic value, though again no action was taken. The death by execution of Charles I in 1649 removed the exclusive royal prerogative of coining copper or brass money and, the dearth of small change being acute, the time was thus ripe for the large and widely spread issue of tokens which form the main body of this catalogue.

The Tokens

Physical composition

The great majority of the tokens were struck, in copper or brass, on round flans of rather thin metal. Very rarely they occur tin-coated. Some issues are found in both copper and brass, and occasionally (notably in

Worcestershire and Ireland) they were made on flans of one metal with a central plug of the other.

Lead or pewter was used on a small scale and a few of these pieces were cast in moulds, not struck. A very few tokens of London are known in leather; these are exceedingly rare today, for obvious reasons.

About half a dozen different token types are known in silver. These are all considered to be restrikes, i.e. made considerably later than the period of their circulation. They are mentioned in the catalogue at the appropriate places. Two or three have reportedly been struck in iron.

The period of issue

The earliest date is 1648: several different issues in and near London are known for this year. At this period the new year still began on March 25, i.e. March 24, 1648 was immediately followed by March 25, 1649. By this calendar Charles I was thus beheaded on January 30, 1648. Whether the first tokens of the series were struck before his death is not known, but it is more likely that they first appeared very soon afterwards. Following this, they spread from London to all counties in England and, starting about 1656, to all Welsh counties except Cardiganshire.

Tokens became gradually more plentiful in England and Wales with a final spurt in the peak years 1666–7, after which quantities struck declined with increasing rapidity. There had been a notable lull in the late 1650s and early 1660s, coinciding with the belief that first the Commonwealth Protectorate, then the Restoration Government, would issue official copper coins. The decline of the later 1660s was due to the prosecution of some issuers, and simply the growing realisation that official action was at last on the way. The royal pardon was sought and obtained by several local authorities for having issued tokens; pardons were also granted to shopkeepers in the London area.

In 1672 a proclamation was issued by the King making current the new regal farthings and halfpence and forbidding the use and issue of tokens (see Appendix). This was immediately very effective, but not quite fully so. In 1674 we know that tokens were still being used by some traders in Chester and Norwich, but the threat of legal proceedings was enough to stop them doing so. Another proclamation was issued with this in mind (see Appendix).

The story in Ireland was somewhat different. A war quite unlike that in England had been fought there throughout the 1640s and, tragic though the consequences were for Ireland, it is for the numismatist interesting because of the resultant emergency coinages, official and quasi-official. These included several local issues in copper not unlike tokens, but strictly outside the scope of this catalogue. Following the monarchy's suspension, the conquest of Ireland by Cromwell's Puritan army continued until complete in 1652. In the next year the country was declared part of the Protectorate, and the granting of free trade with England and Wales brought hope of increasing prosperity to merchants. 1653 is the earliest date known for Irish tokens, although Kinsale corporation authorized an issue of £50-worth of (undated) farthings in the previous year. Issuers are known from all counties except Mayo.

In 1660 the newly-restored Charles II granted to Sir Thomas Armstrong a monopoly patent to coin farthings for Ireland and in 1661 banned the circulation of tokens there by proclamation. The resulting coinage was similar to the royal tokens of Charles I but considerably heavier; nevertheless it was opposed by the Irish authorities and not struck in great quantity. Token issues, which had virtually ceased after 1660 – as far as can be ascertained from the rarity of dated specimens – recommenced in 1663 on a big scale, until another proclamation in 1673 forbade their circulation. However, unlike England and Wales, there was no new regal coinage to take their place. Despite the issue of the larger-sized 'St. Patrick' halfpence and farthings at about this time – apparently a semi-official coinage – the shortage of small change resulted in a final period of tokens from about 1675 to 1679. At this time also, older tokens were counterstruck to make them pass at lower values. From 1680 a proper regal coinage of halfpennies in adequate quantity was put into circulation and no more tokens were issued.

In the Isle of Man penny tokens were issued by John Murrey in 1668. Irish tokens of Mic Wilson of Dublin, known as 'butchers' halfpence', and the slightly later 'St. Patrick' coins were circulating freely in Man by the late 1670s. Tynwald, the Manx parliament, enacted that none of these Irish pieces should pass as currency after the end of 1679, but at the same time decreed that the King's (English) farthings and halfpence and Murrey's pence could still be used. This is a unique case of legalisation of a token at this time in the British Isles. It is believed that Murrey, or a descendant, redeemed most of his tokens after the issue of an official Manx coinage in 1709.

Denominations

The first dated halfpenny that exists is for 1656; previous to this, all tokens are believed to have been farthings. For some time the halfpenny was the more unusual denomination but after about 1664 it is commoner than the farthing. The increasing call by traders for halfpenny tokens was not because of rising prices but due to the absence in circulation of the official silver halfpenny (the Commonwealth coinage was demonetized late in 1661) and the greater profit from the issue thereof to both manufacturer and trader alike. Notwithstanding this, a preference for farthings remained strong in many areas, e.g. Norfolk.

Pennies apparently first appeared in 1663, with a Welsh issue. They were the usual denomination in North Wales, common among Cheshire issuers, and occasional in Shropshire, Lancashire and Yorkshire and in London where they were mainly used by coffee-house owners. Elsewhere they were largely unknown, however, and are easily the least common value, apart from a few extremely rare higher-value denominations in London and Southwark.

The foregoing paragraphs apply to England and Wales; for Ireland the picture is again different. Here the usual denomination was the penny right from the start, but in size the tokens were comparable in many cases only to the smallest English farthings. Where halfpence and farthings were issued, they were, oddly, larger on average than pennies, certainly to begin with.

Sizes, shapes, and weights

Farthings vary in diameter from approximately 14 mm to 22 mm with only a handful of exceptions. Most of the municipal farthings are in the 20 to 22 mm range and state their denomination; private traders' tokens are usually 14 to 16 mm and only rarely actually mention their face value.

Halfpennies are the most consistent in size, very seldom being less than 17 mm or more than 20 mm. It is not always clear whether tokens that are silent about their value in this size range are halfpence or farthings, but it is unusual for the denomination *not* to be present on halfpennies. Sometimes it is expressed as II or 'double token', or *ob* – short for *obolus*, an old form for half a penny.

Pennies show the greatest variety in size, being anything from 14 mm to over 25 mm; even tokens from the same locality differ considerably in diameter.

For the first twenty years or so all issues were struck on round flans, but in or just before 1668, no doubt partly as a gimmick to shore up a business which was just past its peak, manufacturers introduced the option of three new shapes for the flans of halfpenny and penny tokens. In order of frequency of occurrence, they were octagonal, heart-shape, and square, the latter of which could become 'diamond-shaped' if the design and legend were suitably positioned. The heart-, square-, and diamond-shaped pieces are particularly popular with collectors and, being mostly very rare, command high prices today.

Each issue of tokens was made roughly to the same standard size but not, it is believed, to any specific weight. Flans used could vary considerably in thickness. Suffice it to say that the lightest pieces are of about 6 grains, the heaviest being occasionally over 50 grains; among these latter are the late Irish tokens.

The issuers

Originally the tokens were struck for traders, shopkeepers and, in particular, innkeepers and alehouses, and the large majority emanated from these sources. Their issue by local authorities of the day accorded them considerably more respectability, and some of these municipal tokens are the commonest in the whole series, having been minted in the greatest numbers. Some of the gentry also had them made, and it is not impossible that they were included in the wages of workers on estates.

A great variety of trades, professions and occupations is indicated on the tokens, either in words or by the designs used or, most frequently, by the representation of the arms of one of the local trade guilds or London Livery Companies, then at about the height of their influence. Drawings of these coats-of-arms will be found as Figures 1–3. The businesses of grocers and mercers occasioned most of the need for tokens, with bakers, drapers, tallowchandlers and ironmongers also prominent.

Among the most unusual and interesting occupations noted on specimens are those of clockmaker, coachman, limeman, postmaster, rat killer, rector, ropemaker, spectacle-maker, and tollman. A glance through the pages of the catalogue will reveal many other activities, some now long since gone from our highly technological age. The predominance of certain occupations in parts of the country will be noticed, e.g. lace in Buckinghamshire, apothecaries in Nottingham, bay-making in Colchester, weavers in Kidderminster and watermen on the river Thames. Among businesses new in the seventeenth century were those of the tobacconist and pipe-maker. The first coffee-house opened in Oxford in 1650 and soon after this they became fashionable in London, several dozen of them issuing tokens. The occupation of tollman also began during this period – in 1663, with the passing of the first Turnpike Road Bill by parliament.

The trader's description of himself (or herself: a small but significant number of tokens were issued by the fairer sex, mostly widows) could well have been less than the whole story. In country districts, a 'grocer' would have offered many more types of food than the sugar, spices and preserves the term strictly indicated in those days, especially in the equivalent of today's village store; tobacco could well have been retailed. Similarly, while a 'mercer' in a city dealt in silk and other costly fabrics, the same term in a country village might also embrace the trades of a draper, haberdasher and even grocer and tobacconist under one roof. A tallowchandler's stock was chiefly in candles, oil, soap, etc. but small domestic goods would be sold as well. Apothecaries – today's chemists or druggists – acted as local doctors for minor ailments.

A whole family was often involved in a trade or business and the home would be over the shop. From time to time two traders jointly issued tokens; a few issuers had businesses in more than one place. More trade was carried on out-of-doors than today and the issue of a token did not necessarily mean that the trader had fixed premises. An average shopkeeper's income has been estimated at about £45 per annum; a labourer might earn only a third of this. A clergyman would probably be at least as well off as a shopkeeper, while an important merchant could well earn in excess of £200 a year.

As mentioned earlier, innkeepers, tavern landlords and alehouse owners were commonly token-issuers. At the time inns were frequently the main centres of trade. Apart from providing food and drink and temporary accommodation for travellers, the bigger houses, a few of which were staging posts in the developing coaching era, might also have had shops for related businesses and living quarters either adjoining or within the main building. This explains why a large number of shopkeepers' tokens show an inn-sign as their device.

Of the local authorities which issued coin-substitutes, the city of Bristol was first, following its own earlier example in the 1570s. Starting about 1651, they were struck at various times throughout the next twenty years. Their lead was followed eventually by over 90 towns and cities in England, one in Wales and 12 in Ireland. For some places the issues are quite well documented. Interesting and unusual official titles are to be seen on tokens. Apart from Corporation and Mayor, one finds Overseer of the poor, Bailiff, Chamberlain, Churchwarden, Constable, Feoffee, Portreeve, Seneschal and Sword Bearer. Many of the municipal issues have a legend to the effect that they are for the benefit of poor people, of whom there were many, especially in the aftermath of the Civil War.

Makers and manufacture

Only one man has so far been identified as a producer of tokens: David Ramage, who was an engraver of dies employed at the Tower Mint in London. He is known for a number of patterns for official Commonwealth coinage and commemorative medals. A very large number, if not the majority, of seventeenth-century token dies up to 1662 (the year of his death) were made up from letter punches and designs engraved by him. His initial R is witness to this occasionally on traders' pieces, especially on the city issues of Bristol, Oxford and Gloucester, and also the Irish 'Armstrong' coinage of 1660 referred to earlier. Interestingly, the iron dies for these were all apparently made at the Tower, suggesting tacit official approval of Ramage's activities.

In State Papers it is recorded that on 14 March 1649 (=50), he and three other moneyers in the Mint seized tools belonging to one Reeves of White Cross Street, used 'in making copper farthings unlicenced, which if made at all, should be done in the Tower'. He was also referred to in a tract of 1660, quoted by Peck, as

> one Rammage farthing-maker in the Tower, whose aime in all this business is, to suppress all tools for making farthings but his own; the

> said Rammage having proffered a large weekly sum to be paid to one party, if all the presses for making farthings may be but taken away about London but only his, so that he may have the sole trade in his hands.

Apart from Ramage, then, we do not know *who* was responsible for tokens, but similar style and the use of identical punches on many later pieces suggest that a fairly small number of engravers was involved throughout the period. It seems likely that over 90% of dies were sunk in London and the initial issue of tokens struck there too, certainly in the case of English and Welsh tokens. While some Irish pieces are recognisably the work of London die-sinkers, many others, including probably all the post-1672 issues, are of local origin. Tokens of this latter group are also of interest in that they were usually struck in collars with grained or ornamented edges; two even have inscribed edges on which, unfortunately, less than a handful of letters can seldom be read.

Preserved at the Ashmolean Museum, Oxford, are a pair of dies for the halfpenny token of Samuel Bacon of Kineton, Warwickshire, and a pair for the Corporation halfpenny of Henley-on-Thames. The City of Gloucester Museum has the obverse die for Mayor Thomas Price's farthing. A description of a coining-press for making the tokens of Edward Wood of Chesterfield, Derbyshire, was given by Dr Samuel Pegge in the Gentleman's Magazine of November 1757 (see Appendix): that this simple type of mill and screw press was used for nearly the whole series is interesting, particularly as the system was not finally adopted for regal coinage until 1662. This evidence apart, there is apparently no contemporary record of how they were made.

Metal for the tokens was nearly always provided in the form of ready-made, individual blanks. Sometimes one comes across a token struck on another; whether this happened by accident or design is often unclear. In Ireland, several types (? all from the North) are known overstruck on other *coins*, especially French *doubles tournois*. Brockages, i.e. pieces with one side being an incuse mirror image of the other, are also found. This kind of mis-striking occurs when a coin, newly struck, either sticks to one of the dies or by mistake is not removed from it; a virgin blank then inserted is struck by a die on one side and by the remaining coin on the other.

As presumed earlier, the first striking of a token issue would be made in London as a rule. However, the Chesterfield press mentioned above was found in the house of the issuer's grandson; and there is no reason to doubt that most serviceable dies were given or sold to the issuers for possible future use. The dies themselves were roughly square and set in blocks for striking. It follows that although the dies could be positioned with aligned edges, obverses could be in up to four different positions relative to the reverse. Many seventeenth-century tokens occur with more than one die axis position, some with all four possibilities, indicating separate periods of manufacture.

A few facts and figures may be of interest here. It has been estimated that a pair of dies could produce up to 15,000 examples in the case of the Bristol tokens of 1652 and 1662, £300- and £500-worth of which, respectively, are believed to have been put into circulation. The town of Poole, Dorset, in 1667 obtained £19 4s. worth of farthings (i.e. 18,432 tokens) for £10; fifteen years previously, the city of Oxford spent £20 and was supplied with about 100,000 tokens. These statistics, and the quantities of these and other tokens surviving, lead one to an educated guess that for many private tradesmen £1-worth of face value, or even less, would be sufficient.

The manufacturers doubtless had agents, travelling widely up and down the country, who perhaps showed examples of work already completed and took orders, advising issuers and establishing what their tokens should show and say. Contact would probably have been kept with issuers by the agents, hoping for repeat business. The occurrence of the same date on all or most of the tokens of one area suggests busy activity here by these itinerant salesmen.

Design, style and legends

The basic type of seventeeth century token has an inscription or legend each side surrounding either a central device, a group of initials, or further inscription. Legends are often continued from the obverse to the reverse. The central part, or field, is usually separated from the outer legend by a dotted, lined or cable-patterned border. From the early 1660s there is more variety, e.g. with script lettering instead of capitals, and one or both sides being filled entirely with a design or a legend. Private traders' halfpennies were usually larger than farthings, and this presented increased scope for a longer, more interesting, perhaps humorous, legend. Most of the notable phrases are recorded in the catalogue listings. The greater space was sometimes used for more attractive designs, often with charming results. All of this gives us an insight into the everyday life of the period.

Tokens nearly always bear the name of their issuers, whether traders or local authorities. If the name of a tavern or inn was spelt out on the token it often left room only for the initials of the issuer, as was frequently the case in London. The place-name of issue is very seldom absent. In central London precise information is the rule in the form of street-names, etc.; sometimes these details are seen on issues in provincial cities and towns.

The face value of the token is typically in the centre of one side, and for the halfpenny is in three lines, e.g. HIS/HALFE/PENY. As mentioned before, farthings are commonly not denominated. A central position is also favourite for the issuer's initials, when (usually) shown. Often these are in the form of a triangle, with the first letter of the surname placed above two letters alongside each other: the husband's usually on the left, the wife's on the right. This was a custom of the time; and is occasionally still seen on old buildings today. Not infrequently initials occur in wrong positions on some dies. In some parts of the country the fashion was not to mention wives, so a man's initials alone do not necessarily signify bachelorhood. More often than not, a date is given.

The most fascinating aspect of the inscriptions on these pieces is the wonderful variety of their spelling. The town of Peterborough, Northamptonshire, for example, is spelt in thirteen different ways, most of them phonetically quite reasonable! It would perhaps not be fair to say that twelve of these were *wrong*, as with no set standard, several different renderings of the same word seem to have been acceptable in those days. Even the spelling of an issuer's name was sometimes varied on a die made at a later period. All this, however, was of little concern to a populace of whom most were semi-literate at best. Although the catalogue lists do not give complete readings of token legends, the information provided will show the reader plenty of examples of the variety of spelling ideas of the time. It is important to remember that, with capital letters, an I was always used for J, a V always for U; thus each of these letters could be used as a vowel or a consonant.

Throughout the listings will be found also some examples of contemporary humour. Rhyming inscriptions were popular, with minor classics like 'Although but brass yet let me pass', 'Take these that will, I'll change them still', 'Welcome you be to trade with me', 'When you please, I'll change these', and on a square token, 'Square dealing is best'. Punning devices were sometimes used to illustrate an issuer's or town's name. The surnames Bull, Cox, Finch, Hancock, Harbottle (a hare and a bottle), Horne and Lambe among others were all given suitable treatment; the Chertsey town piece has a church, the Taunton one a letter T and tun, and of course the Mayor of Oxford's token shows an ox crossing a ford. Some punning ideas are not perhaps so obvious today, one issuer Conny having *coneys* or rabbits as the device, for example. After the Restoration, the expression of royalist sentiments is frequently found.

Naturally, the chief design feature is usually the pictorial device. Most commonly met with are representations – often simplified and incomplete – of the arms of the local trading guilds, or Livery Companies of London. Those of the Grocers and Mercers appear most often, and the Bakers', Drapers', Tallowchandlers', and Ironmongers' arms are also very commonly represented. Illustrations of the various Company arms which appear on tokens can be found as Figures 1–3. Small sections of these arms also indicate a trade: a single dove could denote that the issuer was a chandler, three cloves would suggest a grocer, a goat's head a cordwainer. An object associated with the occupation or handicraft of issuers is often portrayed, e.g. scales, scissors or shears, a sword, a windmill, tobacco-pipes, a hat, a roll of cloth, two men carrying a barrel (for a brewer), a woolpack, a shuttle, a bible (for a bookseller or stationer), a sugar-loaf (for a grocer), a stocking or leg, a packhorse, the head of a Turk (for a coffee house or shop), and so on. An apothecary might indicate his trade by a mortar and pestle, a unicorn, a pot of lilies, a cross, a cock or a skull, apart from his Company arms. The arms of a good number of families are featured.

Inns always had a sign in those days and this is rarely absent from their tokens. Thus we find crowns, lions, harts and bulls galore, among many others; London is very rich in these and has many uniquely interesting ones. As mentioned earlier, a trader might show an inn-sign on his token, so a device portrayed is not conclusive evidence of the exact activity of the issuer; however, we are often aided in this respect by the spelling out of his business. Merchants' marks – a hark back to a much earlier form of identification – occur frequently. A few old local landmarks are also depicted, albeit simply .It can be stated here that in Ireland most issuers simply describe themselves as MERCHANT or MARCHANT or an abbreviation of these; the term is but rarely seen on English tokens.

The tokens vary in style from simple and rather crude to neat and accomplished. The work of Ràmage is always competent and sometimes of a high, though not surprisingly never of exceptional, standard. The same letter- and design-punches were repeatedly used, on tokens struck for issuers in entirely different parts of the country; the savings in time, labour and expense were thus considerable. Speaking very generally, earlier tokens are usually neat and unspectacular; those of the middle period (later 1650s to early 1660s) show some decline in standard; the later pieces are better again, often more elaborate, with more originality and diversity of type. Apart from the many stops and embellishments used on the tokens, in the form of mullets, cinquefoils, roses, diamonds, pellets, etc. throughout their issue, a common ornamentation of the last period was a simple device of a small flowering plant used around issuers' initials in the fields.

After inspecting quantities of seventeenth-century tokens, an interested numismatist will soon be able to make intelligent guesses from their style as to the rough period of issue in the case of undated pieces. Milne, in his work on Oxfordshire, invented the following classification system for borders on tokens:

A	Round dots	E	Oval dots, lengthways
B	Diamonds	F	Cable pattern, thin
C	Oblong labels	G	Cable pattern, thick
D	Oval dots, sideways	H	Plain line

Many tokens have an inner border, and nearly all an outer one.

Published research by Milne and, for Buckinghamshire and Nottinghamshire, by Peter Preston-Morley has given us the following information with regard to dated tokens.

Outer border: type B, not used *before* 1659, except once on a *lead* piece in

1656; type C, not used *after* 1666; type D, not used *after* 1665. Ramage does not appear to have used type B. Inner border: type a, not used *before* 1657; types c and d, not used *before* 1660; type e, not used *after* 1665; types f and g, used throughout; type h, not used *before* 1656; type b was used but rarely; an inner border is not present on some tokens of all periods. While it must be emphasised that these results, from just three counties, are by no means conclusive, they might be useful in rough dating.

Usage

In towns where several traders had businesses in close proximity to one another, tokens of a known issuer would be acceptable in other shops, and boxes with small compartments were used to separate the different ones. When sufficient had been accumulated, a trader would exchange tokens either for silver coin or for his own tokens. If the local authority was a token-issuer, its specimens would no doubt be thought of as good as real money. In London there were so many tokens that exchanging them was a business for some; one Richard Rich of Drury Lane issued a halfpenny on which he described himself CHANGER OF FARTHINGS.

Apart from their advantages discussed in previous pages, tokens were also conveyors of the message that the issuer had a business and as such were a useful advertising medium. The extreme limitations as to their possibilities of circulation, however, and the realisation that a great profit was being made by their use, was a cause of dissatisfaction with them. Specimens have been found a long way from 'home', but these are probably strays; nevertheless, those struck for local authorities would have had a wider circulation than their town or city limits. We know that tokens issued by the cities of Norwich, Salisbury and Worcester were primarily to replace those of private traders.

It is fascinating to discover how many different people issued tokens in various villages, towns and cities in these islands, thus offering interesting clues to the relative importance of places at the time. Compare, for example, Liverpool's 13 issuers, Manchester's 16 and Birmingham's 24 with over 90 for Norwich and over 4000 for London. In Bristol, the city corporation farthings obviously filled most needs for small change, only six private issues having been noticed thus far.

Very little contemporary record of the use of tokens exists. Unfortunately Pepys' diary does not mention them once, though he visited many hostelries that issued them. Incidentally, no London token refers to the Great Fire of 1666, though there were some issuers in Pudding Lane where the fire is thought to have started. The London diarist Evelyn wrote in 1697, in *Numismata: a Discourse on Medals Antient and Modern*:

> The tokens which every tavern and tippling-house (in the days of late anarchy amongst us) presumed to stamp and utter for immediate exchange as they were passable through the neighbourhood, which,

> though seldom reaching further than the next street or two, may happily in after-time come to exercise and busie the learned critic, what they should signify, and fill whole volumes with their conjectures.

How right he was!

Only a few 'hoards' of seventeenth-century tokens are known to have been discovered. The largest was found in 1936 at Witham, Essex, and consisted of 170 farthings of George Robinson. A group of farthings of Robert Bell of Thirsk, Yorkshire, thought to have consisted originally of over 50 specimens, was on the market about five years ago. Other smaller finds have included 16 specimens of the halfpenny of Edward Ashe of Tideswell, Derbyshire and some examples of Zachariah Lightwood's octagonal halfpenny of Yoxall, Staffordshire, along with a die the whereabouts of which is unfortunately now unknown. Hundreds of tokens, lost or thrown away separately, have been unearthed with the aid of metal detectors in recent years, particularly along the banks of the Thames.

The return of official coinage

From the early days of the Commonwealth there were ideas and plans for a coinage of farthings, of near-intrinsic value, in copper or tin. In May 1650 there was agreement in principle that the State should strike suitable coins, and in the early 1650s petitions were presented by private entrepreneurs, notably Thomas Violet and Thomas Dunstervile, for minor coinage. Patterns were struck; one, made in pewter in 1654, saw limited circulation for a while, but these efforts came to nothing.

Official patterns with Oliver Cromwell's portrait were struck about 1658, but he died in September of that year. His successor as Protector, Richard Cromwell, went so far as to agree, in April 1659, to the terms of another petition with the backing of Violet for the coinage of farthings of about 55 grains each in 'fine rose copper', from which the Exchequer would benefit to the tune of one shilling for every 22-shillings' worth issued. But Richard resigned a month later.

With the restoration of the monarchy in 1660, there was a new crop of official proposals and private petitions for low value coinage in copper or brass. Although, as we have seen, a coinage of farthings soon resulted for Ireland, there was no such progress in England. More patterns were struck in connection with these ideas. The designs on official farthing patterns dated 1665 were very closely followed on those of 1671 and on the coinage of halfpennies and farthings at last made current in England and Wales in Charles II's proclamation of 16 August 1672. Again, the picture in Ireland was different, official coinage not re-appearing until 1680.

Following their suppression, these tokens disappeared quickly. Some were redeemed by their issuers but many were not. Vast numbers were melted down or discarded and they were collected by very few until the nineteenth century.

CATALOGUE

Format

The lists in the following pages mention most of the important details that appear on the tokens, although in order to save space complete readings of the inscriptions are not given. The legends all note the place of issue, with exceptions listed in Index 2. Index 1 will be found helpful in identifying strange-sounding localities, but it does anyway provide a full gazetteer of places from which tokens were issued. For the novice, the photographs give plenty of examples of the sorts of full inscriptions used.

My aim, as was Williamson's, has been to list all specimens under the county in which the place of issue was at the time. I have mainly followed Williamson except where noted in a few places. In order to retain his basic system of numbering, the separate listings for London (not a county in the seventeenth century) and the *Borough* of Southwark have been retained, as has his simple method for Wales and Ireland, avoiding separating counties within these countries; in all these ideas, Williamson himself copied Boyne.

In quite a number of instances, more than one of the sub-editors whose services Williamson used for many of the county schedules claimed the same token to belong to his 'patch'. Often, subsequent research has proved which of these was correct and I have made a suitable note where appropriate. In some cases, though, the question has not been settled with any certainty; furthermore, a new location, with no definite evidence, has been mooted for a few tokens listed only once in Williamson. Where there are two possibilities for the correct placing of an issue, I have listed the piece under what I consider the more likely county, with a reference at the less likely one. If I can be proved wrong in any of these opinions, I shall be glad that someone's research into local historical records will have been worthwhile!

As mentioned in the Introduction, tokens are occasionally found overstruck on others and where classification of the undertype is possible great distances between the two issuers' locations can sometimes be identified.

The descriptions provided for the tokens, then, are abbreviated somewhat, but give the following information:

1 Williamson's number Some of these represent minor varieties of legend or design and are not listed separately in the present catalogue. But more than one die variety is known of many individual Williamson numbers, an extreme example being Gloucestershire 18, of which 27 or more obverses *and* reverses have been noted; such are not listed separately here unless they show major changes in legends or designs. All additional entries are major new types or varieties and are denoted by figures followed by a *capital* letter A, or B, etc.; some of these were listed by Williamson in his 'Uncertain' section but have since been more definitely placed, and a few were in his 'Addenda', but most are specimens noted since 1891. In a small number of instances a number will be seen followed by a *small* letter or an asterisk (*): these were noted thus by Williamson himself under the same county.

2 Issuer's name Shown as it appears on the token itself, in capital letters or *script*. Sometimes it is a correction of Williamson's description. Where only the issuer's initials are shown on specimens, I have noted them followed by full stops which probably do not occur on the pieces themselves; other punctuation I have used in the descriptions is also for the purpose of neater presentation only. Some tokens discovered *post* Williamson, for which the style of lettering has not been recorded, are indicated by normal small letters, as are all the city and town pieces which do not tell us more than their place-name.

Occasionally letters and numbers are found retrograde or inverted on tokens, or two Vs used to make a W; such variations have not been indicated in the listings here. Alternative spellings of a name have been noted in parenthesis; usually this means that both (or all) varieties exist, but in some examples one version may have been wrongly recorded in the past and this is often impossible to prove. In multi-variety situations, I have not attempted to give *exact* combinations of readings on individual tokens. A long dash denotes that a *word* is exactly the same as on the preceding piece.

3 Initial of spouse If shown on the token, this is listed in parenthesis after the issuer's name or initials. Rarely, the initial is of another relative, perhaps in partnership with the issuer. When it occurs it should be positioned in the field of one side of the token to the right of the issuer's, both letters being below the initial of the surname in the form of a pyramid; occasionally they are wrongly placed. In the case of a few Irish tokens, it is just possible that (M) might indicate 'merchant'.

4 Denomination ¼ = farthing, ½ = halfpenny, 1d = penny. Farthings rarely express their value. Halfpence, and the pennies of England and Wales, usually do; those that do not are denoted (½) or (1d). In Ireland, tokens silent about their denomination are usually assumed to be pence. (See also the section 'Denominations' in the Introduction.)

5 Date (if any) Sometimes only the last two figures appear on the token. In the lists, for convenience, they are recorded with an apostrophe (e.g. '49, '68, etc.) which does not occur on the specimen concerned. When varieties exist with both partial and full dates, this is indicated, e.g. (16) 59. A long dash means that a date is the same as on the preceding piece.

6 Further inscription and/or design Where the occupation of the issuer appears, I have listed it as shown on the token. When it occurs *in addition to* a representation of one of the London Livery Companies' arms, the arms are noted only if not the expected ones. Similarly, a device very commonly associated with a trade is not referred to where that trade is described on the token itself, e.g. a wheatsheaf in the case of a BAKER. The Companies' arms are usually depicted very basically, sometimes crudely too. No indication is given as to whether or not they are on a shield; such information is mentioned, however, if a token exists in types with *and* without shield. 'Arms' (alone) is the description provided when these are of uncertain type, i.e. possibly they are of the family, or imaginary, or simply not properly visible. No attempt has been made at full heraldic description.

Where the plural has been used in design descriptions without further qualification, it is to be taken to mean *two* of that item, except where there is an obvious *group* of something, e.g. a stick of candles, in which case there are more than two. With various sub-editors in 'Williamson' describing similar tokens differently, it is obvious that the same motif was identified in more than one way. The present work will also be found wanting in this respect, but not to the same extent as Williamson's.

A small number of tokens exists with *and* without an inner circle surrounding the design: these are not differentiated. A few of the dies made up by Ramage bear his inital R: these are identified only when similar pieces do *not* have this letter (e.g. the Bristol city issues). A semi-colon between recordings of types signifies that what appears *before* it is on the *obverse* of the piece, and what appears *after* it is on the *reverse*. With Irish tokens only, the word MERCHANT or MARCHANT, or an abbreviation of either, occurs very frequently, and I have not noted this unless it is important in helping to identify one variety from another.

If no design details are given, it can be assumed that the issuer's initials and/or the token's face value are the main features in the fields (unless of course the type is completely indistinguishable); one or both of these data are on almost all seventeenth century tokens. Initials sometimes appear in the form of a monogram. No mention has been made of the cinquefoils, diamonds, mullets etc. used as ornamentation to fill in otherwise empty spaces in the legends or fields. On Irish tokens other objects such as crescents or hearts are also ignored.

Many of the remarks made at section 2 (*Issuer's name*) apply here also, except that a long dash denotes an identical section of legend, or very similar main type, to that of the token preceding.

7 Further notes (if any) Unless stated, all tokens are struck in copper or brass and are round in shape. Exceptions to this norm are all noted. Some varieties exist in copper and in brass, but no distinction between them is made here. A few tokens were counterstamped with initials and some Irish pennies with a lower value. These are noted when known, but countermarks of devices such as a ship, sun, etc., very occasionally found on Irish tokens, are not listed.

8 Market value Prices are given where my researches have suggested that there is a fair chance of a collector obtaining the specimen in his or her lifetime! Unfortunately so many tokens are extremely rare – a large majority in the case of London, several English counties, Wales and Ireland – that there are many gaps in the pricing; however, a minimum valuation for these is provided at the beginning of each county or country. Location and the shape of tokens are the chief factors in assessing value. There are far more collectors of local tokens in some counties compared with others and obviously demand will affect values; for instance, a Northumberland token could bring about six times as much as a London one of approximately similar rarity and design interest. The cheapest heart-shaped token is listed at £100.

All prices are for tokens in *fine* condition; they are a close guide to Seaby's selling prices at the time of going to press. A token – or coin – in *fine* (F) condition is worn but with the main features of the designs and inscriptions distinct. This can be considered a perfectly acceptable quality, although for collectors of Irish tokens a less good state of preservation has to be sufficient more often than not. Specimens in *very fine* condition are worth about 1½ times the F price in the case of rarer pieces and up to 2½ times for most of the commonest varieties. *Very fine* (VF) means that there is only light wear on the raised surfaces. Few seventeenth-century tokens turn up today in *extremely fine* (EF) condition, i.e. with almost no circulation, but with perhaps slight surface marks. An EF specimen might be worth 1½ to 2½ times a VF example. The condition factor with this series, though, is not nearly so important as with later tokens and, indeed, coins generally.

Seldom do these gradings alone describe the state of preservation of a numismatic item, however. Weakness in striking, an uneven or chipped flan, corrosion of various kinds, discolouration, and other damage all affect desirability and, hence, value. So this catalogue will rarely give an exact value for any token.

Forgeries Contemporary counterfeiting of seventeenth-century tokens was non-existent in almost all of England and Wales, but some Irish pieces are considered to be copies because of their crude style. A number of the Mic Wilson halfpennies of Dublin dated 1672 are believed counterfeit. So far, the only later forgeries noticed are a group apparently produced about or nearly one hundred years ago on flans larger and heavier than usual. They are of a quite different, rather crude, style to that of normal seventeenth-century pieces and are known of tokens of Berkshire, Derbyshire, Nottinghamshire and Yorkshire. A feature of those that have a group of three initials is that the first letter of the surname is *below* those of the Christian names. Probably of a slightly earlier period are some fantasy City of Bristol pieces dated 1511, 1591 and 1598. Notes in the listings about all these will be found at the relevant places.

Abbreviations

Æ	*aes*. Copper or brass
AR	*argentum*. Silver
b.s.	Both sides
Cmkd.	Countermarked
n.d.	Not dated
Obv.	obverse. First or main side of token
Pb	*plumbeus*. Lead or pewter
Rev.	reverse. Second or less important side of token

Bibliographical Abbreviations

BNJ	British Numismatic Journal, published by the British Numismatic Society
NC	Numismatic Chronicle, published by the Royal Numismatic Society
SCA	Spink Coin Auction
SCMB	Seaby's Coin and Medal Bulletin
SNC	Spink's Numismatic Circular
TCSB	Token Corresponding Society's Bulletin
W	Williamson (see General Bibliography)

ENGLAND

Bedfordshire

Major reference: J. H. Blundell, *Bedfordshire Seventeenth Century Tokens* (Ventnor, I.o.W., 1928). 105 copies only, with 3 plates; updating and revision of 'Williamson', more notes, locations of specimens.

Further new tokens recorded from J. G. Milne, 'Seventeenth-Century Tokens: The Browne Willis Cabinet' (*BNJ*, 1951); and R. H. Thompson, *Sylloge of Coins of the British Isles, 31. The Norweb Collection. Part 1: Bedfordshire to Devon* (London, 1984).

See also: T. D. Whittet, 'A Survey of Apothecaries' Tokens, part 3: Bedfordshire' (*The Pharmaceutical Journal*, 9 July 1983); and *SCMB*, July 1959.

Minimum price for unvalued tokens: £60

Ampthill

1A THOMAS HARVYE (M) ¼ 1664
1 —— (M) ¼ 1666 £40
2 IOHN IMPIEIL (A) ¼ 1663 DRESSER
2A — IMPIE (A) ¼ — FLAX DRESSER

Barton-in-the-Clay

3 WILLIAM HOPKINS (E) ½ £18

Bedford

4 PAVLL BAMFORTH (E) ¼ 1665
5, 6 ANTHONY BOVLTON (S) ½ 1667 GROCER £20
7 IOHN CLARKE (S) ¼ Crossed keys £22
8 THOMAS COX (I) ¼ 1664
9 WILLIAM FALDO (A) ¼ 1659 £22
10 ROBERT FARMAN (E) ½ 1667 BAKER £28
11 ROBERT FITTZHVGH (M) ¼ 1654 £30
12, 13 HENRY FITTZHVGH ¼ 1655 £16
14 HVGH HOLTON ½ 1666 Frying pan
15 WILLIAM ISAAC (M) ¼ 1666 £28
16 PHILLIP NICHOLLES (S) ¼ 1659 Grocers' Arms
17 THOMAS PARE (E) ¼ 1656 3 cloves £28
18 IOHN PAVLIN (D) ¼ 1654 Grocers' Arms £20
19 RALPH SMYTH (S) ½ 1668 LINNEN DRAPER £22
20 (See *Kent* 194)

Biggleswade

21 OVERSEERS ½ Cripple; spinning-wheel. *Heart-shape.* **Plate 1** £100
22 IOHN BODDINGTON (K) ½ 1669 DRAPER £25
23 IOHN BRAY (S) ½ 1668 AT YE SWAN £25
24 WILLIAM PARNELL (E) ¼ Mercers' Arms £17
25 THOMAS TOMPKINS (A) ¼ Falcon £22

Blunham

26 GEORGE FARR (E) ¼ 1666

Bourne (End)

26A IOSEPH LAKE ½ 1668 Man at forge

Cardington

27 WILLIAM WILMOT ¼ '64

Clifton

28 IOHN SAMM (H) ¼ 1664 Drapers' Arms. **Plate 1** £28

Clophill
29 IOHN CARTER (S) ¼ 1666 Tobacco-roll £30

Cople
30 IOSEPH LAKE ½ 1668 Man at forge
31 As last, but no place-name in legend £35

Cranfield
32 IOHN BANDY ¼ 1668 Scales £25
33 ELING LEB(A *or* E)TT ½ Scales
34 RICHARD YOVNG (A) ¼ 1670 Scales

Dunstable
35 (See *Oxon.* 85)
36 EDWARD CHESTER (E) ½ 1667 BAKER £20
36A ROBERT (D(EANE?) (E) ¼
36B WILLIAM ELEMENT (E) ¼ Angel
36C — — ¼ 1667 —
37 DANIELL FINCH (S) ½ 1668 Merchant Taylors' Arms £50
38 — — (S) (½) — — £45
39 DANIELL FOSSEY (E) ½ 1668 Greyhound with hare in mouth, pipes, tobacco-roll £18
40 WILLIAM FOSSEY (½) 1667 Swan £17
41 EDWARD TIPLADY (M) ½ Grocers' Arms £50
42 IOHN WHITLEY (M) ¼ Drapers' Arms £60
43 NATHANIELL WIMPEW (I) ½ Hart

Eaton Bray
43A THOMAS BRIDGES ½ 1669 Man making candles. **Plate 1** £25
44 WALTER RICHARDS ½ 3 fleurs-de-lis

Eaton Socon
44A THOMAS COLLINGS (probably *Bucks.* 59)
44B RICHARD ROBINSON (probably *Bucks.* 60)
44C IOHN SMITH (A) ½ 1668 AT YE, cock

Elstow
45 ROBERT HOLDSTOCK (A) ½ 1668

Goldington
46 GILBERT ASHLEY (I) ½ 1668
47 Similar, with ROVND after place-name £70

Great Barford
47A MARY BRINE (probably *Warwicks.* 23)
48 EDMVND WARD ½ Bull £28
49 (See *Oxon.* 49)

Harrold
50 IOHN BLETSOE ½ 1668 £28

Henlow
51/2 THOMAS VNDERWOOD (E) ¼ 1668

Hockliffe
53–5 (See *London* 1352–4)

Houghton Regis
56 IOSEPH COLEMAN (E) ½ 1667
57 — — (E) ½ 1668

Husborne Crawley
58 EDMVND GREENE (F) ½ 1668 £45

Kempston
58A RICHARD BOVGHTON (E) ¼ 1656 3 cloves
59 SAMVEL PERSON (E) ¼ 1664

Langford
60/1 OVERSEERS ½ 1668 £40

Leighton Buzzard
62 BENEDICT COLES (A) ½ 1667 Scales £22
63 ISAAC HANNELL ½ 1667 Pipes, tobacco
64 WILLIAM GVRNEY ¼ TALOW CHANDLER
64A IEREMY KING (C) ¼ Grocers' Arms
65 (Misreading of 44)
66 IOSEPH SEAYRE (M) ¼ 1663 LINEN DRAPER £60

Lidlington
67 IOHN DAWBORNE ½ 1668 Grocers' Arms £24
68 — — (E) ¼ n.d. — £32
69 (Probably *Sussex* 121)

Luton
70 RICH HOPKINS ¼ 1666 AT RED, lion
71/2 ABRAHAM PEETER ¼ 1653 Grocers' Arms £28
73 IOHN ROWLEY (I) ¼ 1657 £35

Markyate Street
73A RICHARD BARNES ¼ Mercers' Arms* £40
73B THOMAS DEARMOR ¼ 1666

Maulden
73C MATHIAS TOMPKINS (S) ¼ 1667 St. George & dragon

Millbrook
74 RICHARD NORRIS (A) (½) 1671 Lion
75 GREGORY DOWLINGE ¼ 1666 Mercers' Arms

Milton Ernest
76 HENRY SAVAGE (E) ½ Plough

Oakley
77 IOHN FOWLER (S) ½ 1668 Crossed keys £25
77A HVMPHREY MORGAN ½ 1669 Scales

Pavenham
78 WILLIAM ASHTON ½ 1667 Grocers' Arms £60

Potton
79 RICHARD ATKINSON (K) ¼ 1661 Stag £35
80 HVGH CONNY ½ 1666 3 rabbits (conies) £25
81 IOHN HARPER ¼ 1657 IN MIDLESX £18

* Specimens on wider and heavier flans are known in copper and silver; all are probably of much later manufacture.

81A WALLTER LETTICE IVNIOR ¼ 1666 Grocers' Arms
82 HENRY RVGELEY ½ 1666 St. George & dragon £25
82A ANDREW SELBY (same as *Hunts.* 7)
83 RICHARD THORNE ½ 1667 3 garbs

Riseley
83A MARY EARLE ½ 1668 3 pipes £30

Shefford
84 IOSEPH BOVLSTRED (A) ¼ 1667 Grocers' Arms £35
85 IOSEPH CROCKER (E) ½ 1670 LINEN DRAPER £28
86 IOSEPH FOSE ¼ Grocers' Arms; Mercers' Arms £30
87 WILLIAM GROVES ¼ 1666 Grocers' Arms, SHEFFORD
88 — — ¼ — — SHEFFEIELD (error)
89 ISAAC SHEPPARD (E) ¼ 1664 £22

Shillington
90 FRANCES CARTER ¼ 1656 £30
91 IONATHAN CARTER ½ 1667

Silsoe
92 RICHARD DAVIS (A) ¼ 1668 Mercers' Arms £35

Stevington
93 RALPH HARVIE (S) ¼ 1657 2-headed eagle
94 — — (P) ½ Scales
95 EDWARD READE ½ 1667 Scales £55

Turvey
96 GEORGE BABINGTON ½ 1667 £50
97 IOHN WOODIN (D) ¼ Scales £50
97A — — (D) ¼ 1659 —

Upper Dean
98 ROBERT DAI ¼ 1667
99 — DAY ½ 1668 £60

Wilden
100 THOMAS SPRINGE ½ 1667 GROCER £50

Woburn
101 FRANCIS COLLMAN (S) ½ 1667 £17
102 RICH GASLEY (A) ½ 1666 Drapers' Arms
103 THOMAS HILL (A) ¼ 1666 Scales £30
103A — — (A) ¼ 1664 —
104/5 (see *Bucks.* 154B, 154C)
106 NATHANIEL LAWSON (E) ¼ 1664 Drapers' Arms
107 FRANCIS SEAGRE ½ 1667 Royal oak

Wootton
107A EDWARD WALLINGTON (probably *Oxon.* 253)

Berkshire

Major reference: Vincent West, 'Berkshire Seventeenth Century Tokens' (*SNC*, July/Aug. 1976) and 'Additional Notes on Berkshire Seventeenth Century Tokens' (*SNC*, Apr. 1981).

Further new tokens recorded from the Lowsley collection (sold at Sotheby's, 20 Apr. 1936); *SNC List*, Apr. 1947; and R. H. Thompson, *Sylloge* . . . (see under Bedfordshire).

See also *SCMB*, Dec. 1950; T. D. Whittet, 'A Survey of Apothecaries' Tokens', parts 4 and 5. (*The Pharmaceutical Journal*, 26 Nov. 1983 and 12 May 1984); and P. Preston-Morley and H. Pegg (see under Nottinghamshire): notes on a late 19th cent. forgery.

Minimum price for unvalued tokens: £50

Abingdon

1 ROBERT BLACKALLER ½ MERCER £25
2 ROBERT LIFORD ¼ Spectacles, scissors; comb, fish-hook. MILLINER £35
3 RICHARD ELY ¼ LAMB £20
4 THOMAS GEAGLE ½ AT THE BRIDWELL, 3 clubs* £18
5 IOHN HALL (B) ½ 1667 GROCER £40
6 THO. HARTWELL ½ Lion, OF ABINGDON; crown, OF HIGHWORTH £45
7 HENRY MEALES ¼ 1657 (without BAKER) £14
7A —— ¼ — (without BAKER)
8 SARAH PLEYDELL ½ 1667 Mercers' Arms £15
9 (See *Cambs.* 1)
10 WILLIAM STEVENSON (M) ¼ GROCER £13
11 IOHN WELLS ¼ 1667 Man making candles £20

Blewbury

12 IOHN LEWENDON (A) ¼ Grocers' Arms
13 GEORGE STANTON (E) ½ 1670 Mercers' Arms £40
14 —— (E) ¼ 1665 — £30
15 —— ¼ n.d. — £35

Bray

15A IOHN KEENE ¼ BARGMAN AT THE CROWE

Bucklebury

16 IOHN MOORECOCK (I) ¼ 1666 Bladebone £40

Chilton

16A SAMVELL COOKE (I) ¼ 1664

* Copies are known (late 19th cent.) of crude style

Cookham

17 MARTHA SPOT ½ 1668 AT YE KINGS HEAD £40

Coxwell

18 (See *Essex* 87A)

Faringdon

19 IOHN BARRETT (H) ¼ 1656 Man making candles £20
20 —— (M) ¼ 1662
21 PHIL(L)IP COL(L)YER (E) ¼ Ironmongers' Arms
22 THOMAS COWLEY (M) ¼ '57 Grocers' Arms
23 RICHARD FOWLER (A) ½ 1669 Stays. *Heart-shape* £125
23A As last but without date
24 —— (A) ¼ 1663 Grocers' Arms £17
25 —— (I) ¼ 1657 —
26 EDWARD GOLDINGE (A) ½ 1668 Barber-Surgeons' Arms £20
27 THOMAS SHEPARD (A) ¼ '68 Bell
28 EDWARD STEVENS ¼ 1652 Grocers' Arms £18
28A —— ¼. In *pb* (Probably *Oxon* 102A)
29 SYMON TVRNER (M) ¼ 1667 MERCER

Hagbourne

30/2 THOMAS HVMFREY *or* THO HVMFERY (A) ¼ Mercers' Arms £15
31 (Probably misreading of 32)

Harwell

33 IOHN HANSON (A) ¼ 1666 Rose. **Plate 1** £35

Hungerford

34 *William Bell* ½ 1668 *vintner at the Bear* £18

35 IOHN BVTLER (E) ¼ Tallowchandlers' Arms £20
36 IOHN LVCVS ¼ Rose
37 TIMOTHIE LVCVS (F) ¼ 3 cloves £25
38 IOSEPH SARE ¼ Man making candles

Ilsley
39 RICHARD WESTON ½ 1669 Man holding scales £20

Kintbury
39A IOHN BVRDON (N) ¼ Grocers' Arms

Lambourn
40 IOHN FARMER ½ 1665 AT THE RED LYON £35
41 HENRY KNIGHTON (C) ¼ 1652 Crown £45
42 — — (C) ¼ 1665 —
43 — — (C) ½ 1666 — £18

Longcot
44 ALBERT WILLIAMS (A) ½ 1671 MERCER

Longworth
45 THOMAS MORRIS ¼ GROCER £22

Maidenhead
46 WILLIAM BATTES (G) ¼ 1659 Mercers' Arms £22
47 ROBERT BENNETT (K) ¼ Bust
48 IOHN CHERRY ¼ Cherry tree £30
48A E.R. (D) ¼ 1652 AT THE GEORGE
49 EDMOND STONE ¼ Mercers' Arms £8
49A Similar, but 3 instead of 5 points to crown. **Plate 1** £10
50 IOSEPH TAYLOR ½ 1669 Still

Newbury
51/5 BOROVGH ¼ 1657 Castle, 3 turrets £7
52 — ¼ — — 4 turrets £7
53 (Flawed *rev.* die of 52)
54 — ¼ 1657 Castle, 5 turrets £7
56 THOMAS COWSLADE (C) ¼ Antlered lion, GROCER
57 WILLIAM HARRISON (S) ¼ 1657 Grocers' Arms £40
58 IOHN HILL (S) ¼ Skull
59 IOHN NAISH (S) ¼ 1652 GROCER £25
60 IONAS NORAWAY IVNIOR (S) ¼ GROCER £25
61 IOSEPH SAYER ¼ Castle; bible. RECTOR. **Plate 1** £60
62 IOHN SPENCER ¼ Grocers' Arms
63 (See *Salop* 53)

Old Windsor
63A HENRY LINE (F) ½ AT YE BELLS OF OLDSEY

Reading
64 RICHARD BAGLY ¼ Man making candles £40
65 SOLOMON BARNARD (E) ¼ 1653 Rabbit £18
66 MARY BLOWER ¼ 1652 Grocers' Arms £20
67 IAMES BLVNT (E) ¼ 1666 AT BLACK, horse
68 HENRY BOAD (A) ¼ 1664 King's Arms £32
69 EDWARD BOWLAND (E) ¼ 1666 Woolpack £30
70 FRANCES BROWN (K) ¼ BAKER £32
71 IOHN BROWNE (C) ¼ AT 3, fishes
72 RICHARD BROWNE (A) ¼ BAKER
73 WILLIAM BVRLY (E) ¼ 1655 Hand holding glove £16
74 THOMAS BYE (I) ¼ Mill cramp; sack of flour, MEALEMAN £28
75 WILLIAM CASTELL ¼ 1666 Castle
76 HVGH CHAMPION ½ 1669 LINEN DRAPR, HIS HARTY DVBBLE TOKEN. *Heart-shape*
77 (78 struck over *Hants*. 123)
78 WILLIAM CHAMPE (T) ¼ 1658 £25
79 RICHARD COTTAM ½ 1669 DISTILLER
80 ROBERT CREED ¼ 1655 Grocers' Arms
80A — — ¼ 1658 —
80B THOMAS EAST (A) ¼ 1664 Hooded head facing
81 NICHOLAS EDWARDS (E) (½) 1667 Tallowchandlers' Arms
82 WILL GAND (M) ¼ Chained dog, GROCR
83 ALCE GILL ¼ 1666 WIDDOW, Bakers' Arms
84 RICHARD HELLOWS (M) ¼ 1656 Stockings
85 IOHN HARRISON (M) ¼ 1666 Candlestick
86 IOHN HARVIE (M) ¼ Tailor's shears **Plate 1** £35
87 HENRY HEAD (C) ¼ 1652 Plough £25
88 WILLIAM IAMES (A) ¼ 1664 Castle £35
89 THO KING IVNIOR ¼ 1666 Crown £20
90 MARTHA KNIGHT ¼ 1669 LIN DRAPR
91 MOSES LAMB (R) ¼ 1658 Shears
92 RICHARD LEVENS (M) ¼ Cordwainers' Arms £35
93 IOHN LOADER ¼ Ship, CHANDLER
94 WILLIAM LOVEGROVE (E) ¼ 1664 Roll of cloth £45
95 THO MACHIN (M) ¼ APOTHECARY
96 WILLIAM MALTHVS ¼ 1658 £28
97 CLEMENT MARLOW (G) ¼ AT THE BELL £22
98 DANIELL MARTEN (E) ¼ 1652
99 — MARTIN (E) ¼ 1653 GARDNER £18
100 IOH MILESON (I) ¼ Mortar and pestle
101 HVMPHREY MILLS ¼ DRAPER
102 IOHN PAICE (E) ¼ 1666 AT THE, angel £30
103 IOHN PETERS ¼ AT THE COCK
104 THOMAS PHIPPS (E) ¼ 1652 Man making candles £18
105 IOHN PHIPS (E) ¼ 1655 Tallowchandlers' Arms £35
106 ROBERT PIDGION (E) ¼ 1663 £40
107 THOMAS PINECK (A) ¼ Mermaid £25
108 EDWARD PINNILL (A) ¼ 1665 £30
109 (Probably misreading of 108)
110 NICHOLAS PRINCE (A) ¼ Prince of Wales' feathers, GROCER

111 IOHN REMNANT (M) ¼ 1669 Mallet
111A IOHN SHIPWAY ½ 1667 Hat
112 ROBERT SMART (A) ¼ Bread? £28
113 IOELL STEVENS (D) ¼ Grocers' Arms £25
114 IOSEPH STOCKWELL (E) ¼ Shuttle
115 RICHARD STOCKWELL (E) ¼ 1656 Salters' Arms £18
116 IOHN SWIFT (A) ¼ AT THE ROSE £40
117 FRANCIS TASSELL (E) ¼ 1663 Bust of Chas II £22
118 WILLIAM TAYLOR (M) ¼ 1658 St George & dragon £16
119 REYNOLD THORNBROVGH ¼ Bull's head, VINTNER £32
120 IOHN THORP ½ 1665 AT THE GOALE, King's Arms
121 THOMAS VNDERWOOD (M) ¼ 1666 Surgeon's bleeding instrument £25
122 HENRY WHITELL (I) ¼ 1656 Woman making cheese £20
123 IOHN WILDER THE ELDER (A) ¼ Pelican and young £38
124 IOHN WILDER THE YOVNGER (T) ¼ 1652 £25
125 IOHN WILDER YE ELDER (A) ¼ 1663. Pelican and young
126 THOMAS WINCKELLS (A) ¼ 3 stars, BAKER £18

Sonning
127 THOMAS BALL ¼ Bakers' Arms
128 FRANCIS FEILDER ¼ 1664 Sugar-loaf £50

Speenhamland
128A IOSEPH SEALY ¼ 1667 Castle; angel £70

Wallingford
129 IOHN ANGIER ¼ 1669 IRONMONGER £18
130 IAMES ANSLOW (A) ½ 1669 AT YE GEORG £17
131 ANTHONY BOVLTER ¼ 1664 Grocers' Arms £12
132 IOHN BVCKLAND (M) ¼ Man making candles £14
133 PHILIP ELDRED (A) ¼ '59 Family Arms, APOTHICARY £22
134 WILLIAM ELIOT ½ 1669 AT THE, elephant and castle £20
135 ION GOODWIN ¼ Family Arms, DRAPER £18
136 ANN HALL (A) ¼ 1652 Arms £14
137 SAMVELL PEARCE (A) ¼ St George & dragon £22
138 THO PHIPS (S) ¼ 1664 City of London Arms, 3 doves £28
139 WILLIAM POLHAMPTON ½ 1668 3 castles £13
140 WILLIAM QVELCH ½ 1669 Tobacco-roll £20
141 THOMAS RVSDEN (A) ¼ 3 sugar-loaves £14
142 RICHARD WHITE ½ 1669 Mermaid £25
143 SILLVANVS WIGGINS (A) ¼ '69 YE, lamb £20

Wantage
144 WILLIAM ALBWORTH ¼ 1652 Crossed keys £25
144A ZACHEVS BEALE ¼ Crossed tobacco pipes
145 IOHN BEALLE ¼ Tobacco-roll £22
146 IOHN CLEMENT ¼ Grocers' Arms £25
147 (Probably misreading of 146)
148 WILLIAM CVLLY (I) ¼ 1660 Apothecaries' Arms £25
149 THOMAS GROVE (M) ¼ AT YE, crown
150 (See *London* 3313)
151 IOHN HVNSDON (E) ¼ 1667 Weavers' Arms
152 THO HVRDMAN (I) ¼ AT THE BEARE £20
153 GEORGE KERBY ½ 1669 AT YE BEARE
154 WILLIAM MASMORE ¼ 1653 Grocers' Arms £12
155 — — ¼ 1657 —
156 IEFFERY MASMORE ¼ 1663 Grocers' Arms* £18
157 EDWARD PENER ¼ 1654 Fleur-de-lis
158 IOH(N) SEYMOR (M) ¼ AT GOLD lion, MERCI £15
159 RICHARD STAMP (A) ½ 1669 Fleur-de-lis
159A — STAMPE ½ 1671 —
160 IOHN WEBB (E) ¼ 1667 Lion £32
161 IOHN WHITFEILD ¼ Arms, MEARCER
162 *Michaell Willams* ½ 1669 DIER. *Heart-shape*

Windsor (or **New Windsor**)
163 THOMAS ADAMES (I) ¼ 1652 Tallowchandlers' Arms £32
164 SAMVALL BANAT ¼ 1657 Soldier bestriding king; shoemaker fitting woman with shoe
164A SAMVEL BENET (½) FROM WINDSOR TO YE EAGLE & CHILD IN THE STRAND, etc. Coach and horses; queen's head. *Octagonal*
164B *Samuel Benet* (½) Similar legends, but script. Coach and one horse; queen's head. *Octagonal*
165 MOSES BRVCH ¼ 1666 Family Arms, APOTHECARY £30
166 W.C. (E) ¼ AT THE CHECKER
167 WILL CAMPION ½ 1669 IN PEASCOD STREET, horse
167A WILLIAM CHVRCH ¼ 1668 Cock
168 HAMMAN FARNHAD (E) ¼ 1657 Bakers' Arms £35
169 IOHN FINCH (E) ¼ 3 birds £45
169A WILLIAM GALLAND ¼ Bell
170 IOHN GOSSE ½ 1669 MAVLSTER IN PEASCOD STREET, crossed shovels. *Octagonal* £35
170A WILLIAM HERENDEN (A) ¼ 1651 Scallop-shell, APOTHYCARYE
171 FRANCIS HILL (A) ¼ 1666 Arrow, DRAPER
171A EDWARD LLOYD (Probably *London* 2522A)
172 GEORGE PENNINGTON (C) ¼ 1656 Mermaid
173 DANIELL QVARTERMAN (E) ¼ AT THE GARTER
173A IOHN RANDALL ¼ 1655 3 doves

* Copies are known (late 19th cent.) of crude style

174 IOHN WYRON (M) ¼ 1653 Fish-hook £45

Winkfield

175 THOMAS TEELLING ¼ '69 Tobacco-roll

Wokingham

176 W.A. ¼. Both sides as *rev.* of 177
177 WILL ANDARSON ¼ Grocers' Arms £18
177A —— (M) ¼ —
178 SIMON BANISTER ½ 1668 AT THE, St George & dragon
179 IOHN CLEMENTS (M) ¼ Pitcher £30
180 —— ½ —
180A GEORGE FIELD ¼ Tallowchandlers' Arms
181 THOMAS GRAPE (D) ¼ 1667 Lion £40
182 —— (D) ¼ 1668 — £22
182A —— (D) ¼ 1664 — £28
183 —— (D) ¼ n.d. —
184 RICHARD LARANCE (A) ¼ Wheatsheaf £17
185 THOMAS MAY ¼ Man making candles £45
186 (See *Bucks.* 38)
187 RICHARD SMITH ¼ Mercers' Arms
188 —— (A) ¼ Man making candles £35
189 ANTHONY SPEER (F) ¼ Family Arms

Yattendon

189A THOMAS PATY (E) ¼ Sugar-loaf

Buckinghamshire

Major references: George Berry and Peter Morley, 'A Revised Survey of the Seventeenth Century Tokens of Buckinghamshire' (*BNJ*, 1973). 2 plates; updating and revision of 'Williamson', more notes, corrections to previous listings, detailed classification of the tokens, locations of specimens and numbers examined.

J. O. Manton and E. Hollis, *Buckinghamshire Trade Tokens Issued in the Seventeenth Century* (Aylesbury, 1933; most of it previously published in *BNJ*, 1925—30). 75 copies only. Useful for background information and complete readings of tokens not repeated by Berry and Morley.

See also: W. R. Hooper, 'Notes . . .' (see under Devonshire), for further details of Colnbrook issuers; E. Hollis, 'Some Additional Trade Tokens of Bucks.' (*Records of Bucks.*, 1932, vol. 12, no. 6); G. Berry, 'New Light on the Seventeenth-Century Token Issuers of Chepping Wycombe' (*Records of Bucks.* vol. 18, no. 2); and T. D. Whittet, 'A Survey of Apothecaries' Tokens, part 5: Buckinghamshire' (*The Pharmaceutical Journal*, 12 May 1984).

Believed entirely unpublished: 47A.

Minimum price for unvalued tokens: £60

Amersham

1A ANDREW BAROWES ¼ 1652 CLOTHWORKER
1 —BVRROWES (F) ½ 1665 Clothworkers' Arms £30
2 IOHN COCKE (M) ¼ 1666 Unicorn
3 FRANCIS LANE (G) ¼ 1666 FL monogram
4 ELIZABETH RVTT ½ 1668 Shuttle £40
5 WILLIAM STATHAM (B) ¼ 1653 £38
6 RICHARD WEBB (S) ½ '66 Hand holding axe over leaf £30

Aylesbury

7 IOSEPH BELL (H) ¼ 1659 Mercers' Arms
8 WILLIAM BVRGAS ½ 1670 Turk's head
8A — BVRGES ½ — Turk pouring coffee. *Square*
9 RICHARD BVTLER (S) ¼ 1666 Crown £30
10 GYLES CHILDE (D) ¼ MERCER £15
11 EDWARD COPE (D) ¼ Drapers' Arms £12
11A STEPHEN DAGNELL (I) ¼ 1656 Book. In *pb*
12 W.D. (E) ¼ 1657 AT YE KINGS HEAD, Henry VIII £32
12A IOHN DOSSET (I) ¼ 1670 Malt shovel
13 ALEXANDER TROTT (A) ½ 1669 GROCER
14 IOSEPH FREER (M) ¼ 1652 MARCER £30
15 IOHN HILL ½ 1665 TALLOW CHANDLER £35
16 THOMAS HILL (R) ¼ MERCER £35
16A IOSEPH SAXTON ¼ St George & dragon
17 THOMAS STRATFORD (M) ½ 1667
17A W.W. (I) ¼ TALLOW CHANNDLER
18 FRANCIS WETHERED ¼ 1660 Mercers' Arms, DRAPER

Beaconsfield

19 T.C. (I) ¼ £32
20 IOHN FOSCET ½ 1669 Paschal lamb £30
21 HENRY TRIPP (A) ½ 1668 Stick of candles £45
22 THOMAS COCKE (K) ¼ Cock
23 I.G. (M) ¼ 1658 Letter B £40
24 WILLIAM WILLIS (F) ½ 1668 Bull £45

Brill

25 THOMAS CATER (E) ½ 1671
25A WILLIAM CLARK (E) ½ 1669 Mercers' Arms
26 WILLIAM GOLDAR (A) ¼ MERSER
27 (Misreading of 28)
28 I.H. ¼ AT THE HALF MONE £45
29 ELIZ SCARLETT ½ 1669 Grocers' Arms

Broughton

29A IOHN WILSON ¼ Scales

Buckingham

30 ELIZABETH CRAWLEY ¼ 1668 Heron, HER OB £45
31 WILLIAM ATTON (E) ¼ 1663 Bells, DRAPER £40
32 IOHN HARTLEE ¼ Heart £28
33 — — ¼ 1650 — £30
34 — HARTLEY ¼ 1660 —
34A — — ½ — Heart, tree, OB £35
35 IOHN HARTLEY IVNIOR (½) 1665 £35
35A IOHN KEW ½ 1668
36 IOHN RENNALS (E) ½ 1668 Strip of lace £35
36A As last, but no initials
37 PETER REYNOLDES (F) ¼ '58 Strip of lace
38 GEORGE ROBINS ¼ Holy Lamb, MERCER £32

Chalfont St Peter

39 IOHN BENNITT (O) ½ 1668 AT THE, greyhound £50
40 IARVICE GOOD (M) ¼ Greyhound
41 *Edward White* ¼ 1664 Crossed keys

Chesham

42 *Richard Amond* (D) ¼ 1664 Clothworkers' Arms £60
43 WILLIAM CHILDE (M) ¼ BREWER £38
44 WILLIAM G(R *or* V)OME (S) ½ 1671 Shears £60
45 RISE DAVIS (E) ½ 1671
46 ABRAHAM GARRAWAY (M) (½) 1671 Crossed pipes
47 IOHN GROVER (I) ¼ 1655 £50
47A — — (G) ½ 1671 Boy smoking pipe
48 IAMES IOYSE (M) ¼ 1658
49 *Thomas Hall* ½ Tobacco-roll; Grocers' Arms, *Mercer. Heart-shape* £120
49A THOMAS SLAVTER (M) ½ 1669 Cordwainers' Arms
50 SAMVEL TRECHER (I) ½ 1665 MERCER £35
51 — — (G) ¼ 1653 £45
52 IOHN TYLER (A) ¼ 1665 Mercers' Arms
53 RICHARD WARE (P) ¼ 1653 £40
53A SAMVELL WARE (S) ¼ 1658
54 (See *Essex* 342)

Colnbrook

54A THOMAS BVRCOMBE (D) ¼ Hart £22
54B IOHN FORISE (S) ¼ 1667 AT YE, bear
54C ALCE GOAD ½ 1669 AT THE BELL
54D IOHN GVY (B) ¼ 1652 Cock, CHANDLER £28
54E WIDOW (S) HOMES ¼ AT YE BALL
54F IOHN HOSEY (I) ¼ AT THE ANGELL
54G SAMVELL MILLS (M) ¼ '57 Ostrich £50
54H EDMVND SLOCOMBE (D) ¼ 1653 3 stags £28

Edlesborough

55 DANIELL FINCH (S) ½ 1666 £35

Emberton

56 IOHN PEIRCESON ¼ 1668 Scales
57 ANTHONY SCALDWELL (A) ¼ 1664 Scales £35

Eton

58 (See *Beds.* 43A)
59 THOMAS COLLINGS ½ 1669 Fleur-de-lis
60 RICHARD ROBINSON (A) ¼ 1666 Crossed pipes
61 (See *Beds.* 44C)
62 (Misreading of 61)

Fenny Stratford

63 ROBERT HONNOR (L) ¼ 1655 Grocers' Arms £45
64 — — (L) ¼ '67
65 WILLIAM INNS (A) ¼ 1651 £32
66 IOHN SMALBONS (E) ¼ 1656 Hat £32

Haddenham

67 (See *Cambs.* 131)

Hambledon

67A IOHN LANE (M) ½ 1669 Horseshoe

Horton

67B GEORGE GOAD (M) ½ 1669

Hughenden

68 FRANCIS BARNABY (A) ¼ Vintners' Arms, GROCER £40
69 (Misreading of 68)
70 FRANCIS BARNABY ½ Vintners' Arms, GROCER £35

Horwood, Great or **Little**

71 HENRY FEILDEN ½ 1668 Acorn
72 IOHN CARTER ½ 1668 Scales
73 HVGH WILLEATT (A) ½ Crowned rose £45
74 FRANCIS WOODCOCK (E) ½ Haberdashers' Arms £45
75 — — (E) ¼ — £32
75A — WOODCOCKE (F) ½ £60

Iver

76 NICHOLAS MERVIN (E) ¼ BAKER £40

Ivinghoe

77 ROBERT BARNES (S) ¼ Scales, MERCER
78 (Misreading of 79)
79 HENRY BVTLER ½ '67 BAKER £55
79A IOHN TOMES (S) ¼ Horse, MERCER

Lavendon

80 EDMOND BALTSWELL (A) ¼ Bakers' Arms

Leckhamstead

81 ABRAHAM TAYLOR ½ 1669 AT YE COCK £50

Little Brickhill

82 CHARLES LORD ½ 1669 Man making candles

Marlow, Great

83 ALICE BOVLES (surname struck over PARKER) ½ Queen's bust

83A ALICE BOVLER ½ —
84 — PARKER ½ —
85 STEPHEN HARRIS (D) ¼ Scales
86 —— (D) ¼ 1669 Scales, side of bacon
87 THOMAS LANE ¼ 1666
88 PETER RIVERS (A) (½) 1667 Family Arms
89 THO SMITH (I) ¼ Crossed guns
90 SILVESTER WIDMERE (K) ¼ Griffin £60

Mursley
91 HENRY PITKIN ½ 1668 SILKE WEAVER

Newport Pagnell
92 WILLIAM BREDEN (E) ¼ Scales
93 IOHN BVRGIS (S) ¼ 1668 Scales £40
94 IOSIAS CHAPMAN ¼ Scales
95 IOHN CHILD (R) ¼ Scales
96 *John Child* ½ 1667 Tobacco, pipes. In *pb*
97 EDWARD COOPER (E) ½ Scales
97A —— ¼ (? design)
98 —— ¼ 1667 Grocers' Arms £55
98A IAMES DAVIS (E) ¼ Skinners' Arms
99 IOHN DAVIS (I) ¼ Drapers' Arms
100 ROB HOOTON (E) ¼
101 SAMVELL LAMBERT ½ Scales £14
102 IOHN NORMAN ¼ Scales
103 —— (E) ¼ Grocers' Arms
104 THOMAS PERROTT (E) ¼ Heart
105 W.S. (F) ¼ Scales £38
105A IOHN THORNTON (E) ¼ Thorn bush

Newton Longville
105B IEFFERY WILLISON (I) ½ 1667 Tobacco, pipes

North Crawley
106 NICHOLAS STEELE (M) ¼ Scales

Northall
106A WILLIAM ASHBY (A) ½ 1666
106B —— (A) ½ 1668

Olney
107 IOHN AMPS (R) ¼ 1662 Scales £20
108 ROBERT ASPRAY (M) ¼ 1662 Scales £18
109 IAMES BRIERLY (M) ¼ 1658 Scales £32
110 MOSES FREEMAN (E) ¼ 1668 Scales £20
111 IOHN GAYNES (S) ¼ 1652 Scales £14
112 IOSEPH SCRIVENER (E) ¼ 1668 Scales £25

Princes Risborough
113 EDWARD BARNABY (W) ½ 1665 £35
114 —— (W) ¼ 3 tuns
115 THOMAS HEADEACH (E) ½ 1669 Fleur-de-lis. *Square.* **Plate 1**

Shenley
115A IOSEPH INNS (E) ¼ 1670. *Octagonal*

Sherington
116 EDWARD BRITNELL (A) ¼ Scales

Soulbery
116A IOHN NEALE (F) ¼ Fleece

Steeple Claydon
117 WILLIAM NORMAN (I) ½ 1668

Stewkley
118 THOMAS COLES ½ 1667 Grocers' Arms £38

Stony Stratford
119 FRANCIS ANDERTON ¼ Grocers' Arms
120 ROBERT ANDERTON (M) ¼ 3 cloves £28
121 IOHN BOTRILL (A) ¼ Cordwainers' Arms
122 HVGH BLATSO (M) ¼ Drapers' Arms
123 THOMAS BVRGES (A) ¼ 1657 Bakers' Arms
124 CHRISTOPH CLIFTON (I) ¼ Pot of lilies £45
125 MATHEW FINALL (F) ¼ Phoenix and nest
126 THOMAS FORFEIT (A) ½ Griffin
126A IOHN GOMFORD ¼?
127 HENREY HONNOR ½ 1664 £38
128 WILLIAM MARSHALL (M) ¼ Lion
129 FRANCIS PENN ¼ Mercers' Arms £42
130 IOHN PENN (M) ½ 1669 £35
131 WILLIAM SMITH (E) ½ 1668
132 RICHARD VEASEY (E) ¼ Lion

Swanbourne
133 IOHN BAVIN ¼ 1652 Dove

Thornborough
134 EDWARD PVRSSELL ½ 1668 £18

Tingewick
135 GEORGE DRVRY (M) ½ 1669 Mercers' Arms £35
136 IOHN DVRRANT ½ 1668 Fleur-de-lis

Waddesdon
136A HENRY AND ELIZABETH BATTERSON ½ AT THE BELL
137 RICHARD SVTHEREY (M) ¼ CARRIER

Warrington
138 THOMAS NORRIS (M) ¼ 1668 Scales £45

Wendover
139 GEORGE BROWN (A) ½ Haberdashers' Arms, CHAPMAN £32
140 IOHN DVNCOMBE (E) ¼ 1664 Hat
140A IOHN FOSSCET (M) ¼ Paschal Lamb
141 FRANCIS FVNGE (E) ½ 1668 £35
142 RALPH HILL (E) ¼ 1655 Rose £38
143 GABRIELL PRENTICE (A) ¼ 1664 Grocers' Arms
144 THOMAS STOKINS (P) ¼ 1656 £38

Winslow
145 MATHEW BISHOP (D) (½) 1666 3 boars' heads £50

146 —— (D) ¼ n.d. —
147A IOHN CRAWLY AND MR DIMOCK ½ 1666 Hand holding axe over leaf
147 As last, but IO punched in over MR £40
148 IOHN FORREST (M) ½ 1666 Bakers' Arms £38
149 WILLIAM GILES (M) (½) 1666 Hat £45
150 — GYLES (M) ¼ n.d. — £35
151 THOMAS GODW(I *or* Y)N (I) ½ £40
152 DANIELL SAYER ¼ Grocers' Arms £50
153 THOMAS SMALLBONES (A) ¼ Hat
154 IOHN WATT (K) ½ '64 £40

Wooburn

154A ROBERT DREW (A) ¼ 1664 Rose
154B IONATHAN KINGHAM ½ MIL, water-wheel; mill-rind £45
154C Similar, mill-rind divides initials I.K. £50

Woughton-on-the-Green

154D WILLIAM COALE (E) ¼ Grocers' Arms

Wycombe (incl. **Great, High** and **West Wycombe**)

155 THOMAS ATKINES (E) ½ 1668 £25
156 THOMAS BATES ¼ 1661 Plumes
156A —— ¼ — Plumes in pot
156B SAMVELL BOVDREY (I) ¼ King's bust
157 THOMAS BVTTERFEILD ½ Wheatsheaf £50
158 (Misreading of 159)
159 THO BVTTERFIELD ¼ Wheatsheaf £50
160 THO DIMARSH (A) ¼ 1668 Sugar-loaf
161 WILLIAM FISHER (A) ¼ 1652 Clothworkers' Arms £50
162 ROBERT FRIER ¼ Rose £40
163 IEREMIAH GRAY (M) ¼ Swan chained £20
164 IOHN HARDING (M) ¼
165 THOMAS HARDING (E) ¼ 1668
166 FRANSIS INGEBY ¼ 1666 £45
167 IOHN IVSON (M) ½ 1669 Chequer board £35
168 THOMAS LEECH (A) ½ 1667 Lion £35
169 RICH LVCAS (D) ½ 1670 Lion, RATHER DEAD THEN DISLOYAL £25
170 (Worn specimen of 169)
171 RICHARD LVCAS (D) ¼ 1653 Lion with rod £22
172 IOHN MORRIS ½ 1666 Stick of candles £50
173 —— ¼ ——
174 RICHARD PREIST (E) ¼ 1662 Crown
175 (Misreading of 176)
176 ALEXANDER PARNAM (K) ¼ 1668 Greyhound
177 IOHN ROWELL (M) ½ 1667 Joiners' Arms £40
177A THOMAS TAYLOR (E) ¼ Roll of lace
177B ROBERT WATSON (M) ¼ 1666 Saracen's head
177C THOMAS WHEATLY (S) ¼ Wheatsheaf
178 ROBERT WHITTON (K) ¼ Stag £25
179 EDWARD WINCH (P) ½ 1666 Family Arms £38

Cambridgeshire

New tokens recorded from W. Gilbert, 'Unpublished Seventeenth Century Tokens in the Collection of William Gilbert' (*NC*, 1927); and R. H. Thompson, *Sylloge* . . . (see under Bedfordshire).

See also W. Gilbert, 'Cambridgeshire Seventeenth Century Tokens' (*SNC*, May/June 1917): varieties; Kenneth A. Jacob, 'Notes on Some Seventeenth-Century Cambridge Tokens' (*BNJ*, 1963) and 'The Cambridge Trade Tokens of the 17th and 18th Centuries and the Traders who issued them' (*Cambridgeshire Local History Council Bulletin*, 1971–5); D. W. Dykes and K. A. Jacob, 'A Mythical Seventeenth Century Halfpenny of Cambridge' (*BNJ*, 1965); Reg Holmes assisted by Pamela Blakeman, *Ely Tokens* (Ely, 1983): a booklet giving details of issuers and enlarged photographs, including die varieties; T. D. Whittet, 'A Survey of Apothecaries' Tokens, part 6: Cambridgeshire' (*The Pharmaceutical Journal*, 30 June 1984); and *BNJ*, 1984.

Believed entirely unpublished: 140A.

Minimum price for unvalued tokens: £45

Abington

1 THOMAS SMITH (M) ¼ '58 Ship, crescent, GROCER

2–6 (See *Berks*. 2, 7, 8, 10, 11)

Arrington Bridge

7 HENRY ATKINS ½ AT THE, turnstile £22

Brinkley

8 IOHN GROWSE (M) ½ Tallowchandlers' Arms

Burwell

9 OLLIVER HARLIE (M) ¼ Haberdashers' Arms £45

Cambridge

10 IAMES ALDERS ¼ Lion £25

11, 12 RICHARD ALLEN (I) ¼ ROSE TAVERNE £12

13 (Probably misreading of 10)

14 NICHOLAS APTHORP ¼ Globe on stand £20

15 WILL BASSETT (K) ½ 1669 MERCER*

16 IOHN BIRD ¼ 1667 Merchant Taylors' Arms £11

17 (Probably a worn example of 16)

18 IOHN BLACKLY (A) ¼ Bakers' Arms £15

19 IONATHAN BROWNE (I) ¼ Grocers' Arms £17

20 WILL BRYAN (H) ¼ 1652 3 cloves, CONFECTIONER £11

21 I.B. (E) ¼ VNDER THE ROASE, Bakers' Arms £30

* An error token for *Wales* 30

22 EDWARD CHALLIS ¼ 1663 Haberdashers' Arms £20

23 —— ¼ n.d. — £25

24 FRANCIS CHALLIS ¼ 1653 Stick of candles £25

25/6 IOHN CHAPLYN (M) ¼ Stick of candles £9

27 —— (M) ¼ 1667 — £14

28/9 ED CLARK (A) ¼ 1652 HABERDASHER £10

30/1 (Probably misreadings of 28/9)

32 PETER COLLINS ¼ 1656 Hand holding glove; initials W.M. £12

33 —— ¼ ——— small R in *obv.* field £18

34 RICHARD COOKE ½ 1669 AT PEASE HILL, talbot £20

35 IOHN CRASKE (A) ½ 1667 Grocers' Arms £25

36 THOMAS DARRANT (M) ¼ Griffin £12

37 IOHN DOD ½ 1667 AT THE RED HART AND ANTELOP £20

38 IOHN EWIN (A) ¼ 1652 Man making candles

39 THOMAS EWIN (E) ½ 1668 Man making candles £11

40 E.F. (E) ¼ 1651 AT THE MITER

41 GEORGE FELLSTED (A) ¼ Pestles in mortar £13

42 THOMAS FELSTED (D) ¼ 1664 Bakers' Arms £12

43 THOMAS FENN ¼ Woolpack £12

44 IOHN FINCH ¼ MARKET PLACE £35

45 THO FOX ¼ AT THE BLACK BVLL £20

46 IOHN FROHOCK (M) ¼ 1670 Family Arms £13

47 WILL GORHAM (M) ¼ Arms, crest, GROCER
48 FRANCIS HAMPSON ¼ 1667 Crossed pipes, tobacco-roll £30
49 ROBERT HARWOOD (C) ¼ 1660 £15
50 IAMES HAWKE (M) ¼ Grocers' Arms £25
51 — — (M) ¼ 1667 — £25
52 IOSEPH HEATH (H) ¼ 1666 Family Arms £7
53 (See *Southwark* 203)
54 ELIZEBETH HOGHTON ¼ £20
55 EDWARD IENNINGS ¼ Stick of candles £18
56 FRANCIS IERMAN ½ 1667 Grocers' Arms £12
57 STEPHEN IOHNSON (A) ¼ 1669 Hart (or unicorn)
58/9 IOSEPH LINSEY ½ 1663 2-headed eagle £12
60 SAMVELL LONG ¼ 1665 AT THE LILLY POT £40
61 (Not a trade token; individually made, probably unique)
62 CHRISTOFER MAIES ¼ Stick of candles £14
63 IOHN MARSTON ½ IN TRVMP-INGTON STREET, hand pouring coffee from pot into cups £18
64 OWEN MAYFIELD (S) ¼ 1658 Mitre £15
65 IOHN NEWTON (A) ¼ 1652 Grocers' Arms £20
66 IOHN NICKLES (I) ¼ AT BLEW, anchor, MARKET HILL £35
67 IOHN PECKE (M) ½ 1668 Bakers' Arms £15
68 SANDIS PEYTON (M) ¼ Family Arms, crest £18
69 IAMES POTTER (E) ¼ 1667 £18
70 (Probably misreading of 71/2)
71/2 THOMAS POWELL (E) ½ 1666 Group of lozenges £9
72A — — (I) ½ — —
73 — — (E) ½ 1667 — £20
74 HENERY RAPER (M) ¼ GROCER £18
75 — — (M) ¼ 1660 Shears
76 FRANCIS RVSSELL (A) ¼ 1663 Family Arms, crest £18
77 HENERY SMITH (M) ¼ Haberdashers' Arms £17
78 WILLIAM SMITH (E) ½ 1670 Leathersellers' Arms £17
79 IOHN SPARKES (M) ¼ 1653 BAKER £18
80 BENIAMIN SPENCE ½ 1668 Grocers' Arms, CHANDLER £25
81 IOSEPH TIFFORD ¼ 1659 3 cloves £20
82 WILL WATERSON (E) ¼ 1657 CARYER £18
83 WILLAM WELLS (S) ¼ 3 TVNS TAVERN £17
84 PHILLIP WILLIAMS (M) ¼ Bakers' Arms £14

Caxton

85 HVGH CONNY ½ 1666 CAXTON & ELSWORTH, 3 conies
86 ROBERT MILLARD ½ 1668 Pie crust, BAKER £28

Chatteris

87 THOMAS COAPE ½ 1670 AT THE, gate £45
88 THOMAS DRING (I) ½ 1667
88A IOHN FRENCH (same as *Hunts*. 27)
89 WILLIAM SMITH ½ 1670 Cooper making cask £25

Chesterton

90 WILLIAM LIMBER (D) ¼ Hart £22

Cottenham

91 PHILIP CHAMBERS ½ 1668 Man with club over shoulder £38

Croydon

92–5 (See *Surrey* 40–2, 45)

Doddington

96 ROBERT ADAMS ½ 1668 £35
97 (Same as 149)
98 IOHN IOHNSON ½ 1669 Windmill £45

Elsworth

99 (Same as 85)

Eltisley

100 ISAAC DES . . . (E) ¼ 16?? Arms

Ely

101 HENRY AVSTIN ¼ 1667 WEAVER £32
102 THOMAS CHADRTON (A) ¼ AT THE WHITE SWAN
103 WILLIAM CHEVILL (S) ¼ 1667 Merchant Taylors' Arms
104 LVKE CROCKSON (S) ¼ Stick of candles £22
105/6 CORNELIVS *or* CORNL(L *or* E)VS FVLLER ¼ 1654 Haberdashers' Arms £12
107 IOHN GAYER (A) ¼ Fishmongers' Arms £20
108 WILLIAM GOTOBED ¼ 1662 Skinners' Arms £42
109 IOHN KNOWLS (A) ¼ 1667 AT THE, ship £28
110 THOMAS LENSLEY (A) ¼ 1664 Platter (?) £25
111 WILLIAM LETTEN (K) ¼ AT ROSE & CROWN £40
112/3 NICHOLAS MAL(L)ABAR ¼ 1658 Woolpack £18
114 WILLIAM MARSH ¼ Scales, GROCER
115 THOMAS PORTER ¼ 1663 Grocers' Arms £17
116/7 IOHN READE ¼ 1656 Fishmongers' Arms, GROCER £14
118 RALPH SKITTAR (M) ¼ 1659 Bakers' Arms £28
119 WILLIAM TANNER (M) ¼ Sparger, BREWER £15
120 WILLIAM TVCKINTON ¼ Stick of candles, CHANDLER £22
121/3 WILL TVRKINTON ¼ 1661 — £10
122 WILLIAM WAGSTAFE ¼ Fishmongers' Arms, MERCER £13
124 — — ¼ Family Arms, MERCER £20
125 IOHN WEATHERHEAD (R) ¼ 1666 BAKER £38

Fordham

126 (Probably *Norfolk* 45)

Gamlingay
127 STEPHEN APTHORPE ¼ 1657 Grocers' Arms
128 —— ¼ 1659 — £22
129 —— ¼ 1666 — £22
130 IOSEPH HARVIE (M) ½ 1667 Grocers' Arms £17

Haddenham
131 IOHN MOR(EF or FI) ELD ¼ Man walking CARRIER £28

Hinxton
132 IOHN NORTH ½ 1667 Grocers' Arms £25

Histon
133 CHRISTOP CHALLICE ¼ 1670 Fleece

Hockington (Oakington)
134–6 (See *Devon* 226, 226A)

Ickleton
137 GEORGE FORDHAM ¼ CAMBRIDGSH
138 —— ¼ IN ESSEX, wheatsheaf

Isleham
139 ROBERT MOODEY (G) ¼ 1664 Mercers' Arms £24
140 WILLIAM READE (E) ¼ 1666 £35
140A —— (E) ¼ 1664
141 ELIZABETH ALLEN ¼ 1667 Chequers £38

Linton
142 IOHN BITTIN ¼ 1657 Griffin £20
143 ROBERT HALLS ¼ 1667 Scales £17
144 IOHN HARVY (S) ¼ CHANDLER £28
145 ROBERT MOORE ¼ 1667 Grocers' Arms

Littleport
146 OVERSEERS OF YE POOR ¼ 1668 Frying pan? £17

Littlington
147 (Probably *Sussex* 121)

Manea
148 IOHN SANDERS ½ 1671 Initials I.M. £35

March
149 ROB ADAMS ¼ 1670 Stick of candles
149A IOSEPH (BL?)VDWICK ½ 1669 Drapers' (?) Arms
150 THOMAS HARRYSON (M) ¼ 1657 HABERDASHER £24
151 — HA(O *or* R)RISON (M) ¼ 1667 Haberdashers' Arms £30
152 — HARRISON (M) ½ 1669 £28
153 IOHN INGROM ¼ 1666 £28
154 ROBERT NEALE ¼ 1656 GROCER £32
155 THOMAS TOWERS ½ 1669 Tower £38

Newmarket
156/7/9, 161–5 (See *Suffolk*, various between 265 and 279; one of the two parishes here was formerly in Cambs.)
158 (See *London* 645)
160 (Probably *London* 646A)

Newton
166 (See *Bucks.* 105B)

Over
167 THOMAS SKINNER ¼ 3 hammers, MERCER

Soham
168 ROB CROW ½ 1671 BAKER, A HALFE PENY £32
169 —— (P) (½) — BAKER, lion £35
170 THOMAS TROWELL (M) ¼ 1664 Stick of candles £38
171 HOVELL IOANES (F) ¼ 1654 Grocers' Arms £28
172 —— (F) ¼ 1658 — £45
173 NATHANIELL STEARNE (G) ¼ 1667 Grocers' Arms £20
174 MARY KENT, IOHN KENT OF HORNSWELL (same as *Suffolk* 152)

Stanton
175 (Probably *Suffolk* 304)

Sutton
176 IOHN CLEMENT ¼ 1656 3 tuns £22
177 IOHN BVRKHVEST ¼ 1657 Grocers' Arms £14
178 (Probably *Devon* 278)

Swaffham
179–81 (See *Norfolk* 247–50)

Swaffham Bulbeck
182 WILLIAM COE ¼ Woolpack £50

Swavesey
183 WILLIAM BVRTEN (S) ¼ 1656 £22

Thorney
184 EDWARD TAYLOR ¼ Bakers' Arms

Upwell
185–9 (See *Norfolk* 260–5; the parish is in both counties)

West Wratting
190 EDWARD CRANDFEILD (D) ¼ Grocers' Arms

Whittlesey
191 THOMAS DAVIE (E) ½ 1668 Grocers' Arms £24
192 —— ¼ — Initials W.D.
193 IOHN EADES ¼ 1657 Bakers' Arms
194 ROBERT IVES (I) ¼ 1667 Woolcomb £22
195 —— (I) ¼ n.d. Woolcomb (incorrectly drawn) £25
196 SIL(VESTER?) IVES (E) ¼ Woolcomb
197 GEORGE LAMBE ¼ Grocers' Arms £40
198 WILLIAM SEARLE ¼ Grocers' Arms £28

(Little) Wilbraham

199 IOHN TVRNER (S) ¼ 1666 £25

Willingham

200 IOHN NORRIS (A) ½ 1669

Wisbech

201 IOHN BELLAMY (I) ¼ 1665 Grocers' Arms £35

202 —— (I) ½ 1667 — GROCER £22

203 —— (I) ¼ — £28

204 HENRY COLDWELL ½ 1668 HABA-DASHER £28

205 —— ¼ n.d. —

206 IOHN FINCH ¼ 1666 Grocers' Arms £14

207 —— ¼ n.d. — £14

208 RICHARD HARRISON ¼ 1664 Haberdashers' Arms

209 IOHN MOYES (E) ¼ 1664 Grocers' Arms £40

210 ANTHONY RACHELL (E) ¼ 1667 Cog-wheel £32

211 HENRY TVNARD (I) ¼ 1657 Bakers' Arms £14

212 —— (I) ¼ 1662 — £30

213 —— (I) ¼ 1663 — £14

Wood Ditton

214 KIMWOOD NORTON ½ 1670 Windmill

Cheshire

New tokens recorded from N. Heywood, 'Further Notes on Lancashire and Cheshire Tokens' (*Transactions of the Lancashire and Cheshire Antiquarian Society*, 1912); W. Gilbert, 'Unpublished . . .' (see under Cambridgeshire); *SNC List*, May 1947; R. H. Thompson, *Sylloge* . . . (see under Bedfordshire); *SCA* 19, 3 Mar. 1982 and 51, 16 Apr. 1986; and T. D. Whittet, 'A Survey of Apothecaries' Tokens, part 7: Cheshire' (*The Pharmaceutical Journal*, 8 Dec. 1984).

Believed entirely unpublished: 46A, 58A, 76A.

Minimum price for unvalued tokens: £135

Audlem

1 THOMAS BATEMAN (I) 1d 1670
2 ROBERT BIRCHALL 1d 1669

Bramhall

3 IOHN BROWNE ½ 1669 £120

Chester

3A THOMAS ASPINWALL 1d 1666 IN THE BRIDGE STREET
4 THOMAS BAKER ½ Lion, POST MASTER. **Plate 1**
5 NATH BASSNET 1d 1668 APOTHICARY
6 SARAH BENNET ½ 1668 AT YE 3 TVNNS
6A WILLIAM BENNETT 1d Wheatsheaf, GROCER
7 ROGER BRERETON ½ 1666 Grocers' Arms
8 RICHARD BRISCOE 1d 1670 Royal oak
9 RALPH BVRROVGHS 1d 1670 Crown
10 WILLIAM CRVE 1d 1668
11 ANNE EARLE 1d 1668
12 SAMVEL ELCOCKE 1d 1669 Family Arms; phoenix
13 ROBERT FLETCHER 1d AT YE HALF MOON
13A THOMAS GAMVL 1d 3 hammers, crescent, IRONMONGER. *Heart-shape*
13B IOHN GRIFFITH ¼ Arms (? Cordwainers') In *pb*
14 WILLIAM HARVEY 1d '69 AT YE STARR, Ostrich with horseshoe in mouth
15 SAMVELL HEATH 1d 1670 CONFECTIONER. *Heart-shape*
16 THOMAS HEATH 1d 1667 APOTHECARY
17 ROBERT HEWITT ½ 1667 City Arms; Grocers' Arms
18 WILL HEWITT ½ 1667 Arms
19 RALPH HOCKNELL (M) ½ 1666 Ironmongers' Arms
20 IOHN HOVGH ½ 1666 AT THE, swan
21 IAMES HVTCHINSON 1d 1669 Tallowchandlers' Arms £70
22 NATHAN IOLLIE 1d '68 IN NORTHGAT STREET AT YE PHEASANT £120
23 CADWALADER IONES 1d 1669 IRONMONGER
24 IAMES KNOWSLEY ½ 1667 City Arms
25 PETER LEE ¼ Ram's head
26 THOMAS MINSHVLL 1d 1666
27 RICH MYNSHAL ¼ Star and crescent
28 LEWIS PERRY 1d 1669 Hands joined
29 ROBERT RADFORD (M) 1d 1668 IN BRIDGE STREETE, Family Arms
30 SAM RADFORD 1d 1668 IN YE BRIDGE STREETE, Demi-griffin crest
31 ROB RIDGE (F) ½ 1666 Ship
31A IOHN ROBERTS 1d 1669 Harp, IRONMONGER
32 THOMAS ROBINSON 1d 1669 Anchor
33 IOHN SALMON 1d 1667 Family Arms, Haberdashers' Arms £110
33A —— 1d 1670 —— WILL GIVE FOR THIS A PENY
34 THOMAS SIMPSON ½ 1667 City Arms
34A As 34 but HALFE erased to raise value to one penny
35 WILLIAM SNEAD 1d 1668 Scythe and snead (= pole)
36 PETER STRINGER 1d 1667 Family Arms
37 IOHN TRAVERS ¼ 1663 Family Arms
38 HENRY WILLIAMS 1d 1667 Ironmongers' Arms £70
39 —— 1d n.d. —
40 (See *Sussex* 70)
41 LEWIS WILLIAMS ½ 1667

Congleton

42 RICHARD COTTON ½ 1667 Family Arms

43 RICHARD EATON ½ 1666 Grocers' Arms
44 IOHN GLOVER ½ 1667
45 THOMAS WELCH (A) ¼ Feltmakers' Arms
46 —— (A) ½ 1666— £120

Egremont

46A IOHN GEITSKELL ½ 1666 Bust of Chas II, MERCER

Knutsford

47 PHILLIP ANTROBVS ½ 1671 Mercers' Arms
48 IAMES IOHNSON ½ 1668 Grocers' Arms. *Octagonal*
49 RICHARD LEIGH (C) ¼ Lion, MERCER
50 IAMES SWINTON ½ 1667. *Octagonal* £55
50A IOHN SWINTON ½ n.d. Arms. *Octagonal*

Macclesfield

51 SAM ENDON ½ 1671 Man smoking between tobacco-roll and scales, WELCOM YOV BE TO TRADE WTH ME. **Plate 1** £80
52 SAMVELL LEAH (I) ¼ Grocers' Arms £100
53 NATHANIELL POOLE ½ 1668 Mercers' Arms. *Heart-shape* £185
54 FRANCIS SWINDELL ½ 1669 SQVARE DEALING IS BEST. *Square*
55 IOHN TOWERTON ¼ Boy smoking, tobacco-roll under arm £110
56 EDWARD WOOD ½ MERCER £90

Middlewich

57 NATHENEL BEARD ½ Scales, CHANDLER
58 THOMAS COTTON ½ 1669 ALTHOVGH BVT BRASS YET LET ME PASS. *Heart-shape* £225
58A RICHARD HASSALL (E) ½ 1667 Mercers' Arms

Nantwich

58B RICHARD BARKER (E) ½ 1665
59 RICHARD BICKERTON ½ 1666
60 GEORGE BEESTON (E) ½ Grocers' Arms
61 THOMAS BROMHALL (E) ½ 1665 £90
62 *William Cappur* ½ 1666 Ship
63 (Probably misreading of 62)
64 DANIEL IACKSON 1d 1669 Mercers' Arms. *Octagonal*
65 THOMAS IACKSON ½ 1666 Ironmongers' Arms £100
65A —— ½ (?) n.d.
66 ELIZABETH PRICE ½ 1666 Family Arms £110
67 IOHN TENCH (M) ½ 1666
68 —— (M) ¼ 1665 Mercers' Arms
69 IAMES WILSON (A) ½ 1666
69A GEORGE WOOD ½ Haberdashers' Arms

Sandbach

69B IOHN BOWYER ¼ Goldsmiths' Arms
70 IONAH BOWYER ½ 1667 Mercers' Arms

Stockport

71 HENRY ANDERVE (M) ½ 1667
72 IOHN ANDREWS (E) ½ Grocers' Arms; City of London Arms
73 IOHN BROOK ½ 1670
74 WALTER COATES ½ 1667 Horse caparisoned
75 IOHN HVLME ½ 1666
76 FRANCIS NEWTON (E) ½ 1669
76A —— (E) ½ 1667
77 MARGERET NICHOLSON ½ 1667 Mercers' Arms £75
78 RALPH AND ELIZ NICHOLSON ½ 1667 Mercers' Arms £110
79 THOMAS SMITH (I) ½ 1666 £80

Cornwall

Major reference: J. A. D. Mayne & J. A. Williams, *Coins & Tokens of Cornwall* (Exeter, 1985). Updating of 'Williamson', more notes, and specimen locations of some of the additions. The successor to J. A. Williams' *Cornish Tokens* (Truro [1970]), which latter has fewer errors in the descriptions of the tokens.

Further new tokens recorded from R. H. Thompson, *Sylloge* . . . (see under Bedfordshire); and *NC*, 1902.

See also T. D. Whittet, 'A Survey of Apothecaries' Tokens, part 8: Cornwall and Cumberland' (*The Pharmaceutical Journal*, 26 Jan. 1985).

Believed entirely unpublished: 3C, 31B, 32A, 41A, 67A.

Minimum price for unvalued tokens: £90

Bodmin
1A HENRY DAGGE ¼ 1664 Mercers' Arms
1 IOHN HARRIS (A) ¼ Grocers' Arms
2 RICHARD MANATON (P) ¼ 1664 Family Arms
3 THOMAS WILLS (F) ¼ 3 griffins on shield

Boscastle
3A PENMIN GAYER ¼ 1659 Mercers' Arms

Buripps (?)
3B ARTHVR TRY ¼ 1666

Callington
3C TRISTRAM DOIDGE ½ 1670 Stick of candles
4 IOHN WILLS ¼ 1667 Man making candles
4* (Probably misreading of 4)

Camelford
4A SAMVELL GAYER ¼ 1668
4B NICHOLAS HENDER ¼ Mercers' Arms

Falmouth (and **Smithwicke**)
5 THOMAS HOLDEN (A) ¼ 1668 Arms £65
6 RICHARD LOBB ¼ 1655 Arms b.s.
7 NICHOLAS KEATE ¼ Family Arms
8 BENIAMIN PENDER (A) ¼ 1664 Arms
9 — PYNDOR ¼ 1665 Mercers' Arms
10 HENRY PENIELL (M) ¼ 1666 AT YE, 7 stars
11 MICHELL RVSSELL (A) ¼ 3 escallops £65
11A —— (A) ¼ Family Arms on shield

Fowey
12 IOHN GOODALL ¼ 1657
13 IOHN MAIOR (M) ¼ 1657 Grocers' Arms
14 PETER TOLLER ¼ 1660 £90

Grampound
14A M.G. (A) ¼ 1657 AT YE SPREAD EAGLE

Helston
15 ROBERT COCKE ¼ 1666 Griffin
16 WILLIAM PENHALVRICK ¼ 1667 £50
17 IOHN PENHELICK (M) ¼ 1666 Family Arms
18 HENRY PENHELLICK ¼ 1659 Family Arms
19 PETER PRISKE ¼ 1668 £42
20 RICHARD ROGERS (T) ¼ 1668 Mercers' Arms £60

Kilkhampton
21 IOHN COVRTIS ¼ 1667

Launceston
22 DEGORY BEWES ¼ OF SANT STEPHENS, Mercers' Arms £85
23 THOMAS BEWES ¼ '59 3 castles
24 OSWOLD KINGDON ¼ Tallowchandlers' Arms
25 RICH KINGDOME ¼ Haberdashers' Arms
25A ANDREWE SHEARE ¼ 1667 Mercers' Arms

Liskeard
26 BENIAMIN CHAPMAN ¼ Mercers' Arms £60
27 —— ¼ Rose
28 —— ¼ 1666 Mercers' Arms £80
29 IOHN CHAPMAN ¼
30 IOSEPH CLOAKE (M) ¼ Grocers' Arms
31 —— (M) ¼ 1664 — £85
31A ELIZABETH COLE ¼ 1664 Scales
31B HENRY HELLYAR ¼ 1668 3 ostriches
32 RICHARD KEMP ¼ '60 3 fleurs-de-lis £70
32A IOSEPH VPCOTT ¼ Cock
33 GEORGE WHITFORDE ½ Arms. *Heart-shape*

Looe (and **East Looe**)
34 WILLIAM AMBROSE ¼ 1664 Dolphin
35 IOHN CHANDLER ¼
35A IOANE CHUBB ¼ 1655
36 PEETER COADE ¼ Mercers' Arms
37 ELIZABETH HENDRA ¼ 1668 Ship
38 BENIAMEN OBEN ¼ 1656 Mercers' Arms
39 RICHARD STADGELL ¼ 1669 Anchor

Lostwithiel
40 IOHN ALLIN ¼ Grocers' Arms £60
41 RICHARD WEBER ¼ 1658
41A —— ¼ 1659
42 —WEBBER ¼ 1664 £45

Ludgvan
43 RICHARD SCADDAM ¼ 1666

Marazion
44 THOMAS COREY (P) ¼ 1668

Mevagissey
45 IOHN KEAGLE (B) ¼ 1664 Fleur-de-lis £85
46 IAMES BONYTHON (M) ¼ 1651 3 fleurs-de-lis

Millbrook
47 (Probably *Beds.* 74)

Mylor
47A IOHN BRODWAY ¼ 1669 Tobacco-roll

Newport
48 IOHN KERTON (I) ½ 1668 3 sheep in fold
49 —— (I) ¼ n.d. —
50 (See *Bucks.* 103)
51 (More likely *Salop.* 51A)

Padstow
51A IOSIAS PIPER ¼ 1659
52 PETER SWYMMER (G) ¼ 1664 (date on *obv.*)
52A PEETER SWIMER (G) ¼ — (date on *rev.*) **Plate 1**

Penare
53 FRANCES OSGOOD (V) ¼ Angel

Penryn
53A SAMPSON BLOYES ¼ 1653
54 MICHAEL COODE ¼ 1667 Armorial bearings
55 MICHAELL— ¼ 1669 3 doves £65
56 IAMES KEMPE ¼ 1668 3 garbs (?) on shield
57 IOHN PEARCE ¼ 1666 Haberdashers' Arms £50
58 ANDREW RIDER (C) ¼ 1664 Bell £65
59 THOMAS SPRY ¼ 1667 Family Arms. **Plate 1** £38
60 VRSVLA SPVRR ¼ 1668 £75
61 THOMAS WORTH ¼ 1665 2-headed eagle £55

Penzance
62 RALPH BEARD ¼ 1667 Mullet b.s.
63 IOHN BLVNT (I) ¼ 1665 3 lions on shield £65
64 IOHN CLEVERDON ¼ Mercers' Arms
65 ANTHONY GVBBS ¼ 1667 Fleur-de-lis
66 P.L. ¼ Head of John the Baptist; castle, falcon and crescent £75
67 IOHN TREVETHAN ¼ '63 Griffin between 3 fleurs-de-lis

Probus
67A FRANCIS LOOGER ¼ Cross
68 IOHN LOOGER ¼ 1668 Cross

Redruth
69 ANTHONY COCKE ¼ 1666 3 cocks £35
70 —— (M) ¼ — 3 cocks on shield (Family Arms) £42
71 STEPHEN HARRIS (I) ¼ Mercers' Arms

Saltash
72 IOHN FOSTER ½ 1670 Anchor £80
73 CHRISTOPHER STEPHENS ½ 1669 Men in rowing boat
74 PETER STEPHENS ½ 1667 Ship £55
74A —STEVENS (I) ¼ 1665 —
75 THOMAS SWETNAM ½ 1669 Vintners' Arms

Scilly, Isles of
75A IOHN COSSEN ¼ 1666
76 THOMAS EKINES ½ 3 men around globe; merchant's mark £60

St Agnes
77 EDWARD NEWSAM ¼ 1666 Family Arms; bust of Saint £85

St Austell
77A LAWRENCE GROWDON (I) ¼ Dolphin
78 IOHN TREFRY ¼ 1669
79 —— ¼ — Mercers' Arms

St Columb
80 IOHN OXNAM ¼ 1664 Mercers' Arms
81 RICHARD EDWARDS ¼ 1663 Mercers' Arms

St Ives
82 HENRY CORDALL (E) ¼ 1658 Haberdashers' Arms
82A —— (E) ¼ 1657 —
83 WILLIAM HARRISON ¼ 1657 £55
84 IAMES HEATON ½ 1667 £55
85 IOHN HICKMAN (E) ¼ 1660 Salters' Arms £55
86 IOHN HICKMAN IVNIOR ½ 1668 Salters' Arms £60
87 IOHN HVTCHINS ¼ 1667 £60
88 RICHARD HVTCHINS (W) ¼ 1666 3 roses
89 IOHN KINGE ¼ 1667 Crossed swords £60
90 (See *Hunts.* 49)

St Mawes
91 WILL KNAPTON (S) ¼ 1666 Vintners' Arms, initials W.S.N.

St Neot

92 (See *Hunts*. 57)
93 WALTER HODGE (E) ¼ Shuttle

Stratton

93A THOMAS BANT ¼ King's Arms
94 IOHN CANN ¼ 1652 Mercers' Arms
94A SAMVEL GAYER ¼ 1664
94B WILLIAM VGLOW ¼ Mercers' Arms

Tregony

95 HENRY SLADE (I) ¼ '58 Grocers' Arms

Truro

96 HENERY BVRGAS (A) ¼ 1657 Blazing star
97 ANDREW CROCKER ¼ 1668 £75
98 RICHARD FREEMAN (M) ¼ Mercers' Arms £65
99 WILLIAM IACKMAN (I) 1666 Haberdashers' Arms
99A IOSEPH LAVGHORNE ¼ 1657 Ship
99B — LA(HA?)THORNE ¼ 1671 —
100 MATHEW ROWETT (A) ¼ 1668 Mercers' Arms £75
101 HENRY SLADE (I) ¼ 1660
102 — — (I) ¼ 1663
103 WILLIAM SMITH ¼ Ship
104 THOMAS TREWILLOW ¼ 1667 3 owls *b.s.*
104A — TREWOOLA ¼ 1669 3 owls; crowned rose
105 SAMVELL WEALE (F) ¼ 1663 Post-boy

Unknown Locality

106 T.R. ¼ 1667 MERCER
107 (See *Lincs*. 233A)

Cumberland

New token recorded from W. Gilbert, 'Unpublished . . .' (see under Cambridgeshire).

See also T. D. Whittet, 'A Survey . . .' (see under Cornwall).

Minimum price for unvalued tokens: £150

Broughton

1 IOHN LAMPLVGH ½ COAL PITTS, castle. *Octagonal*

1A IOHN WILSON (Probably *Bucks*. 29A)

Cockermouth

2 A.B. ¼ '64 I AM FOR A PVBLIQVE GOOD **Plate 1** £40

2A IOHN FALLOWFEILLD (S) ¼ 1669 MERCER

3 LEO SCOTT (K) ¼ I AM FOR BETTER CHENG

4 THOMAS WATSON (I) ¼ '64 St George & dragon

Kirklinton

5 THOMAS BARRETT (M) ¼ 1666 Woolpack

Derbyshire

New tokens recorded from *NC*, 1931; *SNC List*, May 1947; Glendining sale, 14 Apr. 1964, and T. D. Whittet, 'A Survey of Apothecaries' Tokens, part 9: Derbyshire, (*The Pharmaceutical Journal*, 20 July 1985).

See also P. Preston-Morley and H. Pegg (see under Nottinghamshire): notes on late 19th cent. forgeries.

Believed entirely unpublished: 58A, 93A, 96A, 101A.

Minimum price for unvalued tokens: £65

Alfreton
1A TIMOTHIE COATES ½ 1664 Family Arms
1 CORNELIAS LAVNDER ½ 1663 Mercers' Arms
2 ROBERT WRIGHT ½ 1668 Beehive. *Heart-shape*

Alsop-en-le-Dale
3 WILLIAM BRION ½?

Ashbourne
4 HENRY ADAMS ½ 1669 CHANDLER
5 IOHN ATKINS ½ 1667 MERCER
6 THOMAS BAGVLEY ½ Mercers' Arms
7 WILLIAM BRVNT ½ 1671 (7)
8 WILLIAM FROGGATT ½ 1664 Arms
9 CHARLES HOLME ½ 1666 Lion £70
10 IOHN MARRATT ½ 1671*
11 DANIELL MORLEY ½ 1669
12 WILLIAM OWSBORNE ½ '71 Coachman driving coach and pair
13 IOSEPH SHERWINN ½ 1666 PEWTERER
14 MARIE SLEIGH ½ Mercers' Arms
15 IOHN VALENTINE (M) ¼? 1668 Cutlers' Arms
16 RICHARD WATSON ½ 1663 Haberdashers' Arms £70

Ashford
17 ROBERT BIRDS 1d 1671 Value in wreath

Bakewell
18 IOHN DICKENS ½ 1669 Arm holding covered cup £30
19, 20 THOM(E *or* A)S GRAMM(E *or* A)R (M) (½) Mercers' Arms
21 THOMAS GRAYMER ½ 1669 Mercers' Arms. *Square* £165

Baslow
22 SAMVEL PALMER ½ 1667

* Copies are known (late 19th cent.) of crude style

Belper
23 IOSEPH CLARKE ¼ AT LANE END, crown
24 IAMES IACKSON (R) ½ Grocers' Arms

Birchover
25 HVMPHREY SMITH (E) 1d 1671

Bolsover
26 IOHN AKERS (M) ½ Grapes
27 RICHARD SOVTHWORTH ½ 1667 Grocers' Arms
28 — — ¼ n.d. —

Bonsall
29 IOHN BALME ½ 1670 BVTCHER
30 IOHN DVDLEY ¼ Grocers' Arms
31 HENRY HILLE ½ 1671 BVCHER

Brailsford
32 WILLIAM WEBB ½ 1671 Tallowchandlers' Arms

Brampton
33 IOHN DEARE (E) ½ 1669 £70
34 P.C.M. ¼ 1671 Scissors
35 (Probably *Northants*. 13A)

Brassington
36 DANIELL BAGSHAW ¼ 1663 Ironmongers' Arms

Castleton
37/8 ROB(ERT) THORNHILL ½ Bull standing under tree

Chapel-en-le-Frith
39 NICHOLAS SMITH ½ 1671 Anvil

Chesterfield
40 RICHARD CLARKE (A) ½ AT THE ANGELL £28
41 — — (A) ¼ —
42 IAMES DVTTON ½ 1666 Lion £65
43 (Probably same as 44)
44 SAMVELL INMAN ½ 1667 Grocers' Arms
45 WILLIAM MILLNES ½ 1667 Grocers' Arms

46 THOMAS RADFORD ½ 1666 Haberdashers' Arms
47 EDWARD WOOD ½ APOTHECARY £45
48 RICHARD WOOD ¼ 3 sportsmen and dog

Crich

49 THOMAS LOWE ½ 1669 BVTCHER

Derby

50 RICHARD BAKEWELL ½ 1666 2 doves, GOOD MORROW VALENTINE
51 IOHN BANCRAFT ½ 1667 Rolls of bread
52 THOMAS BEEBYE ½ 1664 Tallowchandlers' Arms
53 GEORGE BLAGRAVE ½ 1668 Hand with sceptre; crown
54 ANN BLOODWORTH ½ 1669 Cordwainers' Arms, CORDWAINERS ARMS
55 ANNE — ½ — — SHOMAKERS ARMES
55A THOMAS BOTT ½ MERCER
55B — — ½ 1669 —
56 THOMAS BROOKS ½ 1668 Hat and feather
57 RICHARD CORDIN ½ 1667 Vintners' Arms
58 HENRY CORDEN ½ Bust of Charles II
58A — — ¼ Mercers' Arms
59 WILLIAM DAWSON ½ 1669 DIER £28
60 EDWARD DENTY ½ 1667 Queen's head
61 NATHANIEL DOVGHTY ½ 1666 MERCER
62 IOHN DVNNIDGE (D) ¼ 1663 Grocers' Arms
63 IOHN DVNNIDG IVNIOR ½ 1664 Grocers' Arms
64 ROBERT FEARBROTHER ½ 1669 Tallowchandlers' Arms £60
65 IOHN FERGVSON ½ 1666
66 WILLIAM FREIRSON ½ 1668
67 (Same as 68)
68 SAMVELL FLECHER ½ 1664
69 HENRY HAYWARD ½ 1665 Bust of Chas. II
70 IOHN HODGKINSON ½ 1670 APOTHEC
71 HENRY HOLMES ½ 1664 Apothecaries' Arms
72 — — ½ 1666 — (no shield)
73 RICH KNOWLES ½ 1671 WOOLL PACKER
74 RICHARD LISTER, RICHARD PIGGEN ½ 1666 Horse £60
75 — — — — ½ 1667 —
76 ROBERT LICHFORD ½ 1669 Saddlers' Arms £60
77 — — ½ 1667 —
78 THOMAS LOCKHART ½ 1668 SHOEMAKER
79 — LOCKHAR ½ — shoe, SHOOEMAKER
80 IOSEPH MOORE ½ 1667
81 — — ½ 1665 £55
82 HENRY MORE (E) ½ 1668*
83 THOMAS MORE ½
84 WILLIAM NEWCOME (½) TOVCH NOT MINE ANOINTED £42
84A WILLIAME — ½ —
85 W.N. ½ Similar, but ANNOINTED
86 LVKE NEYLD ½ 1667 Harp; Turk's head, MORAT. *Octagonal* £75
87 (Probably same as 89)
88 MORAT ½ Turk's head. *Octagonal*
89 WILLIAM NVCOME (M) ¼ 1657 Hart
90 IAMES PALMER ½ 1667 Flower
90A LEONARD SADD ½ 1668 APOTHECAR
91 BENIAMIN SMEDLEY ½ 1664 AT, Cordwainers' Arms £60
92 GEORGE SOWTHER (M) ½ 1667*
93 THOMAS STRONG ½ 1666
93A IOHN TAYLOR ½ Arms

Dore

94 ROBERT VNWEN ½ Hammer and pincers

Dronfield

95 IOHN BATE ½ 1666 Mercers' Arms £70
96 HENRY BLYTH ½ 1666 Apothecaries' Arms

Duffield

96A WILLIAM LEE ½ 1666 3 hooks
97 IOHN MALYN (K) ½ 1669
98 DOROTHY ROSSINGTON ½ 1669 Griffin's head

Eckington

99 HENRY HASLEHVRST ½ 1667
100 — — ½ 1665
101 HENRY SALE ½ 1669 MERCER

Grindleford

101A WILLIAM HAVLEY ½ Hand crest, BAKER

Hartington

102 THOMAS BATEMAN ½ 1670 Arms

Higham

103 IOHN LOWE ½ 1669 BVTCHER. *Heart-shape*
104 EDWARD PARKES (A) ¼ Huntsman, hound

High Peak

105 COLE MINES (½) Shalcross Arms; Shalcross crest £50

Melbourne

106 NATHAN SMEDLEY (P) ½ MERCER*

Repton

107 MATHEW WILKINSON ½ 1671 Crown

Riseley

108 (See *Beds.* 83A)

Stony Middleton

109 DENNIS RAGG ½ 1670 3 objects

* Copies are known (late 19th cent.) of crude style

Tideswell

110 EDWARD ASHE ½ 1667 Grocers' Arms £28
111 *William Ashe* ½ 1670. *Square*
112 ROBERT BAGSHAW (S) ½ 1667*
113 GERVASE GENT ½ Family Arms, crest
114 RICHARD MIDDLETON ½ 1669 Cross £50

Winster

115 RALPH BOWERS (E) ¼ 1666 Grocers' Arms

Wirksworth

116 IOHN BOOTH ¼ Mercers' Arms £70
117 IOHN BVXTON ½ DYER
118 ELEAZER COATS ¼ Family Arms
119 PETER COVLBORN ½ Mercers' Arms
120 RICHARD HEAPE ¼ Mercers' Arms
121 ANTHONY KEMPE ¼ 1666 King's Arms
122 ?? HER ½ Mercers' Arms
123 THOMAS WIGLEY ¼ Grocers' Arms*

Youlgreave

124 ROBERT BIRDS ¼ Grocers' Arms*

* Copies are known (late 19th cent.) of crude style

Devon

Major reference: W. R. Hooper, 'Notes on a Collection of Devonshire Seventeenth Century Tokens' (*Transactions of the Devonshire Association for the Advancement of Science, Literature and Art*, Vol. LXXVII, 1945).

Further new tokens recorded from the Lowsley collection (sold at Sotheby's, 3/4 May 1899); *SNC*, Mar. 1900 and June 1947; A. J. V. Radford, 'Devonshire Tokens of the Seventeenth Century' (*Transactions of the D.A.A.S.L.A.*, Vol. XXXIX, 1907); *BNJ*, 1914; Glendining's sale, 8 Oct. 1919; W. Gilbert, 'Unpublished . . .' (see under Cambridgeshire); Faulkner collection (sold at Glendining's, 21 May 1940); *SCMB*, May 1966; John Andrews, William Elston and Norman Shiel, *Exeter Coinage* (Exeter, 1980); R. H. Thompson, *Sylloge . . .* (see under Bedfordshire); *SCA* 35, 11 Apr. 1984; Sotheby's sale, 19 July 1984; Christie's sale, 7 Mar. 1985.

See also R. G. Harry, '17th Century Plymouth Tokens' (*Coins and Medals*, Mar. 1975).

Believed entirely unpublished: 7A, 7B, 300B, 345A, 353A, 361A.

Minimum price for unvalued tokens: £50

Appledore
1 PHILLIP COMMAN ¼ '64 Harp
2 —— (H) ¼ '68 —
3 THO GRIBLE ¼ Ship

Ashburton
4 AYSHBVRTON ½ 1670 Town Arms. **Plate 1** £28
5 WALTER FVRNACE ½ 1668
6 ROBERT IEFRY (G) ½ 1668 £28
7 —— ½ — Queen's head £35
7A ANNE MALKLEL ½
7B ANN MALLAKE ½ Family Arms
8 MOSES TOZER ¼ £32

Aveton Gifford
9 THOMAS MARTIN (S) ¼ 1659 2 hearts
9A THOMAS PETMEN (M) ¼ 1659 Man making candles

Axminster
10 AXMISTER AND NO OTHER PLACE ¼ T.W., pot of lilies (Town piece) £14
11 WILL BLATCHFORD ¼ Mercers' Arms £50
12 THOMAS WHITTY (D) ¼ Tobacco-roll, pipe £18

Bampton
13 HENRY BALL (E) ¼ 1666 Clothworkers' Arms £50
14 —— (M) ¼ n.d. 3 balls
15 IOHN BALL ¼ 1652 Grocers' Arms £30
16 DANIELL GLAS ½ 1666 Mercers' Arms £30
17 WILLIAM YEANDEL (A) ½ 1669 Cordwainers' Arms

Barnstaple
17A IOHN BALLER (I) ¼ Weavers' Arms
17B ROBERT COMES ¼ Mercers' Arms
18 IONAS HAVWKWELL (K) ¼ '68 Weavers' Arms £45
19 WILLIAM HILL ¼ 1656 Castle £30
20 PHILLIP SOMERS (G) ¼ 1662 Star £45
21 NATHANIEL S(I *or* Y)MONS ½ 1657 Family Arms £45
22 — SYMONS ¼ — Trefoil £30
23 IOHN WEBBER ¼ 1666 Tankard £30
24 RICHARD WEBER ½ 1669 Castle
25 —— ¼ 1667 Pewterers' Arms £32

Bideford
26 BIDEFORD Corporation ¼ 1659 Town Arms £30
27 —— ½ 1670 — £28
28 HENRY BRAYEARLE ¼ 1663 £32
28A GILBERT COOZE ¼ Apothecaries' Arms
29 GEORGE DAVIS ¼ 1668 Barber-Surgeons' Arms
30 IOSIAS ELLIOT ¼ Double triangle in shield £28
31 THOMAS LEACH ¼ 1657 £35

Bishop's Teignton
32 IOHN GRANTE (E) ½ 1670

Bovey Tracey
33 WILLIAM PERIAM (A) ¼ Axe £55

Bow (Nymet Tracey)
33A HENRY MILFVRD ¼ 1659
33B — MILFORD (E) ½ 1668 Shuttle

Bradninch
34 THOMAS PEARCE ¼ 1658 MERCER £45
35 HENRY RICHARDS ½ 1666 Cordwainers' Arms £22

Bridgetown
36 WILLIAM BRADFORD (E) ½ AT THE, boar £32
37 IAMES CHED (M) ¼ 1659 Hand

Chulmleigh
37A EDWARD BOWHAY ¼ 1669 Basket?
38 IOHN BOWRING (M) ½ 1670 Woolcomb
38A NICHOLAS MANLEY (M) ½ 1671 King's Arms
39 ALICE MOORE ½ 1668 Bell
40 HVMFREY MORGAN ¼ 1658 Scissors
40A HVMPHRY — ½ 1669 Scales, MERCER
41 IAMES SHEPHARD ½ 1669 MALTSTER £40

Colebrooke
42–8 (See *Bucks*. 54A, B, D–H)

Cullompton
49 WALTER CHALLS (S) ¼ 1651 Rose £22
50 TRVSTRAM CLARKE (A) ¼ Man making candles
51 IOHN HARRIS (M) ½ 1666 £22
52 HENRY HOPPING (D) ½ 1666 Pack-horse, CARRIER £20
53 IOHN MVDFORD (M) ½ 1667 Woolpack £28
54 WILLIAM SKINNER (S) ¼ 3 fleurs-de-lis

Colyton
55 EDWARD BVRD (M) ¼ 1657 Bird. **Plate 1** £16
56 BENIAMIN MASSEY ¼ Anchor in heart, MERCER £22
57 N.P. (E) ¼ 1659 Rose £28
58 NATHANIEL PARKMAN (E) ¼ 1666 — £32
59 — — ½ 1668 — £38
60 NATHANIELL SWEET ¼ 1657 Anchor

Crediton
61 NICHOLAS BODLEY (H) ¼ 1668 Scales
61A IOHN BODLY (A) ¼ 1665 Mercers' Arms
61B THOMAS BVCKINGHAM (E) ¼ 1668 Yoke
62 WILLIAM DANIELL (M) ¼ 1664 Sheep £25
63 IONATHAN FRYER (T) ¼ Grocers' Arms
64 IACOB IRISH ½ ROB TAIL(D *or* L)ER £35
65 IOHN KNIGHT (S) ¼ 1665 Shuttle £48
66 IOSEPH MEDLTON ¼ 1667 Rose
67 GILBERT NICOALS (M) ¼ 1665 IN SANDFORD, pail

Culmstock
68 IOHN DAVY (M) ¼ Merchant's mark
69 EDWARD LANE (F) ¼ 1654 Woolpack £30
70 RICHARD SHVTT ¼ 1654
71 IOHN SOVTHWOOD (I) ¼ 1657 Mercers' Arms £40

Dartmouth
72 DARTMOVTH ½ King seated in antique ship £22
73 — ¼ — £28
74 ROBERT BIFFEN (B) ¼ 1663 Globe £50
75 HENRY BYRD (H) ¼ 1664 Rose
76 PHILLIP CARY ¼ 1663 Apothecaries' Arms £18
76A HANNA & SARAH CVBITT ¼ Glove
77 HENRY HVNT (D) ¼ 1669
78 EDMVN IEFFRIE (E) ¼ 1657 £28
79 EDMOND IEFF(E)RIE (A) ¼ 1668
79A ROBERT ROOD (T) ¼ Pellet
80 THOMAZIN SIKES ¼ Grocers' Arms £22
80A WILLIAM TAYLER (I) ¼ Man making candles
81 ELIZABETH WIKS ¼ £42

Dodbrooke
82 WILLIAM MASKELL ¼ 1666 Ancient galley

Exeter
83 HENRY AXWORTH ¼ £32
83A I.B. ¼ '64 AT ST. MARTINS GATE
84 IOHN BAKER (V) ¼ 1663 Indian with bow and arrow £42
85 FRANCIS BASS (C) ¼ 1665 Heart?
86 IOHN BENNET (S) ¼ 1657 £25
87 WILLIAM BENNET (T) ¼ 1668
88 ABISHA BROCAS ¼ BOOKSELLER
89 ACHIER BROCAS ¼ 1670 Turk's head; coffee-pot
90 ACHIOR — ¼ 1669 — hand holding coffee-pot
91 IOHN BVRELL ¼ 1671 GROCER
92 STEPHEN BVRTON ¼ 1659
93 RALPH BVRIGN ¼ VINTNER NEW INN
94 SAMVELL CALLE ¼ Man smoking; covered cup, GOVLDSMITH £55
95 IOHN CANTER ¼ 1666 Fleur-de-lis
96 I. CHALWELL ¼ 1660
97 IOHN CHALLWELL ¼ 1662
98 IOHN COGAN (B) ¼ '64 AT ST. MARTIN'S GATE
99 IOHN COLLIBEER (A) ¼ 1666 Weavers' Arms £45
100 WILL COPLESTON (P) ¼ 1668 Grocers' Arms
100A — — (P) ¼ 1663 —
101 IOHN DAGGE (A) ¼ 1653 Lion
102 IOHN DANNIE(L *or* LL) ¼ 1664 Lion £42

103 IOHN DVNNING (S) ¼ 1668 Man smoking £32
104 THOMAS FORWARD (E) ¼ 1668 3 keys
105 ROBERT FOSTER (M) ¼ 1668 Shuttle
106 RICHARD FREKE (M) ¼ 1659 Grocers' Arms £20
107 THOMAS GILBERT ¼ 1666 £25
108 ANDREW GLANFEILD (I) ¼ 1668 Man making candles £32
109 THO GLOYNE ¼ 1657 IRONMONGER £42
110 RICHARD GOSWELL ¼ 1668
111 WILLIAM GRAVITT (E) ¼ AT SIDWELL, Heart
112 I.H. (S) ¼ 1658 Bell
112A I.H. (M) ¼ 1666 Ropemaker's wheel
113 ELIZABETH HAKENS ¼ 1663
114 IVDETH HATCHLEY ¼ NEARE EASTGATE
115 IOSEPH HELLIOR (S) ¼ 1666
116 EDWARD HICKMAN ¼ 1659 Ironmongers' Arms
117 MICHAELL HIDE ¼ 1670 BOOK SELLER
118 THOMAS HITCHE (E) ¼ 1668 Tobacco-roll £42
119 MARTIN HOPKINS (A) ¼ 1666 Man holding scales
120 HENRY HVGH ¼ 1662 £28
121 ROGGER HVMPHREY ¼ 1663 P crowned
122 PHILLIP IERMAN ¼ 1663 GROCER
122A —— ¼ 1666 —
123 THOMAS IONES ¼ 1669 Man smoking
124 WILLIAM IOHNS (P) ¼ AT THE SVNN £32
125 —— (P) ¼ 1670 Sun
126 WILLIAM KEAGLEY (M) ¼ 1664 Fleur-de-lis £30
127 IOHN LEDGINGHAM ¼ 1660 2 V's joined (one inverted)
128 MARY LISSON ¼ 1661 Rose
129 RICHARD LVNN ¼ 1664 Comb £45
130 IOHN MABAR (R) ¼ 1663 Grocers' Arms
131 IOHN MATHEW ¼ 1662
132 WILLIAM MAY ¼ 1663 Lantern £24
133 IOSEPH MAVOIT ¼ 1657 Grocers' Arms
134 (A holy communion token)
135 MARIE MOVNTIOY ¼ 1666 Mercers' Arms
136 P.P. ¼ 1671 NECIESSARY CHANGE
137 YE RED LION ½ FOR NESSESARY CHANGE
138 THOMAS PAFFORD (L) ¼ 1668 Mercers' Arms £25
139 AMBROSE PAIGE ¼ 1658 Castle
140 —— ¼ 1666 —
141 CHRISTOPHER PA(I *or* Y)NE ¼ 1666 DYER
142 HENERY PALMER ¼ Dagger £20
143 IOHN PALLMER (M) ¼ 1667 Mercers' Arms £30
144 IOHN PEARCE ¼ 1663 Haberdashers' Arms
145 IOSEPH PEARCE ¼ 1666 £32
146 WILL PEARCE IVNIOR (M) ¼ 1668 Fleur-de-lis
146A Will Peace Senior ¼?
147 ROBART PENN (E) ¼ 1658 CHANDLER
148 IOSIAS PERRY ¼ 1666
149 ANTHONY POTTER ¼ 1664 Scales
150 GRACE POTTLE ¼ 1665
151 ANN POWLE ¼ 1666 WITHOVT WEST GATE, 3-legged pot £38
152 IOHN PYM (S) ¼ 1668 Griffin's head
153 IASPER RADCLIFF (M) ¼ 1659 Castle
153A THOMAS RATTORD (L) ¼ 1668 Mercers' Arms
154 NICHOLAS REDWOOD ¼ 1651 Ironmongers' Arms
155 ELINOR ROOPE ¼ 1669 IN ST SIDWELL PARRISH
156 IOHN RVSSELL (G) ¼ 1669
157 IOHN SAVNDERS ¼ 1668 Blacksmiths' Arms
158 NICHOLAS SAVORY ¼ 1663 £32
158A —— ¼ 1662
159 GRACE SEARELLE ¼ IN SOVTHGATE STREETE £38
160 IAMES SLADE ¼ 1666 Clothworkers' Arms
161 IOHN SLADE ¼ 1658
162 RICH(ARD) TAMLING ¼ 1666 Lion
163 THOMAS TEMPLER (I) ¼ 1668 2 lit candles
163A RICH TILLEY (A) ¼ 1657 NEAR ST STEPHENSBOWE, Bakers' Arms
164 IOHN TREWMAN ¼ 1668 3 wool bags
165 W.W. ¼ 1666 AT THE MAIREMAID £50
166 THOMAS WHITE ¼ 1659 £40
166A IOHN WHITTING ¼ 1666
167 RICHARD WINBALL ¼ 1659 Stick of candles in crescent; Tallowchandlers' Arms £35
168 WILLIAM WILLIAMS (A) ¼ Lion
169 WILLIAM WOLLMAN ¼ 1669 Tobacco-roll; stick of candles
170 —— ¼ 1668 — stick of candles and dipping tray £50
170A EDWARD WOOD ¼ 1657 Crowned rose

Exmouth

171 THOMAS LAIGH ¼

Halberton

172 SIMON HVSSEY (D) ¼ 1667 Clothworkers' Arms

Hartland

172A MARY MOVNTIOY ¼ 1667 Mercers' Arms
173 IOHN RANDELL ¼ '64 Shuttle

Hatherleigh

174 IOHN GIDLEY (A) ¼ 1665

Hemyock

175 ROBERT SELLECKE ¼ Horn

Holsworthy

176 HENRY CAD (A) ¼ 1667 Anchor

177 GEORGE HINGSTON (A) ¼ 1669

Honiton
178 THOMAS ASH (B) ¼ 1664 Salters' Arms £22
179 DANIEL CLEEVELAND (M) ¼ Lion
180 WILLIAM DARBY ¼ 1663 Apothecaries' Arms £35
181 IOHN HALL (R) ¼ 1663 £20
182 —— (R) ¼ 1667 £25
183 THOMAS HVMPHRYS (A) ¼ 1668 Lion £28
184 GEORGE HVMPHREYE (I) ¼ 1666 Horse £20
185 IOHN MINIFIE (I) ¼
186 RICHARD NORTHCOT ¼ 1660 MERCER £20
187 SAMVEL POWNING (A) ¼ 1663 Lion
188 IOHN RICHARDS (M) ¼ 1657 MARCHANT £20
189 —— (M) ¼ 1663 — £40
190 ROGER SACHELL (E) ¼ 1657
191 ORLANDO SEARLE (A) ½ 1667 Shears
192 HENRY TANNER (E) ¼ 1664 Hat with feather £28

Ivybridge
193 A.M. (B) ¼ 1657 AT THE GOAT

Kenton
194 IOHN WHITROE ¼ 1654

Kingsbridge
195 IAMES BOWEN (T) ¼ Mercers' Arms £32
196 NATH FRANCKLIN ¼ Mercers' Arms
197 EDWARD HAYMAN (I) ¼ '59 St George & dragon £45
198 THOMAS HVNT (S) ¼ St George & dragon
199 I.H. (M) ¼ 1657 Mercers' Arms, HEAD OF THE MAYDEN
200 IOHN TRIPE (C) ¼ 1659 Ship

Kingswear
201 IAMES BVTLER (K) ¼ Still

Lympstone
202 IOHN REED (E) ¼ 1666 £55

Modbury
203 IONATHAN ELLE ¼ 1662 Bearded, full-face bust; tobacco-roll
204 IONATHEN — ¼ 1664 Hat; tobacco-roll
205 —— (H) ¼ 1668 — £38
206 THOMAS POTTELL (M) ¼ 1668 Family Arms
207 N.S., H.S., S.R. (½) Mercers' Arms
207A ——— ¼ —

Moreton Hampstead
208 YE 8 MEN & FEEFFEES ½ 1670 Church £42
209 MORETON HEMPSTED ½ ——
210 THOMAS AISH (S) ½ 1666
211 (See *Lincs.* 205A)
211A IOSEPH TANTEN ¼ 1659
212 IOHN TVCKER (I) ½ 1668 Scissors £22

Newton Abbot
212A WILLIAM CLEAKE ¼ Mercers' Arms
213 WM FVRNEAVX ½ 1670 Family Arms
214 ELIZABETH MANINGE ½ 1668
215/6 IOHN MANINGE (E) ½ 1669 £22
216A RICHARD REYNELL ¼ Mercers' Arms

Newton Bushel
216B WILL FVRNEAVX (A) ¼ Merchant Taylors' Arms
217 RICHARD REYNELL ¼ Mercers' Arms

Okehampton
218 CHRISTOPHER DREWE ¼ Mercers' Arms
218A —— ¼ 1652 £50
218B IOHN GAYRE ½ Grocers' Arms
219 HESTER GEYRE ¼ 1652 £50
219A —— ¼ 1656
220 THOMAS IANES (M) ¼ 1666 Scales
221 —— (M) ½ 1667 —
222 WILLIAM PINGSTON ½ Woolpack
223 IOHN SHEBBEARE ½ 1667 Family Arms £50
224 — SHEBBER ¼ n.d. Grocers' Arms
225 FRANCIS SQVIRE (G) ½ Tobacco-roll, pipe, MERCER
226 I.G. (M) ½ 1657
226A I.G. (M) ½ 1658

Oreston
227 WILLIAM AND ARTHVR COLLINGS ¼ Hands joined

Ottery St Mary
228 RICHARD CORNISH (R) ¼ Woolpack £28
229 HANNYBALL FOLLET (B) ¼ 1666 Lion £25
230 RICHARD HVLL (E) ¼ 1666 Woolpack
231 I.M. (E) ¼ 1656 AT THE RED LION £50
232 HENERY MARCKER (I) ½ 1667 £32
232A IOHN MENNACK (A) ½ 1669 Horse
233 IOHN MOSSE (E) ¼ 1664 Lion
234 RICHARD NESBITT (R) ¼
235 THOMAS OSMOND (D) ¼ 2-headed eagle £28
236 NATHANIELL SWEET (M) ¼ 1658 Man smoking £40
237 RICHARD TEAPE (M) ¼ 1666 £25

Plymouth
238 ABRAHAM APPLEBEE (M) ¼ 1666 Ship £35
239 MARY BAKER ¼ 1667
240 MAXEMILLIAN BOVSH ¼ 1658 Trefoil; 3 cinquefoils
241 ELIZABETH BYLAND ¼ 1667 Coopers' Arms £38
242 HENRY CLARKE (M) ¼ 1667 Lion £32
243 NICHOLAS COLE ¼ 1665 Rose £45
244 IOHN COOKE (M) ¼ Arms
245 HENRY DAVIS ½ 1669
246 BENIAMIN DVNNING ¼ 1666 Castle

247 MARGRET EATON ¼ 1655 Apothecaries' Arms
248 GRACE ELLIOTT (A) ¼ Mercers' Arms
249 IVDITH FORD ¼ 1669
250 EDWARD GEFFERY (E) ¼ 1664 Town Arms
251 IOACHIM GEVERS (A) ¼ 1656 Castle £35
252 RALPH GORDGE (M) ¼ 3 gurges
253 RICHARD HAMLYN (P) ¼ 1659 Grapes
254 CHRISTOPHER HATCH (R) ¼ 1658 Swan with 2 necks
255 MICHAEL HOOKE ½ 1667 Grocers' Arms
256 IAMES IRIESH (E) ¼ 1667 AT YE 3, fish-hooks
257 IAMES IACKSON (G) ¼ 1651 AT THE SVNN £22
258 WM MOVNTSTEPHENS (P) ¼ 1670
259 SAMVELL NORTHCOTT ¼ 1653 POSTMA
260 ROGER OLIVER ¼ 1663 Arms, MERCER £30
260A IOHN PARETT ¼ 1667 Pair of dividers
261 EDWARD PATESON (A) ¼ Drapers' Arms £38
262 IOHN PAYNE ¼ 1656 Pelican feeding young £40
263 SIMON PAYNTER (A) ¼ 1657 Town Arms
264 RICHARD PERRY (D) ¼ 1658 Man making candles
265 THOMAS PHILLIPPS (M) ¼ Mercers' Arms
266 IOSIAS PICKES (E) ¼ 1657 Anchor
267 HENRY PIKE ¼ AT THE THREE CRANES
268 THO PIKE ¼ 1657 AT YE 4 CASTLES, Town Arms
269 THOMAS POWELL (I) ¼ 1669 Woolcomb
269A SARAH REED ¼ 1671 Sun
270 WILLIAM REEPE (I) ¼ 1666 £45
270A IOHN STONE (A) ¼ 1666
271 WILLIAM TOM ½ 1667 Family Arms, GROCER
272 — TOMS ¼ 1663 Family Arms
273 ADAM TVRTLY ¼ Grocers' Arms
274 WILLIAM WARREN (I) ¼ 1656 Fleece
275 — — ¼ n.d. —
276 WILLIAM WEEKS (S) ¼ 1659 Clasped book
277 IOHN WILLIAMS ¼ STATIONER £42
278 SAMVEL SEELEY ½ 1657 Grocers' Arms

St Thomas (Exeter)
279 DAVID HARTE ¼ 1666 3 men at workshop; woolcomb £40
280 — HART ¼ n.d. £22
281 WILLIAM SNOW ¼ Scales £25
282 — — ¼ 1671 —

Salcombe
283 THOMAS COLLMAN ¼ Glaziers' Arms £38
284 FRANCIS FORD (E) ¼ 1659 Dolphin
284A THOMAS GELEMAN (E) ¼ Arms

Sampford Peverell
285 IOHN STONE (M) ½ 1670

Sandford
286 WILLIAM MANLY (I) ¼
287 GILBERT NICOALLS (M) ¼ 1666 Shuttle (See also no. 67)

Sheepwash
288 BARTHOLOMEW VENTON (E) ½ 1668

Silverton
289 HENRY WALTER ½ 1666 Horse £45
290 I.Y. ¼ 1660 £25

Sidbury
291 M.P. ¼ Eagle; sun

South Molton
292 IOHN ANTHONEY ¼ 1667 Merchant's mark
292A — ANTHONY ½ n.d. — £55
293 SAMVELL BADCOCK ¼ Cock
294 RICHARD BOWDEN (E) ¼ '69 Stocking, annulets £35
295 — — (E) (½) 1669 — — £28
296 ED BROAD ½ Mercers' Arms, WHEN YOU PLEASE ILE CHAINGE THESE
297 EDWARD — (M) ¼ Mercers' Arms
298 WILLIAM DOWNES (E) ¼ 1652 Bell
299 HENRY IESS (C) ½ 1668 2 shuttles
299A As last but no initials
300 HENRY IESS (C) ¼ 1668 2 shuttles
300A — — (C) ¼ 1667 —
300B ANDREW KENT (A) ¼ 1664 Grocers' Arms
301 THOMAS LAKE (M) ¼ Horse saddled and bridled
302 CHRISTOPHER MAY (E) ½ 1668 Fleur-de-lis
303 — — (E) ¼ n.d. —
303A GEORGE SHARLAND ¼ 1659 Bread roll (?)

Tavistock
304 DAVID CONDY ¼ 1666 Clothworkers' Arms £50
304A WILLIAM HOARE ¼ 1666 Grocers' Arms
305 RICHARD HVCHINGS ¼ 1666 Grocers' Arms £50

(North) Tawton
306 IAMES DAGGARY (E) ½ Dagger £35
306A ROGER GOSTWYKE ½ Arms

(South) Tawton
307 IOHN LETHBRIDGE (M) ½ SOVTH TAWTON CHAGFORD AND MORETON £18

Teignmouth
308 THOMAS IORDAN ¼ 1652

Thorncombe
309 ROGER BRIANT ¼ 1657 Shears
310 SAMVELL STAPLE (E) ¼ '68 Scales £28

Thorverton
311 IOHN THOMAS (W) ¼ Dolphin

Tiverton

312 THOMAS ALLDREAD ½ 1667 Clothworkers' Arms
313 FRANCIS BELLAMY ¼ '64 Fleece
314 RICHARD BELLAMY (H) ¼ 1661 Fleece £30
315 IAMES CLARKE (E) ½ 1666 £30
316 THOMAS DAYMAN (A) ¼ '58 Family Arms
317 WILLIAM DAYMAN ½ 1666 Family Arms
318 — — (A) ¼ BARRINTON, 3 diamonds
319 — DIAMAN (A) ¼ 3 diamonds £55
320 THOMAS FOWLER ¼ 1652 MERCERS' Arms £22
321 ROGER FROST (R) ½ Shuttle
322 IOHN GODDARD ¼ 1657 £28
323 FRANCIS HOW (A) ¼ 1659 Cloth brush? £32
324 GREGORY MAVRY (S) ¼ 1667 3 moor cocks £28
325 MICHAELL OTWAY (W) ½ 1666 £25
326 IOHN PATEE ¼ 1661 £35
327 — PATY ½ 1664 Cock £25
328 THOMAS SAMFORD (A) ¼ Fleur-de-lis £28
329/30 AQVILA SKINNER (C) ¼ 3 fleurs-de-lis £20
331 RICH STRANGAR (P) ¼ TALLOW CHANLER £40
332 IOHN VPCOTT ¼ 1657 £50
333 WILLIAM WARREN (T) ½ 1666 MERCER £28
334 THOMAS WEBBER (K) ¼ 1666 Diamond
335 THOMAS WHICHAR (K) ¼ '57 Diamond £32
336 RICHARD WOOD (E) ¼ 1663 £25
337 T.I. ¼ 1657 AT THE RED LION

Topsham

338 SVSAN DRAKE ¼ Wyvern £30
338A IOSHVA FRY ½ 1669 AT THE SHIP
339 ROBERT NEWCOMBE (S) ¼ 1668 Fleur-de-lis £50
339A — NEWCOMB (S) ¼ 1658 —
339B ALEXANDER PEAKE (A) ¼ 1655
339C HONAR PINSON ½ 1668 Ship
339D BENNONY SEWARD ¼ 1650 Arms £18
340 PETER TRAPNELL (D) ¼ 1668 MERCER £32

Torrington, Great

341 GREAT TORRINGTON ¼ 1668 Borough
342 ARTHVRE AYRE (A) ¼ Arms
343 ANTHONY DENIS (B) ½ Stick of candles £22
344 IAMES GLOYNE ½ 1669 Packhorse £35
345 RALPH HARBOTTLE (E) ¼ Bottle on hare
345A ALEXANDER PENHARWOOD ¼ 1659
346 THO POWELL (E) ¼ '71 MERCER
347 GEORGE TITHERLY (D) ¼ 1666 £35
347A GEORGE TVCKER (O) ¼ 1666
348 *Richard Tucker* ¼ 1668 £38

Totnes

349 IAMES COCKEY (E) ¼ 1668 Cock
350 EDMOND CORBYN (S) ½ 1668 Cavalier's hat £25
351 IOHN CROSSE ½ 1669 Cross £45
352 MARY FARWELL ¼ 1658 Arms
353 PETER GAILARD (E) ¼ 1657 Barber-Surgeons' Arms
353A HENRY LANGWORTHY ¼ 1653
354 IEAMS MARTYN ¼
355 — — ¼ 1653 £25
356 WILLM RVMBELLO (I) ¼ Weavers' Arms £30
357 IOHN RENNELL ¼ Hoop, VINTNER
358 PETOLOMVS SAMPSON ¼ Mercers' Arms
359 PETER WILLIAMS (T) ¼ Haberdashers' Arms

Uffculme

360 ROBERT BATT ½ 1671 Clothworkers' Arms
361 IOHN BARNEFELLD (M) ½ 1671
361A — — ¼ n.d. (?)
362 HVMPHREY BOWDEN ½ 1666 Clothworkers' Arms
363 — — (E) ¼ n.d. —
364 IOHN DYER (M) ¼ 1658 £50
365 FRANCIS PRATT (E) ¼ 1666

Uplyme

366/7 IOHN LID(D)ON (M) ¼ 1667 Mop £12

(South) Zeal

368 IOHN LETHBRIDGE ½ 3 wheatsheaves

Dorset

Major reference: H. Symonds, 'Additions to and Amendments of the Dorset Section of Dr. Williamson's Edition of W. Boyne's *Trade Tokens issued in the Seventeenth Century*' (*Proceedings of the Dorset Natural History and Antiquarian Field Club*, Vol. XXIX, 1908). 1 plate.

Further new tokens recorded from W. Gilbert, 'Unpublished . . .' (see under Cambridgeshire); Herbert Allen Seaby and Peter John Seaby, *A Catalogue of the Copper Coins and Tokens of the British Isles* (London, 1949); and *SCA* 19, 3 Mar. 1982 and 51, 16 Apr. 1986.

Believed entirely unpublished: 130A.

Minimum price for unvalued tokens: £50

Abbotsbury

1 IOHN BAILY (E) ¼ Hand holding dagger
2 SAMVELL MILLER ¼ 2 pistols crossed

Beaminster

3 HENRY BRAYNE ¼ 1657 Mercers' Arms £32
4 WILLIAM CONWAYE ¼ 1667 Woolcomb £45
5 LANCELOT COX ¼ 1667 Skull pierced by arrow
6 ROBERT HALLET ¼ 1667 Lion, MERCER
7 LANCELOTT KEATE ¼ 1668 2 hands holding instrument £35

Bere Regis

8 THOMAS SPEARE ¼ £25

Blandford Forum

9 CORPORATION ¼ 1669 FOR THE VSE OF YE POORE £14
10 THOMAS BRIDLE (M) ¼ 1659 Mercers' Arms £25
11 RICHARD EMBRIS (S) ½ 1666 Crown
12 HENRY FORREST ¼ 1663 £18
13 IOHN GOVLD ¼ AT THE CROWNE
14 THOMAS GOVLD (R) ¼ 1664 Lion £22
15 —— (R) ¼ AT THE LYON, lion
16 NICHO GOVLDESBVRGH ¼ 1663 £22
17 IOHN MEW ¼ 1655 Grocers' Arms £35
18 WILLIAM MINCK ¼ 1657
19 —MIINCK ¼ 1654 £22
19A —— ¼ — Mercers' Arms
20/1 IOHN PAIGE *or* PAGE (T) ¼ 1656 Grocers' Arms £20
22 WALLTER RIDIOVT ¼ 1662 £45
23 —— ¼ 1652 £17
24 DANIEL SHEPHEARD (M) ¼ Haberdashers' Arms £50
25 EDWARD SPEED (A) ¼ Angel £22
26/7 WILLIAM ST(A *or* O)YNER ¼ Scales, GROCER £25
28 WILLIAM WARE (E) ¼ 1668 Neckband £35
29 WILL WOLFER(E)YES ¼ Grocers' Arms

Bridport

30/1 RICHD BAGG ¼ 1657 Stocking, MERCER £22
32 THOMAS BAGG ¼ Grocers' Arms. **Plate 1**
33 ROB BISHOPP ¼ Apothecaries' Arms £25
34 WILLIAM BVLL ¼ Bull's head £22
35 WILL—(E) ¼— £45
36 (Probably misreading of 37)
37 WILLIAM BVRTE (S) ¼ 1669 Columbine
38 (Probably misreading of 37)
39 THOMAS DASSELL ¼ 1669 Bull £50
40 BEN DEVENISH (M) ¼ Tobacco-roll
41 FRANCIS HASTINGS ¼ 1657 Bull's head £35
42 EDWARD PILLEN ¼ 1668 Unicorn
43 DANYELL TAYLOR ¼ 1666 Mortar and pestle £35

Broadwinsor

44 ALICE IONES ¼ 1667 Sugar-loaf

Cerne Abbas

45 IOHN RANDOLL ¼ Grocers' Arms £16

Chalbury

46 (See *Oxon.* 54A)

Corfe Castle

47 EDWARD HARVEY ¼ 1657 £35
48/9 EDWARD KE(Y *or* N)NELL (E) ¼ 1666 £30
50 RICHARD PAINTER (S) ¼ 1666 Man holding woolcomb £40

Cranborne

51 ROBERT ALNER ¼ 1669 Drapers' Arms

52 NICHOLAS BARNES ¼ 1659 Grocers' Arms £40
52A HENRY CASTELL ¼ 1666 Castle

Dorchester

53–6 DORCHESTER ¼ 1669 Town arms £6
57 Similar, in *pb*
58/9 THOMAS ALLEN ¼ Mercers' Arms £25
60/1 (See *Oxon.* 82A, 83)
62 IOHN CARDROW ¼ Drapers' Arms £35
63 EDWARD CHEAPMAN ¼ 1668 Tobacco-roll £38
64 RICHARD CHENEY ¼ 1666 Grocers' Arms £20
65 — — ¼ 1659 — £16
66/7 SIMON EYRE (½) 1667 Boot, 3 leaves £22
66A S.E. (½) — — —
68 (See *Oxon.* 84A)
69 THO GOVLD ½ 1667 Maypole ornament(?); merchant's mark. **Plate 1** £25
70/1 THOMAS HALL ¼ 1656 Castle; Grocers' Arms £12
72 — — ¼ 1666 — — £17
73 WILLIAM MAYCOCK ¼ 1658 Grocers' Arms £20
74 — — ¼ 1666 —
75 LAWRENCE RIGHTON (½) 1669 Ironmongers' Arms £35
76 IOHN ROY ¼ 1660 Upholsterers' Arms
77 IASPER SAMWAYS ½ 1668 GROCER £45
78 — — ½ 1666 —
79 — — ¼ 1668 —
80 PHILLIP STANSBIE (½) 1667 Salters' Arms
81 — — ¼ '68 — £40
82–4 — — ¼ n.d. — £13
85 SAMVELL WILLIAMS (H) ¼ Grocers' Arms

Evershot

86/7 (Probably both misreadings of 88)
88 IOHN FFISHER ¼ 1658 MERCER £55

Frampton

89 (See *Glos.* 76)

Halstock

90 WILLIAM CLARKE (G) ¼ Packhorse

Lyme Regis

91–4 LYME RS (*or* R *or* RES) ¼ 1669 Town Arms £8
95 — RS ¼ 1653. In *pb*
95A IOHN HACKWOOD ¼ 1658 Cutlass; 2 pistols
96 AMVELL HART (Senior) ¼ 1655 Heart; pot of lilies £13
97 AMMIEL HART (Junior) ¼ 1668 — — £16
98 (Probably misreading of 97)
99 ABRAHAM PITTS ¼ 1657 Ship £25

Maiden Newton

100 R.B. ¼ DRAPER

Melcombe Regis

101/2 THOMAS HIDE ¼ Ship £20
103 GEORGE PLEY ¼ 1656 WAYMOVTH AND MELCOM, Ship
104 IOHN SWETNAM (A) ¼ DRAPER, MELCONB, initial A *below* I.S.
105 — — (A) ¼ — MELTON, normal initial positions £38

Milton Abbas

106 GEORGE CLEEVE ¼ 1669 Drapers' Arms £55
107 ZANCHY HARVYN ¼ 1651 Grocers' Arms

Poole

108/9 FOR THE MAIOR ¼ 1667 Borough Arms £14
110 CONSTANTINE BEAVMONT (R) ¼ 1667 £28
111 SAMVELL BRAMBLE (S) ¼ 1666 £28
112/3 ROBERT CLEVES ¼ Grocers' Arms, MERCER £30
114 MOSES DVRELL (I) ¼ 1666
115 I.H. (A) ½ 1666 AT THE GEORGE £45
116 ELIZABETH MILLEDGE ¼ 1666 Antelope £28
116A — — ¼ 1668 —
117 WILLIAM MINTY ¼ 1657 MERCER £25
118 MICHAELL OKE ½ 1668 AT YE OKE TREE £24
119 (Probably misreading of 120)
120/1 GEORGE OL(L *or* E)IVE (A) ¼ 1665 CHANDLER, lobster, stick of candles
122 RICHARD OLLIVER ¼ 1656 Grocers' Arms
122A — — ¼ 1655 —
123 GEORGE PHILLIPS (A) ¼ 1653 Dolphin
124 IOHN ROGERS ¼ 1668
125 DENNIS SMITH ¼ 1663 Stocking; ship £25
126 RICH SMITH ¼ Sword, A FREEMAN EINGLAND £35
127 STEPHEN STREETE ¼ 1657 MERCER
128 EDWARD TIZARD ½ 1671 CHANDLER £35
129 (Probably misreading of 128)
130 EDWARD TIZARD (E) ¼ 1665 Man making candles
130A EDWARD WARD ¼ 1665 Crown

Purbeck

131 EDWARD ABBOTT ½ 1667 Leg

Shaftesbury

132 SHAFTSBVRIE ¼ 1669 Town Arms, MOVNT PALADORE £15
133 THOMAS BALL (A) ¼ 1667 Shuttle
134 THOMAS BRICKSEY (E) ½ Hat, feathers
135 (Misreading of 134)
136 EDWARD BVRD (M) ¼ Lion £18
137 IOSEPH BYLES (S) ¼ Tallowchandlers' Arms £16
138 IOHN CALL (M) ¼ 1668 AT THE, King's Arms
139 IOHN COLE ¼ Mercers' Arms £28
140 WILLIAM DAMPNY (M) ½ 1668 Grocers' Arms £28
141 (Probably misreading of 136)

142 NATHANIEL FORDE ¼ FELTMAKER £28
143 THOMAS HACKNY ¼ 1665 Grocers' Arms £25
144 HENRY HVMBER ¼ AT THE BELL
145–7 PETER KING IVNIOR (M) ¼ 1657 Mercers' Arms £18
148 IOHN LEGGE (S) ¼ 1658 Grocers' Arms £18
149 THOMAS MASTERS ¼ '68 GROCER
150 WILLIAM MATHEW (M) ¼ 1667 Packhorse
151 RICHARD PRITTELL (M) ¼ Packhorse £20
152 RICHARD SOPP ¼ 1665 Leg £30
153 CHRISTOFER WARE ¼ Arms; merchant's mark £30
154 ALEXANDER WEEKES ½ AT YE, rose and crown

Sherborne
155 SHERBORN ¼ 1669 Mitre, FOR THE POOR £10
156/7 ROBERT ALFORD (M) ¼ Crowned rose
158 IOHN BVSHROD ½ 1668 Lion £42
159/60 GEORG CON(N)INGTON (D) ¼ Prince of Wales' feathers
161 THOMAS COOPER ¼ 1667 £40
162 GVSTAVVS HORNE (S) ½ 1667 MERCER
163 WILLIAM MOLBY (G) ¼ AT YE CROWN, wife's initial above husband's
163A Similar but initials in usual positions
164 (Probably misreading of 163)
165 W.O. (R) ¼ Hart, WELCOM
166 RICHARD OLDES ¼ Mercers' Arms £32
167 IOHN PITEMAN (I) ¼ '58 2 pistols £32
168 (Probably msireading of 167)
169 IOH PITMAN (I) ¼ '59 — FOR DORSET AND SOMERSETSHIRE £45
170 CHRISTOPHER PORT (A) ¼ 1669 Neck ornament (?)
171 RICHARD POVNSFOOT (E) ¼ 1667 Castle
172 WILLIAM RIDEOVT ¼ 1666 Dot in centre b.s. £45
173 H.R. ¼ '57 Dolphin on water £45
174 (Probably misreading of 173)
175 IOHN SHERLOCK ¼ 1666 Hour-glass £40
176 BENIAMIN SNOOKE ¼ 1664 Mercers' Arms £30
177 IOH STVCKIE ¼ 1659 Ram's head on shield, GLOVER £28
178 IOHN WARMAN (A) ¼ 1669 Merchant's mark
179 IOHN WATS (A) ¼ 1666
180 IOHN WHETCOMBE ¼ 1657 Family Arms £20
181 ISACK WILLIAMS ¼ 1664 Mortar and pestle
182 —— ¼ 1658 —
183 —— ¼ 1666 —

Stalbridge
184 IAMES CANE (K) ¼ 1666 Glove
184A THEOPHILVS COLLINS (M) ¼ 1669 3 cloves
185 THOMAS SNOOKE (K) ¼ 1658 Fleur-de-lis £32

Stowborough
186 NICHOLAS NORTHOVER ¼ 1657

Sturminster Newton
187 HENRY CROSSE ¼ 1664
188 ROBERT PORTER (F) ¼ Mercers' Arms £50

Thorncombe
189/90 (See *Devon* 309, 310)

Wareham
191 WILLIAM CLEEVES ¼ 1655
192 HENRY HARBIN ¼ 1657 £35
193 ANTHONY TREW ¼ £28

Weymouth
194 WEYMOVTH ¼ 1669 Town Arms, FOR THE POOR £15
195 BARTHOLOMEW BEERE (S) ¼ 1658 Grocers' Arms £32
196 (Misreading of 195)
197 IOHN BEERE (I) ¼ Grocers' Arms £25
198 IAMES BVDD (I) ½ 1666 Grocers' Arms £15
199 THOMAS HIDE ¼ 1664 Ship £17
200 IOH HODDER ¼ Rose £18
201 WILLIAM POOKE ¼ Grocers' Arms £28
202 FRANCIS REED ¼ Grocers' Arms £16
203 —— ½ 1669 — GROCER £30
204 IOHN SENIOR (R) ¼ Mercers' Arms £30
205 —— (R) ¼ 1663 Fleur-de-lis
206 IAMES STVDLEY ¼ 1664 Wheatsheaf; merchant's mark £50
207 THOMAS TVNSTALL (A) ¼ Ship
208 —— (A) ¼ 1667 — £32

Wimborne
209 WIMBORNE ½ 1669 2 women washing in tub, FOR THE VSE OF THE POORE. **Plate 1** £32
210 IOHN ANSTEY ¼ MERCER £42
211 WILLIAM BATEN (M) ¼ Grocers' Arms £25
212 IEFFERY BVDDEN (A) ¼ 1666 WEAVER £45
213 WILLIAM CATTEN ¼ 1666
214 PETER COX ½ 1667 FELTMAKER
215 DAVID DEANE (B) ¼ 1657 £17
216 —— (B) ¼ 1668 £20
217 (Probably misreading of 216)
218 IOHN DEANE (M) ¼ 1666 £38
219 WILL EASTON ¼ Shuttle, LINNEN WEAVER £32
220 ROBERT EKINS (I) ¼ 1670 Arms
221 IOHN FARRE ¼ GLOVER £30
222 THOMAS FLORY ½ 1670 £32
223 IOHN KING (I) ½ 1669 Horse drawing waggon £35

Wool
224 MIL WEBSTER (A) ¼ AT THE WHITE HART

The existence of nos. 21, 49, 74, 78, 94 (reading RES) and 98 must also be open to doubt.

Durham

New tokens recorded from *SNC*, June 1947.

See also B. L. Carter, 'Some Historical Notes on the Seventeenth Century Tokens of Co. Durham' (*SNC*, Nov. 1957).

Minimum price for unvalued tokens: £70

Barnard Castle

1 MICHAELL ALDERSON (A) ½ 1666 * £45
2 MICAELL — ¼ Crown
3 THOMAS BVLL ½ 1666 * £32
4 CRISTOPHER BVRFEY ¼ *
5 IOHN GOLIGHTLY (½) *
6 — — (I) ¼ *
7 WILL HVTCHINSON ¼ * £20
8 ANTHONY MARKENDAILE ½ 1666 * £38
9 — MARKENDAIL(E *or* L) ¼ 3 fleurs-de-lis £55
10 CHRISTOPHER PINKNEY (E) ½ 1666 Crown £35
11 GEORGE SANDERSON (½) 1665 * £65
12 MATTHIAS SOWERBY ½ 1666 * £38
13 MATHIAS — ¼ * £30
14 — — ¼ Rose £50

Billingham

15 RICHARD CHAPMAN ¼ '66 Mercers' Arms *

Bishop Auckland

16 WILLIAM CRADOCK (E) ¼ 1666 Arms
17 MICHAELL STOBBART ¼ * £55

Darlington

18 ROBERT COARSON ¼ 1666 Tobacco-roll * **Plate 1** £60
19, 20 MICHAELL MIDDLETON ½ Crown * £55
21 RICHARD SCAIFE ¼ 1666 Grocers' Arms * £65
22 HENRY SHAW ¼ 1667 Tobacco-roll *
22A RALPH WILKINSON ¼ *

Durham

23 IOHN BOWEY ¼ '66 APOTHECARY
24 (Probably misreading of 31, or 25)
25 R. CHILTON ¼ *
26 GEORGE COMYNT, GEORGE COOPER ¼ '66 Queen's head crowned £65
27 WILLIAM DENT ¼ 1666 APOTHECARY £40
28 WILL DIXON ¼ 1663 AT YE, queen's head £50
29, 30 WILLIAM GREEVESON ¼ 2 angels holding crown £20
31 GEORGE HODSHON ¼ * £45
32 CVTHBERT HETCHINSON ¼ 1664 King's Arms £55
33 WILL HVTCHESON (E) ¼ Stationer's Arms, BOOKSELLER £75
34, 34* WILLIAM IORDAN ¼ * £25
35 RALPH NICHOLSON ¼ * £50
36 IOHN PEACOCK ¼ 1662 St George & dragon
37 IOHN RICHARDSON ¼ 1664 Grocer's Arms; Family Arms £55
38 NIC RICHARDSON ¼ 1661 Rose and crown £30
39 WILLIAM ROPER ¼ Grocers' Arms £30
40 GEORGE SHIERS (E) ¼ 1666 Star
41 IOHN STOKELD (M) ¼ 1661 MERCER
42–5 WILLIAM WILKINSON *or* WILKE(N)SON ¼ 1661 3 fleurs-de-lis £20

Gateshead

46 IOHN BEDFORD (A) ¼ Goat's head arms £45
Electrotypes are known of this token and no. 47.

Hartlepool

47 ROGER DOBSON (E) ¼ 1662 Hart £45

Stockton

48 ROBERT IAKSON ¼ * £70
49 IOHN WELLS ¼ 1666 Name in legend * £45
50 — WELS ¼ — Name in centre * £40

Sunderland

51 WILLIAM FAWCET (A) ¼ Family Arms
51A LANCELOTT WARDELL (E) ¼ 1659 Drapers' Arms

* Tokens thus marked show, in addition, a crowned bust of Charles II

Essex

Major references: Edward and Eileen Judson, *A Re-listing of the Seventeenth Century Trade Tokens of Essex* (Little Bardfeld, 1973).

Peter Seaby, 'A Guide to the Token Coinage of the 17th Century: Essex' (*SCMB*, Jan. to Apr. 1961). Useful for locations of specimens.

W. Gilbert, 'The Token Coinage of Essex in the Seventeenth Century' (*Transactions of the Essex Archaeological Society*, Vols. XIII, XIV and XVII [1914–25]). Useful for extra notes on many issuers.

See also E. N. Mason, *Ancient Tokens of Colchester*: further background information; and W. Gilbert, 'Unpublished . . .' (see under Cambridgeshire).

Believed entirely unpublished: 51A, 160A, 182A, 182B.

Minimum price for unvalued tokens: £55

Aveley

1A THOMAS PRIME (M) ¼ 1659 Man making candles

1 ELIZABETH VAVGHAN ½ 1669

Bardfield

2 ROBERT BOWYER (F) ¼ Chequers £38

3 FRANCES MAY ½ 1669 Stag £50

4 IOHN NOONE (M) ¼ Bunch of flowers

Barking

5 THOMAS AMES (M) ¼ Man making candles £40

6 RICHARD BRITTEN ¼ Man making candles; arms

7 NICKLES CLER (R) ¼ 1650 BAKER £40

7A —— (R) ¼ 1665 —

— ROBERT DVKE (S) ½ 1667 Anchor

9 D.G. (A) ¼ 1650 THE HAND AND BOWLE £50

10 R.L. ¼ AT THE COALE YARD, arms* £35

11 WILLIAM MARTIN (P) ¼ AT THE KEY, ship £42

12 THOMAS MORE (A) ¼ 1660 Scales, BAKER

13 WILLIAM REECA (V) ¼ 1665 IN FISHER STREET £42

14 THOMAS WEST (A) ¼

15 —— (A) ¼ MEALMAN AND CHANDLER

Billericay

16 IOSEPH FISHPOOLE ½ 1669 Woolpack above fishbone £28

17 MILES HACKLVITT ½ 1666 3 tobacco pipes £20

18 EDWARD RHETT (E) ¼ Sugar-loaf

19 ABRAHAM THRESHER ½ 3 fleurs-de-lis £38

* See also *London* 2073.

20 SAMVELL WAYTE (H) ¼ Fleur-de-lis £42

Blackmore

21 ROBERT PEACHEY ¼ Sugar-loaf

Black Notley

22 IOHN ATTEWELL (I) ½ 1670 3 stags' heads £38

Bocking

23 ABRAHAM ANSELL (M) ¼ BAKER

24 HENREY ARDLEY ¼ 1652 Man making candles £22

25 IOSEPH BOOSEY ¼ Grocers' Arms

26 NATHANIELL BOOSEY (H) ½ £20

27 IOHN DAWEDATE (S) ¼ 1666 Woolpack £50

27A IOHN DOBSON (E) ¼ Woolpack

28 (Misreading of 23)

29 THOMAS MERILL ½ 1667 £20

30 RICHARD WADE (H) ½ 1667 £20

Braintree

31 IOHN ALLEN (G) ¼ 1657 Soldier

32 —— (G) ¼ n.d. — £40

33 I.A. (G) ¼ —— TVRNE A PENNY

33A —— (G) ¼ 1656 ——

34 IOSEPH BOTT (M) ¼ Woolpack £25

35 ROBERT CRANE ¼ Stick of candles £35

36 IOHN HVNWICKE ¼ Sugar-loaf

37 WILLIAM MARTIN ¼ Tobacco-pipes crossed £28

38 THOMAS MIRRILLS ½ 1670 Shoemaker's last

39 WILLIAM OSBORNE (M) ¼ BAKER £30

40 PEETER PEARCCE ¼ Shepherd, dog sitting £40

40A —— ¼ — dog standing on hind legs £45

41 PETER PEERS ¼ 1670 Shepherd, dog

42 HENRY THORNBACK (M) ½ 1668 £25
43 WILLIAM VNGLE (S) ½ 1667 DVBBLE TOKEN

Brentwood
44 THOMAS ABROOKE ¼ Stag
45 FRANCIS ALEYN (M) ¼ AT THE ANGEL
46 IOHN BETES ½ 1669 Clove on sugar-loaf
46A ABELL LIFORD (M) ¼ 1666 Crown
46B IONATHAN POPE ½ 1665 St George & dragon
46C —— (E) ½ 1669 —
47 IOHN RAYMENT (E) ½ 1669 Lion £65
48 IOHN RHETT (E) ½ 1669 Stick of candles
48A EDWARD SHELTON (E) ¼ Scallop-shell

Brook Street
49 ROBERT SHEPHERD (K) ½ 1668 AT WHIT, lion

Bures
49A THOMAS DANIELL (See *Suffolk* 36A; part of parish in Essex)

Burnham
49B ROBERT BENNET (D) ½ 1669
49C THOMAS WILLIS ¼ 1659 Mercers' Arms

Chelmsford
50 FRANCIS ARWAK (E *or* ER) ¼ n.d. Arms £28
51 — ARWAKER ¼ 1660 —
51A —— ½ 1668 —
52 IOHN BASTABLE (H) ¼ 1657 3 sugar-loaves, GROCR £55
52A IOHN BLOMEFEILD ¼ GROCR
53 NATHNIALL BOWND ¼ Arms £45
54 HENRY CORDALL ¼ 1658 Hand holding glove £22
55 —— ½ 1668 Clothworkers' Arms. *Heart-shape*
56 MARY CVRTIS ½ 1667
56A —— ½ 1668
57 SAMVELL CVRTIS ¼ '64 Savage holding club
58 WILLIAM HARMAN (M) ¼ 1657 3 tuns £50
59 THO HAVEN ¼ 1669 3 keys, LOCKSMITH
60 —— ½ ———
61 WILLIAM HVCHENSON ¼ Rabbit
61A —— ¼ 1658 —
62 RICHARD IAMES (G) ¼ 1666 £38
63 GEORGE IEFFRIES (M) ¼ 1656 Grocers' Arms £38
64 THOMAS IOSLIN ¼ 3 cloves, GROCER
65 GEORG KNIGHTSBRIDG (A) ¼ 1656 Arms
66 IOHN MARSH (A) ¼ 1657 Grocers' Arms
67 PETER ROBINSON (M) ¼ GROCER
67A IOHN STVCKE (M) ¼ 1666 Arms
68 IOHN TVRNER ½ 1667 AT THE WHITE HORSE £50
69 SAMVELL WHEELY (M) ¼ 1666 Hammer
70 IOHN WILKINSVN (S) ½ 1669 Bakers' Arms
71 LAWRANCE WILKINSON ¼ 1667 Men with barrel; Bakers' Arms
72 IOHN WRIGHT (L) ¼ Grocers' Arms £30

Chipping Ongar
73 IACOB ARCHER (M) ¼ '57 Clothworkers' Arms £30

Clavering
74 EDWARD PAMPHELON ¼? Bust left

Coggeshall
75 THOMAS BECKWITH (A) ½ Tallowchandlers' Arms £28
76 HENRY BENYAN ¼ Griffin with flag
77 SAMVEL COX ¼ Hand holding pen £32
78 IOHN DIGBY ¼ Fleur-de-lis, GROCER
79 THOMAS GVYON ¼ 1667 Rose £38
80 WILLIAM GVYON (R) ½ 1670 Fleur-de-lis £28
81 IOHN LARK (M) ¼ 1667 St George & dragon £38
82 FRANCIS LAY (D) ½ AT THE, swan £38
83 MOSES LOVE ¼ Shuttle, SLAY MAKER £40
84 ROBERT PVRCAS (A) ¼ Grocers' Arms £20
85 BENIAMIN SAMSON (E) ¼ 1665 Samson holding jawbone £18
86 EDMOND SPICER ¼ Sugar-loaf; merchant's mark
87 AMBROS SVTTON (S) ¼ 1665 Greyhound's head crest £40

(Little) Coggeshall
87A IOHN HA(N *or* RV)EY (A) ¼ Arms

Colchester
88 (Same as 113)
89 ROBERT ADSON ½ 1668 Bust of Chas. II £18
90 WILLIAM ALLDRED (M) ¼ Unicorn £15
91 MICHAELL ARNOLD ¼ Mermaid £13
92 NATHANIEL BARKER (L) ¼ 1669 Man making candles £32
93 CHRISTOPHER BAYLES (M) ¼ Sugar-loaf £18
94 THO BAYLES ¼ GROCER £20
95 IOHN BEACON ¼ 1667 £50
96 MATHEW BONNEY ½ 1665 Bakers' Arms £15
97 RICHARD BOYSE ½ 1668 Lion £20
98 THOMAS BVRGES ¼ EST STREET, Mercers' Arms £20
99 RICHARD BVSH ¼ Vase of flowers £16
100 PAVL CANNAM (M) ¼ Woolpack £20
101 THOMAS CARTER ¼ 1667 £12
102 FRANCIS CLARK ¼ 1660 Heart
103 — CLARKE ¼ 1658 — £50
103A —— ¼ 1656 —
104 RICHARD COCKE (A) ¼ '58 Cock £30
105 — COCK (A) ¼ n.d. — £13
106 WILLIAM COFELL ¼ 1658
107 ISAAC COLMAN ¼ 1667 Apothecaries' Arms, GROCR £35

108 IOHN COVENEY ¼ 1657 £20
109 —— ¼ 1663
110 IOHN DEBERT (B) ¼ 1666 Clothworkers' Arms £12
111 —DEBART (B) ¼ 1667— £13
112 IOHN EDLYN (E) ¼ Fleur-de-lis
113 —ADLYN (E) ¼
114 WILLIAM FERRIS (M) ¼ 1665 £10
115 ANDR FORMANTEL IVNIOR ¼ 1662 £11
116 ——— ¼ n.d. £10
117 RICHARD GREENE (M) ¼ IN EASTS STRET £28
117A —— (M) ¼ IN AF STREET
118 WILLIAM HARTLEY (B) ¼ Angel £15
119/20 THOMAS HOW(O *or* A)RD ¼ 1670 £28
121 THOMAS KILDERBEE (M) ¼ 1666 £25
122 IOHN KING (A) ¼ Tobacco-roll, GROCER £22
123 HENRY LAMBE ¼ 1655 Bird £10
124 —— ¼ 1663— £25
125 IOHN LAMBE ¼ 1656 Star £12
126 —— ¼ n.d. —
127 THO LAMBE ¼ 1654 AT BVTT(I *or* L)S GATE, Holy Lamb £10
128 ABRA LANGLEY IVNR (A) ¼ 1667 Crown, BAY MAKR £11
129 MARTIN LANGLEY (E) ¼ IN EAST STREETE, cockatrice £25
130 IOHN LAWRENCE ¼ 1662 £12
131 NATHANIELL LAWRENCE ¼ £10
132 THO LVMKIN ¼ IN TRENETY PARRISH, merchant's mark £20
133 IOHN (M *or* N)ILBANCK ¼ 1655 2-headed eagle £14
134 IACOB MILLER (M) ¼ 1662 £12
135/6 WILLIAM MOOR(E *or* F) (M) ¼ Merchant's mark, BAYS MAKER £11
137 ELIAS MOORTIER (S) ¼ Fleur-de-lis £14
138 —— (S) ¼ Shuttle £30
139 THOMAS PEEKE ¼ WYRE STREET, chained dog £10
140 PETER PELLE ¼ 1669 Merchant's mark, BAY MAKER £12
141 IOHN PRINCETT ¼ IN EAST STREET £25
142 IOHN RAYNER (M) ¼ IN ST PETERS £12
143 THOMAS RENOLDS ¼ BAY MAKER (or in one word) £8
144 RICHARD RICH ¼ 1656 Lion £12
145 IACOB RINGER (D) ½ 1670 Merchant's mark, BAYMAKR £25
146 ALEX SATTERTHWAITE ½ 1668 Town Arms* £18
147 IOHN SCOLDEN (S) ¼ 1670 BAY MAKER £28
148 IOHN SEWELL ¼ 1653 GROCER £12
149 —— ¼ 1667— £25
150/1 NATHANIEL STRICKS(T)ON (A) ¼ 1658 £12
152 DANIELL STVD (A) ½ BAKER £18
153 G.T. ½ 1668 Merchant's mark in shield, crest £11
154 I.T. ½ 1668 Merchant's mark in shield, crest £11
155 —— ½ — MARTIN LANE ——
156 IAMES TAYSPELL ¼ NORTH GATE £15
157 GILES TOYSPELL ¼ 1666 Swan £16
158 ABRAHAM VOLL (A) ¼ 1668 Merchant's mark £11
159 —— (A) ¼ — Initials *both* sides
160 IACOB VOL (R) ¼ Merchant's mark, BAY MAKER £10
160A IAMES WARNER ? (R) ¼ Tobacco-roll
161 IONAS WHALE (S) ¼ BAKER £11
162 IOHN WINNOCK ½ 1670 Fleur-de-lis £25

* Cf. the token of Thomas Satterthwaite (*London* 3221)

Danbury

162A DANIELL DOE (E) ¼ 1666 Fleur-de-lis

Dedham

163 NATHANIELL BACKLER ¼ Initials D.D. £25
164 IOSEPH GLESON ¼ 1664 Horse £18
165 SAMVELL SALTER ¼ 1656 Horse galloping £25

Dunmow

166 THOMAS BVRGES ½ 1669 Woolpack, packing-staff £25
167 EDWARD KEATCHENER ¼ Crossed keys, LOKSMITH £28

Epping

168 GEORGE DEY (R) ½ 1668 St George & dragon. *Heart-shape*
169 FRANCIS FVRRILL (S) ¼ 1667 AT WHIT, horse
169A EBENEZER GO(D *or* L)LEDGE ¼ 1666 Saddlers' Arms
170 MATHEW GRACE ¼ 1667 Lion, SKINNER
171 RICHARD GRAYGOOSE (M) ¼ CHANDLER £60
171A THOMAS GROVES (M) ½ 1669 Merchant Taylors' Arms
171B RICHARD KINTON (E) ½ AT YE, crown, IN HOVLDER
171C —— (E) ½ AT WHIT, lion, IN HOVLDER
172 IOHN LOE (M) ¼ 1667 SHOP KEEPER
172A HENRY PRISE ¼ 1667 BRASIER
173 GEORGE SMITH (P) ¼ 1667 Man making candles
174 NIMPHAS STACE ¼ 1656 Grocers' Arms
174A IOHN TAVERNER (I) ¼ Grocers' Arms, MARSER
175 WILL TODD ½ 1668 BLACKSMITH

Felsted

176 HENRY BIGG ½ 1669 Mortar and pestle £38
177 THOMAS BRIBRIST ¼ Bust of Chas. II £38

Finchingfield
178 ANDREW FVLLER ¼ Star
179 WIL GREENE (D) ¼ AT Y, bell £42
180 WILL — (I) ½ 1667 Crowned lion

Fobbing
180A FRANCES HALL ½ Tobacco pipes

Foxearth
181 THO BRINKNELL ¼ 1657

Good Easter
182 IOHN LICHFIELD ¼ 1658 Grocers' Arms

Grays
182A IOHN LLAWD (E) ¼ 1662 YE BVLL
182B — — (E) ¼ — Bull, IOHN LLAWYD on *rev.* (no place name)

Great Chesterford
183/a IOHN HOWSDEN (E) ½ 1670 D(O)VBLE TOKEN £55
184 BENIAMIN ORWELL (M) ¼ 1667 £30

Great Easton
185 EDWARD MOARE ¼ 3 cloves

Great Oakley
185A EDWARD BRICE ¼ Lion

Great Sampford
186 WILLIAM HEWES ¼ £60

Halstead
187 ELIZABETH CHAPMAN ¼ £25
188 IOHN FINCH ½ Malt-shovel; finch £25
189 IOHN FORES ¼ Bust of Chas. II
190 NATHAN HECKFORD ¼ £40
191 WILLIAM NEWMAN ¼ £22
192 ROWLAND SATH (B) ¼ 1669 £25
193 NATHANIELL WADE ¼ £22

Harlow
194 SAMVELL YOVNG AND IOHN HVCHIN ¼

Harwich
195 IOHN ATKINSON (V) ¼ Skull over hour-glass £60
196 THOMAS BRADSHAWE ¼ 1667 Apothecaries' Arms £45
197 ANDREW DEBNAM (M) ¼ Fishmongers' Arms £42
198 WILLIAM HVBERT (E) ¼ 1664 Scales £28
199 IOHN ROLFE (E) ¼ 1666 £38
200 IOHN SMITH (E) ¼ Scales £30
201 IOHN VANDEWALL (M) ¼ 1652 Scales £18

Hatfield Broadoak
201A IOHN SCEVBY ¼ Oak tree
201B — SCRVBY (S) ¼ 1666 —
202 W. M. SPILTIMBER ¼ 1658 Oak tree £55
203 (Misreading of 202)

Hedingham, Castle and **Sible**
204 THOMAS FIRMIN ¼ Castle
205 THOMAS HEWES ¼ Castle £16
205A HVES ¼ 1657 —
206 CLEMENT PASK ¼ Mercers' Arms £20
207 IOHN VNWIN ¼ Woolpack £22
208 ROBERT WALFORD ¼ Woolpack £16
209 WILLIAM CANT ¼ 1667 Clothworkers' Arms £25
210 IOHN KING (I) ¼ 1668 £25
211 THOMAS PLVME (M) ½ 1670

Henham
212 ROBERT HALLS ½ 1667 Scales

High Easter
212A IAMES SCRVBIE ¼ Dove

High Roding
212B THOMAS SMITH (M) ¼

Hornchurch
213 IOSHVA BVRLE (R) ½ 1668 £42
214 WILLIAM HALLWAY ½ 1671 Lion

Ilford
215 WILLIAM KEMPETON ¼ Sugar-loaf
216 GEORGE TAYLOR (I) ¼ 1665 Angel holding sword

Ingatestone
217 IOHN AND THOMAS BARKER ½ 1668 £48
218 GEORGE EVANES (I) ¼ Dove
219 — — (M) ¼ —
220 — — ½ 1668 — £32
220A IOHN GODFREY ½ 1668, Hart; initials W.A.G.

Kelvedon
221 IOHN HANCE (I) ¼ 1669 Bundle of yarn, CLOTHER £38
222 RICHARD SIDEY (S) ½ 1669 Sugar-loaf £55

Leigh
222A THOMAS HARRISON (M) ¼ 1664
223 GEORGE KING ½ 1668 3 tobacco-rolls £35
224 IOSEPH LAMB (B) ¼ 1664 Lamb £50
225 R.S. (I) ¼ 1664 AT THE ANCKER
226 THOMAS WALL (A) ¼ 1666 Scissors
226A — — (E) ¼ — —

Leighbeck
226B IOHN LAMBE ½ 1668 Paschal lamb; Grocers' Arms

Leytonstone
227 IOHN EVANS ½ 1668 AT THE, huntsman and dog
228 *Iohn Unwin* ½ Archer shooting stag. *Octagonal*

Littleton
228A GEORGE FORDHAM ¼ Wheatsheaf

Maldon
229 IOHN HARRISON ¼ Grocers' Arms £38
230 PHILLIP RALLING (A) ¼ Grocers' Arms
231 IAMES ROBIENT ¼ Grocers' Arms £50
232 (See *Beds*. 73C)

Manewden
233 THOMAS BVLL ½ 1669 Barber-Surgeons' Arms £50

Manningtree
234 HENRY CARTER (G) ½ 1669 CHYRVRGEON £48
235 IERVEMY ERDS ¼ 1653 Mercers' Arms £35
236 THEOPHILVS HARVEY (R) ¼ 1669 King's Arms

Moulsham
236A CHARLES CLARKE (M) ¼ Dyers' Arms £70
237 THOMAS IOYCE ¼ 1666 Wooden pail
238 IOHN LITTLE ¼ 1666 Woman spinning
239 WILLM SWEETING (S) ¼ 1665 Wheelbarrow

Much Baddow
240 IOHN LANGSTON ½ AT THE WHIT HORS

Much Clafton (Great Clacton)
241 WILL ANGER ¼ 1654 Unicorn £25
242 WILLIAM MVNT (M) ¼ 1664 £28

Newport Pond
242B RICHARD DORE (probably *Hants*. 99)
242a FRANCIS HVCHERSON (½) 1668
243 —— ½ 1669 £20
244 THOMAS HVCHERSON (A) ¼ 1658
244A WILLIAM ROWE (probably *Salop* 51A)
245 THOMAS RVNHAM ½ 1667 AT YE, bull £38
246 HENRY WOODLEY ¼ 1657 £55

Orsett
(See 284)

Pebmarsh
247 WILLIAM SEWELL (I) ¼ 1667 £45

Pentlow
248 ABRAHAM DAKING (M) ¼ Stag £60

Plaistow
249 IOHN CORIE (M) ¼ 1657 MEALMAN
250 I.F. (M) ¼ AT THE DOGGS HEAD IN THE POTT
250A THOMAS HALBEART ¼ 1666 Scales
251 IOHN PHILLIPS (M) ½ 1670 AT THE, dog and pot £50
251A —— (M) ¼ ———
252 THOMAS POLLARD ½ 1668 AT THE, ship £55

Pleshey
253 HVMFREY SARIENT ¼ '59 Crest; Arms

Prittlewell
253A N.B. (M) ¼ 1660 Arms

Purfleet
254 SAMVEL IRONS ½ 1669 Limekiln £75

Quendon
255 H.B. (E) ½ 1669 Bust of Chas. II £28
256 WILLIAM WINSTANLEY ½ 1669 Drapers' Arms £55

Rainham
256A ELIZABETH GOEVER ½ 1661

Rayleigh
257 REBECCA BARNES ¼ Bull

Ridgewell
258 IOHN NEVILL (I) ¼ 1668

Rochford
258A EDWARD BAYES (A) ¼ 1657 Star
259 IOHN HARVEY ½ 1668 Butchers' Arms (part) £60
260 ROBERT HAWDEN (I) ¼ Drapers' Arms

Romford
261 RICHARD CHARVELL ½ 1668 Hand holding shears £45
261A *Henry Dawes* ½ 1668 Lion. *Octagonal*
262 FRANCIS DILKE ½ 1668 Angel. *Square*
263 IOHN IEFFRSON (A) ¼ 1657 Sun
263A ELIZABETH MARCVM ¼ Lamb, BAKER
264 MICHEALL MARKEM (D) ¼ 1653 Bakers' Arms £45
265 W.M. (M) ¼ 1651 AT THE CROWNE
266 IOHN PARKER (E) ½ 1669 Sugar-loaf £45
267 IAMES SCOTT ½ 1668 Sugar-loaf £45
268 GEORG(E) SILKE (E) ¼ AT THE ANGELL £55
268A GEORGE — ¼ —
269 THOMAS STEEVENS ¼ 1651 Sugar-loaf £25
270 *Will Willis* ½ 1667 Hammer and pincers crossed £40

Saffron Walden
271 NATHANIELL CATTLIN ½ 1668 Shuttle £32
272 (Misreading of 273)
273 RICHARD KENTISH ¼ Head of black boy
274 SAMVELL LEADER ¼ 1653 Tobacco-pipes £20
275 WILLIAM LEADER ½ 1668 Pipes crossed £30
276 ANNE MATHEWS ¼ 1656 Grocers' Arms £22
277 THOMAS MEHEW ¼ 1658 Grocers' Arms £32
278 THOMAS PA(T *or* L)MER ¼ Drapers' Arms £38
279 IOHN POTTER (A) ¼ 1656 Hart; initials A.M.* £55
280 (Probably same as 281)
281 EDWARD TOMPSON (K) ¼ 1659 £32

* Same reverse as that of W.276

282 WILLIAM WILDMAN ¼ 1656 Fishes £18
283 —— ¼ 1667 — £16

Orsett
284 WILL(IAM) CLARKE (P) ¼ 1659 Grocers' Arms

St Osyth
285 IOHN GVNFEILD ¼ 1665 Drapers' Arms £55
286 RICHARD STANLY ¼ '58 Tree

South Benfleet
287 WALLIAM THOMPSON ½ Blacksmiths' Arms

Southminster
287A IOHN COOPER (A) ¼ 1664 Bust of Chas. II
288 ANNE ELLIES ¼ 3 crowns
289 ELIZABETH IEFFERY ¼ 2-headed eagle
289A IOHN IEFFERY ¼ 1670 Mercers' Arms
290 WILLIAM LONE ¼ Drapers' Arms
290A —— (A) (½) FOR NECESSARY CHANGE

Springfield
291 IASPER EVE ½ 1669 Fruiterers' Arms £22

Stebbing
292 BARGE ALLEN ½ AT THE, 3 hats
293 (Same as 295)
294 RICH BOWYER ¼. In *pb*
295 RICHARD SAYER ½ 1667 Hat £30

Stansted Mountfitchet
296 (See *Herts.* 186A)
297 BENIAMIN GIFING (M) ¼ 1666
298 GEORGE PERRIN ½ 1669 AT YE BELL

Steeple Bumpstead
299 MARTIN DIKE ¼ 1657 Drapers' Arms £45

Stisted
300 IAMES BONVN (B) ¼ 1666 Shears £35
301 —— ½ 1670 —
302 WILLIAM FOVLSVM ¼ 1657 £55

Stock
303 GILBERT GARRARD (A) ¼ 1660 Fleur-de-lis
304 EDWARD SOMES (M) ½ 1667 Fleur-de-lis
305 ROWLAND SADLER (M) ½ 1669 3 pipes
305A GEORGE WEILE (A) ¼ AT THE COCK

Stratford
305B I.B. (Listed under *Suffolk* 317)
306 ABELL BONO ½ AT YE WHITE, swan
306A *Abell Bono* (A) ½ *at ye white*, swan. *Octagonal*
307 (See *Suffolk* 318)
307A IOHN CLARKE (Listed under *Suffolk* 319)
307B *William Greenwood* ½ Hart. *Heart-shape*
307C THOMAS IAMES (S) ½ 1670 Hand holding scissors
308 THOMAS IOLEY ½ 1667 Hand holding bird
309 (See *Warwicks.* 146B)
309A IOHN WILLMOR (E) ¼ 1650

Takeley
310 SAMVELL TAYLER ½ 1667 Scales £35

Terling
311 THOMAS TARVERNER (E) ¼ 1658 Bull

Thaxted
312 IAMES CAMPE (M) ¼ 1670 Drapers' Arms £45
313 IOHN HAVERS (A) ½ 1670 Saracen's head
314 WILL MASON (M) ¼ 1662 AT THE, bell £45
315 WILLIAM PVRCHAS ½ 1666 Still £32
316 IOSEPTH SMITH (I) ¼ 1652 Man making candles £22
317 IOSEPH — ¼. In *pb*
318 NATHANIELL SMITH (K) ¼ Swords crossed
319 GEORGE STVBBING (A) ¼ 1656 Funnel. In *pb*
320 —— (A) ¼ 1666 — In *Æ* £38

Thorpe-le-Soken
321 GEORGE NICHOLSON ¼ Grocers' Arms; crowned initials £35
321A —— ¼ — no crown £30
322 IOH SMITH (S) ¼ CHANDLER £40

Tillingham
322A IOHN PRESTON (M) ½ 1668 Castle over arms

Tollesbury
323 WILLIAM LVCKEN (E) ¼ '68 Stag

Tolleshunt Darcy
324 GEORGE NICHOLSON ¼ Grocers' Arms; scallop-shell £50

Toppesfield
324A THO BENTALL (F) ¼ Arms (lion)
324B IOSEPH WALFORD ¼ 1652 Mercers' Arms
325 — WOLFORD ¼ 1659 —

Waltham
326 (See *Leics.* 105A)

Waltham Abbey
327 WILLIAM DEANE (S) ½ 1668 AT THE, King's Arms £60
328 IOHN HODGES ½ 1668 Grocers' Arms, GROCER £50
329 —— (I) ¼ Grocers' Arms £30
330 — HODGIS (I) ¼ 1666 Stick of candles
331 MIHILL ROBINSON (S) ¼ Grocers' Arms
332 THOMAS TYLAR ½ 1668. *Heart-shape* £180
333 THOMAS WARRIN (S) ½ 1668 3 tobacco-pipes
334 HENRY WEB (F) ¼ Drapers' Arms

(Great) Waltham
335 IOHN POOLE ½ 1667 GROCER

(Little) Waltham
336 IOHN GOODEVE ½ 1668 Grocers' Arms £30

West Ham
337 THOMAS BAILY ½ 1668 AT THE, savage with club and dog
338 *Gabriel Brewer* ½ 1668 Dolphin. *Octagonal*
339 THOMAS COPLEY (S) ½ AT YE VNICORN
340 IOANE COYDE ½ 1667 King's Arms
341 (Probably *Sussex* 181A)
341A *Margret Graves* ½ Men saluting. *Octagonal*
342 *Thomas Simes* ½ 1668 2 logger-heads, *Wee are* 3. *Octagonal* £100

Wethersfield
342A SAMVELL FITCH ¼ Mercers' Arms
343 THOMAS LIVERMER (E) ¼ Bust of Chas. II

Wivenhoe
344 IOHN PARKER (M) ¼ AT THE FALKEN, bird holding sceptre £22

Wickham Bishops
345 LAVRENCE BROWN IVNIOR ½ 1669 Hand £65

Witham
345A THOMAS BARKER (M) ¼
346 ROB BARWELL (M) ¼ Merchant's mark, CLOTHYER £40
346A ROBERT CLARKE ¼ 1667 3 swans
347 IOHN FREEBVRNE IVNIOR ¼ 1667 Rose crowned £15
348 THOMAS GARDENER (E) ¼ Woolpack £30
349 IOHN HOWLETT (E) ¼ 1667 Cordwainers' Arms
350 IOHN IACKSON (A) ½ 1669 Fleur-de-lis, CLOTHIER £35
351 GEORGE ROBINSON (D) ¼ 1669 Still. **Plate 1** £6
351A — — (D) ¼ — —. In *pb*
352 RICHARD SWINBORNE ½ 1668 Hart £20
353 SAMVELL WALL (E) ¼ 1653 2-headed eagle £38

Woodham Mortimer
354 RALPH COKER (A) ¼ Swan

Writtle
355 DANIELL LENORD (E) ½ 1668

(Little) Yeldham
356 THOMAS BVCHER ¼ Bakers' Arms £45

Gloucestershire

New tokens recorded from J. E. Pritchard, 'Bristol Tokens of the Sixteenth and Seventeenth Centuries' (*Proceedings of the Clifton Antiquarian Club*, Vol. IV part III, 1899; and addenda in *NC*, 1902); the Macfadyen collection (sold at Sotheby's, 15 July 1907) *SNC*, July 1947; J. G. Milne, 'The Browne Willis Cabinet' (*BNJ*, 1951); L. V. Grinsell, C. E. Blunt and Michael Dolley, *Sylloge of Coins of the British Isles, 19. Bristol and Gloucester Museums* (London, 1973); and *SCA* 7, 5 Dec. 1979 and 19, 3 Mar. 1982.

See also *SCMB*, Nov. 1957; L. V. Grinsell, *A Brief Numismatic History of Bristol* (Bristol, 1962): 1 plate, more background information; I. E. Gray, 'Some 17th-century Token-issuers' (*Transactions of the Bristol and Gloucestershire Archaeological Society*, Vol. 84, 1965); R. H. Thompson, 'Unrecorded Bristol Tokens 1598: Some Reservations regarding their Authenticity' (*SNC*, Sep. 1972), and '*Gloucester Farthings, 1657–1662*' (*BNJ*, 1975): analysis and history of the city issues, with one plate.

Believed entirely unpublished: 36A, 134A.

Minimum price for unvalued tokens: £50

Awre
1 ROBERT DOVER (E) ¼ 1652 OF THE PARISH, vine
2 — — (E) ¼ — OF THE VINE

Barton Hundred
3 THO WATKINS ½ 1668 Tallowchandlers' Arms £28

Berkeley
4 IOHN SMITH ½ 1669 MERCER £50

Bisley
5 EDWARD ALDRIDGE ½ 1670 Scales, CHANDLER £22

Blockley
6 THOMAS WARNER (V) ¼ 1657 Cropper's shears

Bourton-on-the-Water
7 RICHARD BOSWELL (M) ½ 1669 £28
8 (Probably misreading of 9)
9 EDWARD LAMLY ½ 1669 BAKER £25

Brand Green
9A IOHN IAMS (A) ¼ 1666 Weavers' Arms

Bristol
10 (A late 19th cent. concoction)
11 City ¼ n.d. (1651) Ship issuing from castle. (Also cast) £14
12 — ¼ 1652R (= Ramage) —. **Plate 1** £5
13/4 (Probably misreadings of 12)
15 City ¼ 1652R As 12, I R on design. (*Cast*) £12
16 — ¼ 1660 Ship issuing from castle £15
17 — ¼ 1660R— £10
18 — ¼ 1662R— £5
19 — ¼ 1662 — £10
20 — ¼ 1670 — £8
21 — ¼ n.d. (? c. 1597) —. *Square or rectangular* £75
22 — ¼ n.d. (c. 1577–83) Arms in shield, ship issuing right. *Square or rectangular* £75
22A Similar but ship issuing left. *Square or rectangular*. **Plate 1**
22B IOHN BRADWAY ¼ AT THE MREMAYD ON THE BACKE
22C IOHN BROWN ¼ 1567 GROCER. In *pb**
22D WILLIAM COOKE (M) ¼ Sugar-loaf between 3 cloves
22E *John Jenkins* ¼ Monogram
23 THOMAS RICRAFT ¼ IN WINE STREET, sheaf of arrows
23A M.W. (B) ¼ AT THE BORES HEAD IN WINE STREET

(Chipping) Campden
24 WILLIAM COLTMAN ½ 1667 Mercers' Arms £18

* The date is most likely an error for 1657.

25 IOHN DICKINS ¼ 1657 Drapers' Arms £28
26 GEORGE FREEMAN (M) ¼ 3 cloves £18
27 (Probably misreading of 28)
28 IOHN MOSELY (S) ¼ 1657 Mercers' Arms £20
29 THOMAS PERRY ½ 1667 Sugar loaf, MERCER £30
30 VALENTIN SMITH (D) ¼ 1651 Wheatsheaf £12
31 WILLIAM YEATE ½ 1666 Bust of Chas. II, MERCER £18
32 —— (M) ¼ n.d. Grocers' Arms. — £20

Charlton Kings

33 THOMAS ASHMEADE (E) ¼ Grocers' Arms £25

Cheltenham

34 SAMVELL ARROWSMITH (M) ¼ 1663 Family Arms £45
35 NICHOLAS ASHMEADE (A) ¼ Grocers' Arms £28
35A GYLES HOBS ¼ Mercers' Arms
36 THOMAS HVMPHERIS (M) ½ 1669 3 birds on wheatsheaf, BAKER
36A L.I. ¼ 1652 TALLOW CHANDLER
37 R.I. (M) ¼ 1652 TALLOW CHANDLER £28
38 EDWARD IOHNSONS (M) ¼ Mercers' Arms (not in shield) £42
39 — IOHNSON (M) ¼ Mercers' Arms (no inner circle) £15
40 IOHN MASON ½ 1667 MERCER £18
41 THOMAS MASON (M) ½ 1669 Family Arms £14

Chipping Sodbury

42 STEPHEN SMITH ¼ 1669 Lion £30

Cirencester

43 (? Misreading of another token?)
44 CIRENCESTER ¼ 1668 Phoenix in flames, serpent in beak £15
44A — ¼ —— no serpent £20
45 OBADIAH ARROWSMITH ½ 1668 Grocers' Arms, MERCER. *Heart-shape* £125
46 ANTHONY CHANCE ¼ MERCER £14
47 WILLIAM CONSTABLE ½ 1668 £14
48 —— ½ 1669. *Octagonal* £35
49 *William Constable* ½ —. *Octagonal* £25
50 WILLIAM CONSTABLE ¼ n.d. MERCER £11
51 THOMAS EDWARDS (M) ¼ Military boot £18
52 EDMVND FERIBY (E) ¼ £16
53 GEORGE FEREBEE ¼ 1666 Arms £20
54 EDMVND FREEMAN (M) ¼ 1665 Grocers' Arms
55 —— (M) ¼ 1655 — £16
56 ELIZABETH KEMBLE ¼ 1657 Mercers' Arms £16
57 BRYAN MILLS (E) ¼ 1657 £14
58 IO NELMES (M) ¼ 1668 GROCER £22
59 RALPH OLIVER ¼ 1664
60 REBEKVH OSBORNE ¼ 3 cloves £20
61 THOMAS OSBVRNE ¼ 3 cloves £16
62 (Misreading of 63)
63 THOMAS PERRY (A) ¼ 3 doves £28
64 WILLIAM PETTY (I) ¼ 1667 £25
65 CALEB SELFE ¼ 1666 Crowned rose £15
66 ISAAC SMALL ½ Merchant's mark £11
67 EDWARD TAYLER (R) ¼ £25
68 RALPH WILLETT ¼ Merchant's mark £50

Clifton

69 (See *Beds.* 28)

Cuckold's Brook

70 THO PILL (D) ¼ Clothworkers' Arms £45

Dursley

71 WILLIAM PARTRIDGE (E) ¼ Bird, MERCER £14
72 SAMVELL SIMONS (E) ¼ 1667 Man making candles £18
73 IOHN WATTKINS (A) ¼ Star £35
74 OBEDIAH WEBB (E) ¼ Fleece, MERCER £10

Edgeworth

75 (Probably *Middx.* 40A)

Frampton-on-Severn

76 IOHN MAYNARD ½ 1667 MERCER

Gloucester

77/9 LVKE NOVRSE MAIOR ¼ 1657 City Arms, with R (= Ramage) £11
78 ——— ¼ —— no R £20
80 THOMAS PRICE MAIOR ¼ 1667 — £18
81 GLOVCESTER ¼ 1669 — £8
81A Samuel Allen ¼? (grocer)
82 MATHIAS BOWER ¼ 1666
83 I.C. (A) ¼ 1654 AT THE NEGS HEAD £15
84 RICHARD CHANDLER ¼ SADLER £22
85 (Probably same as 86)
86 RICHARD COCKES (S) ¼ 1652 Cock £20
87 DANIELL COLLINS (B) ¼ Arms and crest, MERCER*
88 THOMAS COOKE (M) ¼ CHANDLER £15
89 IOH DONNE ¼ Postman on horseback, blowing horn £30
90 THOMAS GOODWIN ¼
91 IOHN HOBSON (I) ¼ 1652 M(A *or* E)RCER £28
92/3 HENORY *or* HENRY KNOWLES ¼ Flesh-pot £15
94 NICHOLAS LANE ¼ 1656 APOTH £20
95 GILES LYE (H) ¼ CHANDLER £12
96 (Probably misreading of 88)
97 (Probably misreading of 98)
98 IOHN PVRLETT (R) ¼ 1653 Coopers' Arms
99 W.P. (I) ¼ 1654 THE ROOSE AND CROWNE £18

* Also known in silver (of later manufacture)

100 WALTER TAYNTON (E) ¼ 1651 Grocers' Arms £14
101 W.W. (A) ¼ 1650 AT THE RAEN TAVERNE, raven £14
102/3 NATHANIELL WE(B *or* E)B (M) ¼ Brewers' Arms, BROVER

Gloucestershire Hundred
104 T.L. ½ 1669 Castle £20

Hampton Road
105/6 T.C. ¼ £14
107 MILES ROBERTS (S) ¼ 1664 Man making candles £25
108 NATHANIELL SKERTON (H) (½) 1670 AT YE, King's head £22
109 — — ¼ — — —
110 NATHANIELL YOVNG ¼ 1668 St George & dragon £18

Hawkesbury
111 THOMAS WALKER ¼ 1657 AT THE HORSE

Kempsford
112 IOHN MASLIN (M) ½ 1669 Tallow-chandlers' Arms. *Octagonal* £80

Lechlade
113 RALPH LANGLEY ½ 1669 Grocers' Arms. *Octagonal* £55
114 THOMAS SMITH (E) ¼ Grocers' Arms £42

Lower Gitting
115 ANTHONY FREEMAN (M) ¼ Crown

Marshfield
116 WILLIAM HOSEE (M) ¼ 1651 £14
117 MATHEW MEADE (M) ½ 1669 Mercers' Arms
118 ELLIAS OSBORNE (M) ¼ 1651 MERCER
119 ELIAS — ¼ 1664 Drapers' Arms
120 (Probably misreading of 121)
121 ELIAS OSBVRN (M) ¼ MERCER £50
122 THOMAS WATERFORD (M) ¼ 1667 Grocers' Arms £20

Mitcheldean
122A IAMES BRIDGMAN ¼?
123/4 THO GARRAWAY (E) ¼ Grocers' Arms £22
125 THOMAS GARWAY (A) ½ —
126 EDWARD MORSE (A) ½ Merchant's mark, CLOTHIER £18
127 IOHN NASH (E) ¼ 1669 Mercers' Arms
128 — — (E) ¼ 1656 —
128A DANIEL PHILPOT (I) ¼ Mercers' Arms, CHANDLER
129 WALTER RVDG (M) ½ 1667
130 THOMAS WALLYN (P) ½ 1667 £25

Moreton-in-the-Marsh
131 RICH ALBERT ¼ 1666 Stick of candles £45
132 ROWLAND FREEMAN (E) ¼ Grocers' Arms, MERCER £45
132A Similar but without MERCER

Newent
133 THOMAS MASTER (S) ¼ 1653 Dolphin £25
134 WILLIAM NELME (H) ½ 1667 Grocers' Arms £35
134A — — ½ 1666 3 cloves on shield

Newnham
135 IAMES IEFFERES ½ 1667 Rose; initials I.A.S. £48
135A — — (A) ¼ n.d. Rose, NEWNHAM
135B — IEFRYES (A) ¼ — — NVNOM GLOSTERSHEAR
135C THOMAS SMITH ¼ 3 sugar loaves
136 STEPHEN WILLCOCKS (S) ½ 1667 Cutlers' Arms £18
137/8 — WIL(L)COCKS (S) ¼ n.d. — £25

Northleach
139 RICHARD BVTLER AND WILL NEALE ½ '70 Bakers' Arms £25
140 THOMAS PAGE (M) ¼ Falcon, NORTH LEETCH £17
141 Similar but NORLEGE £15
142 EDWARD SMITH (A) ¼ 1651
143 WILLIAM SOVCH (H) ¼ Grocers' Arms £20
144 WILLIAM STONE ½ 1669 Crown, date on *obv. Octagonal* £28
144A Similar but *round*, date on *rev.*

Painswick
145 ROBERT SIMONS (H) ¼ Man making candles £22
146 ROB — (H) ¼ 1667 — £18
147/8 GILES SMITH (A) ¼ 1664 Grocers' Arms £22
149/50 (Probably both misreadings of 148)

Stanley St Leonard
151 RICHARD ELLIOTTS ¼ Cordwainers' Arms

Starton
152 EDWARD CAGWORTH (T) ½ 1669 Blacksmiths' Arms £30

Stow-on-the-Wold
153 THOMAS BROMSGROVE (E) ½ 1670 Apothecaries' Arms £32
154 FRANCIS DIX (A) ¼ 1666 Crown £28
155 THOMAS GIBBS (A) ¼ 1658 Fleur-de-lis £18
156 IOHN KEECH (H) ¼ 1666 King's Arms
157 WILLIAM MINCE (A) ¼ Mercers' Arms £18
158 HAZELWOOD WELLS (S) ¼ Grocers' Arms

Stroud
159 SAMVELL BVBB ½ 1664 Tree £22
160 WILLIAM HOPTON ¼ 1655 3 crosses crosslet fitchée £18

161 —— ¼ — 3 cloves £20
161A —— ¼ 1667 5 crosses £55
162 RICHARD WAKE ¼ 1664 Man making candles

Tetbury

163 BVRROVG(H *or* E) ¼ 1669 Town Arms, IS OWND £7
164 BVRROVGH ¼ n.d. — WIL BE OWND
165 (Probably a misreading of 163)
166 OBADIAH ARROWS(M)ITH (A) ¼ Haberdashers' Arms, BAYLEF £18
167 IOHN STEPHENS (L) ¼ 1664 Tallowchandlers' Arms £25
168 (Probably a misreading of 169)
169 ANTIPAS SWINERTON (M) ¼ WOLLMAN £18
170 SAMVELL TEAKLE (E) ¼ CLOTHIER £18

Tewkesbury

171 LAWRENCE AMBREY ¼ Shears £14
172 CHRISTOPHER ATKINSON ½ 1667 £18
173 ELINOR ATKINSON ¼ Rose £20
174 THOMAS ATKINSON ½ (16)67 Leg £25
175 THOMAS BRIAN (P) ½ 1667 Ship £20
176 SAMVELL CANNER ¼ Tankard, PEWTERER £40
177 WILLIAM HAIDON (E) ¼ Horseshoe £22
178 WILLIAM HALE (P) ½ 1662 £16
179 WILLIAM HATTON (I) ¼ '63 Grocers' Arms £18
179A —— BARTHOLOMEW READE ½ Mercers' Arms, 3 cloves £40
180 PHILLIP HEYWARD ½ 1668 MERCER £18
181 (Probably a misreading of 182)
182 SAM HOLLAND (M) AND ROBT PORTER (P) ½ £22
183 (Probably a misreading of 184)
184 THOMAS IEANES ½ 1669 Castle on *obv.*
185 SAMVELL IEYNES ½ 1669 Castle
186 THOMAS IEYNES ½ 1669 Castle on *rev.* £18
187 SAMVEL IEENES (M) ¼ Glove £18
188 FRANCS IEFFERIS (A) ¼ 1652 Cheese-knife £45
189 DANIELL KEMBLE (A) ½ 1666 Drapers' Arms £40
190 EDWARD LAIGHT (E) ½ 1668 Lion £14
191 NICHOLAS MEARSON (S) ¼ 1659 Blacksmiths' Arms £22
192 IOHN MILLINGTON (P) ¼ Grocers' Arms
193/4 SAMVEL MOSSE *or* SAMWELL MOST (M) ¼ 1653 Holy Lamb £20
195 SAM MOSS (M) & THO CLARKE (H) ½ 1664 £35
196 IOHN OVLEF (S) ¼ Dove with olive branch £20
197 THOMAS PALMER (M) ¼ Open book £22
198 IOHN PEIRCE (M) ¼ 1654 Weaver's shuttle £20
199 RICH PENNELL & THO NVTT ½ 1668 Leathersellers' Arms GLOVERS
200 IOSEPH SHEENE (H) ½ 1663 £13
201 SAMVELL SMYTH ½ 1666 £14
202 NICH STAIGHT (M) ¼ Apothecaries' Arms, OPIFERQVE PER ORBEM DICOR
203 NICHOLAS — (M) ¼ — (no motto)
203A John Surmon ¼?
204 E.W. ½ 1666 £12
205 PERC(E *or* I)VALL WRIGHT, DANIEL KEMBLE ½ £20

Thornbury

206 THORNBVRY Borough ¼ 1670 Barrel and knot £16

Wickwar

207 GEORGE HOART ¼ 1669 Lion £20

Winchcombe

208 CLE DARKS ½ 1672 Glove £28
209 DAVIDE HARVY (A) ½ Shoulder of mutton £30
210 WILLIAM HOWLET (H) ¼ 1666 Woolpack? £35
211 WILLIAM IOANES (K) ¼ Armourers' Arms £32
212 — IONES ¼ 1666 Roll of tobacco or cloth £18
213 NICHOLAS PEARSON (M) ½ 1670. *Octagonal* £50
214 GEORGE SKINER (E) ¼ 1663 Man making candles £16
215/7 G(E)ORGE SKIN(N)ER (E) ¼ 1657 — £14
216 GEORGE SKINER (E) ¼ 1666 —
218 (Probably same as 215/7)
219 WILLIAM STEPHENS (D) ½ 1671 Grocers' Arms £30

Woodchester

220 ANDREW ROGERS ¼ 1670 £16
221 DANIELL YEATES ¼ Man making candles £18

Wotton-under-Edge

222 THE MAIOR AND ALDERMEN ¼ 1669 Woolpack £15
223 (Probably misreading of 222)
224 LAZARVS KEMPP (M) ¼ Apothecaries' Arms £50
225 I.S. (M) ¼ AT THE MAREMAID £18
226 DANIELL STODARD (S) ½ 1667 Fleece £20
226A EDWARD WALLINGTON (S) ¼ MERCER £18

Hampshire
(including the Isle of Wight)

Major reference: J. L. Wetton (Editor), *The Hampshire Seventeenth Century Traders' Tokens* (Lymington, 1964). 22 plates; updating and revision of 'Williamson', more notes, and locations of specimens.

Further new tokens recorded from the Lowsley collection (sold at Sotheby's, 3/4 May 1899); and D. P. White, 'A Hampshire Token Overstrike' (*TCSB*, vol. 1 no. 7, Oct. 1972).

See also H. E. Jacobs, 'The Seventeenth Century Tokens of the Isle of Wight' (*SNC*, Sep. 1927); and H. Good, 'A New Romsey Token' (*SNC*, May 1985).

Believed entirely unpublished: 73A, 126A.

Minimum price for unvalued tokens: £50

Alresford

1 IARVAS ABIN (A) ½ 1666 AT THE, St George & dragon £15
1A IERVES — (A) ¼ — — —
2 IERVAS — (A) ½ 1667 AT THE GEORGE, — £24
2A RICHARD HOCKLEY ¼ 1652 Grocers' Arms
2B — — ¼ 1657 —
3 IAMES WITHERS (I) ½ Man making candles £20
4 IA — (I) ¼ — TALLOW CHANDLER £25

Alton

5 Town ¼, I.H., T.B., W.W.T., 1652 £12
5A — ¼, W.T.W., 1650. In *pb*
6 — ¼, I.H., L.L., W.W.T., 1652 £18
7 — ¼ — — — 1666 £16
8 — ¼ — — — 1664 £22
9 THOMAS BRAIMAN (H) ¼ £38
10 (Probably *Suffolk* 250)

Andover

11 Town ¼ 1658 Cripple, REMEMBER THE POORE £20
12 — ¼ 1666 — FOR THE POORE £18
12A — ¼ 1664 — —
13 — ½ 1666 — Town Arms, FOR YE POORES BENEFIT £12
14 — ¼ — — — — £9
15 ROBERT BIRD ¼ GROCER £22
16 BENIAMIN BRADBORNE (M) ¼ GROCER
17 RICHARD BLAKE ½ MERCER £48
18 NVCOM COKETT (F) ¼ 1666 £22
19 WILLIAM CORNELIVS (M) ¼ Glove £18
20 WILLIAM GOLD (M) ¼ Mercers' Arms £14
21 ROBERT MILLETT ¼ Grocers' Arms
22 THOMAS OLIVES ¼ 1656 CHANDLER
23 (Misreading of 19)
24 THOMAS PAINE (B) ¼ Man making candles £14
25 IOHN SEAGROVE (B) ¼ Grocers' Arms
25A — — ¼ 1669 —
26 IOHN STANIFORD (I) ¼ 1666 Woolpack, CLOTHIER
27 WILLIAM SWEETAPLE (A) ¼ 1655 Grocers' Arms
28 *Anthony Tatnell* (A) ¼ 1666 Dolphin £25
29 ABRAHAM WALLER (E) ¼ 1655 Grocers' Arms £14
30 WILLIAM WALLER (D) ¼ 1665 Grocers' Arms

Basingstoke

31 HENRY BARFFOOT (S) ¼ 1669 Lion £20
31A — BAR(E *or* F)FOOT (S) ¼ 1665 —
32 ROBERT BLVNDEN (K) ¼ Rabbit £15
33/4 IOHN COLEMAN THE ELDER (I) ¼ 1652 Falcon with bells and jesses £16
35 SAMVEL KICHENER (M) ¼ Tallow-chandlers' Arms £20
36 IOSEPH MANSFEILD ½ 1669 Sword and helmet, GROCER, HIS HARTY DVBBLE TOKEN. *Heartshape* £135
37/9 BARNARD REEVE *or* REVE (M) ¼ Angel, arms crossed £13
38 — REVE (M) ¼ Angel holding scroll £14
40 THOMAS SPIAR ½ 1669 Shuttles
41 IOHN TRIMMER (M) ¼ 1670 Hat £38
42 IOHN WATTS IVNOR (M) ¼ Man making candles £20

43 GEORGE WHITE ¼ Mortar and pestle £25

Bishops Waltham
44 IAMES BLLAKLLEY ½ 1666 Grocers' Arms £45
45 IAMES BRAFET ¼ MERCER
46 THOMAS PENFORD ½ 1666 Grocers' Arms £15

Blackwater
46A IONATHAN IENINGS (M) ¼ Arms
47 IOHN WRIGHT ½ 1667 £17

Blissford
47A ANTHONY ROBBINS (I) ¼ 1669

Brading, Isle of Wight
48 THOMAS MAYLE (R) ½ 1670 Bakers' Arms

Castlehold, Isle of Wight
49 EDWARD KNIGHT ¼ Castle £35
50 IEAMES SMITH (E) ¼ Castle £38

Christchurch
51 HVMPHRY RICHARDS (E) ½ Bridge
52 HENRY RICHMAN ½ 1669 Shears
53 HENRY RODGERS ½ 1670 King's Arms
54 IOHN WELCHMAN ¼ Mercers' Arms £28

(West) Cowes, Isle of Wight
55 IOSEPH BARTON ½ THE KINGS ARMS £25
56 THO BRADFEILD (S) ¼ 1666
57 PETER COVRTNELL (S) ¼ '67 £35
58 DANIELL GILES (B) ¼ 1667 £40
59 ROBERT MOORE ¼ Still
59A IOHN WARLAWS ½ 1668 AT ROYAL EXCHANG, building

Crondall
60 E.P. (A) ¼ Drapers' Arms £50
60A EDWARD PECK ¼ 1667 —

East Meon
61 IOHN WITCOMBE (M) ¼ '66 AT YE, angel

Emsworth
62 THOMAS WHEELER (B) ¼ 1667 Mercers' Arms £28

Fareham
63 WILLIAM DIDLESFOLD ¼ 1658 Mercers' Arms
64 — — ¼ n.d. — MERCER*
64A ROBERT HAVKES ½ 1668 Blacksmiths' Arms
64B RICHARD PESCOD (M) ½ Bust of Chas. II

Farnborough
65 IOHN SMITH ½ 1668 AT THE, King's head

Fordingbridge
65A R.C. (A) ¼ 1669 Stag, MERCER
66 SAMVEL HARRIS ¼ Shuttle £25

* From same obv. die as *Surrey* 34

Freshwater, Isle of Wight
67 SAM BARTON ½ '68 Mercers' Arms £55

Gosport
68 NICHOLAS BRADWAY (A) ¼ 1655 £28
69 IOHN BRAMLEY ½ 1667 AT YE RED LYON, lion £30
69A — — ½ — AT YE RED, lion
70 ANNE GRAINGER ½ 1667 £30
71 WILL HVNT (A) ¼ 1668 Rolls of bread, BAKER £50
72 STEPHEN LOCK (D) ¼ 1667 Crossed keys £28
73 IOHN MORGAN (I) ½ 1667 AT YE ROYALL SOVERAIGN, ship £28
73A Gregory Pencher ¼ Tree
74 ELIZABETH SEYMOR ¼ 1667 Anchor

Hambledon
75 (See *Bucks.* 67A)
76 RICHARD STENT (M) ¼ 1666 £20

Hartford Bridge
77 THOMAS RAWLENGSON (E) ½ AT YE WT HART

Hartley Row
78 THO IVSTICE (M) ¼ St George & dragon
79 ROBERT RAYE ¼ 1663 Arms £38
80 IAMES SMETH (E) ½ 1669 AT YE FENIX

Havant
81 THOMAS HILDRVP (M) ¼ TALOWCHAND £22
81A — HILLDROP (S) ¼ 1667 CHANDLER
82 THOMAS YOVNG (M) ¼ 1653 £22

Hook
83 ANN ATKINSON ½ AT THE BLACK RAVEN £38

Hurstbourne
84 ROBERT MVNDAY ¼ 1664 Grocers' Arms

Kingsclere
85 NICHOLAS GREENE (A) ¼ 3 swords, dove

Liphook
86 W.S. (E) ¼ 1668 Anchor £32
87 HENRY CHITTY ¼ 1667

Lymington
88 BARTHOLOMEW BVLKLY ¼ Grocers' Arms £22
89 IOHN BARWICK ½ 1667 £45
89A IOHN EDWARDS ¼ 1666
90 THOMAS GLEVIN (E) ¼ Grocers' Arms
91 (Misreading of 90)
92 BARTHOLOMEW HARMOOD ¼ Grocers' Arms £15
93 IOHN HARMOOD ¼ 1666 Man making candles £30
94 PHINE(H)AS WRIGHT ½ 1667 £20

Newport, Isle of Wight
95 Town ½ n.d. Ship £18

96 Town ¼ 1664— £22
96A —(½)—— (20mm.+ diameter) £28
97 ANN BARFORD ¼ Stationers' Arms £50
98 STEPHEN BARTON (E) ½ 1664 £15
99 RICHARD DORE ¼ 1654 £32
100 IOHN EDWARDS (M) ½ 1668
101 IOSEPH FOSTER (M) ¼ 1657
102 —— (M) ½ 1669
103 WILL HANNAM ¼ Tallowchandlers' Arms £48
104 WILLIAM HAPGOOD ½ 1668 Apothecaries' Arms
105 (Misreading of 111)
106 THOMAS IVNINGE ¼ 1654 Pot of lilies
107 IOHN IOLLIFFE (E) ¼ 1655 £32
108 EDWARD KNIGHT ¼ Castle
109 ARTHVR LEGG (I) ¼ 1656 Grocers' Arms £48
110 ANTHONY MAYNARD (E) ¼ Apothecaries' Arms £35
111 IOHN HOOKE (E) ¼ Grocers' Arms
112/3 ELIZ MAYNARD ¼ £22
114 CVTHBERT MILLS (E) ½ 1670 £50
115 W. NEWLAND (G) ¼ Grocers' Arms £32
116 FRANCIS SEARLE (I) ½ 1670 Brewers' Arms £30
117 (See *Bucks.* 105A)
117A EDWARD WHISTLER ½ 1667
118 IOSEPH WHITHEAD (K) ¼ 1664 £32

Niton

119 (Misreading of 9)
120 (See *Worcs.* 118)

Odiham

121 FRANCIS BAKER (S) ¼ Drapers' Arms £48
122 EDWARD MANNERING (E) ¼ 1656 Grocers' Arms £24
123 ROBERT MAY (A) ¼ 1653 Mercers' Arms £15
124 —— (A) ½ 1669— £25
125 IOHN SPIER (A) ¼ 1668 £28
126 —— (A) ¼ 1665 Shovel £30
126A THOMAS WYNNALL ½ St George & dragon

Overton

126B FRANCIS CARTER (K) ¼ 1665 Man making candles
127 IOHN PVRDVE (I) ½ 1670 AT YE WHITE HARTE £18
128 (Misreading of 129)
129 WILLIAM SPIER ½ 1668 Tallowchandlers' Arms £25

Petersfield

130 IOHN HORSENAILE (S) ½ 1668 Stays
131 THOMAS IAQVES ¼ AT THE *or* IN, hart £18
132 —— ¼ AT THE HARTE, hart £25
132A IOHN IONES ¼ Sugar-loaf £50
133 IOHN WALKER (M) ½ 1668 £22
133A Similar but ½ instead of HIS HALFE PENNY on *rev.* £45

Portsmouth

133B IAMES AVSTEN ¼ Bakers' Arms £35
134 IOHN AYLWARD (M) ¼ Candles, dipping-case £16
135 IOHN BALLARD (A) ¼ 1653
136 ELIZABETH BISSELL (W) ¼ 1657 3 anchors £20
137/8 CHRISTO BRVNCKER *or* CHRISTEFER BRVNKER (M) ¼ n.d. Bell £14
138A CRISTOPHER BRVNKER (M) ¼ 1667—
138B — BRVNCKER ½ Bell
139 ALEXANDER CARTER (K) ¼ Scales
139A THOMAS CARTER (E) ¼ 1664 Hat £38
139B IOHN EASTMAN (M) ¼ 1667 3 cloves
140 PHIL(L)IP ELMES (I) ¼ Crossed swords £32
141 WILLIAM ENGLISH (I) ¼ 1667 Paschal lamb £22
142/3 RICHARD FAVL(K *or* C)ONER (A) ½ '68 Bust of Chas. II. *Octagonal* £75
144 EDWARD FLOOD (W) ¼ Crescent and star £30
144A IEANE GARNHAM ¼ Pelican at nest £35
144B THOMAS HANCOCK ½ 1669 Cock
145 ROBERT HARFORD ½ 1669 Hand holding pen £24
146 ROBERT HAWCKES (E) ¼ Blacksmiths' Arms £30
147/8 HENRY IENNER (S) ¼ 1656 £15
149 THO IELLIT (E) ¼ AT WHIT, hart
150 IAMES LOCK (M) ¼ 1667
150A — LOCKE (M) ¼ Still
151 IOHN KENT ½ 1670 AT NEPTVNS COVRT, Neptune. *Octagonal** £42
151A RICHARD LARDNER ¼ 1655
152 FRANCIS LVCAS ¼ 1666 Ship £17
153 RICHARD MARKS ½ 1671 Fishing boat
153A THOMAS MILLS ¼
154 IOHN PATTEN (A) ¼ 1667 £14
155 THOMAS PARKES (E) ¼ Dolphin £30
156 EDWARD PEARSE (M) ½ 1667 AT YE HVLKE, ship's hulk £20
156A —— (M) ¼ '67 AT YE, ship's hulk
157 NICHOLAS PEIRSON (S) ¼ 1653 £30
158 —— (S) ¼ 1666 £42
159 RICHARD PRIEST (I) ¼ Squirrel £18
160 PAVL RICHARDS (E) ¼ 1656 £32
161 WILLIAM SMEDMORE ½ 1670 AT, fountain £32
162 (Misreading of 161)
163 RICHARD THOMAS (I) ¼ ON THE POINTE, stag
164 WALTER THVRMAN (I) ¼ '60 Roll of cloth £25
165 ROBERT TIPPETS (E) ¼ 1666 Barber-Surgeons' Arms £20
166 RICHARD WHITE (M) ¼ 1656 £35
167 THOMAS WILSON ½ AT THE, plume of feathers, VPON YE POINT

* Also known on *round* flan (? error)

Ringwood
167A NICK BELBIN (I) ½ Hat, HABADASHER
168 RICHARD BELBIN (M) ½ 1668 Sugar-loaf
169 THOMAS BLANCH ¼ Rose and crown £35
169A BENIAMIN HIGHMORE ½ 1668 Arms
169B IAMES PHEITEPLACE (E) ¼ Stick of candles*
170 TRISTRAM TVRGES (G) ¼ 1666 Arms £28

Romsey
171 CORPORATION ½ 1669 Portcullis, FOR YE BENEFIT OF YE POOR £12
172 — ¼ — — FOR YE BENEFIT OF THE POORE £55
172A WALTER BELL (H) ¼ 1665 Cordwainers' Arms
173 IOHN HACKE (I) ½ 1667 AT THE, bell £20
174 ISAAC KNIGHT (F) ¼ 1664 Grocers' Arms £45
175 WILLIAM KNIGHT (A) ¼ Grocers' Arms £16
176 IOHN MOVNTAYNE (F) ¼ Man making candles £24
177 IOHN PVCKRIDGE (M) ½ 1668 £11
178 CLEMENT WARREN (I) ½ 1667 Mercers' Arms £13
179/80 EDMVND Y(O *or* I)NGE (A) ¼ 1664 3 crowns £18

Ryde, Isle of Wight
181 NICHOLAS OAKLEY (M) ¼ 1664 £32
182 WILLIAM PHILLIPS (E) ½ '67 Vintners' Arms

Soake (Winchester)
183 NATHANIELL ROBBERTS ½ 1668 Tallowchandlers' Arms £24

Southampton
184 CORPORATION ½ Town Arms £12
185 — ¼ — £12
186 ANTONY BARROW ¼ Grocers' Arms
187 CHRISTOPHER BELL ¼ Family Arms £22
188 WILLIAM BOWER (C) ¼ 1666 Grocers' Arms £30
189 RICHARD CORNELLIVS ¼ 1660 Barrel £35
190 SAMVELL DOWNES ½ 1668 Bakers' Arms £35
191 GEORGE FREEMAN ½ 1668 AT YE WHIT, horse £28
192 IOHN GOTER ¼ 3 stars (?), 3 roses
193 WILLIAM IOLLIFE (I) ¼ 1666 Grocers' Arms £22
194 — LOLLIFE ¼ Grocers' Arms £30
195 CORNELIVS MACHAM ½ 1667 Grocers' Arms £16
196 — — ¼ 1664 — £20
197 — — ½ 1667 Initials
198 WILLIAM MACHAM ¼ Grocers' Arms

* A farthing of this issuer, dated 166(5?), has been recorded overstruck with *obv.* and *rev.* of 196

199 HENRY MILLER (M) ¼ 1664 Grocers' Arms £30
200 HENRY NORBORNE (A) ½ 1668 Family Arms £28
201 IOSEPH SMITH ¼ Mercers' Arms
202 IACOB WARD ¼ Scales £20

Titchfield
203 WILLIAM HACK (E) ½ 1668 AT THE, St George & dragon £50
204 WILLI HOVGHTON ¼ 1652 Grocers' Arms £32
205 HENRY RAY (E) ¼ Scissors

Wallop
206 HVGH CHITTY ½ 1666 Shears £25

West Meon
207 IOHN FOSTER (I) ½ 1670 Saltire £35

Whitchurch
208 ALLEN HARPER (I) ¼ Grocers' Arms £30
209 IOHN PEARCE (M) ¼ Grocers' Arms
210 EDWARD WAIGHT (I) ¼ 1667 Grocers' Arms £25

Winchester
211 City ½ 1669 City Arms £14
212 — ¼ — — £55
213 WILLIAM BVTLER (I) ½ 1669 Grocers' Arms £28
214 — — (I) ¼ 1657 — £11
215 IOHN CLEER ½ GROCER £40
216 PETER CROSS ½ 1667 GROCER £38
217 (Misreading of 216)
218 (See *Wilts.* 235)
219 MICHAELL FITCHAT (I) ½ 1667 Crossed swords £15
220 WILL FLETCHER IVN (M) ¼ AT KINGSGATE, Grocers' Arms £18
221 IOHN LAMPARD (M) ¼ Grocers' Arms £25
222 ROBERT MICHILL (S) ¼ Grocers' Arms £32
223/4 WILL(I)AM OVER (M) ¼ AT (YE) EASTGATE, Grocers' Arms £11
225 GODSON PENTON (P) ½ 1667
226 NICHOLAS PVRDVE (K) ¼ Grocers' Arms £28
227 IOHN PVRDVE ½ 1667 Ironmongers' Arms £35
228 ROBERT STEELE ½ 1667 GROCER £18
229 WILLIAM TAYLOR ½ 1667 Grocers' Arms £18
230 — TAYLER (R) ¼ Grocers' Arms £32
231 (Misreading of 222)
232 DOROTHY WINTER ½ 1667 IN KINGS GATE STREET, pot of lilies £20
233 ANTHONY WISEMAN (M) ¼ 1657 DRAPER £12

Yarmouth, Isle of Wight
234 IOHN PRICE ½ 1670 Greyhound
235 (Misreading of 236)
236 IOHN PRICE ¼ St George & dragon
237 WILL(IAM) HIDE (B) ½ 1667 Ship. **Plate 2** £28

Yateley
238 IAMES LECH (H) ¼ 1670 Butchers' Arms £38

Herefordshire

New tokens recorded from *NC*, 1902; W. Gilbert, 'Unpublished . . .' (see under Cambridgeshire); the Faulkner collection (sold at Glendining's, 21 May 1940); *SNC*, July 1947; *TCSB*, Vol. 2 nos. 5/6, Nov./Dec. 1974; *SCA* 7, 5 Dec. 1979.

Believed entirely unpublished: 36A, 43A, 52A, 64B, 67A.

Minimum price for unvalued tokens: £75

Bromyard

1–3 IOHN BA(ME *or* YN)HAM (F) ¼ Family crest £75
2A — BAYNHAM (Mule: see *Wales* 66B)
3A — — ½ 1664 Family crest

Hereford

4, 5 City (½) 1662 City Arms, CITTY ARMES; sword, HEN IONES SWORDBERER £30
6 — (½) 1663 — — — —
7 — ¼ 1662 — ARMES; sword, H. IONES SWORD BERER £55
8 WILLIAM BARNES ½ 1661 *Ob* in lozenge
9 — — ¼ 1666
10 ROGER BOVLCOT ½ Fleur-de-lis
11 — — ¼ —
12 THOMAS ELLTON ½ 1666 Weavers' Arms £55
13 THO HANCOX ½ 1668 BOOKESELLER
14 I.H. ¼ Rose; Mercers' Arms £35
15/6 IOHN HILL ½ '57 Centre oval b.s. £30
17 GILES HOVLDER ½ 1668 Leathersellers' Arms, GLOVER. *Heart-shape*
18 EDMOND HVCK (M) ¼ Rose and crown
19 THOMAS HVTCHINS ½ 1668 Anchor, GLOVER. *Heart-shape* £150
20 BARNABY IENKINS ½ 1666 Leathersellers' Arms
21 IOHN LANE ½ 1661 Horse; Initials in heart
22/3 THOMAS MATHEWS ½ 1661 *Ob* £70
24 ROGER MORGAN ¼ Fleur-de-lis
24A — — ½ 1671 —. *Octagonal*
25 IOHN MOSS (I) ¼ Fleece £55
26 THOMAS POWELL ½ 1669 7 stars
27 HVGH RODD ½ City Arms; elephant and castle
28 — — ¼ — —
28A (Mule: see *Staffs*. 63)
29 IOHN RODD (F) ½? 1670 Cavalier's hat. *Square*
30 SAMVELL SAVNDERS ½ Ironmongers' Arms £40
31 THOMAS SEABORNE ¼ 1652 3 lions £55
32 LYSON THOMAS ½ 1668 IRONMONGER
33 ROBERT WATTS ½ 1667 Lion
34 WILL WELCH ½ 1663 SILK WEAVER £30
34A — — ½ 1665 — £65

Kington

35 IOHN BREYNTON ½ 1667 MERCER
36 FRANCIS DAVIES ½ 1665 MERCER
36A THO GIPPS (A) ¼ Family Arms
37 EDWARD GRONNOVS (E) ½ 1670 Mercers' Arms
38 — — (E) ¼ Mercers' Arms
39 IAMES GRONNONS ½ 1669 MERCER; I DOE AS I WOVLD BE DONE BY
40 IAMES LLOYD (M) ¼ 1660 MAESSER
41 — — (M) ½ 1664 MERCER
41A IAMES MEREDITH (E) (½) Bunch of grapes?
42 IOHN ROWDON ½ 1664 Family Arms, MERCER
43 ANTHONY SEARCH (M) ¼ Grocers' Arms, MERCER
43A WILL SHIPHEARD (M) ¼ 1664 Sheep
43B WILLIAM SHEPPARD (M) ½
44 RALPH TVRFORD ½ 1668 APOTHECARY
45 NICHOLAS VORE ½ 1664 Ironmongers' Arms
46 RICHARD VOARE ½ 1668 IRONMONGER; SQVARE DEALING. *Square*

Ledbury

47 WILLIAM BERROW (E) ¼ Grocers' Arms
48 WILLIAM BROWNE (I) ¼ Glaziers' Arms (part)
49 RICHARD COX (A) ½ 1667
49A IOBE MANINGS ½ 1670 Bell
50 WILLIAM MATHEWES (M) ¼ 1653 Drug jar
51 WILLIAM HOOPER, THO PAGE ½ 1667 Weavers' Arms
52 REIGHNALD RANDOLPH ½ 1668 Blacksmiths' Arms £60

52A RENOLD — ¼ 1659 —
53 IO STONE (H) ½ Sugar-loaf
54 SAMVELL WILSON, IOHN WHITE ½ 1663 £48

Leominster
55 ELIZABETH BEDFORD ½ 1667 Sugar-loaf £70
56 IEROMY CLARKE (T) ¼ 1663 Mercers' Arms
57 WILLIAM CLENT (E) ¼ 1666 BOOK SELLER
58 SAMPSON EDWARDES (K) ½ 1668 Bakers' Arms
59 THOMAS FOORDE (S) ¼ Mercers' Arms
60 THO HARDWICK IVNIOR ½ Hart £50
61 IOHN NAISH (M) ½ 1669 Glovers' Arms, GLOVER
61A M.P. (I) ¼ 1659 Drapers' Arms
62 FRAN PERSE ½ 1666 Mercers' Arms
63 NATHANIELL SMITH (M) ½ 1667
64 IOHN STEAD ¼ Shield both sides
64A THOMAS WILDE (S) ¼ Sheep's head

Pembridge
64B James Bwngo ¼ Arms
65 THOMAS BENGOVGH (P) ½ 1665 £60
65A — — (P) ½ 1667

Ross
66 IAMES FISHER ½ 1666 Mercers' Arms £70
66A FRANCIS HARRIS ½ 1670 2-headed eagle
67 IOHN HILL ½ '66 Centre oval b.s.
67A — — ½ '59 —
68 — — (E) ¼ MERCER
69 THOMAS MERRICK 1d 1680?
69A THOMAS RODD (B) ¼ 1666 APOTHECARY
70 IOHN TAYLOR (T) ½ 1667 CHANDLER
71 THOMAS TAYLOR (E) ¼ 1656

Weobley
72 IAMES CLARKE (½) 1659, 3 rabbits, MERCER £70
73 RICHARD CLARK ½ 1667 Hand holding bird, MERCER

Hertfordshire

Major reference: Peter Seaby, 'A Guide to the Token Coinage of the 17th Century: Hertfordshire' (*SCMB*, May to July 1961). Updating and revision of Williamson, and locations of specimens.

Further new tokens recorded from H.C.A., 'Stanstead Abbots: Tradesmen's Tokens' (*SCMB,* Apr. 1948); *SCMB*, Feb. 1958; East Hertfordshire Archaeological Society, *Newsletter no. 15* (1964); and George Berry and Bryen Wood, 'A Small Hoard of Seventeenth-Century Tokens, Bushey, Herts., 1965' (*BNJ,* 1975).

See also *NC*, 1893: notes on some unpublished tokens; W. Longman, 'Notes on some Hertfordshire Issuers of Seventeenth Century Tokens' (*SNC*, Mar. 1908).

Believed entirely unpublished: 36A, 54A, 225A.

Minimum price for unvalued tokens: £50

Ashwell

1 VALENTINE LEE (G) ¼ 1669 AT YE, wheatsheaf £20
2 THOMAS MACKERIS (E) ¼ 1665 Stick of candles £18
3 IOHN SELL IVNIOR (A) ¼ Grocers' Arms £18

Baldock

4 EDWARD CRAFFTES (M) ¼ 1670 Bust of Chas. II
5 IO CROWCH ¼ 1658 CHANDLER £25
6 PHILLIP DEERE ¼ Tallowchandlers' Arms; stick of candles £48
7 IOHN GODFREYE (E) ¼ 1652 GROCER £14
8 EDWARD HIGHLY (S) ¼ 1652 £14
9 IOHN IZARD (E) ¼ £22
10, 11 WILLIAM KENNET (I) ¼ 1658 St George & Dragon £16
11A WILL KNIGHT (E) ¼ AT YE TALBOT
12 (Probably misreading of *Surrey* 6)
13 WILLIAM SEAMER (L) ¼ 1672
14/5 RICHARD SHEPHERD (M) ¼ 1665 Grocers' Arms £18
16 WILL WARRE (A) ¼ GROCER £12

Barkway

17 IOHN KENT (S) ¼ 1667 GROCER £48
18 THOMAS RAVENS (G) ¼ Grocers' Arms, CHANDLER £25

Barley

19 PHAROH OLD ½ 1670 Swan

Barnet

20 WILLIAM BARNES (S) ½ Tobacco-roll, pipes
21 PEETER BLACKWELL (A) ½ '66 AT YE ANTELOPE £24
22 —— (A) ½ 1668 AT THE ANTELOPE £35
23 IOANE BVLL ½ 1667 Scales £40
24 —— ½ 1668 —
25/6 IAMES BVRGES (S) ¼ Drapers' Arms £25
27 WILLIAM PRESTWOOD (E) ½ AT YE MERMAYDE
28/9 IOHN ROTHERHAM ¼ 1655 Stick of candles £14
30/1 — ROTHERH(AM *or* A) ¼ 1653 — £32
32 N.S. (A) ¼ 1651 AT THE HOOPE £28
33 SAMVELL STONARD ¼ 1668 Drapers' Arms
34 SAMLL WILKINSON ½ AT THE FLOWER DE LVCE

Batchworth Bridge

34A IOHN WEADEN ½ 1667 Bridge

Bovingdon

35 IASON GOVLD ½ 1670

Berkhampsted

36 WILLIAM BABB (K) ½ 1667
36A —— (K) ½ 1666. In *pb* (?)
37 IOHN CARVELL (M) ½ 1667
38 WILLIAM PRESTON (I) ½ 1668 £42
39 IOHN SEELING (E) ¼ 1655 £42

Bishops Stortford

40 EDWARD AYNSWORTH ½ Reindeer
41 E.A. (E) ¼ — YE RAINE DEARE

42 (Misreading of 43)
43 ANN BRITTAINE ½ 1669 IN SOVTH STREET, crossed keys. *Octagonal* £65
44 WILL CHANDLER ¼ Bust of bishop £50
45 HVMPHREY DIXON ½ 1667 Grocers' Arms; crozier £30
46/7 EDWARD GARDNER ½ 1668 Woolpack £28
48 (Uniface (*obv.*) or brockage of 46)
49 RICHARD GINN ¼ 1666 Half-moon £45
50 FRANCES MATHVS ¼ Initials b.s. £28
51/2 FRANC(E *or* I)S — ¼ Rose £50
53 GEORGE PATTESON ¼ Castle
54 IOHN READ ½ Crossed keys. *Octagonal*
54A —— (M) ½ Initials. *Octagonal*
55/6 SIMON RVTLAND (T) ¼ Grocers' Arms £38
57 IOHN SMITH ½ 1667 Man smoking
58 WILLIAM WESTWOOD ½ 1667 3 sugar-loaves, GROCER

Braughing

59 WILLIAM ROWSON (M) (½) 1668 Crossed keys; crossed tobacco-pipes

Brent Pelham

60 *Ralph Wheeler* (A) ½ Panniers

Buntingford

61 MARY BATSFORD ¼ 1667 Grocers' Arms
62 IAMES CAMPE (M) ¼ DRAPER
63 THOMAS EDRIDGE ¼ Haberdashers' Arms
64 MARY EDWARDS ½ 1669 Bell £32
65 WILLIAM FERRIS ½ 1669 Sheep
66 —— ½ — Woolpack £28
67 (Misreading of 68)
68 ADAM IOVRY (I) ½ 1669 Crossed keys. *Octagonal* £80
69, 70 EDMON LYON (A) ¼ 1666
71 ANDREW WOOTTON (M) ½ 1669 TALLOW CHANDLER. *Heart-shape*

Bushey

71A IEREMIAH DELL (E) ¼ 1664 Malt-shovel
72 RALPH FEILD ½ 1669 3 tobacco-pipes; wine cup
73 WILL LITCHFIELD, IOHN PILE ½ 1669 Lion with arrow; malt-shovel £32
74 (Misreading of 73)

Cheshunt

75 IAMES BVLL ¼ 1666 Bull
76 RICHARD FEILDING (E) ¼ 1659 IN CHESSON STREETE
77 SAM GOODAKER ½ 1668 City of London Arms. *Heart-shape* £150
78 THOMAS MEDLICOTT (B) ¼ 1664 Wheatsheaf £32
79 *John Teckoe* ½ 1669 Queen's head
80 IOHN WRIGHT (I) ¼ 1660 Stick of candles £18

Chipperfield

81 THOMAS BIGG (M) ½ 1669 Weavers' Arms

Eastwick

82 IOH CRAMPHORN (M) ¼ 1662 AT YE, vine £48

Elstree

82A IOHN AXTELL (S) ½ '67 MERSER

Furneaux Pelham

83 FELIX CALVERD (I) ½ 1668 £32
84 THOMAS PHIPPE ¼ 1671 HIS TOKEN £55

Hatfield

85 ROBERT BARNARD ½ 1666 AT THE GEORGE £28
86 IOSEPH FAIRCLOTH ¼ Bell
87 THOMAS FAIRECLOTH (E) ¼ Grocers' Arms £40
87A WILLIAM OTWAY ½ 1666 AT YE RED, lion
88/9 (See *Essex* 201A, 201B)
90 THOMAS SERIN (E) ½ 1667 AT YE, chequers £18
91 ELIZABETH SELWOOD ¼ Mercers' Arms
92 IOHN THOMAS ½ 1666 AT THE HOLY LAMB, Paschal lamb

Hemel Hempstead

93 H.A. ¼ 1658 Crown, hands holding comb and hair
94 WILLIAM CLIFTON (M) ½ 1669 Hand holding pen £25
95/6 WILLIAM GLADMAN ½ Fox and goose £40
97 NICOLAS KING (G) ¼ 1653 £35
98 IOHN NORRIS (M) ½ 1667 AT THE, swan £45
99 IOHN ROLPH ½ 1668 Bull £38
100 THOMAS TVRNEY ½ 1664 £24

Hertford

101 EMERRE BRADLE ¼ '68 BAKER
102 IOSEPH BROWNE (E) ¼ GROCER £38
103 WILLIAM CARTER ¼ GROCER
104 IOHN KING (S) ¼ 1652 GROCER
105 THOMAS LOWE ½ 1668 Drapers' Arms
106 THOMAS PRAT (M) ¼ Chequers
107 ABRAHAM RVTT (M) ¼ 1666 Ironmongers' Arms £45
108 GORGE SEELY ¼ 1652 Grocers' Arms
109 ROB STADDER (S) ¼ AT THE SWAN

Hitchin

110 IOSEPH BAKER (E) ¼ 1663 £15
111/2 EDWARD COOKE (A) ¼ £22
113 FRANCIS CROVT (E) ¼ 1657, IN AN S
114 W. DRAGE ½ 1667 Apothecaries' Arms, OPIFERQ' PER ORBEM DICOR £20
115 FRAN FEILD ¼ 1667 IN BANCROFT STREET £28
116 WILLIAM FVLLER ¼ Man making candles
117 THOMAS HAYWARD (A) ½ 1667 £28
118 THOMAS HEALEY (L) ¼ 1659 £22

119 DAN HVRST (A) ¼ Man standing with sieve, OATEMEALEMAKER £20
120 ANDREW LANGLY (M) ¼ 1667 AT YE, 2 sugar-loaves
121 ISAAC ROYSE ¼ 1656 BREWER £38
122 IOHN RVGELEY ½ 1667 Family Arms £12
123 IOHN THORNTON (A) ¼ 1664 Sugar-loaf £16
124 MARY TRISTTRAM ¼ 1666 3 hats £13
125 HENRY WARNER (S) ¼ 1664 Stick of candles £16

Hoddesdon
126 IOHN CLARKE ½ 1668 AT THE, 2 brewers with barrel. *Octagonal*
127 ABRAHAM DIXE (M) ¼ 1665 Grocers' Arms
128 MARTHA GIBBS ½ AT THE, bull
129 *Mathew Harold* (M) ¼ *meale man*
130 (Probably misreading of 131)
131 WILLIAM PEDLEY ½ 1668 Mercers' Arms
131A IOHN SMIGERSGILL ½ 1668 Man making candles

Hunsdon
132 MARGRET WHORELY ¼ Sugar-loaf

Kimpton
133 WILLIAM SHORTOR ¼ 1668 Bakers' Arms

King's Langley
134 (Probably misreading of 135)
135 CHRISTOR BVCKCVK (M) ¼ 1656
136 IAMES GOODWIN (F) ½ 1668 AT THE, rose and crown £45

Lemsford Mills
137 IOSEPH HARDHAM (M) ½ 1666

Little Hadham
138 FELIX COLVART ¼ Family Arms

Little Munden
139 ANNE KEIMTON ¼ '65 Monkey dressed as woman; stick of candles £42

Markyate Street
140/1 (See *Beds.* 73A, 73B; in the 17th century the place was in Bedfordshire)

Much Hadham
141A IOHN COCKETT ½ 1668 3 cloves
141B MARGERY COCKETT ¼ 1666
142 ELIZABETH COLEMAN ¼ Drapers' Arms
143 — COLMAN (½) —
144 THO DONCASTER (A) ¼ 1666 AT WHIT, lion

Northaw
145 (See *Bucks.* 106B)

Pirton
146 (Misreading of 149)
147 IOHN FARMER (E) ½ 1668 Tobacco-roll £60
148 — FARMAR ¼ 1656 —; Grocers' Arms
149 (Probably *Surrey* 207)
150 (See *Wilts.* 157A)

Puckeridge
151 *George Benn* ¼ Crossed tobacco pipes £38
152 *Arthur Brayne* ¼ Crossed tobacco pipes
153 *George Rogers* ¼ Pipes crossed, cloves

Redbourn
153A *George Carpenter* ½ 1669 Royal oak
154 IOHN HALSEY ½ AT YE BLACK LYON
155 IAMES HANNELL (K) ½ 1669 Woolpack. *Heart-shape*
156 IOH TYLER (A) ¼ Scales

Rickmansworth
157/8 IOHN SKIDMORE ½ 1666 Mercers' Arms £20
159 (Uniface? (*obv.*) of 157/8; perhaps a later striking)
159A GEORGE WINGFEILD (A) ¼ Grocers' Arms

Royston
160 THOMAS BILL ¼ 1664 £35
161/2 EDWARD CROVCH (A) ¼ Stick of candles £32
163 RICHARD GODFREE (E) ¼ Man making candles £16
164 THOMAS GODFREY ¼ Sugar-loaf, CHANDLER
165/6 IAMES PARTRICH (C) ¼ Mitre, VINTNER £16
167 — — (C) ¼ 1668 Mitre
168 BENIAMIN SCRVBIE (E) ¼ GROCER £30
169 IAMES SWAN ¼ GROCER
170 WILLIAM WIND (E) ¼ 1657 City of London Arms £45

St Albans
171 RALPH BRADBVRY (E) ¼ Grocers' Arms £28
172/3 EDWARD CAMFIELD (E) ¼ 1656 £18
174 (Misreading of 175)
175 *John Cowlee ½ Backer. Octagonal* £70
176 RICHARD FINCH (M) ¼ 1666 Swan
177 HENRY GLADMAN ½ 1666 AT THE, St George & dragon £20
177A THOMAS HVDGSON (S) ½ MEALEMAN
178 THOMAS NASH (D) ½ 1669 Savage holding dart £20
179 IOHN TISDALLE (E) ½ 1667

Sawbridgeworth
179A IOHN AND SARA EVE ¼ Arms
180 (See *London* 2438A)
181 IEREMIAH HERNE (E) ½ 1669
182 THOMAS KING (F) ¼ 1669 Crossed swords

Shenley
183 IOHN CLARKE (A) ¼ 1666 Heart £35

184 (See *Bucks*. 115A)

Standon

185 THOMAS DANIELL (M) ¼ 1656 Grocers' Arms
186 *Henry Hicks* ¼ Shoe; crossed tobacco pipes

Stanstead Abbots

186A ROBERT BRADLY ½ MEALMAN AT YE LION
186B IOHN BVRNAP (E) ¼ 1656 GROCER
186C MARY TRAYHEARNE ¼ Female figure; rose, DEALR

Stevenage

187 THOMAS FLETCHER ¼ 1668 Scales £32
188 PETER LANGTHORNE (E) ¼ 1666 Blacksmiths' Arms £32
189 *Henry Barnes* (A) ¼ 1667 £28
190 ROBERT SMITH ½ 1667 Man making candles £30
191 —-— ¼ —— £42

Stocking Pelham

192 THOMAS WHEELER (M) ½ '68 AT YE, hart £60

Therfield

193 WILLIAM HARE (S) ¼ Greyhound

Tring

194 WILLIAM AXTELL ½ 1668 Crowned rose
195 NORRIA COOCKE ¼ 1657 Mercers' Arms
195A HASTING PARROT (A) ¼ 1668 Bell
196 WILLIAM SOMNER (M) ¼ Bakers' Arms £55
196A WILLIAM SPICER (F) ½ Woolstaple; uncrowned head

Wadesmill

197 EDWARD LAWRENCE ½ 1669 AT YE, turnstile £38
198 (Uniface (*obv.*) or brockage of 197)

Walkern

199 THOMAS CHAPMAN (M) ¼ 1667 Grocers' Arms £50
199A FRANCES EXTON (M, G) ¼ 1666

Waltham Cross

200 THO LIDERDALL (E) ½ 1668 Dress £32
201 (See *Leics*. 105A)
202 *John Teckoe* ½ Name in monogram £48

Ware

203 PEETER BOWES (E) ¼ 1653
203A IOHN CRISPP (M) ¼ 1666 AT THE, lion
203B THOMAS FITT (M) ½ 1667 OSTLER
203C IOHN GILLAM (S) ¼ 1668 AT YE, cock
204 IOHN GOTHERIDGE (E) ¼ GROCER £45
205 RICHARD GVTTERIDGE (E) ¼ GROCER
206 THOMAS GVTTERDGE (R) ¼ GROCER
207 HENRY HARTE (I) ¼ 1667 Saracen's head
208 IONATHAN IOHNSON ¼ 1666 Cordwainers' Arms £48
209 E.P. (A) ¼ AT THE BRIDGE FOOT, GROCER
210 GEORG KILBEY ½ AT THE COACH AND HORSES
211 THOMAS WALKER (A) ¼ 1665 Griffin

Watford

212 GEORGE BROCKETT (S) ½ 1668 AT YE, swan
213 WILLIAM BVCKOKE ½ 1667 Hat
214 EDWARD EWER (M) ½ 1666 Glove £35
215 FRANCIS HILL ¼ Rose
216 T. IARMAN (A), I. BVRGES (M) ½ 1669 Dove b.s.
216A T. IERMAN, I. BVRGES ¼ 1653 Loaf b.s. In *pb*
217 IOHN LEMON (S) ¼ Tobacco-roll
218 IOHN MORSE (I) ½ 1666 Skeleton holding hour-glass and dart £38
219 IOHN NEALE (H) ½ 1664 TALLOW CHANDLER £48
220 IOHN & IONATHON NEWMAN ½ Lion, TALLOW CHANDLER £50
221 CAP ROCKE ¼ 1649 Initials A.M.R., AT THE, stag £38
222 GEORG SMEANTH ½ 1668 Man smoking, tobacco under arm
223 THO & GEORGE SMITH ½ 1668 —
224 WILLIAM WHITTAKER (H) ½ 1668 MERCER £17

Watton-at-Stone

224A KATHERINE ALLEYN ¼ 1668

Welwyn

224B RICHARD FOARD ¼? 1667 Grocers' Arms

Weston

224C THOMAS COVLSON (A) ¼ 1668 Prince of Wales' feathers

Wheathampstead

225 IAMES GREENE ¼ 1659 Grocers' Arms
225A —— ¼ 1657 —

Wormley

226 HENRY SPARKS (A) ¼ 1665 Grocers' Arms

Huntingdonshire

New tokens recorded from W. Gilbert, 'Unpublished . . .' (see under Cambridgeshire); and *SNC*, Aug./Sep. 1947.

See also Capt. J. A. M. Vipan, *Coins, Medals and Local Tradesmen's Tokens of the XVII, XVIII & XIXth Centuries in the Peterborough Museum* (Peterborough Natural History, Scientific and Archaeological Society, 1908). Has useful notes on a few St Neots issuers.

Minimum price for unvalued tokens: £45

Alconbury Weston
1 THOMAS ACHVRCH (A) ½
1A ROB WHITEHEAD ¼ 1659

Buckden
2 WILLIAM REEVE (M) ½ 1667 £50

Catworth
3 IOHN TALBOTT ½ 1668 £17

Earith
3A THOMAS IOHNSON (I) ¼ 1656

Elton
4 IOHN MARCH ½ IVEN (= June) 1667 AT YE, crown £24

Eynesbury
5 HENERY ASHLEY (A) ¼ 1668 £30
6 ROBERT BVLL ½ 1667 Horse's head bridled
7 ANDREW SELBY ½ 1668 EYNSBVREY AND POTEN, fleur-de-lis £13

Fenny Stanton
8 TOBIAS HARDMEAT ½ Hive £45

Glatton
9 (Probably same as *Beds.* 28)

Godmanchester
10 HENRY BECK (K) ½ 1669 Sugar-loaf £22
11 ROBERT CARLES ¼ '58 Grocers' Arms
12 SAMVELL CONNYE ¼ Cock £22
13 IOHN SKEGGS ½ 1668 2-headed eagle £28
14 WILLIAM WRIGHT (M) ½ 1666 £32

Hemingford Gray
14A RICHARD BARINGER ¼ 3 shuttles

Huntingdon
15 MARY CHAMBERS ¼ '57 Crown £32
16 RICHARD KNIGHT (M) ½ 1667 £40
17 WILLIAM LAMBE ½ 1668 Royal oak £28
18 T.P., R.H. ¼ 1653 GROCER £22
19 ROBERT RABIE (P) ¼ 1653 DRAPER £20

Kimbolton
20 IOSIAH KING (A) ¼ 1656
21 IOHN WOLLASTON ¼ 3 cloves £18

Offord Cluny
22 (Probably misreading of 23)
23 IOHN BRADLY (K) ¼ 1660 St George & dragon

Ramsey
24 IOHN BECKE (M) ½ GROCER £20
25 MILES BERRIFFE ¼ 1666 Haberdashers' Arms £25
26 W.F. (S) ¼ THE GEORGE, St George & dragon
27 IOHN FRENCH ½ 1669 RAMSEY AND CHATTERIS, Drapers' Arms £40
28 IAMES IARMAN ½ 1669 Arrow* £20
29 — — ¼ 1663 Arrow-head £18
30 IAMES SHARPE ¼ Grocers' Arms £20
31 WILLIAM SHARPE (F) ½ 1666 £35
32 IOHN WILLIAMES ½ 1668 ST. IVES AND RAMSEY. Plough; pipes crossed £40

St Ives
33 *Overseers* ½ 1669 Women washing in tub, POOR WOMEN £20
34 — ¼ — — — £35
35 THOMAS ANDREWS (E) ¼ 1663 Bull
36 THOMAS BERRIFFE (M) ¼ Haberdashers' Arms £25
37 ARON BROWNE ¼ 1659 Anchor
37A HENRY CORDALL (Probably *Cornwall* 82)
38 THOMAS FILBEE (R) ½ Crown £42
39 HEN GOODFELLOW (M) ¼ Grocers' Arms
40 EDWARD HALLSEY ¼ 1663 Salters' Arms £35
41 — — (I) ¼ 1667 Sugar-loaf £24

* Also known in silver, of later manufacture

42 IOHN IBBOTT (M) ¼ 1663 Salters' Arms £42
43 THO IOHNSON ½ INFEILD AND ST. IVES. Rose and crown; Arms £24
44 WILL NOTTINGHAM ¼ 1663 £32
45 ROBERT PAIGE (I) ¼ 1663 Tallowchandlers' Arms
46 WILLIAM AND IOB PERRET (I) ¼ Bull £18
47 MARTIN PRATT (S) ½ Angel
48 EDWARD RABIE (½) Crown; 3 tuns £22
49 IONATHAN READ (R) ¼ Haberdashers' Arms £24
50 THOMAS REWSE ½ St George & dragon £24
51 THOMAS STOCKER (M) ½ Dolphin

St Neots
52 OVERSEERS ½ Women seated making lace, ST. EEDS £60
53 As last but ST. NEOTS £55
54 THOMAS ANNIS ½ 1667 Apothecaries' Arms £24
55 ROBERT DOMAN (E) ¼ 1664 DRAPER £18
57 THOMAS HANCOCKE ½ 1667 Frying pan £20
58 IOHN HATLY ½ 1668 Rolls of bread, BAKER £24
56/9 — HATLEY ¼ Sword between stars; monogram of name
60 IOHN NEWMAN (M) ¼ Grocers' Arms £16
61 THOMAS NEWMAN (E) ½ 1667 Mercers' Arms £16
62 IOB PERRETT (M) ¼ 1666 Salters' Arms £25

Sawtry
63 ROBERT MICHELL ½ 1667 Tallowchandlers' Arms £20

Somersham
64 NATHANIELL DREW ½ AT THE, bull £32
65 RICH KILLINGLY ½ 1671 AT YE GREAT BVLL
66 IOHN SMITH ½ 1670 Man chopping wood £28

Spaldwick
66A HENRY BVLL ¼ 1657 £60

Stilton
67 IOHN EVERELL (E) ½ 1667 Sugar-loaf £18
68 WILLIAM FLOWER ½ 1666 TOLEMAN £25
69 RICHARD GINN (M) ½ 1668 Butchers' Arms £20
70 (Probably misreading of 72)
71 IOHN METHERINGHAM (M) ½ 1668 AT YE GLOBE £18
72 *Thomas Wanless* ½ 1669 Angel. *Octagonal*

Woodhurst
73 WILLIAM BVRGIS (S) ½ 1668 £25

Kent

New tokens recorded from the Hodgkin collection (sold at Sotheby's, 22 Apr. 1914); W. Gilbert, 'Unpublished . . .' (see under Cambridgeshire); and *SNC*, Jan. 1980.

See also H. W. Rolfe, *Kentish Tokens of the Seventeenth Century* (London, 1862), for more background information; and V. J. Newbury, 'Tokens of Sheppey issued in the Seventeenth Century' (*Kent Numismatic Society Bulletin*), 1959–60, for notes on the issuers.

Believed entirely unpublished: 61A, 89A, 121A, 244A, 246A, 285A, 285B, 293A, 296A, 346A, 351A, 475A, 507A, 535A, 550A, 572A, 573A, 586A.

Minimum price for unvalued tokens: £45

Appledore
1 IOHN BOVRNE (S) ½ 1669 King's Arms

Ashford
2 IAMES BASSETT ½ 1669 St George & dragon £42
3 FRANCES BAYLEF (I) ¼ AT THE PYD BVLL £18
4 WILLIAM BOTTING (S) ½ 1669 Malt-shovel £18
5 BENIAMIN BOWYER ½ 1664 Haberdashers' Arms £32
6 IAMES CHITTENDEN (M) ½ 1669 Drinking pot £32
7 THOMAS CLERKE (E) ½ 1668 AT YE PYD BVLL
8 IOHN DENN (M) ½ 1669 £25
9 THOMAS FENNER (M) ¼ '57 Grocers' Arms £38
10 THOMAS FLINT (S) ¼ 1664 £40
11 WILLIAM OSBORNE (P) ¼ 1663 Grocers' Arms £30
12, 13 THOMAS R(E *or* V)DFEILD (A) ¼ Chequers
14 MARY STEED ½ 1669 £22
15 ROBERT WAGE (M) ½ 1668 £32
16 ROBERT WALBE ½ '69 Shears. *Octagonal*
17 HEN WISE (E) ½ 1664 Grocers' Arms
18 SAMVELL WOOD ½ 1666 Saracen's head £12

Aylesford
19 (Probably *Hants.* 2A)
20 EDMON SMITH (M) ¼ Grocers' Arms

Benenden
21 RICHARD GRANT (M) ¼ Grocers' Arms

Bexley
22 IOHN THORNDELL (S) ½ 1667 Ox, axe

Biddenden
23 RICHARD FOSTER ½ 1668 Lion
24 RICH — (I) ½ Lion
25 ALEXANDER HOMESBY (H) ½ £28
26 ALIXANDER HOLMSBY ¼ 1658 £38
27 ALEXANDER LINDRIDGE (M) ½ 1671
28 THOMAS SCEELLES (M) ¼ 1666 Ship

Brasted
29 WILLIAM LINES (M) ¼ 1666

Brenchley
30 WILLIAM WOODGAT (M) ¼ 1654 Grocers' Arms
31 — — (M) ¼ 1659. *Rev.* dated 1654
32 — WOODGATE (M) (½) 1664 (date below name)
32A — — (M) ¼ 1664 (name around date)
33 — — ½ 1667

Bromley
34 THOMAS GHOST ½ AT THE, hart
35 ROBERT KINGE (M) ¼ Keys crossed
36 MICAELL LEE (E) ¼ 1664 AT WHITE, hart
37 IOHN PERCIVALL (E) ½ 1667 Tobacco-roll
38 WILLIAM WALDRON (A) ½ Man making candles £24

Brookland
39 IOHN EVE (K) ½ 1671 GROCER £50
40 — — (K) ¼ Grocers' Arms
41 IOHN HARRISON (½) Goat

Canterbury
42 THO BAKER ½ 1667 Hand holding scales, CHEESMONGR £14

43 FRANCIS BANICK (M) ¼ Wheatsheaf £22
44 THOMAS BEST (M) ¼ 1650 Vintners' Arms, COOPER
45 THO BVLLOCK ¼ AT THE BVLL HEAD
46 THOMAS BVRDEN (V) ½ 1667 Vase of flowers £40
47 IOHN CARDON (D) ¼ 1656 Roll of bread. **Plate 2** £11
48 HENRY CARPENTER ½ 1667 £20
49 HENREY — (S) ¼ 1658 £16
50 IAMES CHEEVER ½ 1663 Hand holding shears £8
51 — — ¼ '57 — £15
52 — — ¼ '62 — £22
53 EDWARD CRAYFORD (B) ¼ Black boy smoking, GROCER £45
54 THO ENFIELD ½ 1666 IN MERCERY LANE, Grocers' Arms £18
55 THOMAS — (S) ¼ 1666 — —
56 ANTHONY FAGG (M) ¼ GROCER £18
57 THOMAS FEILD ½ 1666 Saracen's head £12
58 EDWARD FRAY (S) ½ 1667 Tallowchandlers' Arms £11
59 THOMAS HVTTEN 1d 1669 Pewterers' Arms, PEVTERER; griffin. *Octagonal* £40
60 THOMAS IENINGES ½ 1669 Man making candles, smoking £18
61 — IENINGS (B) ¼ GROCER £11
61A — IENINGE ¼ Grocers' Arms. In *pb*
62 M.K. (S) ¼ 1653 AT THE SHIP
63 FRANCIS MAPLISDEN ½ 1666 Bunch of hops on *obv.* £20
64 — MAPELSDAN ½ — Bunch of hops on *rev.*
65 WALTER MAPLISDEN (S) ¼ Dove with olive-branch £11
66 IEREMIAH MASTERSON (M) ½ AT, chequers. *Octagonal* £18
67 THOMAS MAYNE ½ 1664 Still, GROCER £20
68 THO — (M) ¼ 1654 — — £16
590 — — ¼ 16(43?) Grocers' Arms. In *pb*
69 THOMAS OCKMAN ½ Family Arms £16
70 — — (E) ¼ —
71 I.P. (M) ¼ 1653 THE SARISONS HEAD £38
72 D.R. (M) ¼ AT THE MAIRMAYD £20
73 T.S. (M) ¼ AT THE 3 MARRENORS £25
74 IOSEPH SHERWOOD (A) ¼ Woolpack, GROCER
75 IOHN SIMPSON (I) ¼ 1653 Lion £22
76 RICHARD SMITH (E) ¼ Grocers' Arms £16
77/8 SIBB SMITH ¼ NEER WEST GATE £15
79 WILL TERREY (E) ¼ AT THE GLOBE £18
80 E.W. (A) ¼ AT THE 3 KINGS £35
81 E.W. (M) ¼ — £14
82 RICHARD WHITE (A) ¼ 1656 Comb, BARBER £40
83/4 IARVISE WILLMATT ½ 1664 Horse £28

Charing

85 THOMAS CHAPMAN (F) ½ 1666 AT YE RED, lion
86 ALLEXANDER HART ½ 1667 GROCER
87 IOHN MORS (M) ¼ 1651 Grocers' Arms

Chatham

88 IOHN ADAMS (S) ¼ 1657 Cannon, GVNER
88A ASHLY BRETLIFFE (A) ¼ 1659 Ship
89 FRANCIS BRETT (S) ¼ 1666 Comb £40
89A RICHARD COTTAM (M) ¼ 1657 3 pipes
90 RICHARD CRESWELL (H) ¼ 1666 MEALMAN
91 ROBERT DIER (I) ½ Catherine-wheel
92 WILLLIAM HARDIN (A) ¼ Arms £32
93 IOSHVA HOLLAND (M) ¼ 1668 Cask
94 IOHN IEFFERY (E) ¼ Cheese-knife £30
95 RICHARD IEN (E) ½ 1668 Horseshoe £45
96 RICHARD IENNMAN (P) ¼ Bugle-horn £28
97 WALTER IONES (I) ½ 1667 AT YE NAGS HED, horse's head and bunch of grapes
98 W.I. (S) ¼ 1662 AT THE GLOBE £28
99 — — (S) ¼ 1667 — £35
100 IOHN KNIGHT (O) ¼ Crown
101 SAMVELL MABBOR (S) ¼ 1657 Grocers' Arms
102 IOHN MARVELL (D) ¼ 1666 Frying-pan £38
103 RICHARD MATHEWS (M) ¼ Merchant Taylors' Arms
104 WALTER RAMSDEN ¼ Cannon; anchor £40
105 T.S. (M) ¼ 1657 AT THE GLOBE
106 FRANCIS SANDERS (A) ¼ Merchant Taylors' Arms £30
107 ROBERT SMITH ½ 1671 AT YE OLD KINGS ARMES
108 — — (I) ½ — AT YE OLD, King's Arms
109 IOHN TIHVRST ¼ 1666 BREWER £32
110 IOSEPH WYMSHVRST (M) ¼ 1656 Merchant Taylors' Arms £40
111 — — (M) ¼ n.d. —

Chilham

112 IOHN COLEMAN ½ 1664 Arms £22
113 IAMES ODDEN ½ 1664 Grocers' Arms £20
114 — — ¼ 1659 —
115 WILLIAM PLVMER ¼ Grocers' Arms £30

Cowden

116 IAM IEANES (M) ¼ Stick of candles on crescent moon, 7 stars around, TALLOW CHAN
117 IOHN OSBORNE ¼ 1663 MERCER
117A — OSBVRNE ¼ 1658 —

Cranbrook

118 IOHN AVERY (F) ¼ 3 doves, MERCER

119 THOMAS BVTTERREY (M) ¼ 1666 Man making candles, MERCER
120 THOMAS DANIEL ¼ Grocers' Arms
121 RICH FRANCKWELL (E) ¼ '57 King's head with crown and sceptre
121A G.K. (C) ½ 1666 Lion, lamb
122 THOMAS MANDY (R) ¼ 1666
123 ROBERT MARCH (C) ¼ 1657 MERCER
124 PETER MASTER (A) ¼ Grocers' Arms, MERCER
125 THOMAS MVN (M) ¼ DRAPER
126 IOHN PARTON (D) ½ 1669
127 WILLIAM WACHER (M) ¼ 3 sugar-loaves
128 MARY WILLIS (I) ½ 1669 Pewterers' Arms

Crundale

129 (See *Hants*. 60A)

Dartford

130 ROBERT CAPON (I) ½ 1668 Tallowchandlers' Arms £50
131 NICHOLLAS CHAMBERS (M) ¼ 1664 Grocers' Arms
132 THOMAS GILL (A) ¼ 1659 Hand holding scissors
133 ROBERT GLOVER (I) ¼ Bull
134 WILLIAM HVISH (A) ¼ Cock
135 ISAAC MANNING ¼ 1664 Family Arms
136 THO MORLEY ½ AT YE HORSHO
137 HENRY PEIRCE ¼ Sugar-loaf £35
138 —— (M) ¼ —
139 WILLIAM PHILLIPES (S) ¼ Stick of candles within crescent
140 EDWARD ROSE (M) ¼ Rose
141 REBECKA SMITH ¼ Butchers' Arms
142 THOMAS SMITH (M) ¼ Crown
143 ROBERT TAYLOR ½ 1667 Falcon

Deal

144 THOMAS BROTHERS (A) ¼ 1664 Scales
145 WILLIAM BROTHERS ½ 1669 Ship £25
146 ANN CAVTEREL ½ 1669 Scales £30
147 IOHN CLARKE (M) ¼ 1659 Man and still
148/9 IAMES COSTON (E) ¼ 1653 Heart b.s. £11
150 WILLIAM COVLSON (I) ¼ 1659 Eagle and child £50
151 T.F. ¼ 1658 AT THE DOLPHINE £45
152 TIMOTHY GARDNER (S) ¼ 1666 Arms
153 IOHN LOBDELL (I) ½ 1669 Scissors £35
154 THOMAS PARKSOEN (R) ¼ 1658 Grocers' Arms £28
155 IOHN PEARS (I) ¼ 1663 Heart £35
156 IOHN PITTOCK (E) ¼ 1656 Hand. **Plate 1** £18
157 WILLIAM PITTOCKE ½ 1668 Bust of Duke of York £40
158 MOYSES POTTER ¼ Bakers' Arms £28
159 THOMAS POTTER (M) ¼ 1663 Grocers' Arms £32
160 RICHARD STVTLY (M) ¼ 1653 £30
161 PETER VNDERWOOD (E) ¼ Man making candles £15
162 IOHN WATTS (M) ¼ 1664 Fleece £30

Deptford

163 IOHN ANDREWS (I) ¼ 1655 Globe
164 WILLIAM ARCHER ½ 1665 Archer
165 THOMAS BRIOND (R) ¼ 1665 Bakers' Arms
166 GREGORY BVMPSTED (E) ¼ 1656 Catherine-wheel
167 THOMAS CHILD (B) ¼ Sugar-loaf, CHANDLER
168 ROGER CLARKE (E) ½ AT THE ROYAL OAKE £32
169 WILLIAM CRICH ½ Grocers' Arms £28
170 —— (S) ¼ 1663 — £28
171 IOHN CROVCH (A) ¼ 1658 Wheatsheaf £28
172 WILLIAM DRING (V) ¼ 1651 £38
173 MARGERY FVRZER ½ 1667
174 GEORGE GORHAM (A) ½ 1665 Monogram £45
175 —— (A) ¼ 1664 —
176 IOHN HODGES ¼ AT THE 3 GOAT HEAD
177 —— (B) ¼
178 IOHN HOMES (S) ¼ AT THE BALL
179 IOHN HORLOK ¼ AT THE RED LYON
180 RICHARD IEFRY (S) ¼ MEALL MAN
181 MATHEW IESSON ¼ AT THE WHIT LYON £32
182 IOHN KERBEY ½ Sugar-loaf
183 N.L. (D) ¼ 1648 AT THE KINGS HEAD, Head of Jas. I
184 —— (D) ¼ 1649 — £20
185 IOHN LINES (C) ½ 1668 Weavers' Arms
186 RICHARD MANSFEILD ½ 1665 £28
187 ANTHONY MATHEWS (M) ¼ 1659 AT YE, tobacco-roll
188 PETER PEMELL (M) ¼ 1666 Castle
189 M.R. (A) ¼ 1657 AT THE KINGS HEAD, head of Jas. I
190 IOHN SMITH ½ Weavers' Arms
191 WILLIAM STONE (A) ¼ 1652 £25
192 EDWARD SWALLOW (A) ¼ 1656 Talbot
193 —— (A) ¼ 1658 —
194 IOHN WALLIS (M) ½ 1668 AT THE BLEW BORE
195 IAMES WATTERS ½ Scales, MEALMAN £42
196 ISAAC WELCH (E) ¼ 1664 Lion in shield

Doddington

196A RICHARD NIN ½ Scales

Dymchurch

197 ANDREW CLIFFORD (S) ½ Anvil, BLACK SMITH £35

Dover

198 Town ½ 1668 FOR THE POORE, St Martin on horseback dividing cloak with beggar; Town Arms £15
199 Town ¼ '68 Town Arms; St Martin and beggar £15
200 DAVID ADAMSON (M) ¼ 1657 Anchor £22
201 I.B. (A) ¼ 1658 AT THE SKOCH ARMES, unicorn £22
202 IOHN BRIAN (S) ¼ 1652 £18
203 I.C. (M) ¼ AT THE QVEENE OF BOHEMIA £14
204 I.C. (E) ¼ 1652 AT THE GEORGE
205 EDWARD CHAMBERS (E) ¼ 1649 Grocers' Arms £16
206 IANE COLLER ¼ £40
207 RICHARD COOKE ½ 1669 Shovel, SEIGNIOR
208 RICHARD CVLLEN (F) ¼ 1656 Grocers' Arms; merchant's mark. GROCER £32
209/10 C.D. (M) ¼ 1651 AT THE LEOP(O)VLDVS, Emperor's bust £16
211 G.F. (M) ¼ 1666 AT THE LEOPVLDVS. — £38
212 MARTHA FFORD ¼ 1659 £14
213 THOMAS FIDG (M) ¼ AT THE MAYDEN HEAD £11
214 ROBART GALLANT ¼ AT THE WHITE HORSE
215 KATHEREN GARDNER ½ 1667 CHANLER
216 — — ¼ — —
217 THOMAS GREEN (M) ½ 1666 Rose £25
218 IOHN HALL (R) ¼ 1666 £18
219 IOHN HAYNES (E) ¼ 1655 BAKER
220 IAMES HOMARD (E) ¼ BAKER £32
221 WILLIAM KEYLOCKE (M) ¼ 1667 Goldsmiths' Arms
222 PINES KITE (M) ½ 1670 Bakers' Arms £16
223 THO KITE (M) ¼ 1656 Boat rigged £22
224 D.N. (M) ¼ AT THE FRENCH ARMES £15
225 IOHN PARKER ¼ AT THE PEERE, 3 doves £22
226 SAMVEL PARTRICH (M) ¼ MILLENER £30
227 THOMAS PIEARCE IVNIOR ½ 1669 Tallowchandlers' Arms, DVBBLE TOKEN
228 ROGER ROGERS (F) ¼ 1665 Greyhound £40
229 SVSAN SHARNALL ¼ 1656
230 THOMAS SHARNAL (E) ¼ 1658 £20
231 THOMAS STIVEDAY (I) ¼ 1653 £32
232 SARAH SWEETLAND ¼ 1658 Scales
233 SAMVELL TAVENOR (S) ½ 1669 Family Arms
234 IOHN THOMAS (A) ¼ 3 horseshoes, GROCER
235 WILLIAM TILLIT (M) ¼ Coopers' Arms £22
236 — — (M) ¼ 1662 —
237 MARY TVRK ¼ 1659 GROSER
238 WIL WARDEN (M) ¼ AT THE HORS AND HORS SHOOE
239 WILL WELLARD (A) ¼ AT THE COCK, rose £12
240 ROBERT WOODGREEN (E) ¼ 1666 Rose £25
241 ROBART — (E) ¼ 1658 £28

Eastchurch

242 RICHARD EAGLESTON ½ 1665 Blacksmiths' Arms
243/4 WILL MANY(A)RINGE ½ Bust of Duke of York, HABERDASHER

East Farleigh

244A BENIAMIN IARVIS ½

Edenbridge

245 ROB ALCHORNE, WIL ABLET ½ MERCERS £50
246 KATHERINE HVBERD ½ Crown

Elham

246A IOHN FORMAN ¼ 1664 Grocers' Arms; acorn and oakspray
247 WILLIAM PARTRIDGE ½ Grocers' Arms
248 — PARTRIDG ¼ —
249 RICHARD SYMONS (M) ¼ 1664 GROCER

Eltham

250 IOHN BLANDEN (I) ¼ Measure, MALTMAN £50
251 RICHARD GREENE (I) ¼ 1667 Carpenters' Arms
252 N.M. (T) ¼ 1649 THE CASTELL TAVERNE

Erith

253 ROBERT DVTTON (M) ½ 1667
254 (Probably *Hunts.* 3A)
255 BRYAN RVSSELL (M) ¼ 1671
256 FRANCIS TAYLOR (A) ¼ TVRNSTYLE, crown, fleur-de-lis
257 C. T. (M) ¼ COVLLVER WELL TOLLVER
258 ROB TOY (S) ¼ 1666 Hen and chicks £45
259 R.W. (K) ¼ AT THE COCKE

Eynesford

260 IOHN BECKET (E) ¼ 1658 Grocers' Arms

Farnborough

261 WILLIAM BEST ½ 1668 AT THE, St George & dragon

Farningham

262 HENRY POVND ¼ 1658 Grocers' Arms

Faversham

263 GEORGE ALLEN ½ 1666 Horseshoe
264/5 IOHN BE(A)LE ¼ 1649 Mercers' Arms; Grocers' Arms. MERCER
266 WILLIAM BVCK ½ 1669 Stag £45
267 PHILLIP BVTLER ½ 1669 Crown under rainbow. *Square*
268 R.C. (E) ¼ 1651 AT THE QVEENE ARMS
269 IOHN CLEARE ½ 1666 Crown
270 IOHN ELLIS ½ 1667 BACKER £42

271 ROBERT HOGBEN ½ Vintners' Arms £18
272 WILLIAM KNIGHT (I) ½ 1666 Grocers' Arms £25
273 IAMES MARCH (A) ½ 1669 Grocers' Arms
274 POARE NED ½ 1667 Tree £32
275 IOHN PIEARCE ½ 1667 Dolphin. *Octagonal*
276 ROBERT PRESTON ½ 1664 THE QVEENS ARMES £16
277 FRANCIS WATERMAN (S) ¼ Mercers' Arms £12

Folkestone
278 EDWARD FRANKLIN (E) ½ '70 £38
279 — FRANKLING (E) ½ n.d.

Foots Cray
280 IOHN MOORE ½ 1668 AT THE, griffin's head £55
281 MICHAELL PITMAN (E) ¼ Brewers' Arms

Gillingham
282 WILLIAM COLES ½ 1669 Carpenters' Arms; malt-shovel

Godmersham
283 ROBERT OAKLEY ½ Grocers' Arms £55

Goudhurst
284 IOHN AVSTEN (B) ¼ MERCER £25
285 WILLIAM MAYNARD (M) ¼ 1664 MERC
285A RICHARD PVXTY ½ AT THE, Grocers' Arms
285B —— (M) ½ 1669 Grocers' Arms
286 STEPHEN STRINGER (H) ½ 1661 Anchor, value II
287 —— (H) ¼ —— value I

Gravesend
288 IOHN BIDDLE ½ 1670 Bust of Pope, holding cross £30
289 MARGRET BIRD ¼ 1657 Hen and chicks
290 THOMAS BOONE (M) ¼ Tobacco-roll
291 *Mathew Butler* (D) ½ 1668. *Octagonal* £70
292 IOHN CHEESMAN (E) ¼ AT THE SVN
293 THOMAS CLARK (M) ¼ AT BORES HAD, boar's head
293A —— (M) ¼ —— apple in boar's mouth
294 WILLIAM CROVCH ¼ 1658 Hand holding bird £35
295 ROBERT DAY ½ 1667 Scissors, SHOPKEPER £50
296 THOMAS HILL (S) ¼ GROCER £25
296A T.H. (S) ¼ 1651. In *pb*
297 IOHN MAY (A) ¼ 1666 St Christopher carrying Jesus
298 MARCK MEDHOVST (M) ½ MERCER £32
299 WILLIAM OLIVER (M) ¼ Cannon mounted
300 I.P. (D) ¼ 1656 AT THE MAREMAID
301/2 IACOB PARSON *or* PARS(S *or* C)ON (E) ¼ 1651 Hands joined £18
303 IOH PIKE (M) ¼ AT BLACK ANKER
304 (Probably misreading of 305)
305 IOHN REDDELL (E) ¼ Bust of Chas. II
306 A.W. (M) ¼ AT THE SWANE £32
307 THOMAS WARREN (I) ¼ 1671 3 rabbits
308 IOHN WATSON (K) ¼ 1653 Arrow piercing heart £14
309 — WETSON (K) ¼ Tobacco-roll
310 THOMAS WOOD (E) ¼ 1657 Heart b.s.

Greenhithe
311 WILLIAM CHATTWIN ¼ Tallowchandlers' Arms
312 RICHARD SMITH (S) ¼ Goat's head, shoemaker's knife

Greenwich
313 THOMAS ANDREY (E) ½ 1668 Joiners' Arms and crest. *Octagonal*
314–7 E.B. ¼ AT THE G(E)ORGE £17
318 EDWARD BARTLETT (M) ¼ Hart
319 HENREY BEDBERY (R) ¼ ROSE
320 WILLIAM CLEARE (M) ¼ Wheatsheaf
321 THOMAS COLTON ½ 1667 Mercers' Arms
322 WILLIAM DISKETT (S) ¼ 1659 Tobacco-roll
323 ALEX DRIVER (A) ¼ Arms, SILK THROSTER
324 ADAM EDGHELL ½ AT YE 3, fleurs-de-lis £35
325 IOHN ELLIS (H) ¼ Sugar-loaf £25
326 THOMAS FOSTER (E) ½ 1667 AT THE, nag's head
327 HENRY GIPPES ½ 1668 Pot of lilies
328 ROBERT GIRDIS (M) ½ IN YE OVLD BEARE YARD
329 WILLIAM LEE (F) ½ 1666 Brewers' Arms
330 ROBERT(?) MILINGTON ¼ 1663 IRONMONGER
331 E.P. (E) ¼ 1650 AT THE BARE TAVERNE
332 ROBERT POLADAYE (M) ½ 1667 AT THE, still
333 HVGH PVDEFOVRD ½ AT THE WHITE HORSE
334 S.S. (A) ¼ 1649 AT THE SHIP TAVERNE
335 GEORGE SAXBEE (S) ¼ 1650 £32
336 IOHN SHALLCROS (E) ¼ Unicorn
337 CHRISTOPHER SKAYF (½) AT THE STIL
338 THOMAS TVDER (A) ¼ Unicorn £42
339 RICHARD TVSTEN (E) ½ 1667 AT YE, dragon
340 IOHN WARRELL (A) ½ '69 AT THE SHIP TAVERNE
341 —— (A) ¼ THE, ship, TAVERNE

Groombridge
342 RICH CVNSTABLE ½ 1665 MERCER
343 —— ½ 1666 —
344 RICO CONSTABLE ½ 1668 MERCR. *Heart-shape* £180

Hadlow
345 *John Bateman* ½ Greyhound

Harrietsham
346 ROBRT HOVENDEN (I) ¼ Grocers' Arms
346A NICH SVTTEN (H) ½ 1669

Harty
347 IOHN GORGE ½ Man rowing boat

Hawkhurst
348 ARTHVR GIBBONS (M) ½ 1669 Gate
349 IOHN LATTER (E) ½ BVCHER £38
350 THOMAS MERCER (A) ½ CLOTHIER
351 WALTER QVAIFE (E) ½ Arch
351A —— (E) ¼ —

Higham
351B EDWARD PARKES (probably *Derbys.* 104)

High Halden
352 IOHN COOKE ½ 1667 Lion

Hollingbourn
353 GEORGE HARRISON (F) ½ Windmill

Honychild
354 C.S. (½) 1672 Sedley family crest £18

Hythe
355 WILLIAM ADCOCK (E) ¼ 1657 £42
356 FARDINANDO BASSET (M) ¼ 1658 Hart
357 ION BASSETT (T) ½ 1670 Grocers' Arms £28
358 PETER IOHNSON ¼ Bakers' Arms
359 GVY LANGDON (E) ¼ 1659 Grocers' Arms £40
360 DAVID MARCH (I) ½ 1669 Fleece
361 PETER MARSH ½ 1672 Arms

Ightham
362 *Henry Greene* ½ St George and dragon
363 IOHN WAGGHORNE (M) ¼ 1666 Mercers' Arms
364 WILLIAM WHITE ¼ Mercers' Arms

Kemsing
365 (Probably *Beds.* 59)

Kingstone
366 (See *Surrey* 140A)

Larkfield
367 IOHN PACKE ½ AT THE, Blacksmiths' Arms

Lamberhurst
368 RICHARD FRANCES (A) ½ 1669 Arms, crest

Leeds
369 NATHANIELL BENSON (F) ¼ Grocers' Arms £45
369A IERIMY RVMFEILD (E) ½ 1670

Lenham
370 THO AVSTEN (A) ¼ GROCER
371 IOHN DEEDE (I) ¼ 1664 Dog baiting chained bear
372 THOMAS FOORDE ½ 1667 Grocers' Arms
373 IOHN LAKE (E) ¼ 1667 Grocers' Arms £40

Lewisham
374 IOHN FREEMAN (I) ½ 1665 AT WHIT, bear with chain

Lydd
375 THOMAS EDERICKE ¼ 1657 St George & dragon
376 WILLIAM SVDELL (F) ½ 1669 £40
377 —— ¼ 1662 3 cloves
378 THO WATERS ¼ OF LID OR APELDORE, initials T.W. both sides
379 Similar but initials W.T.

Maidstone
380 THOMAS BOND (L) ¼ 1666 £18
381 ROB BROOKE (W) ½ 1670 IRONMONGER £20
382 ROBERT HEATH ¼ GROCER £18
383 IOHN HOAD ¼ 1657 Windmill
384 GERVIS MAPLISDEN ½ Arms, MERCER £45
385 IAMES RVSE ¼ Grocers' Arms £9
386 THOMAS SWINOKE (K) ¼ 3 men with instruments standing round globe
387 IONATHAN TROVGHTON ½ 1668 Grocers' Arms £15
388 —— (M) ¼ —— £22
389 RICHARD WALKER ¼ 1658 GROCER £11
390 THOMAS WALL ½ 1667 Salters' Arms £25
390A —— ½ ——. In *pb*
391 RALPH WARDE (E) ¼ 1656 Castle £20
392 IOHN WATSON ½ 1670 AT THE, bell
393 ELIZABETH WEBB ¼ GROCER £30
394 WILLIAM WEB (E) ¼ 1649 Grocers' Arms, MERCER £38
395 STEVEN WEEKS (A) ¼ WEAVER. **Plate 2** £11
396 WALTER WEEKES ½ 1669 WEAVER. *Heart-shape*
397 RICHARD WICKING (E) ¼ GROCER £9
398/9 IAMES WOLB(A *or* O)LL ¼ 1664 Grocers' Arms £18

Malling
400 FRANCIS CHAMBERS (E) ¼ Grocers' Arms £45
401 RICH CHAMBERS (M) ¼ 1667 Fleur-de-lis £45
402 SAMVEL FRENCH (I) ¼ 1668 £35
403 THOMAS HILLS (I) ½ 1668 £35

Margate
404 GEORGE FREIND (M) ¼ 3 pipes £28
405 STEVEN GREEDIER ½ Fishmongers' Arms £32
406 CHRESTON HOVDGBEN ¼ Merchant's mark £22

407 IOSEPH IEWELL (E) ½ 1669 Cheese-knife £28
408 RICHARD LANGLEY ½ 1667 Tallowchandlers' Arms, IN KENT
409 Similar but IN TENIT
410 IOSEPH MACKRITH (I) ¼ Sugar-loaf £22
411 SARAH READE ¼ Ship
412 WILLIAM SAVAGE ¼ Grocers' Arms £25
413 IOHN SKINNER ½ 1670 Boat with sail £32

Milton-next-Gravesend

414 WILLIAM BALDWIN ½ 1667 Fleurs-de-lis. *Heart-shape* £135
415 RICHARD BVNCE ½ 1668 Grocers' Arms
416 GEORGE HEAD (M) ½ 1669 Ship £40
417 IOHN IONES (M) ¼ Cross pattée
418 WILLIAM KEMSTER ½ 1668 Bunches of grapes. *Heart-shape*
419 WALTER NINN ¼ 1666 Bakers' Arms £28
420 GEORGE OLLEVER (A) ¼ Sugar-loaf
421 EDWARD PASHLOWE ¼ 1656 Rose
422 WILLIAM READE ½ 1666 Pewterers' Arms £45
423 WILL READ (M) ¼ n.d. — £40
424 IAMES RICHMOND ½ 1666 Glaziers' Arms £40
425 ANTHONY SIFFLET (A) ¼ Ball £42
426 IOHN SMITH (E) ¼ Bird
427 ARTHVR WHITE (M) ¼ AT THE, angel £35

Milton-next-Sittingbourne

428 WILLIAM ALLEN (P) ¼ 1658 Bakers' Arms
429/30 WILL(I)AM BISSY (I) ¼ Grocers' Arms, MERCER £17
431 CHENY BOVRNE (F) ¼ Sugar-loaf £22
432 WILLIAM COVALL (M) ¼ 1659 Brewers' Arms
433 —— (M) ¼ 1664 —
434 RICHARD HENMAN (S) ¼ Talbot £38
435 GEORGE REEVE ½ 1667 Grocers' Arms £28

Minster

436 IOHN DYER ½ Sugar-loaf £15

Newington

437 THOMAS BOORN ½ 1669 GROCER
437A LAWRENCE SHORT (E) ¼ Fruiterers' Arms
438 WILLIAM STANINOVGH ½ 1669 MERCER

Northfleet

439 THOMAS HVMFRE (E) ¼ Beehive
440 ROBERT PEACOCKE ½ 1670 Crown

Orpington

441 IAMES WHITE (M) ½ 1669 Blacksmiths' Arms
442 —— (M) ¼ n.d. —

Otford

443 WILL PHILLIPS ½ 1668 Bust of Chas. II, MERCER

Penshurst

444 HENRY CONSTABLE ½ 1667 Crown, MERCER £42
445 —— ½ 1669 ——
446 MARTEN PYKE (A) ¼ Fleur-de-lis, MERCER

Pluckley

447 EDWARD GOODING (A) ¼ 1663 Grocers' Arms £18

Queenborough

448 HVMPHRY ATWEEKE ½ 1667 AT YE, crown
449 PETER KEN ¼ 1665 Rose
450 THOMAS NORRINGTON (M) ½ Ship £38
451 RICHARD POLEY ½ 1666 Grocers' Arms £30

Ramsgate

452 RICHARD LANGLEY (P) ¼ 1657 Man making candles £20
453 CLEMENT MARCH (M) ¼ 1658 Cheese-knife £14
454 HEN NOLDRED ½ 3 tobacco-rolls £20

Riverhead

455 R.S. ¼ 1653 AT THE OKENTRE £50

Rochester

456 GEORGE ALLINGTON ¼ King's head
457 STEPHEN BONNET (A) ¼ EASTGATE, Joiners' Arms £28
458 ART BROOKER (M) ¼ AT THE CROWNE £38
459 WILLIAM BVRGES (M) ¼ 1669
460 WILLIAM CAMPIAN (F) ¼ 1658 £22
461 ROBERT CART (S) ¼ 1668 £32
462 ROBERT CHVRCHELL (I) ¼ 1669 Merchant Taylors' Arms £32
463 ALICE COBHAM ¼ 1651 Family Arms; family Crest, initials A.C. £12
464 Similar but no initials £28
465 S. IOHN COBHAM ¼ 1666 Family Arms; family Crest £28
466 EDWARD HARRISON ½ 1669 Hand holding scissors
467 RICHARD HVTCHESON (F) ¼ 3 doves
468 IOHN KENNON ¼ Nag's head £28
469 ROBERT LEAKE (E) ¼ 1656 Arms
470 ANTHONYE LOVELL ¼ AT THE KINGS HEAD, Henry VIII facing
471 ANTHONY — (A) ¼ 1657 Bust of Eliz. I
472/3 ROBERT MICHELL (R) ¼ Compasses crossed £30
474 RICHARD NEWBERY (M) ¼ 1666 Black-jack £32
475 THOMAS PALMER (E) ¼ Still £42
475A THOMAS PIGOTT (S) ¼ AT Y, man greeting woman (Salutation)
476 EDWARD SHELLEY (F) ¼ CVRY, Head of Queen of Bohemia

477 SAMVELL STOWE (E) ¼ Prince of Wales' feathers, THE POST
478 IOSEPH TRAVERS (G) ¼ 1666 Tobacco-roll, 4 pipes £25
479 WILLIAM VANDALL (I) ½ 1671 Lion, sun
480 GILBERT YOVNG (S) ¼ 1664 Bell, GROCR £30

Rolvenden
481 IOHN PEMBALL (M) ¼ '58 View of church

(New) Romney
482 RICHARD BAKER (M) ¼ Grocers' Arms £38
483 ISAAC RVTTON ½ AT YE GEORG

Ryarsh
484 EDWARD WALSINGHAM ½ '68 Harrow

St Mary Cray
485 ANN MANING ¼ 1658 Boy holding pipe
486 — — ¼ 1665 —
487 EDWARD SPVRLING (A) ¼ Cannon

Sandhurst
488 IOHN OWEN ½ 1669 Royal oak. *Heart-shape*

Sandwich
489 RICHARD ASHERNIDEN (S) ¼ £35
490 ANNE ATKINS ¼ 1667 Carnation, WIDOW £35
491 IOANNA AVSTIN ¼ 1656
591 W.B. ¼ Bird in shield. In *pb*
492 GEORGE BVRFORD ½ 1666 Grocers' Arms £32
493 IOHN CASBE ½ Fleur-de-lis £38
494 RICHARD CLARKE (A) ¼ 1656 Prince of Wales' feathers
495 IOHN COVCHMAN (E) ¼ 1656
496 RICHARD CRISP ¼ Swords crossed £28
497 IOSEPTH DOE ½ Man making candles £22
498 HENRY FVRNICE ½ Town Arms. **Plate 2** £14
499 — — ¼ — £28
500 THOMAS KINGSFORD ½ POST MASTER £35
501 DANILL PICHLEY (S) ¼ 1656 £22
502 IOHN REVELL ¼ Bell £32
503 IAMES ROBINS ¼ 1655 Arms
592 R.R. ¼ Sailing boat. In *pb*
504/5 RAL(P *or* F)H ROBINS (S) ¼ 1655 Boat with rigging £18
506 DAVID ROGERS (I) ¼ Bunch of grapes
507 THOMAS SANDVM ½ 1667 Tree £32
507A *David Turnur* ¼ *Quarter of an ounce of fine pewter*. In *pb*
508 IOHN VANDEBROVCK ¼ 1656 Merchant's mark; initials (clockwise) I.V.D.B. £32
593 W. ¼ Merchant's mark; pelican feeding young. In *pb*
509 THOMAS YOVNG (M) ¼ 1666 Tobacco-roll £38

Sevenoaks
510 WILLIAM ALLEN ¼ Grocers' Arms £32
511 NICHOLAS BROOKSED (M) ½ Pistol
512 RICHARD CRONKE (A) ¼ 1658 Merchant Taylors' Arms
513 DANIELL DAVES ½ 1668 Bell
514 DANIEL DAVIS (D) ¼ 1666 CHEESMONGER
515 THOMAS GREEN ½ 1668 Mercers' Arms, initials T. C. £42
516 — GREENE ¼ Mercers' Arms £38
517 NATHLL OWEN (E) ½ 1669 MERCER. *Octagonal* £70
518 IOHN THORNTON ¼ '65 Bull
519 WILL WALL (M) ½ 1668 3 sugar-loaves
520 WILLIAM — ¼ 1666 —
521 THOMAS WICKENDEN (I) ¼ 1666 £35

Sheerness
522 RICHARD IONES ½ 1667 SVTTLER

Shurland
523 (½) Herbert family crest; family Arms

Sittingbourne
524 IOHN MILWAY (M) ¼ NEXT THE CROWN, 3 doves £25
525 THOMAS PEARCE ½ 1667 Ironmongers' Arms
526 — — ½ 1669 —
527 WILLIAM WEBB ½ 1670 AT THE, St. George & dragon

Smarden
528 THOMAS HINCKLY (S) ½ 1669 Gate* £22

Snave
529 THOM BRETT ¼ Fleur-de-lis b.s.

Southfleet
529A IOHN GARLAND ¼ Catherine wheel. In *pb*

Speldhurst
530 THO SOANE ½ 1668 Unicorn £45

Stoke
531 WILLIAM GILBART ¼ Sugar-loaf

Strood
532 HENRY ALLEN ¼ AT THE CASTEL, bull's head
533 EDWARD BERBLOCKE (M) ¼ Grocers' Arms
534 *Robert Coverdale* (H) ½ 1668 £35
535 PHILLIP EWER ¼ 1652 £20
535A — — ¼ 1651
536 — — ¼ 1666 £25
537 HENNERE FIGGETT (M) ¼ 1654 £14
538 ANTH LOVELL (S) ¼ '68 Angel
539 CONSTANCE WALSALL ¼ Bird; still
540 CONSTANT — ¼ 1666 Still
541 — — ¼ 1667 — £45

* Most extant specimens have been cancelled by piercing

Sturry
542/3 THOMAS I(HO *or* OH)NSON ¼ 1650 Grocers' Arms; fleur-de-lis £10
544 WILLIAM PICARD (E) ½ 1666

Sutton-at-Hone
545 IOHN CHILD ½ 1667 3 wheatsheaves

Sutton Valence (Town Sutton)
546 (Probably *Cambs*. 177)
547 (Probably *Cambs*. 176)
548 R.G. ¼ AT THE KINGS HEAD, Henry VIII facing £32
549 ISAAC HVNTT ½ 1671 Lion

Tenterden
550 IOHN CHVRCH ½ 1668 Butchers' Arms. *Octagonal*
550A As last but *round*
551 IAMES MEAD ½ 1667 Angel £30
552 IOHN READER ¼ Grocers' Arms, IN KENT £35
553 Similar but IN SVSSEX

Tunbridge
554 WILLIAM FREEMAN (E) ½ 1667 Tobacco-roll £35
555 WILLIAM OVEREY ½ 1669 £40
556 *Stephen Putland* (A) ½ 1666
557 I.E. STRETFEILD ¼ Skinners' Arms, MERCERS IN REATHERF & TVNBRIDGE, initials I.E.S.
558 ROBERT WALICE ¼ Butchers' Arms
559 RICHARD WOOD ½ 1668 £42
560 —— ¼ 1652
561 —— (K) ¼ n.d. Rose

Wateringbury
562 IOHN CAREY ¼ 1669 GROSER

Westerham
563/4 SAMVELL DA(I)LLING (A) ¼ 1653 £22
565 —DALLING (A) ¼ 1664 £38
566 ANTHONY SAXBEY (A) ¼ Man making candles

Westgate (Canterbury)
567 IOHN WRAIGHTE (R) ½ 1668 £25

Willesborough
568 FRANCIS BARTHOLOMEW ½

Wingham
569 IOHN SOLLEY (P) ¼ Lion £25

Woodchurch
570 THO BRISENDEN ½ Butchers' Arms £32

Woolwich
571 SARAH BOWYER ½ 1667 Cannon
572 W.F. (I) ¼ 1656 Scales, AT THE BARBERS POLE
572A IOHN HVTCHINS (E) ½ 1667 Scales
573 IOHN LADBROOKE (A) ½ 1666
573A — LADDBROOCK (A) ¼ 1666
573B WILLIAM MASON (R) ¼ 1657
574 LODWICK POOLE (E) ¼ 1650 Carpenters' Arms
575 E.S. ¼ 1656 Harp, AT THE STATES ARMES
576 RICHARD SCOTT (M) ¼ 1666 Carpenters' Arms
577 IANE TAMPSELL ½ 1667 Joiners' Arms
578 DENIS WATERS ½ 1667

Wrotham
579 CHARLES ALLFREY ¼ Boar's head £55
580 THOMAS CAVERLEY ¼ 1666 Merchant Taylors Arms'

Wye
581 MARIE ALLEN ½ 1666
582 THOMAS ALLEN (R) ¼ AT THE SARASANS HEAD £25
583 IOHN COVLTER (S) ¼ 1652 GROCER £32
584 THOMAS DAN (M) ¼ 1652 Snake, WEAVER £25
585 RICHARD WHITTINGHAM ½ 1667 Winged horse. *Octagonal* £35
586 —— (F) ¼ AT THE FLYING HORSE
586A ¼ AT THE FLYING HORSE, VERY GOOD WINE

Yalding
587/8 DANIELL CHI(L *or* T)TENDEN (A) ½ 1668 £32
589 GABRIEL COVCHMAN ¼ Grocers' Arms

For nos. 590–3, see under Canterbury and Sandwich.

Lancashire

Major reference: N. Heywood, 'Further Notes . . .' (see under Cheshire). Some additions, with notes, and corrections to 'Williamson'.

Further new tokens recorded from W. Boyne (see main Bibliography); the Talbot Ready collection (sold at Sotheby's, 15 Nov. 1920); W. Gilbert, 'Unpublished . . .' (see under Cambridgeshire); *SNC*, Aug./Sep. 1947; J. G. Milne, 'The Browne Willis Cabinet' (*BNJ*, 1951); *SCMB*, Dec. 1958; and *SCA* 28, 28 Apr. 1983.

Believed entirely unpublished: 14A, 31A, 50A, 52A, 62A, 68A, 104A, 107B, 140A, 145A.

Minimum price for unvalued tokens: £135

Ashton-under-Lyne

1 GEORGE BARDSLAYE (E) ½ 1669
2 IONATHAN BVTTERWORTH (A) ½
3 IOHN GOVLDING (½) 1669 Tallowchandlers' Arms
4 IOHN AND MARY HEYWOOD ½ 1667
5 BENIAMIN WALKER ¼ Mercers' Arms, MERCER; monogram of name
5A Halsey Walker ½?

Blackburn

6 IAMES BOLTON ½ 1666 Bolt through tun
7 — — ¼ — —
8 IAMES BRINDLE ½ 1666 Mercers' Arms
9 — — ½ 1667 —
10 RICHARD HAWORTH ½ 1666 Apothecaries' Arms £110
11 ANTHONY WELLS ½ 1667 Mortar and pestle

Bolton

11A *Ellis Bradshaw* ½ 1670 Hand holding bolt
11B RALPH MATTHER (E), HESTER MATTHER 1d 1670 Bolt through tun
12 IAMES MOLLINEX (F) ¼ 1651 Pipes, tobacco-roll
13 *Robert Moss* ½ Bolt through tun
14 *Robert Norris* ½ 1667 Bolt through tun
14A IOHN OKEY ¼ 1651 Acorn, leaves
15 MARY ROBERTS (½) 1666
16 WILLIAM SMALLSHAWE (E) 1d Pipes and tobacco-roll
16A — SMALLSHAW ½ 1669 —. *Octagonal.* **Plate 2**

Burnley

17 LAWRENCE TOWNLEY ½ 1669 Mercers' Arms

Bury

18 SAMVELL WARINGE ½ 1667 Man on horse £60

Chadderton

19 IAMES SCHOLES (M) ½ 1671 Star

Chorley

20 THOMAS ALLANSON (B) ¼ 1653 Pipes, tobacco-roll £90
21 HVGH COOPER ½ 1667 Rose and crown
22 ROB DICCONSON (M) ½ 1667 3 battle-axes
23 THOMAS WASLEY ½ 1666 Cordwainers' Arms
24 IAMES WOLSTENHOLME (E) ½ 1669 Heart pierced with arrows

Chowbent

25 ADAM TWAITE 1d Woolpack
25A — TWISSE 1d 1669 —

Clitheroe

26 ARTHVR ASHTON ¼ Pipes, tobacco-roll
27 THOMAS CVTTLER ½ 1669 Sword
28 EDMVND ROBINSON ½ 1666 Grocers' Arms £75
29 ROBERT TALLBOTT ½ 1669 Talbot
30 IOHN TOWNLEY ½ 1667 Drapers' Arms

Colne

31 OIHN BLAKEY ½ 1667 Merchant's mark
31A ANN ODDIE ½ 1668 Grocers' Arms

Crosby

32 THOMAS ALCOCKE ½ 1667 Drapers' Arms

Garstang

33 WILL LANCASTER ¼ 1663 Stick of candles

Halliwell

34 WILLIAM BOARDMAN (E) ¼ 1666

35 W.B. (A) ¼ 1652 Indian smoking

Halton
36 NICHOLAS TOKIN (A) ¼ Anchor

Haslingden
37 IAMES HARDGREAVES (A) ½ 1667 Scales
38 IOHN LORD (E) ½ 1668 Unicorn

Heaton
39 IOHN DOSON (M) ½ 3 doves

Holland
40 WILLIAM IACKSON ½ 1667 Eagle and child

Huyton
41 THOMAS HODGSON ½ 1666 Grocers' Arms
41A —— 1d 1670 Bull's head

Ince
41B RICHARD PEACOCK 1d 1669 Peacock

Kirby
42 IOHN DENT ½ 1667 Tree, small flowers; bunch of grapes, vine-leaves

Kirkham
43 MARY DAVIS ½ 1671 Grocers' Arms
44 IEFREY WOODS (O) ½ 1670

Lancaster
44A ROBERT BARKER ½ 1669 Sugar-loaf
45 IOHN CRAMPTON ½ 1667 IN LANCASHIRE, crossed keys
46 THOMAS GREENE (E) ¼ Lion
47 IOHN GREENWOOD ¼ Lion
48 IOHN HODGSON ¼ Female figure
49 IOHN LAWSON (M) ¼ Paschal lamb
50 IOHN MASHTER ½ 1668 Apothecaries' Arms
50A CHRISTOPHER PROCKTER (P) ¼
51 WILLIAM PROCKTER (E) 1d 1671 Eagle and child
52 —— (E) ½ 1670 —

Leigh
52A THOMAS HAMOND 1d 1670 Woolpack
53 RICHARD HIGSON (E) ¼ 1666 Woolpack
54 CHARLES RODGERS ½ 1668 Royal oak

Little Lever
55 RICHARD HEWOOD (A) ¼ 1652 Ragged staff

Liverpool
56 PETER ATHERTON ½ 1668 Sugar-loaf
57 GEORGE BENNETT ½ 1666 Ship
57A WILLIAM BVSHELL ½ 1668 Unicorn
58 CHARLES CHRISTIAN 1d 1669 Castle, GROCER £110
59 ADDAM CRVMPTON ¼ 1657
60 RICHARD CRVMPTON ½ 1667 Hope seated on anchor
61 WILLIAM DWERYHOWSE 1d 1670 Arms
62 ROGER GORSVCH 1d 1672 Babes in the wood, MERCER. *Heart-shape*
62A —— 1d 1671 Sheep under tree? —. *Round*
63 RALPH HALL (E) ¼ 1661
64 THOMAS IOHNSON ½ 1666 Grocers' Arms
65 IOHN PEMBERTON ½ 1666 Apothecaries' Arms £90
66 SAMVELL RATHBORNE ½ 1669 Lion
67 EDWARD WILLIAMSON ¼ Drapers' Arms, ALDERMAN £75

Manchester
68 IOHN ABRAHAM (R) ½
68A —— (R) ½ 1667
69 HENRY BARLOW ½ 1667
70 GEORGE BOOTH (I) ½ 1665
70A —— (I) ¼ Grocers' Arms
71 WILLIAM BOWKER ½ 1665
72 ANDREW BVRY 1d 1671 Apothecaries' Arms; City of London Arms
73 IOHN CHARLETON ¼ Apothecaries' Arms
74 IONATHAN EATON ½ 1667 £90
75 RICHARD HVNT ½ 1669 Monogram
76 ISAAC MOSSE (M) ½ 1667
77 IOHN NEILD ½ 1666
78 EMARY OLDFEILD ¼ Grocers' Arms
79 THOMAS PODMORE ½ 1666
80 IOHN RYLANDS (M) ½ 1666
81 IOHN AND MARTHA RYLANDS ½ 1667
82 IOSEPH VIGOR (D) ½ 1663
82A —— (D) ½ 1666
83 SAMVELL WINTER ¼ Grocers' Arms; anchor

Milnrow
84 RICHARD MILNE ½ 1671 Hour-glass
85 (See *London* 1466A)

Newton
86 WILLIAM WILLIAMSON 1d 1667
87 —— ½ 1669
88 (See *Bucks.* 105B)

Oldham
89 LAWRANCE NVTTALL (A) ½ 1669 Crown

Ormskirk
89A HENRY ATHERTON 1d 1671 Family Arms
90 IOHN BERRY (A) ½ 1667
91 IOSHVA CROSBIE ½ 1668 Scales
92 THOMAS CROSBIE ½ 1666 Grocers' Arms
93 THOMAS FARRAR (E) ½ 1666 Drapers' Arms
94 WILLIAM HAYDOCK 1d 1671 Church
95 AMBROSE IACKSON ½ 1667
95A HENRY TORBOCKE ½ 1666 Mercers' Arms

Poulton
96 IAMES SMITH ½ 1667 Drapers' Arms

Prescot
97 MATHEW DEANE ½ 1669 Mercers' Arms
98 IOHN WALL ½ 1666 Dove with olive-branch £110

Preston
99 IAMES ARCHER ½ 1668 Man with bow and arrow
99A HENRY ATHERTON ¼ Family Arms
100 IOSEPH BOLTON ¼ Paschal lamb; Grocers' Arms
101 IOHN CADMAN ½ 1668 PRESTON AND GARSTANG, Apothecaries' Arms
102 ROGER HADDOCK & IOHN RAVALD 1d Grocers' Arms £110
103 IOHN KELLET, THOMAS WOLEY ½ Grocers' Arms; Paschal lamb £110
104 CHRISTOPHER NOWELL ½ 1672 Paschal lamb
104A —— ½ 1671 —
104B CHRISTOPHR — (M) ¼ Family Arms
104C IOH OSBOVRNE, NATHANAEL IACKSON ½ Paschal lamb; Grocers' Arms
105 IOHN SHIELD ¼ 1664 Grocers' Arms
106 RICHARD SVMPNER ¼ Grocers' Arms
107 RICH AND IOHN SVMPNER ½ Paschal lamb; Grocers' Arms

Redvales (Bury)
107A IO ALLEN (A) ¼ 1659 Cat and frog

Ribchester
107B THOMAS CVTTLER ½ 1669 Sword

Risley
108 (See *Beds.* 83A)

Rochdale
109 IOHN BVTTERWORTH ¼ 1662 Queen's bust
110 IAMES HAMAR ¼ 1655 Eagle and child
111 RICHARD KENION ¼ 1666 £100
112 —— (I) ½ 1667 £80
112A ADDAM KERSHAW ¼ 1663 Hat
113 ROBERT MARTLERS ½ 1666 Weavers' Arms
114 IOSVA STRENGFELLOW ¼ Grocers' Arms
114A SAMVEL WILD ¼ 1652 Dog on cord

Rossall
114B RICHARD LIGHBOONE ½ 1669 £110

Shawfield
115 IAMES CHETHAM (M) ½ Talbot

Tarleton
116 TOWNE ½ 1669 Boat; church

Turton
117 W.W. (A) ¼ 1652 AT WOMORSLE CHAPEL

Warrington
118 IOSHVA ABRAHAM (M) ½ 1666 Roll of cloth
118A NATHAN ABRAHAM ½ 1666 Apothecaries' Arms
118B THOMAS BERKENHEAD (K) ½ 1667
119 EDWARD BORRON ½ 1667 Bull; crown
120 —— ½ 1668 ——
121 THOMAS CASSON ½ 1667 Embattled bridge
122 *John Dichfield* ½ 1669 Arms £70
123 SAMVELL LEECH (M) ½ 1666 Arms
124 WILLIAM MORETON (N) ½ 1666 Roll of cloth
125 IANE MVRRY & IO PICKERING ½ 1668 Scales
126 I.P., T.B. ½ 1667
127 MATTHEW PAGE 1d 1672 Ship; dolphin
128 THOMAS PIGOTT ½ Apothecaries' Arms; pot of lilies
129 WILLIAM SCHOFIELD (A) ½ 1666 Sugar-loaf
130 BRVEN SIXSMITH (E) ½ 1666 Drapers' Arms
131 IERIMY SMETHVRST (E) ½ 1669 Man holding spade £110
132 ELIZABETH WOOLLEY ½ 1667 Coronet, plume
133 RICHARD WORRALL (E) ½ 1666 Pot of lilies
134 THOMAS WREXHAM (M) ½ 1666 Grocers' Arms

West Houghton
135 H.M. (D) ¼ 1652 AT DASEY HILLOCKE

Whalley
136 WILLIAM CLAYTON ½ 1667 Hart's horns, MERCER
137 WILLIAM VARLEY ½ 1671 Heart pierced with arrows

Wigan
138 GERARD BANKES ¼ 1652 Family Arms; 3 escallop shells (arms)
138A PAVL BANKS ½ 1669 Windlass, bucket, fleur-de-lis, FOR HIS COALE PITTS
139 GILBERT BARROW (E) ½ 1669 Apothecaries' Arms
140 THOMAS COOPER ½ 1666 Family Crest
140A ?WILL GLOVER? (A?) ¼ 1657 ?Arms
141 WILLIAM LAITHWAITE ½ 1668 Armourers' Arms
142 ROBERT MARKLAND (K) ¼ 1655 Grocers' Arms
142A —— (K) ½ 1664 Mercers' Arms
143 MATHEW MARKLAND (G) ¼ 1664 Tallowchandlers' Arms
144 —— ½ 1666 Family Arms; Crest
145 ROBERT WINSTANLEY (I) ¼ 1652 Dove with olive-branch
145A —— (I?) ½ 1667 Dove (?)

Leicestershire

Major reference: J. Young, 'The Token Coinage of Leicestershire and Rutland in the XVII Century' (*Leicestershire Architectural and Archaeological Society's Transactions*, 1913–4). 1 plate; updating and revision of 'Williamson' with notes on a few issuers, and locations of specimens.

Further new tokens recorded from T. Sheppard, 'A List of Seventeenth Century Tokens of Lincolnshire in the Hull Museum' (*Transactions of the Hull Scientific and Field Naturalists' Club*, Vol. IV pt. III, 1911); W. Gilbert, 'Unpublished . . .' (see under Cambridgeshire); the Carthew collection (*SCMB*, Mar. 1946); and *SCA* 19, 3 Mar. 1982 and 51, 16 Apr. 1986.

Believed entirely unpublished: 13A, 75A.

Minimum price for unvalued tokens: £65

Ashby-de-la-Zouch
1 IOHN ALLATT ½ 1670 Dyers' Arms. *Octagonal*
2 IAMES COWPER ¼ Mill-rind
3 IAMES FARMER ½ 1671 Mercers' Arms
3A —— ¼ 1666 Stag*
3B I.H. ¼ IRONMONGERS ARMES
4 DAVID KING ¼ Mercers' Arms
4A SYMON MARSHALL 1d 1669 Apothecaries' Arms. *Heart-shape*
5 G.T. ¼ 1653 YE SPREAD EAGLE
6 GEORGE SEGRANE ¼ Lion
7 HVGH SHERWOOD ¼ 1656 Grocers' Arms
8 IOSEPH SHERWOOD ¼ 1655 Mercers' Arms; bull's head
9 FRANCIS SIKES ¼ 1669 AT YE RED, lion
10 SAMVELL HOVLDEN ½ 1667 St. George & dragon £65

Belgrave
10A WILL SLY (M) ¼ 1665 Sugar-loaf, MERCER

Belton
11 WILLIAM BARRADELL ½ 1671 Bell £38

Billesdon
12 HVMPHREY PARTRIDGE ½ 1667 Tallowchandlers' Arms £55
13 HENRY SANDERSON ½ 1669 Man making candles £38

Bottesford
13A RICHARD SANSOM ½ 1666 Stick of candles

*This is not an additional entry. It was listed by Williamson as 3A.

(Great) Bowden
14 RICHARD BRONSON ¼ 1658 Packhorse £65

Burrow
15 (See *Lincs.* 49A)

Burton Overy
16 RALPH COLEMAN ¼ Cross on shield £45

Castle Donington
16A HENRY WEBB ½ 1671 Tallowchandlers' Arms

Church Langton
17 WILL ELWOOD ½ 1669 Trowel; stick of candles

Easton Magna
18 (See *Essex* 185)

Hallaton
19 IOHN ELLIS (M) ¼ 1667 Packhorse
20 EDWARD GOODMAY (A) ¼ 3 cloves
20A ROBERT SANDERSON (E) ¼ Man making candles

Hinckley
21 WILLIAM BENTLEY (E) ¼ Arms
22 ROBERT BLOOD ½ 1670 AT THE CROWNE
22A E.C. (Listed under *Warwicks.* 66)
23 IOSEPH CAVE ½ 1666 Grocers' Arms, MERCER
24 —— (E) ¼ Grocers' Arms £55
25 THOMAS DAVELL (R) ½ Bear, IRONMONGER
25A —— (R) ¼ ——
26 THOMAS DAVENPORT (D) ¼ Lion, MERCER
26A IANE ELTON ½ 1667 Apothecaries' Arms

27 NATHANELL GILLBERT ½ 1671 St. George & dragon. *Octagonal*
28 *Nathanl Gilbert ½ 1672 at the George*
28A RICHARD GRIFFIN ½ 1671 Griffin
29 WILLIAM ILIFFE (D) ½
30 —— (D) ¼ 1662 £50

Leicester

31 NATHANIELL BAKER ¼ 1667 Angel £30
32 IOHN BROWNE ½ 1669 Man making candles £28
33 IOHN COLSON ½ Greyhound carrying hare, BAKER
34 DAVID DEAKINS ¼ 1657 BAKER
35 —— ¼ 1664 — £48
36 FRANCIS ELLIOT (W) ¼ 1655 £22
37 IOHN GOODALL (S) ¼ 1666 Hand holding glove £28
38 DANIELL HEGGS (S) ½ 1667 Unicorn £35
39 IANE LASH ½ 1669 King's Arms
40 IAMES LEE (A) ¼ 1656 Mercers' Arms £40
41 IOHN MASON (E) ¼ '62 Crown, BAKER
42 MARY MOVNTNEY ¼ Crown £35
43 RICHARD NOONE (A) ¼ Grocers' Arms
44 W.N. (I) ¼ AT THE RED LYON £50
45 THO OVERING (A) ¼ Crown, VIVE LA ROY £32
46 ROBERT PAGE (E) ½ 1666 St. George & dragon
47 IANE PALLMER ¼ Half-length figure £30
48 IOHN PARES (M) ½ 1666 Hart £25
49 EDWARD READ (M) ½ 1666 Hart £40
50 WILLIAM SAVID(G *or* GE) ½ 1670 Wheatsheaf £28
51 NICHOLAS SMITH 1d 1672 Barrel, BREWER
52 WILLIAM SPENCER ½ BVTCHER
53 THOMAS STVRGES (M) ¼ MERCER £28
54 SAMVELL WILLSON (R) ¼ BAKER £22
55 WILL WOOD (A) ½ 1667 Cordwainers' Arms £55
56 RICHARD WOODROFFE (M) ¼ MERCER

Loughborough

57 MATHEW ALLAIN (A) ¼ Ironmongers' Arms
58 — ALLAM (½) £50
59 IOHN ALLEN ½ NEERE THE, cross on 3 steps
59A — ALEN ¼ NERE THE, —
59B ROB BONOMYS ½ 1664 Bull's head; 3 barrels
60 ROBERT BVNNYS ½ 1666 St. George & dragon; Vintners' Arms
61 IOHN COOPER ½ Apothecaries' Arms
62 HENRY FLOWER (T) ¼ 1669 Hand holding baker's peel
63 IOHN FOWLER (K) ¼ Grocers' Arms £50
64 —— ½ 1665 —
65 WILAM SADLER (M) ¼ 3 fleurs-de-lis
66 HENRY SOMERVILE (M) ½ AT YE CASTLE £55
66A —— (M) ¼ Castle
67 THOMAS STORER (A) ½ AGAINST THE CROSS
68 HENRT FLOWER (T) ½ 1669 Hand holding baker's peel
69 IOHN VARNAM (½) Wheatsheaf £55
69A RICHARD WALTER (M) ½ 1669 Sugar-loaf
70 IOHN ? ½ 1665 Mercers' Arms

Lutterworth

71 PETER MACKCARNES (A) ¼ 1657 MERCER £55
72 —— (A) ¼ 1662 £48
72A GEORGE NEWBY (G) ¼ Grocers' Arms
73 EDWARD REVELL ¼ St. George & dragon
73A WILLIAM SMITH (M) (½) 1669 Cavalier's hat
73B GEORGE TILLEY ½ 1667 King's Arms, MERCER
74 (Listed under *Warwicks.* 98)
74A THO WHITE ¼ 1663 MERCER

Market Bosworth

75 HVGH ADCOCK (E) ½ AT THE, bull's head £35
75A HVMPHREY CHAPMAN ¼ 1657 Mercers' Arms
76 RICHARD THOMPSON (I) ½ MERCER £55

Market Harborough

77 ROBERT BASS ½ 1668 Hart. *Heart-shape*
77A THO COLEMAN (M) ¼ Greyhound
78 ANN GOTT ¼ 1658 Stocking £42
79 AV(GV)STIN(E) HARPER ¼ Grocers' Arms
80 THOMAS HEYRICKE ½ 1668 £35
81 THOMAS HORTON ¼ Drapers' Arms
82 THO LANGDEL ¼ FLAX DRESER
83 ELIZABETH LYNG ¼ Mortar and pestle
84 FRANCES REEVES ½ 1667 Swan £32
85 H.S. (F) ¼ 1651 AT THE SWANN £40
86 HENRY SMITH ¼ Bell
87 WILLIAM THOMPSON (R) (½) Clasped book
88 —— (R) ½ — £55
89 — TOMPSON (R) ¼ 1653 Open book
90 THOMAS WILSHERE (M) ¼ Tobacco-roll

Medbourne

91 GEORGE ALLMOND (E) ¼ 1667 Man standing

Melton Mowbray

92 ROBERT BEATSON (E) ¼ AT YE, 3 Pack-horses
93 IOHN BROWN (A) ½ 1668 CHAVNDLER £30
94 ARTHVR CLOVDSLY (B) ¼ 1664 Stick of candles. **Plate 2** £38
95 THOMAS CLOWDESLEY (S) ½ 1668 £32
96 HENRY CRODDYN (A) ¼ Cross moline on shield
97 EDWARD STOKES (R) ¼ Grocers' Arms
98 ROGER WAITE (R) ½ 1666 3 bugle-horns £28

Mountsorrel

99 RALPH BOSSE ½ 1667 Drapers' Arms

100 IONAS DAVIS ½ 1665 Grocers' Arms £50

101 IOSEPH LOVETT ½ 1667 Tobacco-roll?

Saddington

102 IONATHAN TAYLCOT ½ Pipes crossed, CHANDLER £65

Shepshed

103 IOSEPH BRVXBY ½ 1667 Sheep's head £65

Waltham-on-the-Wolds

104 HENRY DARCKER ½ 1666

105 — DARKER ½ 1668 £55

105A ROBERT NOBLE (M) ¼ 1657 Grocers' Arms

Lincolnshire

Major references: T. W. Townsend, edited by A. Gunstone, *Seventeenth Century Tradesmen's Tokens of Lincolnshire: The Issuers* (Lincolnshire Museums, Occasional Papers, No. 2, 1983). Revision of Smith (see next), with new tokens; notes on most issuers and re-attributions; and A. Smith, *A Catalogue of the Town and Trade Tokens of Lincolnshire issued in the Seventeenth Century* (Horncastle, 1931). 250 copies only. 15 plates; a re-listing of, and corrections to, 'Williamson', with a few extra notes.

Believed entirely unpublished: 184A.

Minimum price for unvalued tokens: £60

Alford

1 WILLIAM CARY ¼ 1659 MERCER £45

2 THOMAS HARRISON ¼ Griffin's head, MERCER £60

3 WILLIAM RODSBIE ¼ Ironmongers' Arms; R and cross

4 WILLIAM SCORTRETH ¼ 1667 3 doves

Ancaster

5 IOHN DRAKE ¼ '63 Ram

6 IOHN SCHOCHEY ¼ 1664 Fleur-de-lis; Grocers' Arms

Aubourn

7, 8 (See *Wilts*. 5, 6)

Barrow-on-Humber

9 BRIAN COVERDAILL ½ Fishing-boat with sail £50

Barton-on-Humber

10 GEORGE BROWN ½ 1669 Stag £60

11 GEORGE KIDSON ½ AT THE, swan £50

11A G.K. ¼ 1662 AT THE SWANN

12 HVGH LONG ½ 1669 Ship

13 RICHARD WOORE ½ 1669 Grocers' Arms

Bolingbroke

13A RICHARD BROKETT ¼ AT BVLLINGBROOK CASTLE

14 IOHN GARTHWAIT ¼ Grocers' Arms

14A ION GARTHWAITE ¼ — GROCR

Boston

15 OVERSERS ½ Town Arms; Crest £16

15A — ½ — — Crescent each side of shield £20

16 ROBERT ATKYN ¼ 1656 Mercers' Arms; 3 cloves

16A *John Brassey* ½ Family Arms. *Octagonal*

17 IOHN BROWNE (A) ¼ 1666 £50

17A WILLIAM BROWN (I) ¼ 1657 Haberdashers' Arms

18 ROBERT BVSTORD ¼ 1657 Bakers' Arms

19 CHRISTOPHER COXAL (D) ¼ n.d. Ironmongers' Arms £50

20 — — (D) ¼ 1666 —

21 WILLIAM EDWARDS (M) ¼ Still

22 THOMAS ETHERINGTON (M) ¼ 1664

23 MARRIAM FRANCIS (D) ½ 1668 Bricklayers' Arms £55

24 BARRON HAIRE (M) ¼ 1656 CHANLER

25 — — (N) ¼ — —

26 WILLIAM HOBSON (M) ¼ Family Arms, BREWER

27 THOMAS IENKINSON (M) ¼ 1666 Hammer, horseshoes

27A W.M. (A) ¼ 1662 Bust of Chas. II, GOD SAVE THE KING

27B WILLIAM MALLORY (A) ¼ — Bust of Chas. II

28 THOMAS MASSAM (M) ¼ 1659 Plough

29 IOHN MOORE (S) ½ 1667 Crown

30 THOMAS NICHOLSON (M) (½) 1666 ROPE MAKER

31 ROBERT PARKER (E) ¼ CVTLOR

32 THOMAS PARRISH (H) ¼ 1667 Blacksmiths' Arms

33 (Same as 34)

34 THOMAS PEARSON (A) ¼ 1663 Stays

35 (See *Staffs*. 4)

36 SAMVELL SKELTON ¼ Grocers' Arms

37 (Undated; minor variety of 38)

38 GEORGE WALKER ¼ Stocking

Bourne

39 WILLIAM BIRRIDGE ½ '64 MERCER £50

40 (See *Sussex* 82)

41 (See *Beds*. 26A)
42 (See *Sussex*. 83)
43 WILL QVENINGBROWH (A) ¼ 1656 Mercers' Arms £40

Brigg
44 IOHN BEALEY (E) ½ 1667
45 PEETER METCALFE ½ 1666 £50
46 WILLIAM MELTON ¼ Grocers' Arms
47 RICHARD STALLARD ¼ 1659 Angel
48 ROBERT TROWAN ½ 1668 Rose £60
48A THOMAS WATERLAND ½ 1668 Tallowchandlers' Arms

Burgh-le-Marsh
49 THOMAS CRACROFT ¼ '66 Fleur-de-lis; cross pattée, MERCER £42
49A IOHN SHAW ¼ 1664 Mercers' Arms £40

Burton-upon-Stather
50 THOMAS LOWTHER ¼ 1665 3 tuns

Caistor
50A EDWARD DENTY ½ 1668 Mercers' Arms
51 IOHN LATHORP ½ 1668 Grocers' Arms £50
52 WILLIAM HANSON (F) ½ 1668 Fleur-de-lis £50
52A WILLIAM WARD ¼ 1656 Grocers' Arms

Coningsby
53 IOHN LVPTON (A) ¼ 1663 Bakers' Arms

Corby Glen
54 THOMAS COLLINGWOOD (K) ½ 1667 Grocers' Arms £50

Claypole
55 NATH HOLT ½ 1664 FAYRE PLAY, GIVE AND TAKE £55

Crowland
56 THE POORES (Town) ½ 1670 Arms of Abbey £22
57 WALLTER BIRD ½ 1668 £48
58 WILLIAM BROWNE ½ 1666
59 ELIZABETH COLLS ¼ 1664 £55
60 IAMES HAMPSON (E) ½ 1666 £50
61 — — ½ — Grocers' Arms
62 ROBERT LOCKET ¼ Grocers' Arms

(Market) Deeping
63 AMBROSE BIRD ¼ Grocers' Arms
64 THOMAS BIRD ¼ 1664 Man making candles
65 WILLIAM BOWMAN ¼ 1664 Grocers' Arms £48
67 GEORGE FRENCH ¼ Drapers' Arms; scales
68 (Misreading of 67)

(West) Deeping
66 THOMAS CHAMBERS ½ 1668. *Heart-shape* £135

Donington
69 RICHARD GREENHILL ½ 1663 Grasshopper £48
70 HENRY CARR ¼ 1657 Mercers' Arms
71 THOMAS PELL ¼ 1664 Mercers' Arms £50

Epworth
72 RICHARD PARNELL (E) (½) Chequers £38
73 ROBERT WRIGHT ½ 1669. *Heart-shape*
74 (Misreading of 75)
75 IOHN MARSHALL (M) ½ 1668
76 THOMAS THORPE ¼ 1664 Mercers' Arms £60
77 — — ½ 1667 THAT GOES TOOE AND FROE

Folkingham
78 IOHN BISSILL (E) ½ Ironmongers' Arms
79 IOHN MICHILL ½ 1669 AT THE 3 PIDGENS
80 RICH QVINGBROW (K) ¼ 1656 £55
81 (Misreading of 80)

Gainsborough
82/3 IOHN A(L *or* I)STROP SENIOR ½ 1666 Rose and crown
84 RICHARD BARBER ½ 1668 Apothecaries' Arms, MERCER
85 MATHEW COATES ½ 1666 Ship
85A — — ¼ — —
86 ROBERT DVCKER ½ 1666 Tallowchandlers' Arms
87 WILLIAM GARLAND ½ 1667 GAINSBROVGH AND EPWORTH
88 NATHANELL GRAY ¼ Stag
89 IOSEPH HODKINS ½ 1666 Ship
90 THOMAS IOHNSON ½ 1666 Mercers' Arms
91 SAMVELL PARKER ½ 1666 MERCER
91A — — ¼ 1663 Mercers' Arms
92 IOHN SMITH ½ 1666 Haberdashers' Arms
93 BRYANTT WALKER ½ 1667 Packhorse with load

Glentham
94 THOMAS IOHNSON ½ 1669 Bakers' Arms

Grantham
95–7 OVERSEERS OF YE POORE ½ 1667 Borough Arms £13
98 ZACHARY LAXTON ¼ 1664
99 WILLIAM CLARKE (K) ¼ 2-headed eagle £48
100 GILBERT CHANTLER (G) ¼ 1654 3 tuns £65
101 EDWARD CODDINGTON (E) ¼ Grocers' Arms £50
102 HENRY COLE (A) ¼ 1657 3 doves
103 THOMAS DOVGHTEY (E) ¼ Rose £48
104 NATH GARTHWAITE (M) ¼ Mercers' Arms
105 ANTHONY HOTCHKIN (M) ¼ '66 Scales, MERCER
106 (Misreading of 105)
107 HENRY HVMES (E) ½ 1666
108 — — (E) ¼ 1657
109 EDW PAWLETT (E) (½) 1666 AT THE BIBLE

110 IOHN PLVMMER (I) ¼ 1663
111 ANDREW POOLE (A) ¼ 1657 Apothecaries' Arms
112 ROBERT TREVILLIAN (A) ¼ Ironmongers' Arms £60
113 THOMAS WALTON (A) ¼ 1659 7 stars
113A —— (A) ¼ 1666 —
113B IOHN WELLS (E) ¼ 3 tuns

Grimsby
114 CHRISTOPHER SCOTT (S) ¼ Grocers' Arms
115 WILLIAM TOD ¼ 1668 Mercers' Arms

Hagworthingham
116 WILL RISHWORTH ¼ 1663 Grocers' Arms

Haxey
117 ANTHONY BARNBY ½ 1669 Heart £45

Heckington
117A IOHN WILLIAMSON ½ 1669 Lion

Helpringham
118 ANTHONY NEWLOVE ½ Grocers' Arms, MERCER £30

Holbeach
119 IOHN BENINGTON ½ 1670 Mercers' Arms £42
120 WILL CARRE ¼ 1666 SADLER
120A RICHARD DAVES ¼ 1658
121 RICHARD WRIGHT (E) ¼ Grocers' Arms

Horbling
121A ROGER HALES ½ 1669 Mercers' Arms

Horncastle
122 RICHARD CATER (M) ¼ Tallowchandlers' Arms
123 IOHN CHAPPMAN ¼ Castle £42
124 (*Obv.* brockage of 123)
125 GEORGE COCKBORNE (½) St George & dragon, HORNECASTELL
126 —— ¼ — HORNCASTELL
127 GEORGE GVISINGE ¼ Mercers' Arms
128 ALEXANDER HOWGRAVE ¼ Grocers' Arms
129 (Misreading of 130)
130 ALEXANDER HOWGRAVE ¼ 1656 Grocers' Arms £42
131 IOHN HVSSEY ½ 1668 Mercers' Arms £35
132 IOHN SMITH ¼ 1669 Dolphin
133 — SMYTH ¼ n.d. Ironmongers' Arms
134 THOMAS VRYE ¼ Arms

Kirton-in-Lindsey
135 EVSTACE HOOKER ½ 1665 £18

(South) Kyme
136 GEORGE CHAPMAN (K) ½ 1669 Sheep

Langton-by-Spilsby
137 WILLIAM ROWETH (M) ½ Spade, GARDINER £65

Lincoln
138 *Citty* ½ 1669 City Arms, *Changd by the Maior. Octagonal* £22
139 — ¼ n.d. City Arms. *Octagonal* £35
140 (Misreading of 141)
141 SAMVELL AISTROP ½ 1668 Mercers' Arms £30
141A — AISTROPPE ½ 1667 —
142/3 — AISTROP *or* SAMVEL ASTRVP ¼ Mercers' Arms £20
144 SAMVEL ASTRVP (M) ¼ 1658 — £28
145 IOHN BABB ¼ 1668 Mercers' Arms £42
146 ROBERT BOWERS (E) ¼ BAKER £42
147 GEO BRACEWELL ¼ Clothworkers' Arms
148 TOBIAS ELLIS ¼ Dog
149 NATHANIELL GRAY (E) ¼ 1663 Vintners' Arms £32
150 ROBERT HALL (A) ½ £38
151 WILLIAM KELSEY ½ 1666 Tallowchandlers' Arms £30
152 THO LONGLEY ½ 1666 MERCER £32
153 IOSEPH LVDINGTON ¼ Mercers' Arms £22
154 —— (½) — £24
155 SAMVEL LVDINTON ¼ Mercers' Arms £18
156 ENOCH MALTON ½ 1666 Fishmongers' Arms
157 WIL MARSHALL ¼ City Arms; Mercers' Arms £30
158 IOHN MIDELBORAH ¼ 1658 Fishmongers' Arms £30
159/60 IOHN OSGOD(B *or* L)EY ½ Fishmongers' Arms £32
161 (Probably misreading of 159)
162 IOHN PHIPER (M) (½) Chequered square on *obv.*
163 Similar but square on *rev.*
164 SAMVELL RIDETT ½ 1666 CHANDLER £30
165 NICHOLAS RODSBY ¼ Apothecaries' Arms £50
166 HENRY SERSON ¼ AT YE FALCON £45
167 (Misreading of 168)
168 EDWARD TOMSON ½ 1666 Ironmongers' Arms
169 —— ¼ n.d. — THE BALE OF LINCOLN £20
169A Similar, VALE in error for BALE £50
170 HENRY WANLESS ½ 1669 Dolphins
171 ANN WILLERTON ¼ 1666 Drapers' Arms £22
172 SAMVELL WILLIAMS (E) ¼ 1657 Stationers' Arms £38
173 ANTHONY WILLOWS ¼ Mercers' Arms £30
174 ANTHONY WRIGHT (R) ¼ Lion's head on coronet £50
175 BARTHOLAMEW YORK ½ £30

Long Sutton
176 FRANCIS CORY ½ 1668 Mercers' Arms £35
177 —— ¼ 1663 —
178 I.S. (M) ¼
179 WILLIAM WALDEN (M) ¼ Grocers' Arms £50
180 —— (M) ¼ 1662 —

Louth
181 OVERSEERS OF THE POOR ½ 1671 Rose crowned. *Diamond-shape* £135
182 IOHN ATKINSON ½ 1669 3 doves £60
183 IOHN BARKER (E) ¼ 1661 Crown £60
184 EDWARD BROWNE ¼ MERCER
184A —— ¼ 1669 Mercers' Arms
185 IOHN CHAPMAN ¼ 1658 Ironmongers' Arms
186 (Misreading of 187)
187 IOHN CHAPMAN ¼ 1663 Ironmongers' Arms £55
188 THOMAS DAVESON ¼ 1666 Sugar-loaf; 5 cinquefoils, 2 stars
189 WILLIAM FOX ¼ 1656 Mercers' Arms; 3 cloves. MERCER
190 —— ¼ 1668 ———
191 (Misreading of 192)
192 CHARLES GREENE ¼ 1666 Armchair
193 WILLIAM HARDY ¼ MERCER £50
194/5 (Misreadings of 196)
196 CHRISTOPHER HEWSON ½ 1669 Tallowchandlers' Arms
197 THOMAS HOLAND ¼ 1666 Axes in saltire
198 (See *Cambs.* 154)
199 IANE SMALL ½ 1668 Apothecaries' Arms £48
200 EDWARD THOVRALD ½ 1670
201 — THVRALD ¼ Unicorn
202 (Misreading of 203)
203 WILL TOMPSON (F) ¼ Poleaxes in saltire

Market Rasen
203A WILLIAM BLOWE (A) ¼ Grocers' Arms
204 WILLIAM CHAPMAN ½ 1668 £24

Marston
205 ANN PARKESON ½ 1669 Scales

Morton-by-Bourne
205A IOHN NEWTON (M) ½ 1667 Man making candles £42

Moulton
206 THOMAS LEFFE (S) ½ 1669 MERCER

Navenby
207 THOMAS BOOLE (S) ¼ Ironmongers' Arms

(North) Reston
208 ELIAS MARTIN (H) (½) 1671 £32

Scotter
209 EDWARD SLEDMORE (M) ½ 1669 Crown over shuttle

Sleaford
210 IAMES ADAMSON (M) ¼ 1656 Mercers' Arms
211 RICHARD CAWDRON ¼ 1664 Mercers' Arms
212 IOHN FARNFEILD (E) ¼ 1656 Grocers' Arms
213 IOHN GARNNER (M) ¼ MERCER
214 CRISTOPHER GREEN (M) ¼ Mercers' Arms £40
215 EMANVELL NEWTON (M) ¼ MERCER
216 CHRISTO STANFEILD (E) ¼ 1659 St George & dragon
216A WALTER TREVILLIAN (S) ¼ 1666 Ironmongers' Arms

Spalding
217 Town ½ 1667 Town Hall, THE POORE £60
218 ED BALL (I) ½ 1666 Cog-wheel £45
219 —— (I) ½ 1668 —
220 (Misreading of 65)
221 SAMVELL CRAFORD ½ 1666 Crown £45
222 IOHN HAVEY (A) ¼ 1655 Grocers' Arms £35
223 *Richard Hutchinson* (M) ½ Lion. *Octagonal* £80
224 IOSEPH NVTTON ½ 1668 Rose crowned £42
225 —— (T) ¼ n.d. —
226 WILLIAM RAGG ¼ 1664 Initials G.S. within monogram
227 CAP WR(A)GG ¼ 4 flax mallets making V's, initials I.I.W.
228 IOHN RAY (M) ½ 1666 Mercers' Arms £42
229 ROBERT RISHTON ¼ 1666 Hart; lion
230 IOHN SHERWOOD ¼ Ironmongers' Arms £50

Spilsby
231 IOHN GAVLE ¼ 1659 Mercers' Arms
232 ROBERT HARRISON ¼ 1659 Unicorn
232A THOMAS PAPE ¼ 1656 Arms (of Beke)
233 IOSEPH SHAW ¼ 1667 Grocers' Arms £60
233A WILLIELMVS TINGCOMBE ¼ 1659 Cross, ECCE SIGNVM

Stamford
234/5 OVERSEERS ½ Town Arms; woolpack £14
236 ROBERT ALGAR (G) ¼ '57 Tallowchandlers' Arms £35
237 LEONARD ASHTON (S) ¼ 1666 Haberdashers' Arms £55
238 FRANCIS BARNWELL ½ 1668 3 pipes
239 FRANCIS BLYTH (M) ¼ '57 Tallowchandlers' Arms £50
240 IOHN BLYTH, CHARLES DEALE ¼ Bakers' Arms; Mercers' Arms £38
241 RICHARD BROOKES (E) ¼ 1666 Bakers' Arms
242 F.D., H.R. ¼ 1657 £42
243 IOHN HARDY, ED DALE ¼ £42

244 IOHN HARDY (M) ¼ 1667 Cordwainers' Arms
245/6 (See *Northants.* 149/50)
247 HVMFREY ILIVE (S) ¼ 1659 Grocers' Arms £42
248 WILL LARET & HVMPH SISCAN ¼ £55
249 HVMPHRY REYNOLDS (S) ¼ 1662 Tallowchandlers' Arms £48
250 THOMAS ROBERTS (M) ¼ 1659 Tallowchandlers' Arms
251 IOHN ROGERS ¼ 1664 Apothecaries' Arms
252 S. WALBVRG, A. MANTON ¼ Grocers' Arms
253/4 WILLIAM WALKER (S) ¼ CHANDL(E)R £50
255 HENRY WATERS (H) ¼ Rabbit

(East) Stockwith
255A THOMAS HOLLAND (M) ½ 1666

Surfleet
256 DANIELL DRINKWATER ½ 1666

Sutton
257 (same as 178)

Swineshead
258 IOHN BRANDO ¼ Lion, MERCR
259 RICHARD STOKES (M) ¼ Mercers' Arms

Tattershall
260 IOHN BODELL (A) ¼ 1650 BREWER
261 FRANCIS COCKE (A) ¼ 3 stars
262 WILL HVNTER ¼ 1660 Bugle
263 EDWARD SHARPE ¼ Grocers' Arms
264 IOHN WILLIAMSON (M) ¼ 1657 Bakers' Arms
265 — — (F) ¼ — —

Wainfleet
265A IOHN BRITTEN ¼? Cage?, TALLOW CHANDLER
266 RICHARD COXON (M) ¼ Grocers' Arms £60
267 THOMAS KENT ¼ 1668 GROCER
267A IOHN RACEE (E) ¼ 1667 AT YE RED, lion
268 IOHN SHAW (R) (½) 1670 Mercers' Arms
269 ROBERT TEMPLE ¼ 1667 Ship; anchor £50

Whitton
269A GEORGE BEALE ½ 1667 St George & dragon £65

Wragby
270 IOHN IONSON ¼ 1666

London

(The City of London, and some localities in the City of Westminster, with a few adjacent areas to the north and east in the former county of Middlesex)

New tokens recorded from J. H. Burn, *A Descriptive Catalogue of the London Traders', Tavern and Coffee-House Tokens Current in the Seventeenth Century* (2nd edition, London, 1855); *SNC*, Sep. 1898, Nov. 1900, Feb. and Nov. 1935, Nov. 1947 to Aug. 1948, Oct. 1948, Apr. to June 1957, May 1976; the Lowsley collection (sold at Sotheby's, 3/4 May 1899); *NC*, 1902, 1925, 1931; W. Charlton, 'Leather Currency' (*BNJ*, 1906); the Macfadyen collection (sold at Sotheby's, 15 July 1907); J. B. Caldecott and G. C. Yates, 'Leaden Tokens' (*BNJ*, 1907); the Hodgkin collection (sold at Sotheby's, 22 Apr. 1914); the Crisp collection (sold at Sotheby's, 20 Apr. 1923); W. Gilbert, 'Unpublished . . .' (see under Cambridgeshire); A. Heal, 'A XVII Century Ms. List of Tokens' (*Notes and Queries*, 7 Jan. to 25 Feb. 1928); *BNJ*, 1932, 1933, 1948, 1979; Seaby's *Coin and Medal List*, Jan. 1939; *SCMB*, Oct. 1950, Sep. 1952, Nov. 1954, June 1955, May 1957, Nov. 1963, Apr. 1967, July 1968, June 1985; H. A. Seaby and P. J. Seaby, *A Catalogue* . . . (see under Dorset); J. G. Milne, 'The Browne Willis Cabinet' (*BNJ*, 1951); Corbitt and Hunter's *Numismatic Gazette*, Mar. 1968; *TCSB*, vol. 1 no. 3, Mar. 1972; Sotheby's sale, 24 Jan. 1979; Robert Sharman, 'Unpublished Seventeenth-Century Tokens Recovered from the Thames' (*SCMB*, May 1983), and 'More Unpublished . . .' (*TCSB*, vol. 4 no. 1, Winter 1984); *SCA* 35, 11 Apr. 1984, 43, 18 Apr. 1985 and 51, 16 Apr. 1986; Michael Mitchiner and Anne Skinner, 'English Tokens, *c.* 1425 to 1672' (*BNJ*, 1984); and R. T. D. Sayle, *Notes on the South East Corner of Chancery Lane*.

See also J. Y. Akerman, *Tradesmen's Tokens Current in London and its Vicinity Between the Years 1648 and 1672* (London, 1849); K. Rogers, 'On Some Issuers of Seventeenth-Century London Tokens' (*NC*, 1928); P. L. Stiles, '17th Century Pewterers' Trade Tokens' (*SCMB*, Oct. 1958); George Berry, 'London Coffee Houses and their Tokens' (*Coins*, Feb. 1972), and 'Sutler to His Majesty's Guard of Foot' (*BNJ*, 1982) but especially *Taverns and Tokens of Pepys' London* (London, 1978: many photographs and other illustrations, analysis of the tokens, much information about the issuers, the places of issue and other background details); and T. D. Whittet, 'A Survey of Apothecaries' Tokens, part 2: London and Southwark' (*The Pharmaceutical Journal*, 5 Feb. 1983), and 'Spectacle Makers' Tokens' (*Worshipful Company of Spectacle Makers, Newsletter*, vol. 1, nos 9, 10, 12, 1984).

Believed entirely unpublished: 10A, 21A, 27A, 31A, 33B, C, 62A, 95A, B, 98A, 106B, 111A, 116B, 128A, 131A, 152A, 169B, C, 183A, 229A, B, 234A, 244A, 254A, 257A, 283A, 285A, 296A, 362A, 386A, 387A, 392A, 395A, 396A, 398A, 408A, 434B, 462A, 477A, 488A, 500A, 549A, 550A,

554A, 601A, 604A, 607B, 612A, 617A, B, 630A, 655A, 659A, 676A, B, 682A, 700A, 705A, 726A, 745A, 747A, 750A, 758A, 761A, 782A, 784A, 788A, 789A, 797A, 805A, 810A, 813A, 823A, 867A, 870A, 877B, 879B, 880A, 943A, 990A, 1001A, 1003A, C, 1013A, 1017A, 1019A, 1033A, 1038A, 1048A, 1097B, 1105A, B, 1108A, 1148A, 1162A, 1167A, 1171A, 1176A, 1180A, 1184A, 1205A, 1239A, 1248A, 1269A, 1281B, 1294A, 1301A, 1304A, 1308A, 1314A, B, C, 1348A, C, 1366A, 1379A, 1382A, 1447A, 1451A, C, 1468A, 1497A, 1542A, 1593A, 1640A, 1653A, 1675A, 1700A, 1735A, 1764A, 1784A, 1873A, 1894A, 1904A, 1927A, 1963A, 1973A, 1977A, 2000A, 2053A, 2063A, 2066A, 2088A, 2132A, B, 2162A, B, 2190A, 2199A, 2215A, B, 2279A, 2294B, 2339A, 2344B, 2346A, 2372A, 2387B, 2407A, B, 2483A, 2490A, B, 2500A, 2502A, 2506A, 2529A, 2585A, 2616A, 2622A, 2652A, 2674A, 2677A, 2678A, 2694B, 2700A, 2722A, 2723A, 2730A, B, 2750A, 2793B, 2794A, 2809A, 2813A, 2834A, 2849A, 2863B, 2898A, 2905A, 2938A, 2952A, B, 3027B, C, E, 3046A, 3084A, 3096A, 3141A, 3142A, 3153A, 3183A, 3195A, 3199B, 3220B, 3261A, 3267A, 3271A, 3315B, 3321B, 3326A, 3362A, 3371A, 3404A, 3424A, 3431A, 3433A, 3439A, 3440A, 3441A, 3443A, 3444A, 3448A, 3471A, 3473B, 3482A, 3487A, 3495B, 3498A, 3517A, 3543C.

Minimum price for unvalued tokens: £35

Abchurch Lane (Lombard Street)
1 T.C. (A) ¼ 1649 AT THE LION
2 NATHANIEL GOOSLY ½ 1666 Wheatsheaf
3 RALPH LVCAS ½ 1665 AT THE WHIT, bear £28
4 *John Milett* (S) ¼ 1664 £30
5 R.P. (S) ¼ 1649 AT THE LAMBE
5A *Jerom Powell ½ Tobacconist*
6 AVGVSTINE RAND ½ Hand pouring coffee from pot to cup
7 D.S. (I) ¼ AT THE WHIT HART
8 W.T. (A) ¼ AT THE BLACK HORSE

Addle Hill (Upper Thames Street)
9 CHARLES DEARE (E) ¼ Sun
10 THOMAS STEDMAN (D) ¼ 1656 Sun
10A —— (S) ¼ n.d. In *pb*

Addle Street (Aldermanbury)
11 A.K. ¼ AT THE SVGER LOFE
12 ROBERT RHETT (K) ½ 1666 Sugar-loaf

Air Street
12A RICHARD FVRNIS (M) ¼ AT YE ANGELL

Aldermanbury
12B IOHN BERKET ½ 1669 AT THE, Curriers' Arms.
12C LOWE HARTLEY 1d 1670 AT YE SIGNE OF YE ALDERMAN
13 ROBERT HILTON (M) ¼ Ball
14 IOHN IOHNSON (S) ½ 1669 Sieve
15 ELLENER PRICKE ¼ Lion

Aldersgate
16 E.A. (½) '68 THE MAIDEN HEAD, Mercers' Arms £25
17 R.A. (D) ¼ AT THE 7 STARS
18 T.A. (E) ¼ AT THE TVNN £18
19 IOHN ANDREWS ¼ 1666 AT YE, bull's head
20 RICHARD AWNSHAM ½ 1667 Swan £30
21 I.B. ¼ 1651 THE MERMAYDE TAVERN, mermaid
21A I.B. ¼ — AT THE MERMAYDE
21B O.B. (M) ¼ AT THE KATRING WHILL
21C DANIELL BAKER (B) ¼ 1667 Hen and chicks
21D EDWARD BAKER ½ 1668 AT THE, St George & dragon
22 IOHN BO . . . (A) ¼ 1650 3 crowns, BREWER
23 T.B. ¼ 1656 Prince of Wales' feathers, AND SVGAR LOAF
24 WILLIAM BOOKHAM ½ 1667 AT THE, bugle-horn
24A Thomas Bourne (A) ¼
25 IACOB CAMFEILD ½ AT YE BLEW, anchor
26 IOSEPH COLLET (M) ¼ Soap-box

27 NICHOLAS COOKE 1d 1666 GROCER AT YE COCK
27A —— 1d 1668 —
28 THOMAS DAMSELL ½ 1667 AT YE, Mercers' Arms, COOKE
29 IOHN DEAKES ½ 1669 AT YE COCK INN
30 RICHARD DOWLEY ¼ Salters' Arms; Arms
31 IOHN DRAPER (A) ½ AT YE BLACK, bull
31A E.F. (A) ¼ THE BLACKMORVSHEAD
32 RICHARD FINCH ½ AT YE LEG AND STAR
33 IOHN FISH ½ Dolphin; anchor
33A —— ¼
33B IAMES FITRIN ½ AT THE, cock?
33C IOHN GLOVER ½ Arms, IRONMONGER
34 THO GROVE (E) ½ 1668 Weight, CHEESMONGER
35 R.H. (S) ¼ AT THE SONN TAVERN
35A IAMES HARDING (A) ¼ Grocers' Arms
36 MATHEW HVTCHINSON (A) ½ Fountain
37 —— (A) ¼ —
38 C.I. (S) ¼ THE SWAN AND SVGAR £32
39 R.I. (A) ¼ AT THE BELL
40 WALTER IONES ½ 7 stars; monogram £25
41 WILL KNIGHT ½ '71 Prince of Wales' feathers; horse
42 WILL LEAMON (A) ¼ AT THE, Prince of Wales' feathers
43 IOHN LISLE (A) ½ AT THE 3, morris-dancers
44 THOMASON MACE ½ Rose under rainbow
45 PETER MORTIMER (M) ¼ Anchor
46 IOHN MYNN (M) ¼ St George & dragon
47 IOHN NORTON (I) ½ 1667 Magpie
48 I.P. (S) ¼ THE DAGGER IN NEV RENTS MARTINS
49 IO READ ½ 1669 AT THE 3 CROWND NEDLS
50 HENRY RVDDLE (B) ½ 1666 Boy on barrel
51 ? R.S. (M) ¼
52 IOHN SHARPE ¼ 1662
53 THOMAS SINGLETON (I) ¼ Sheaf between branches
54 *Michaell Stancliffe* ½ 1667 Castle, *Hosier* £30
55 THO STONE ¼ AT YE CASTLE
56 MICHAELL SYMONDS ½ AT THE, still £25
57 ANN TAYLER ½ A POTTERS SHOP
58 WILLIAM THORPE ¼ Half-moon
59 ROGER WALLMAN ½ '66 AT THE, horse £22
60 IOHN WARNER (A) ½ 1668 Dolphin, bell £10
61 NICHOLAS WARRIN (I) ¼ Hare £28
62 THO WEARG (M) ¼ AT THE SVNN TAR
62A THOMAS WEARGE (M) (½) AT YE SVN TAV
63 MATHEW WHITE (A) ½ AT THE, cock, bottle, crown
64 IOHN WICKINS ½ 1667 Mermaid
65 *The Coffee House* (½?) 1666 Turk's head, SOLYMAN

Aldgate

66 IOHN GAME ½ AT THE COACH AND HORSES
67 IOHN LANGHAM ¼ AT THE GVN, Grocers' Arms
68 SIMON TVRNER 1d NEXT THE PIE. Grocers' Arms; magpie
69 —— ¼ — Magpie; Grocers' Arms
70 ¼ AT THE KINGS HEAD

Aldgate Within

71 N.B. (E) ¼ 1649 AT THE GEORGE
72 R.B. (S) ¼ AT THE SARESENS HEAD, CHANDLER
72A IO BRETT ¼ 1661 AT THE MITER TAVERN
73 RICHARD DRAPER (D) ¼ Globe
73A T.F. (A) ¼ CHEESEMONGER CORNER SHOPE, bear
74 WIL FOR(D *or* DE) (A) ¼ AT THE BEARE
75 T.I. (K) ¼ AT THE SVNN TAVERNE
76 H.L. (E) ¼ THE BLEW BELL, MELL MAN
77 H.N. (S) ¼ '57 AT YE MYTER
78 ROBERT POND ½ 1668 AT THE WHIT, lion
79 ROBERT TAYLOR ½ 1666 AT THE, castle; initials R.E.
80 IOHN TIDDER (A) ¼ '57 Tallowchandlers' Arms
81 T.W. (E) ¼ AT YE HORSHOOE
82 RICHARD WALTON (T) ¼ AT YE STILL

Aldgate Without

83 DOROTHY ATCHESON ¼ Sun; trumpet, CHES MONGER
84 RIC AYLETT (E) ¼ AT THE, rose and crown
84A E.B. (E) ¼ AT THE DRIPIN PAN
85 RICHARD BRADLE . . (A) ¼ YE, stirrup
86 W.D. (A) ¼ 1659 AT THE GVNE
87 E.F. (D) ¼ AT THE HARTS HORNS
88 DAVID GILLAT ½ 1671 AT THE PIE, magpie £22
89 DAVID GRYER ½ 1667 AT THE, chequers
90 GABRIELL HARPER ¼ '59 Angel with scroll; bunch of grapes £32
90A William Hey ¼ 7 stars
91 W.I. (A) ¼ 1648 AT THE PYE, magpie £30
92 THOMAS INGRAME ¼ Harrow; plough
93 IOHN IOHNSON ½ NEAR WHIT CHAPPELL CHVRCH, Merchant-Taylors' Arms. *Octagonal*
94 ANDREW KILDERMORE (E) ¼ Anchor and heart
95 IOH QVICK ½ 1665 IN HIGH STREET, bell
95A D.R. (E) ¼ AT THE DOLFINN
95B F.R. (E) ¼ AT THE DISH PAN
96 THOMAS SLIGHTHOLME ¼ Castle b.s. £35

97 THO SPARKE (M) ¼ AT THE, stirrup
98 THOMAS THACKER (S) ½ 1668 AT THE, bladebone
98A MARGARET THORNE ¼ 3 nuns
99 IOHN VERTVE ½ 1668 AT THE RED, lion
100 C.W. ¼ AT THE BLEW BELL
101 ROBERT WARD (A) ¼ Lion
102 THO WITHERS (M) ½ 1666 AT THE, lady

Artichoke Lane (The Hermitage)
102A John Redding ¼?

Arundel Gardens (Strand)
103 ABRAHAM CVPER (M) ½ 1666 Cupid with bow and arrow

Ave Maria Lane (Ludgate Street)
104 GODFREY ROBINSON ¼ 1658 Hawk

Bacon's Inn (?)
105 IOHN COTTERELL ½ Boar

Baldwin's Gardens (Grays Inn Lane)
106 NICHOLAS SMITH (H) ½ 1666 Wheatsheaf £35
106A HERCVLES WHITHILL ½ 1666 Sugar-Loaf

Ball Alley (London Wall)
106B DAVID TOOLEY (I) ¼ Ball

Barbican
107 EDMOND ALEXANDER (M) ¼ Horsehoe
108 ELIZABETH BABINGTON ¼ 1653
109 HENRY BRAND (I) ¼ AT THE CROSS KEYES
110 IOSEPH BROOKS ¼ 1668 AT YE 3 SVGER LOAVES
111 THOMAS COOPER (A) ¼ 1655 CHANDLER £24
111A PHILIP DAMERELL (E) ¼ 1666 AT YE, plough
112 ROBERT DAWSON ½ AT THE BLACK BEAR
113 SAMVELL DIPPAR (I) ½ AT THE IACOBS WELL
114 R.G. (D) ¼ 1664 AT THE FIVE ROSES
115 EDWARD GROVE (G) ¼ 1665 Stationers' Arms
116 ROBERT HAYES (½?) AT YE COFFE HOVS, *formerly in Pannyer Ally*
116A THOMAS KITCHINMAN ½ 1666 AT YE, tree within garter
116B Samuel Lane ½ 1668 Mermaid
117 WILLIAM LARKIN (I) ¼ 1656 St George & dragon
118 IAMES LEECH ¼ Cupid with arrow, BODIS MAKEER
119 WILLIAM MILTON (E) ¼ 1666 MEAL MAN
120 FRANCIS MORLEY (M) ½ 1668 AT THE, head of Chas. II in royal oak
121 S.P. ¼ 1653 AT THE FIGTRE
121A IOHN REVELL (E) ¼ 1667 Hand holding glove
122 WILLIAM RVDD (A) ¼ 1655 Bull
123 R.S. ¼ AT THE LAMBE £28
124 WILL SANDERS (M) ¼ AT THE GOLDEN, anchor £24
125 WILL SHATCHWELL (I) ¼ Weavers' Arms
126 BRIGGET WOOLLEY ¼ Salters' Arms

Barking Churchyard
127 W.S. (M) ¼ AT THE CROWN AGAINST BARKIN CHVRCH

Barnake Street
128 (See *Southwark* 153A)

Bartholomew Close (Smithfield)
128A Robert Adson (S) ½
129 RICHARD KEMPE ½ 1666 Turk's head
130 WILLIAM RVSSELL (1d) 1671 HIS COFFEE HOVSE £48

Bartholomew Lane (Threadneedle Street)
131 HVGH ADDERLEY ¼ Dolphin
131A ROBERT COAST (G) ¼ Lion
132 ED HEATH (M) ½ AT SR THO GRESHAM
133 WILLIAM LEVETT (M) ¼ Ship

Basinghall Street
134 THO ARMESTRONGE ½ 1668 AT YE, man holding book £25
135 *Richard Buckland* (1d) Turk smoking, man giving him cup
136 RICH LEM (E) ¼ NAGS HED
137 T.M. (I) ¼ AT THE GEORGE £28
138 G.S. ¼ AT THE WHITE HORSE
138A G.S. (A) ¼ —
139 GEORGE STARCKEY ½ AT THE, horse £35
140 WILL TIMBERLACKE (T) ¼ Bearded figure holding book, hat
140A I.W. (M) ¼ 'At the Blue Coat Boy'

Basing Lane (Bread Street, Cheapside)
141 A.A. (P) ¼ 1650 AT THE SEAVEN STARES £35
142 B.A. ¼ 1659 AT THE BALL
143 IOHN BENET (I) ¼ 1650 Grocers' Arms
144 SAMVEL BROXON ¼ 1656 SYLK SHOP, bear
145 IOHN COCK (E) ¼ 1666 Still
146 RALPH EVERSLEY ¼ IN IARETS HALL, crown
147 VINCENT FLETCHER (F) ¼ 1666 Seven stars
148 I.G. ¼ 1652 AT THE WHIT HORS £30
148A W.P. ¼ 1664 AT THE WHIT HORS

149 RICH READ 1d '71 IN RED LION COVRT, bunch of grapes, COOPPER
150 GEORGE SHERLEY ½ AT YE HARTS HORNS

Bearbinder Lane (St Swithin's Lane)
151 T.H. ¼ AT THE LOBSTER
152 IOHN PVLLIN (S) (1d) AT THE BEARE

Bedfordbury (Chandos Street)
152A BARNABY ALLEN ¼ Woman spinning, A YARN SHOPP
153 FRANCES CLARE (P) ¼ Lions supporting crown
154 ELIZ ROW ¼ Ball, skittles
154A IANE SWAINE ¼ 1668 Stick of candles, crescent moon
155 THOMAS WEST (I) ¼ 1663 Stick of candles, crescent moon

Bedford Street (Covent Garden)
156 THOMAS BATCHELER ¼ Tallowchandlers' Arms, CHEESMONGER
156A FRANCIS COOPER (E) ¼ Eagle
157 G.D. ¼ AT THE SHVGER LOFE
158 SAMVELL HOARE (G) (½) AT THE CROSS, keys £16
159 THOMAS LATHWELL ½ Man making candles £35
160 H.P. (K) ¼ AT THE BELCONEY, people looking from balcony £45
161 CHRISTOPHER SEWARD (E) ½ 1664 AT THE, 3 birds £20

Beech Lane (Barbican)
162 PETER BAKER (M) ¼ 1658 Dog and duck
163 ELEZ BVTTERFIELD ¼ AT, hart's horns
163A IOHN CLARKE (C) ½ 1669 AT THE, roll and leaves of tobacco
164 SAMVELL ELCE ¼ 3 crowns, CHANDLER
165 HENRY GREEN (A) ¼ 1669 NEXT DORE TO GLOVERS HALL
166 ROBERT HALES (E) ¼ '59 AT THE, Bakers' Arms
167 EDWARD MARSHALL (I) ½ 1668 3 crowns
168 THOMAS TAYLOR (S) ½ 1668 Butchers' Arms
169 ELIZABETH WOOD ¼ 1656 Goldsmiths' Arms

Bell Alley (Houndsditch)
169A W.I. (R) ¼ IN A CELLAR, cheese-knife. In *pb*

Bell Alley
169B THOMAS VAVGHAN ¼ Stag; anchor (?)

Bell Lane (Spitalfields)
169C G.S. (A) ¼ '59 Men carrying barrel

Bell Yard (Fleet Street)
170 VICTOR DREW ½ 1667 Key within half-moon £32
171 MATHEW FANN (E) ½ 1667 Bakers' Arms
172 WILL IONSON ½ 1667 AT YE DRAKE £30
173 THO LAWRANCE (A) ½ '66 Hart's horns, portcullis
174 IACOB LIONS ½ 1666 Turk's head
175 STEPHEN PORTER ½ 1667 AT YE NAG TAVERN £30
176 W.R. (L) ¼ THE PERCVLIS
177 THOMAS RYVES ½ Portcullis

Bethlem (Bishopsgate Without)
178 C.A. (H) ¼ AT THE THREE TVNS
179 T.B. ¼ THE SINE OF THE HALF MOVN £28
180 RALPH BADGETT (E) ½ 1668 Shoe
181 THOMAS BONNY (M) ½ 1667 AT THE, Clothworkers' Arms
182 IOHN CLAPTON 1d 1669 AT THE COFFEE HOVSE
182A —— ½ 1669 Hand holding coffee-pot over cup
183 EPHRAIM CLITHEROW (G) ¼ AT THE SVNE
183A HENRY GAW (. . .) NE (S) ½ 166? Globe
184 ELIZABETH GROVND ¼ 3 shoes; legging
185 G.H. (A) ¼ 1658 AT THE SALVTATION
186 WILL HILTON ½ 1666 AT BLACK, bull, and small animal
187 ELIAS HOLLOWAY (B) ¼ AT THE, pump
188 E.K. (E) ¼ 1657 AT THE WHITE HART
189 THOMAS LEA(R *or* RE) ¼ 1662 Crescent moon £35
190 W.M. (F) ¼ 1658 . . . SIRPONY HOVS, Arms
190A RICHARD MALLIN (R) ½ 1668 AT YE, frying pan with Pewterers' Arms
191 RALPH PANKE (S) ½ 1667 AT YE, Blacksmiths' Arms
192 BARTHOLOMEW PEELE ½ AT YE BLACK SWAN
193 IAMES REDDALL (S) ¼ AT THE PLOW £28
194 IAMES SANDERSON ¼ Fleur-de-lis
195 HENRY TVRNER (M) ½ 1668 BAKER

Billingsgate
196 S.B. (M) ¼ AT THE QVEENS HEAD, Queen of Bohemia
197 R.C. (A) ¼ AT THE QVEENS HEAD, Queen of Bohemia £25
198 ROB CASH (A) ¼ 1663 Mermaid
199 *John Eldrige* ½ Lion, still. *Octagonal* £28
200 V.H. (I) ¼ 1650 THE MAIRMEAD TAVERN £25
200A VALENTINE HAYWARD (I) ¼ '57 Mermaid, 3 barrels
201 R.M. (S) ¼ THE SALVTAION TAVERN £35
202 WILL PORTER ¼ 1658 WHITE LION

203 T.W. (E) ¼ AT THE DARK HOVSE, ship £35
204 EVERARD WILD (B) ½ AT THE BASKET
205 THE 4 YEOMEN OF THE WATERSIDE ¼ Ship; scallop-shell
206 YEWMEN OF THE WATER SID ¼ Lobster; scallop-shell

Billiter Lane (Aldgate)
207 G. BACHELER (A) ½ 1668 AT YE, anchor
208 G.G. (H) ¼ AT THE ANGELL
209 IOHN HOWKINS (S) ¼ Crooked billet
210 W.L. (K) ¼ 1648 BROVNS ALLY, Holy Lamb
211 WILLIAM PHILLIPS (E) ¼ Rod of Aesculapius
212 WILLIAM WICKINS ¼ 1657 Man making candles £25

Birchin Lane (Cornhill)
213 IOHN COOKE (E) AT BLAC, bull
214 E.D. (A) ¼ AT THE SHIP
215 IAMES FORDE (E) ¼ AT THE COCKE
216 ROGER FORTH ½ 1667 AT THE, cock, bell above £32
216A IOHN HARISON (S) ¼ Crossed keys
217 ROBERT WHITE ½ AT THE BVLL ORDINARY

Bishopsgate
218 H.A. (A) ¼ AT THE BLACK HEART, hart £28
219 W.A. (I) ¼ AT THE SVNN £20
220 F.B. (M) ¼ THE SVGAR LOFE £24
221 H.B. (I) ¼ THE STARR TAVERNE £30
222 IOHN BAKER ½ AT YE FLOWER POTT
223 WILL BENNET (R) ¼ 1657 King's bust, holding globe, sceptre
224 THO BLACKBORNE (S) ¼ Sugar-loaf £20
225 IOHN BOND (M) ¼ AT THE, angel
225A W.C. (E) ¼ AT THE 3 SQVRELS
226 MARY CHILDE ¼ AT, 3 horseshoes
227 CHARLS COLLINS (A) ¼ 1664 Fox £32
228 E.D. ¼ THE SHIP TAVERN £25
229 RICHARD DOWDING ½ 1670 Y(E) WHIT, lion
229A ROBERT FINCH ½ Wheatsheaf
229B THEOPHILVS FROBYSHER (E) ¼ Crown
230 IOHN GASE (I) ¼ BAKER NEARE LEADEN HALL CORNER
231 HENRY GVLLIFER 1d 1668 Angel
232 A.H. (S) ¼ THE SHIP TAVERNE £28
233 G. HARDING (M) ¼ THE BAKER
234 IAMES HASELL ½ 1667 COOK AT, falcon £25
234A William Hearn (T) ¼ Swan
235 IOHN HEARNE (M) ½ 1666 Lion
236 —— ¼ Bunch of grapes
237 HEN HORNE (M) ¼ CHESE MONGER £25
238 IOHN IVES (M) ¼ 1657
239 IOHN IONSON (I) ¼ 1659 Plough, COOK
240 —— (I) ¼ n.d. ——
241 HENRY IORDAN ½ 1666 Man making candles
242 RICH LEVET (A) ¼ 1653 AT THE CRISPIN AND CRISPIANVS £32
243 I.M. (K) ¼ AT THE ACORNE £24
243A I.M. (M) ¼ 'Blew Anchor'
244 R.M. (S) ¼ THE SHVGER LOFE £20
244A RICHARD MILLER ¼ Rose
245 EDM MORRIS (A) ¼ '57 GOVLDEN LYON £24
246 HENRY NAPTON ½ 1670 Pewterers' Arms
247 EDW NOVRSE ¼ 1666 HIS FARTHINGE WORTH OF COPPER NEXT THE BVLL £60
248 THOMAS PEELE (S) ¼ Raven?
249 R.R. (M) ¼ AT THE MITER TAVERN
250 ROBERT ROBERTS (H) ¼ Lobster
251 HENRY RVSSELL (A) ½ 1667 AT THE, horseshoe
251A I.S. (D) ¼ THE FLOWERPOT
252 I.S. (H) ¼ THE TVN AND 3 ARROS £28
253 WALTER SHALLER ½ 1666 Half-moon
254 — SHALTER ½ AT YE, crescent moon
254A IOHN SMITH ¼ AT YE PEHEN
255 IOSEPH STEPHENS ¼ Angel
256 L.T. (M) ¼ THE FLOWER POT £30
257 T.T. (A) ¼ 1658 CHANDLER
257A LEONARD TARRANT (D) ¼ CVLLER MAN
258 THOMAS TEMPLE ½ Castle
259 G.W. (M) ¼ THE KINGS HED TAVERN, bust of Chas. I
260 IOHN WASHBOVRNE ¼ 1661 SALTER
261 HEN WELLINGTON ½ NEAR YE POST HOVS, COFFEE HOVSE
262 IOHN WILSON (A) ¼ Bust of Queen Elizabeth
263 PHILLIP WINFIELD (E) ¼ Bakers' Arms £30
264 ½ '66 Full-faced crowned bust; monogram of issuer's name (? Lewis)

Bishopsgate Without
265 *Benjamin Antrobus* (½) *At the Harrow. Octagonal* £45
266/7 GEORG A(T *or* L)KINES (A) ¼ Sugar-loaf
268 EDWARD BAILEY ½ 1667 Hare
268A John Baily ¼ 'Pen Maker'
269 IOHN BANBVRY ¼ Grocers' Arms
270 IOHN BARNARD ½ AT THE, globe
271 BATHVRST ¼ 3 Sugar-loaves, CONFECTIONER £30
272 W.B. ¼ AT THE TVN AND AROWES
273 IOHN BECHAM (S) ½ IN WHITE GATE ALLEY, figure on horseback blowing horn

274 WILL BENET ½ AT YE WHITE, hart
275 HENRY BVRGIN (M) ¼ Clock-face and hand
276 *Ralph Butcher* ¼ 1666 Lion, stick of candles £25
277 E.C. ¼ AT THE BLEW BOORE, cross pattée; boar £22
278 G.C. (E) ¼ AT THE BLACK LYON, stick of candles
279 I.C. ¼ 1657 AT YE RED LYON £32
280 IOHN CLARK ½ IN RED LION COVRT, cup and cover
281 G.D. (E) ¼ IN WHIT GATE ALLEY, soldiers, one with standard
282 FRANCES DASHWOOD ½ Naked man £24
283 THOMAS DOLLISON ½ 1667 AT YE, plough
283A WILLIAM DVFFILD ½ 1666 Cock
284 PETER EAGLES ½ 1668 2-headed eagle £28
285 THOMAS ENGLISH ½ 1667 Distillers' Arms
285A John Fish (A) ¼ 4 fishes
286 IOSEPH FOSSEY ½ 1668 MEALMAN £28
287 THOMAS FYDGE ½ 1666 Sugar-loaf £28
288 THOMAS GOSS ¼ 1652 Beehive £14
289 IOHN GREENE (L) ¼ Triple crescent, TALLO CH
290 M.H. ¼ AT THE 3 LIBERTS HEADS, Weavers' Arms £24
291 S.H. (A) ¼ 1658 Magpie, SALTER
292 S.H. (A) ¼ BY THE SVN, rose, rays darting from upper part £28
293 T.H. (E) ¼ AT THE WHITE SWAN
294 ARTHVR HALL ½ AT YE SINE OF MY LORD CRAVEN £28
295 IOHN HAMDEN (E) ¼ 1664 3 nuns
296 SAMVELL HAMPSON (A) ¼ n.d. Horse
296A —— (A) ¼ 1658 —
297 *Francis Hardy* ¼ 1666 *Grocer* £25
298 WILLIAM HOLBECH ¼ 3 kings, each holding sceptre and orb
299 SAMVELL HVTTON ½ AT YE CITTY OF NORWICH
300 H.I. (M) ¼ AT THE GRIDE IRON £25
301 W.I. (M) ¼ THE ROSE AND CRO (WN *or* VNE) £24
301A IOHN IAMES (M) ½ '68 AT THE 3, crowns
302 HENRY IORDON (F) ¼ Shuttle, VITLER £22
303 WILLIAM IORDAN (A) ½ AT THE, castle
304 —— (A) ¼ AT YE, castle
305 IOHN KENTISH (M) ¼ 1657
306 IOHN LAM(B *or* L)E ½ IN RED LION COVRT
307 FRANCIS MARTYN ¼ '63 Crown
308 FRANCES — ¼ n.d.
309 THOMAS MIDDLETON (K) ¼ £20
309A G. MORELAND (S) ¼ Cock
310 GEORGE NICOLLS (A) ¼ '57 Harrow
311/2 G.O. (I) ¼ THE HALFE MOONE BREW HOVS(E) £20
313 DOROTHY OVERTON ½ AT THE, packhorse £35
314 CHRISTOPHE PARRAT (E) ¼ Stag
315 ANDREW PARTRIDGE (I) ¼ 1664 Tallowchandlers' Arms
316 EDWARD PLOWMAN ½ AT YE, horse
316A THOMAS PORRAMOR (M) ½
317 IOHN PVLLIN (S) ½ HALF MOON ALLY, Men carrying barrel
318 HEN QVELCH ½ OYLEMAN AT YE, sunflower and barrel
319 E.R. (G) ¼ AT THE RAINEBOWE £25
320 ROBERT ROWLES (A) ¼ Woman churning
321 B.S. (S) ¼ THE GOVLDEN ANCHOR £28
321A G.S. (M) ¼ Bird, MEALMAN
322 E.S. (A) ¼ BY ANGELL ALLY £28
323 R.S. (K) ¼ AT THE MOVTH TAVERN £28
324 SAM SALLWAY (E) ¼ AT YE BLACK RAVEN
325 *Henry Salter* ¼ 1667 Lion, stick of candles £22
326 IOHN SHELLEY ½ '70 Horse-soldier, tobacco-roll
327 WALTER SHOWER ½ 1666 Half-moon
328 WILL SILLET (E) ½ IN DVNINGS ALY, Stag's horns
329 WILL SMALEY (A) ¼ Windmill, BAKER
330 IOHN STANTON ½ 1668 IN DVNINGS ALLY, hand pouring coffee
331 ROBERT STVDD (M) ¼ AT THE, helmet £22
332 THO TVTCHIN ½ Sugar-loaf
333 — TVCHIN ¼ Grocers' Arms; sugar-loaf. GROCER
334 IOHN TVTHILL (E) ¼ Bust of Chas. II £22
335 IOHN W . . . (E) ¼ CHANLER
336 HENERY WARREN (M) ¼ Bird
337 BEN WASHBOVRNE (E) ¼ Mercers' Arms

Blackfriars

338 IOHN CHAMBERLINE ½ 1670 CANTERBVRY COVRT, crowned lion with sword and bundle of arrows
339 WILLIAM CRANWEL (R) ¼ Man making candles
340 *Thomas Hooton* (E) ¼ 1664 £30
341 WILLIAM HOVLDER (A) ¼ Gateway
341A IONATHAN IENINGS (M) ¼ 1659 Goldsmiths' Arms
342 THO INSLEY (S) ¼ AT THE, swan
343 T.K. (D) ¼ AT YE GARDEN HOVS
344 *William Kidder* ¼ 1666 £35
345 W.N. (M) ¼ 1650 AT THE PLOW
346 R.S. (D) ¼ 1659 YE DARKE ENTRY
347 CHARLES SIMKINS (M) ¼ 1657 Drum

348 NICOLAS SIMSON (E) ¼ 1659 Phoenix £38
348A IOSIAS SMITH (S) ¼ Jacob's Well (?)
349 THO SYTTON 1d 1671 AT YE BLACK FRYER, *mum hous*
350 IOHN TVDOR (E) ¼ Angel
350A IOHN WALTER (D) ½ BAKER AT YE PARSH HOVS
351 IOHN WILDMAN (A) ½ '69
352 THOMAS WILSON (A) ¼ Rose
353 PHIL(L)IP YEO (I) ¼ AT THE, fleece

Black Horse Alley (Fleet Street)
354 THO BLVMSVM ½ AT YE KINGES HEAD

Blackmore Street (Drury Lane)
354A EDWARD LOVELL ½ AT YE 2 BLAK, men with spear between, TOBACCON

Blackwall Stairs
354B H.A. (E) ¼ THE COMPANIES ARMS
355 ROBERT EAST ½ AT YE GEORG

Bloomsbury
356 THOMAS CHAPMAN ½ 1664 Crown
357 RICH GADD (H) ¼ 1663 AT YE WHIT, hart
358 IANE KEYES ¼ 1663 Key
359 HENRY LANE ½ 1666 AT YE BLACK BOY
359A THOMAS MYERS (M) ¼ 1663 Man on crescent moon
360 ANDREW PASHLEY ½ AT YE BVLL AND MOVTH £28
361 EDWARD SMITH (L) ¼ Bull
362 ELIZEVS SOVTHERN (S) ½ 1667 £28
362A SIMON SPENCER ½ 1668 Arms
363 RICHARD WARD (E) ½ 1666 OYLE MAN
364 EDMOND WHITE (A) ½ Crown and anchor
365 THOMAS WIGLEY (G) ¼ Cradle
366 ANTHONY IEALE ½ IN KINGS STREET. Arms; harrow

Blowbladder Street (now Newgate Street)
367 ROBERT BOYS ¼ 1664 3 sugar-loaves
368 RICH IOYCE (D) ¼ AT THE, Fruiterers' Arms
369 RICH MOORE (M) ¼ GOLDE BAL

Boss Alley (Thames Street)*
370 W.R. (C) ¼ 1653 AT THE 3 MARRINRS £28

Boswell Court (Carey Street)
371 ELINOR SEAWARD ¼ 1657

Botolph Lane (Lower Thames Street)
372 IOHN CRANE (M) ½ 1666

Bow Lane (Cheapside)
373 WILL BINGHAM (I) ¼ DARK HOVSE, lion
374 PRT BRAILSFORD ¼ Horseshoe

* See also nos. 2920/1

375 D.C. (I) ¼ AT THE HORS SHOO, TOLOW CHAND £25
376 I.D. (A) ¼ 1652 THE MERMAYD TAVERN
377 IOHN DAVIS (M) ¼ 1657 3 arrows
378 IOHN DIX (E) ½ TALLOW CHANDLER
378A HENRY FORSTER (E) ½ AT YE DARK HOVSE, crooked billet
379 MICHELL HIGHAM ¼ AT THE GREN, dragon
380 BARTHOLOMEW HILL (M) ¼ Stag
381 I.K. (C) ¼ AT THE GREENE DRAGON £20
382 IOHN MICHELL (C) ¼ Family Arms, APOTHECARY
382A I.P. (A) ¼ 1652 THE MERMAYD TAVERN
383 W.P. ¼ AT THE BELL
384 ANDREW RAGDALE (B) ¼ Man making candles
385 IOHN WOLRICH ¼ 1650 AT THE COK £25
386 —— (S) ¼ 1652—initials I.S. £22
386A —— (S) ¼ —— initials S.I. (error)
387 —— ¼ 1658 —
387A IOHN WORMWELL (S) ¼ AT YE DARK HOVS, Prince of Wales' feathers
388 ¼ AT THE BLACK TALBVT, MELE SHOP

Bow Street(Westminster)
389 IAMES BEECH ½ 1667 Bunches of grapes in hoop £16
390 IOHN BROWNE (A) ¼ AT THE GRIFIN
390A ROB GOFFE (A) ¼ Bunch of grapes
391 E.O. (F) ¼ AT THE BLEW LION £18
392 H.S. (B) ¼ 1653 THE CR(OS *or* SE) SHVFLES £14
392A H.S. (B) ¼ 1657 THE CROS SHVFLES
393 T.S. (A) ¼ 1659 BACKER £20

Bread Gate
393A THOMAS READER ½ Arms

Bread Street (Cheapside)
394 G.B. (M) ¼ 1649 THE STAR
395 WILLIAM BARNES (I) (½) Still, DISTILER
395A —— (I) ¼ Still
396 I.C. (S) ½ 1665 AT THE MEARMAYD TAVERN
396A THOMAS CH . . . (M) ¼ 1666 Indian holding bow
397 RICHARD CROFT ¼ Angel
398 T.D. (M) ¼ '57 YE MERMAYD TAVERN
398A ROBERT GO . . . SON (A) ¼ Phoenix
399 R.H. (E) ¼ '57 YE WHIT HART TAVERN
400 IOHN IENNENS (½) AT THE, sun; Ironmongers' Arms
400A IOH LARDER (E) ¼
401 EDWARD LEWIS (R) ¼ 1659 Porridge-pot
402 ROB MARSHALL (M) ¼ Mercers' Arms
403 WILL NOBLE ½ 1668 CONFECTIONER AND GROCER

404 R.R. (E) ¼ 1649 AT THE WHITE HORES £25
405 BENIAMIN SALLOWES (M) ¼ 1656 Salters' Arms
406 ARTHVR & THO STONE ¼ Castle
406A IOHN VELEN (E) ¼ AT REDD, cross
407 *Wards Coffee House* (1d) 1671 Turk's head, *Solyman* £42
408 1d AT THE COFFEE HOVSE IN STARR COVRT £48

Brewer Field (?)
408A MARGRET RANDELL ¼ Sugar-loaf

Brick Lane (Spitalfields)
409 IOHN CHVRCHLY ½ Guy, Earl of Warwick, holding boar's head on spear
410 THOMAS COWLY (M) ½ 1666 Sun
411 CHARLES DAY (M) ½ 166(9?) Pentagon. *Heart-shape*
412 GILES DISHLEY ½ Archer £38
413 THOMAS ELY ½ 1666 AT THE GVY OF WARWICK
413A IOHN HARVY ½ 1669
414 SAMVELL NEWMAN ½ 1665 AT THE GVY OF WARWICK

Bride Lane (Fleet Street)
415 WILLIAM ADLEY (I) ½ 1663
416 DANIELL BIRTWISSELL ½ 1666 AT WHITE BEARE
416A EDWARD BOX ¼ AT THE, bear chained. In *pb*
417 R.C. (E) ¼ 1652 AT THE 3 COLTES
418 WILL HEARNE (M) ¼ AT YE WHIT, bear
419 —— ¼ AT Y WHIT, bear
420 WILLIAM P... (M) ¼ 1665 AT THE, ?
421 BARBEREY PAINE ½ 1669

Bridewell (Fleet Street)
421A RICHARD BVTLER ½ Arms, HEMPDRESER
422 A.C. (E) ¼ AT THE SVN TAVERN £22
423 ROBERT CHAPMAN (E) ½ Woodmongers' Arms
423A —— (E) ½ Sword, crown on point
424 —— (E) ¼ —— £28
425 M.E. (A) ¼ 1652 AT THE PYD BVLL £32
426 GILIS RAY (I) ¼ WOODMONG
426A IOHN SMITH (S) ¼ Sun
427 THO TEMPLEMAN (M) ¼ Fleur-de-lis on faggot
428 YE HOSPITAL OF BRIDEWEL ½ City Arms

Broad Street
429 E.B. (A) ¼ 1658 AT THE WHITE HORSE £28
429A E.B. (A) ¼ 1670 —
430 *Silvester Deane* ½ 1667 Hand pouring coffee from pot
431 RICHARD DVNN (M) ¼ AT THE, French Arms
432 IOHN HOW (M) ¼ Helmet
433 HVGH LVMBARD (I) ½ 1667 AT THE, Prince of Wales' feathers
434 STEPHEN MABBERLY (E) ¼ '67 Pewterers' Arms
434A WIL MALLABA ¼ AT HALF MOON, dove with olive branch; stick of candles, crescent moon
434B EDWARD NETHERCOATE (E) ½ 1669 Lion
435 STEPHEN SLANEY ¼ 3 sugar-loaves

Broken Wharf (Thames Street)
436 HVGH ANDRVS ½ 1667 Croppers' shears £28
437 ROB AVSTIN ¼ Bundle of wood, WOODM; dog emerging from wood
438 WILL DOD (E) (½) AT YE WHIT LYON
439 WILL AND ELIZABETH NORTH ¼ Blacksmiths' Arms
439A TR(monogram) P. ¼ 'White Lyon'

Bucklersbury
440 S.R. ¼ '57 AT YE FLOWER DE LVCE, fleur-de-lis; Drapers' Arms

Budge Row (Cannon Street)
440A I.C. (M) ¼ 1649 AT THE SHIPE TAVERNE
441 M.S. (M) ¼ 1657 AT THE DYALL, clock-face
442 FRAN SMITH ¼ AT YE RED, cow; Girdlers' Arms
443 THOMAS SNOW (A) ¼ Raven; stick of candles

Bull and Mouth Street (Aldersgate)
444 DRINGS COFFEE HOVSE 1d 1671

Bulwark Gate (Tower Hill)
445 RICHARD GOODWIN (D) ¼ Lion
446 HENRY HAYWARD (A) ¼ Grocers' Arms
447 R.S. (I) ¼ AT THE CROOKED BILLIT £35
448 THOMAS STARES (E) ¼ 1653 £28
449 THO TONGE (C) ¼ AT THE SHIP

Bury Street, Bevis Marks
450 ISAAC PEADE ½ 1666 Hart

Butcher Row (near Temple Bar)
451 RICHARD CHARTER (I) ¼ Bell
452 MATHEW DVNE (E) ½ AT YE BACON SHOP £28
453 SAMVEL(L) IONES (A) ½ AT THE, fleece
454 SAMVELL — (A) ¼
455 E.M. (H) ¼ YE SWAN
456 EDWARD STARKY (E) ¼ 1657 Bust of Henry VIII

Cannon or **Channell Row** (Westminster)
457 THOMAS MORICE (A) ½ 1666 Gateway with towers

Cannon or **Candlewick Street**
458 I.B. ¼ AT YE BLACK HORSE
459 NATHANIELL BAGNE (S) ¼ Unicorn
460 ANNE BLVNT 1d 1672 Turk's head £42
461 WILLIAM BVRGES ½ 1667 AT LONDON STONE, Coopers' Arms
461A E.C. (H) ¼? '3 blackbirds'
462 THO COLCOCK 1d GROCER AT YE GOVLDEN KEY £48
462A HENRY CROFT (S) ¼ Tree
463 T.E. ¼ THE WHIT LYON TAVERN
464 FRANCIS HEATH (I) ¼ Hercules, club on shoulder, by beacon
464A RICHARD KENNON (M) ¼ AT, peacock
465 B.S. (I) ¼ AT YE WHITE HART £35
466 RICHARD TAYLOR ¼ 1659 Tree
467 SAM TWICKTEN (R) ¼ AT BLACK, swan

Carey Lane (Foster Lane, Cheapside)
468 IOHN HVBBOLD (A) ¼ 1660 POTTER
469 IOHN IACKSON ½ AT YE CROWN
470 —— (M) ¼ Drapers' Arms £30

Carter Lane (near St Paul's)
471 G.A. (P) ¼ THE 3 NEATS TOVNGS
471A M.A. (S) ¼ AT YE LEGG AD SPVR
472 I.B. (M) ¼ THE DOLPHIN
473 ISAAC BARTHOLOMEW (M) ¼ SOPE BOX
474 FRANCIS GVRSON (A) ½ Horse and cart, driver; rose
475 RICHARD HASKER ½ 1664 Globe
476 THO OVTRIDGE 1d Cup, saucer and pipes on table, hand above holding cup; Turk's head. *Octagonal*
477 WILLIAM PROSSER (I) ¼ Goat
477A R.S. (M) ¼

Castle Lane (Petty France or Southwark)
478 THOMAS BLAKE ¼ AT THE, man smoking pipe £28

Castle Street (Long Acre)
479 HENRY GODFREY (S) ½ Brewers carrying barrel

Castle Street (Piccadilly)
480 IOHN BAKER (1d) Sceptres crossed, crown above. *Uniface on oblong flan*
481 THOMAS WHITE (I) ½ '69 Stone-sawyer

Cateaton Street
482 THOMAS BETTON ¼ 3 lions
483 GEORGE FRANCKLIN ½ Bust of Turk holding coffee-cup
483A ROBERT GARRETT ¼ Sugar-loaf, tobacco-roll, GROCER
484 PARTRIDG HATTON (I) ¼ Fleece
484A THOMAS HYATT (I) ¼ Goat
485 THO(MAS) LACY (M) ½ Female bust, ROXCEL LANA
485A THO SMITH (E) ¼ Prince of Wales' feathers, coronet
486 ROB SNOW (A) ¼ AT WHITE, lion
487 I.W. (E) ¼ THE KINGS ARMES TAVERN
488 GEORGE WADE (R) ¼ AT YE, sun
488A THOMAS WARD (B) ¼ Mercers' Arms
489 ROGER WARE ½ 1664 Kings' Arms
490 ¼? AT TE GEORGE

Chancery Lane
491 IOHN BODINGTON ½ AT YE CELLER, bunch of grapes £32
492 WILLIAM BRAMPTON (K) ¼ 1666 Unicorn, MILL(L)INOR
493 IOHN BVSH (D) ¼ AT THE, crown £30
494 E.C. (M) ¼ AT THE CROWNE
495 I.C. (E) ¼ AT THE HORNS
495A DANIELL CHILD (H) ½ 1669 CORN CHANDLER NEERE YE PVMP
496 EDWARD CODDINGTON (M) ¼ Death's head £32
496A W.D. (E) ¼? 'Hornes in Whites Alley'
497 *George Daphin* (½) *Att The Coffee House*
498 I.F. (M) ½ AT THE HOLE IN THE WALL
499 I.F. (M) ¼ 1651 — £18
500 R.H. (M) ¼ THE S IONS HEAD TAVERN £32
500A *John haines ½ at ye Coffee house*
501 BARTH HALL (E) ½ 1668 Goat feeding from tree, MILLENER
502 THOMAS HARRIS ½ 1667 Castle
503 —— (E) ¼ n.d. —
504 IOHN HENTHORNE (M) ½ AT THE ST, John the Baptist, TAVERNE
505 RANDOLPH HOPLEY (G) ¼ Spur
506 ABRA HVDSON ½ APOTHECARY AT YE BLEW BOAR
507 RALPH HVTCHINSON ½ AT YE GRAY FRYER
508 I.I. (S) ½ 1665 LEOPARD TAVERN, spur
509 W.I. (B) ¼ THE POPES HEAD TAVERN
510 T.K. (A) ¼ THE KINGS HEAD TAVERN, bust of Henry VIII. **Plate 2** £24
511 T.L. (E) ¼ AT THE GLOBE TAVERN
512 IOHN LANGSTON ½ '67 AT THE, globe, TAV
513 IOHN LOCKE ½ IN WHITES ALLY
514 WILLIAM MART (K) ½ Bust of Henry VIII
515 RALPH MASSIE ½ 1667 AT YE ROLES TAVERN
516 THOMAS NEWSAM ½ 1666 2-headed eagle

517 D.P. (E) ½ AT YE OVLD PARRS HEAD £32
518 R.P. (½) 1666 AT THE BIBLE
519 (See *Glos.* 128A)
520 HENRY REDMAN ½ 1666 Bust of pope £35
521 *Joh Rider ½ at ye Coffee House at the Rolls gate*
522 WILL ROSSE ½ 1666 AT THE BLACK, 2-headed eagle
523 E.S. (A) ¼ THE WHITE SWAN
523A I.T. ¼? 'George'
524 HVMPHREY TAFT ¼ 1665 AT THE, anchor and sword, CVTLER £24
525 *Robert Terrey ½ Att the Coffee House* £30
526 IOHN TVRNER (D) ½ 1668 AT THE, ? friar's head
527 I.V. (S) ¼ BLACK SPRED EAGLE
528 WILL WOOTTEN ½ AT YE GRAY FRYER
529 F.W. (A) ¼ AT THE GOLDEN CROS £18

Chandos Street (Covent Garden)
529A Edward Barnes ½ Wheatsheaf
530 IOHN BEAVMONT (D) ½ 1667 AT YE GOLDEN, ball
531 THOMAS BECKEMSFEILD ½ 3 kings with sceptres
532 EDWARD BOSWELL (D) ½ 1667 AT 3 ELMES
533 R.C. . . ¼? Key
534 I.K. (D) ¼ AT THE GATE
535 ROB RISBEY (A) ½ 2-headed eagle
535A ROBERT THORPE ¼ Gate (?); horseshoe
536 GEORGE WARNER (A) ¼ Man holding harpoon

Charing Cross; The Mews
537 *Edward Bew* ½ 1664 Queen's bust
538 S.C. ¼ AT THE SENE OF THE HARP
539 THOMAS COOKE ¼ 1662 AT, 3 sugar-loaves (?)
540 THO DARLING ¼ '57 AT 3 TVNS
541 *Judeth Elliss* ½ 1664 Horseshoe
542 W.F. (A) ¼ 1650 THE MEREMAD
543 R.H. (M) ¼ AT THE CHECKER INN
544 MIDLETON HARINTON (A) (½) AT Y BLV, bell, HATTER
545 RICH HAMMOND ¼ 1662 NEXT TO YE WHIT SWAN, GROCER
546 ANDREW HIN(D *or* DE) ½ Hind; 2-headed eagle £35
547 CHRISTOPHER IACOB (I) ¼ Men saluting
548 FRANCIS IEFERIS ¼ AT THE CHERIN CROS TAVERN, cross
549 R.L. ¼ AT YE FETHERS
549A IOHN MAITLAND (M) ¼ 1655
550 MILES MICHELL (I) ¼ Cooks' Arms, MEALMAN
550A Chalres Murry ½ 1668 Man
551 MARKE RIDER ½ 1665 AT THE SWAN
552 THOMAS TONGE (E) ¼ AT THE, lion holding ball
553 I.W. (½) THE PAGEANT TAVERNE, Arch with 3 gates, within garland £45
554 ROBERT WRIGHT (A) ¼ 1664 3 birds

Charles Street (Covent Garden)
554A G.W. (E) ¼ 1654 CHANDLER
555 NOAH WEBB (M) ¼ AT YE FENIX

Charterhouse Lane
556 THOMAS BAREFOOT (P) ¼ Angel
557 RICHARD BENNION (A) ½ AT THE, 3 horses saddled and bridled
558 FRANCIS BENTHAM (M) ¼ Sun £30
559 IOHN BVSH (I) ½ AT YE HARROW £32
560 — — ½ —
561 SAMVELL DAWSON ½ '67 AT YE, nag's head
562 IOHN ELY ½ 1668 AT YE BOARES HEAD
563 T.F. (S) ¼ GREENE MAN AND BALL
564 RICHARD GREENE (E) ¼ St George & dragon
565 IOHN HOWES (M) ¼ Grocers' Arms £25
566 A.L. (A) ½ AT THE FLIEING HORSE £28
567 DVDLEY MEARES (I) ¼ Schoolboy
568 CHRIS SAMWORTH (R) ¼ AT THE, fountain, Bacchus above
569 FRANCIS TVRNER (S) ¼ Rose and crown
570 FELIX WAYLETT (I) ¼ Lion

Charterhouse Square
570A IOHN NATT ¼ Bird holding olive branch. In *pb*

Cheapside
570B W.A. ¼ 'Golden Lady'
571 GEORGE ALLANSON 1d 1672 Cat?
572 EDWARD ATTWOOD (I) ¼ Half-moon
573 T.B. (E) ¼ 1650 THE BVLL HEAD TAVERNE £25
573A DANIELL BLVNDELL ¼ 1664 Mermaid
574 FABIAN BROWNE (A) ¼ Castle (?)
575 T.C. (E) ¼ 1650 THE FEATERS TAVERN
575A ANTHONY CLARK (A) ¼ AT YE STAR
576 IOSEPH CLIFTON ½ 1663 BVLL HEAD YARD £30
577 F.D. (M) ¼ AGAINST THE GREAT COVNDVIT, St George & dragon
578 I.H. (D) ¼ THE DIERS ARMES
579 T.D. ¼ AT THE MITR, FORGET NOT £35
580 E.E. (M) ¼ KINGS HEAD VNDER BOW CHVRCH
581 ROBERT GARDNER (E) ¼ 3 horseshoes
582 HVMPHREY GROSVENOR ¼ Nag's head
583 I.H. (S) ¼ AGAINST THE GREAT COVNDVIT, 3 tuns £30

583A RICHARD HILLER ¼ Bird standing on sun
584 THOMAS IAMES (B) ¼ AT THE, raven
585 EDWARD IARVIS (1d) AT THE GEORG, *Edward* monogram £28
586 CHARLES KIFTELL (1d) 1669 AT THE COFFEE HOVSE £42
587 ROB KIRKHAM ¼ AT, fox; sugar-loaf
588/9 (See after 1308)
590 I.M. (T) ¼ AT YE MEAREMAYD
591 R.M. (M) ¼ 1651 THE MEARMAD TAVERN
592 W.M. (S) ¼ 1652 AT THE STARE TAVERN, star
593 WILL MOSTYN (E) ½ AT YE HEN & CHICKINS
593A THOMAS MVDE ¼ Horseshoe, GROCER
594 GEORGE PEIRCE (M) ¼ 1665 Bull's head £32
595 W.R. (½) AT YE MAREMADE TWIXT MILK STRE WOOD STR HABERDASHER SMALL WARES, merchant's mark
595A FRAN RINGSTEAD ¼ AT, star, TAVERNE
596 RICHARD ROYLE ¼ AT YE RAVEN
597 W.S. (M) ¼ 1648 AT THE STARE TAVORN, star
598 WILLIAM SHARPE ½ IN TRVMP ALEY, man on horseback blowing horn
598A A.T. (C) ¼ 1649 AT THE SARASONS HEAD
599 S.T. (S) ¼ THE MAN IN THE MOON TAVERN £32
600 W.T. (A) ¼ 1652 AT THE BLAKE BOY
601 EZEKIELL WALLIS ¼ AT THE BLEW BOAR £30
601A Sam Wheatley ¼ 1660 Man
602 MARY WOODFALL ¼ Nag's head
603 WILLIAM YATE ¼ 3 keys

Chequer Alley (Moorfields)
604 IOHN MEEKES ½ 1668 YE DARK HOVSE, chequers £38

Chequer Alley (Whitecross Street)
604A IOHN GARDNER (A) ½ 1669 VICTLER. *Octagonal*
604B RICH MORSON ½ 1669 Chequers, PINMAKER

Chequer Yard (Dowgate)
605 H. WELLINGTON ½ 1665 AT YE COFFE HOVS

Chick Lane (West Smithfield)
606 WILLIAM BRATTLE (E) ½ AT THE ROYAL OAK
607 THOMAS COWLY (M) ½ 1666 Sun £30
607A — — (M) ¼ — —
607B WILL CROVCH (M) ¼ 1663 Weavers' Arms, MEALMAN
608 PETER ENGLISH ½ 1668 AT THE, shoulder of mutton; head of St John the Baptist in dish
608A IOHN FISHWICK (F) ¼ Cat seated in boat, catherine-wheel as helm
609 IARVIS GARNON ¼ AT YE CORNER OF CHICK AN FEE LANE, wheatsheaf
610 RACHELL GOVLSMITH ¼ 1665 Salters' Arms, CHANDLER
611 RICHARD HALLET (A) ¼ 1659 Lion of St Mark
612 THOMAS IOHNSON (I) ¼ 1658 Salters' Arms
612A HENRY KETTLE ½ 1671 BREWER
613 HENRY KNIGHT (E) ½ 1669 Still, 3 ?tuns, BREWER £30
614 RICHARD LVKEY (M) ½ AT THE PVMP
615 IOHN MASON ¼ Still
616 RICHARD RAWLINSON ½ 1667 Bakers' Arms
617 ALEXANDER SHARP (I) ¼ 3 pipes
617A RICH SHAW ½ AT YE HOOP AND 3 TVNS, 3 tuns and bunch of grapes
617B AVGVSTINE SMITH (R) ¼ Unicorn
618 R.W. (N) ¼ AT THE GOVLDING LYON
619 ROBERT WEST (A) ½ 1667 Mercers' Arms

Chiswell Street (Finsbury)
620 EDWARD ADAMS ½ 1669 AT YE LAMP
621 RALPH BOWES (M) ¼ 1658 BREWER
622 ROBERT CHIPPERFIELD ½ 1659
623 — CHIPPERFEILD (A) ¼ —
623A RALPH DAVIS ½ AT THE, standing figure holding flag
624 (Probably *Herts.* 76)
625 BARTHOLOMEW FRANCIS ½ 1666 Crown £28
626 *William Panton* ¼ Leg in boot
627 IONATHAN SMITH ½ 1667 Lantern, OYLEMAN
628 I.T. (F) ¼ AT THE PLOVGH £30
629 BRYAN TAILOR (A) ¼ AT GREE MAN
630 IOHN THOMLINSON (S) ½ 1667 AT THE, Robin Hood and Little John £24
630A I.W. (S) ¼ GROCER
631 STEPHEN WILKINSON (L) ¼

Christ's Hospital (Newgate Street)
632 IOHN BANNISTER ½ AT THE MATRONS SELLER, cripple
633 — — ¼ — —
634 SIBBIL THEAME ¼ SHO MAKER

Church Lane (Whitechapel)
635 IAMES HASLER ½ 1669 AT THE, man on horseback blowing horn

636 W.M. (R) ¼ AT YE GENERAL MVNKES HEAD
637 EDW SCALES (E) ½ 1669 AT THE SVN, NEAR WEL CLOS
638 RICHARD SMITH (E) ½ 1665
639 IOHN STONYER (M) ¼ 1658 King David playing harp £32
640 THOMAS WEEDEN (M) ¼ Sugar-loaf

Churchyard Gate (Westminster)
641 ED ROGERS (½) 1659 Horse; Fishmongers' Arms. SALTER £28

Clare Market and **Street; New Market**
641A W.A. ¼?
642 RICHARD ANDREWS ½ AT THE, fountain
643 WILLIAM BIRTBY ½ 1667 FISHMONGER
644 ROGER FRANCKLIN ½ AT THE, lion, HOASSIAR
645 HENRY FRANCIS (E) ½ '67 AT THE 2 KINGS AND STILL
646 IEREMIAH GREEN (A) ½ AT YE KINGS HEAD, bust of Chas. II
646A IOHN HENDERSON ½ AT THE SHIPP
646B IAMES HILL (M) ¼ 1657 OYLE MAN
647 G.I. ¼ '57 GEORGE TAVERN
647A A.K. (E) ¼ '2 kings and still'
648 TERTVLLION LEWIS (G) ¼ SALTER
649 HVM MVNTT ½ 1666 3 candlesticks, IRONMONGER £24
650 THOMAS MOGER (M) ¼ £32
650A ROBERT MYNN ½ AT YE GOLDEN ANCHOR £28
651 ADAM PEARSON ½ IN BEARE YARD AT YE BLEW CAP £35
652 IOHN RENOB 1d COFFEE HOVSE £42
653 GEORG(E) SAMPSON (P) ½ Samson in wig, ass's jawbone in hand
654 GEORG — ¼ 1664 Still
655 RALPH SHERWIN (A) ½ 1668 AT SWAN
655A IANE STAYNER ½ 1666 AT THE GREEN SWAN
655B WIL TAVERNER ¼ Y KYES OF DVNKIRK ACROS TO THE SPANYARD
656 IOHN WALKER (I) ½ 1666 Fishmongers' Arms

Clarendon House
656A ROB SHIPTON (M) ½ AT THE HORSHOO

Clerkenwell
657 CHRISTO ANDERTON (A) ½ 1667 AT YE, crown
658 THOMAS BROWNE (E) ½ 1667 AT THE, sugar-loaf
659 A.C. (E) ¼ YE ROSE (AND *or* &) CROWNE
659A ED COLLMAN ½ 1666 AT YE SHROPSHIRE HOVSE, bell
659B IOHN COWICK ½ AT THE, archer and crescent moon
660 HENRY DANIEL ¼ AT THE, Daniel in lions' den; nag's head
661 THOMAS GIBS ½ 1666 Bust of Chas. I
662 TRISTRAM HEWES (A) ½ 1666 BAKER
663 TRISTRVMP — (A) ¼ Scales, BAKER
664 EDWARD PINCKETHMAN (A) ½ '68 5 bells
665 IOHN ROBERTS (E) ½ AT YE DRVM
666 GILES RVSSELL (M) ¼ 1657 Swan
667 IOHN SCOTT ½ 1667 AT THE TVRN STILE
668 RICHARD STVDLEY (I) ¼ AT THE SHROPSHIERE HOVSE
669 EDWARD WRIGHT (D) ¼ 1658 BAKER

Cloak Lane (Dowgate Hill)
670 N.B. (I) ¼ AT THE WILLOW TREE £35
671 I.B. (P) ¼ AT THE WILLOW TREE £30

Cloth Fair (Smithfield)
672 CHRISTO ASHBOVRN ½ AT THE, sun, CHANDLER
673 WILLIAM BINCKS ½ 1666 AT THE 2 BREWERS
673A THOMAS CANNINGS (M) ½ 1667 Man firing cannon
674 WILLIAM CHANDLER (S) ¼ Hands joined
675 HENRY CRANE (E) ¼ '66 MEALMAN
676 THO CRANFEILD (S) ¼ Fox
676A IOHN DICKSON ¼ AT THE DOGS, dog eating from pot
676B —— ½ AT THE DOGS HEAD IN THE POT. —
677 HENRY DOWNING (R) ¼ Mercers' Arms
678 WILLIAM FAWSON ½ 1667
679 THOMAS GASCOYNE ½ 1668 Merchant-Taylors' Arms
680 RICHARD GIMBART (M) ¼ Men carrying barrel
681 WILLIAM GRAY ½ 1666 Antlers
681A IOHN GREENE ¼ Scissors
682 THOMAS HARLOW (A) ¼ 1669 CHANDLER OVER AGAINST YE BREWERS
682A GEORGE HOLDEN (K) ¼ 1664 AT THE, ship in shield
683 WILLIAM HOW (E) ½ 1667 AT YE HARRO
684 HENRY INGERSOLE ½ 1668 AT YE 3 TVNNES
685 — INGERSOVLE (D) ¼ '58 3 tuns
685A WILLIAM KEAMES (C) ¼ 1663 Harrow
685B THO MILBOVRN (A) ¼ AT Y WHI, bear chained
686 IAMES MILLER ½ 1666 Patten and last

687 ISACK PECKETT ¼ 3 stags; Butchers' Arms
688 *John Poyntting* ½ 1667 Tobacco-roll. *Heart-shape*
689 RICH TAYLER ¼ MEALE
690 MIKHILL TEMPLE (A) ¼ Prince of Wales' feathers
691 GEORGE WALLIS ¼ Tallowchandlers' Arms
692 WILLIAM WITTINGAM (D) ¼ 1657 Wyvern

Cock Alley (Ludgate)
693 HENRY MORICE 1d AT THE BLACK DOGG

Cock Lane (Shoreditch)
694 T.A. (G) ¼ THE COCK
694A L.B. (E) ¼? 'Cock'
694B IOSEPH WARD (M) ¼ Cock

Cock Lane (West Smithfield)
695 ROBERT GREENE (D) ¼ 1656 Fleur-de-lis
696 RICHARD NORMAN (I) ¼ Wheatsheaf and scales, BAKER £35
697 CHARLS OAKES (D) ½ 1667 AT YE SVGER LOAFE, head of Chas. II, royal oak
698 I.S. (D) ¼ THE GREEN LETTICE, latticed square
698A GEORGE THAPE (S) ¼ 1655 AT YE, portcullis
Nos. 694A and 694B may belong here

The Cock Pit
699 IOHN SCOTT (M) ½ Crown over cock, SVTTLER

Colchester Street
700 (See *Essex* 139)

Cole Harbour (Thames Street)
700A Thomas Buckford (I) ¼
701 LANCELOT CHAPMAN (M) ¼ Innholders' Arms
702 HENRY COOPER ½ AT THE, horns, men carrying barrel £28
703 ANDREW E(ILEI *or* LLIE)S (S) ¼ Vintners' Arms
704 — ELLEIS (S) ¼ 1658 Dyers' Arms
705 THOMAS KINGE (E) ½ AT YE DYERS ARMES, Dyers' Arms
705A —— (E) ½ — men carrying barrel

Coleman Street
706 IOHN ABBOTT ½ 1666 Drapers' Arms
707 SAMVELL COLMAN (A) ¼ AT, sugar-loaf and crescent
708 EDWARD FLETCHER (M) ¼ Carpenters' Arms
709 ROB FORDE ¼ Mermaid, GROCER
710 IAMES GRIPP (E) ½ 1666 A COAT MAKER
711 NICHOLAS HARINGTON ½ 1665 AT YE HINE, doe
711A WILLIAM HARTE ¼ Hart; heart
711B THOMAS HVLL (M) ¼ Wheatsheaf
712 NICHOLAS MILLER ½ AT THE, star, TAVERN
712A I.P. (G) ¼ AT THE WHIT HART
713 IOHN SHELDON ½ 1668 IN SWAN ALY, 3 inkhorns
714 IOSEPH SIBLEY ½ 1663 AT YE BLACK, bell £30
714A IOHN WILLETT ½ 1669 AGAINST LONDON WALL, cock in hoop. *Square*

College Hill (Thames Street)
714B GEORGE BOYLSON (A) ¼ St George & dragon
714C IOHN SCVDAMOR (K) ½ 1668 Bust of Chas. II
715 FRANCIS TROWELL ¼ 1664

Cornhill
716 S.C. ¼ 1653 THE 3 GOLDEN LYONS
716A S.C. ¼ 1660 —
717 R.D. (W) ¼ 1656 AT THE BEARE TAVERN
718 T.E. (I) ¼ 1657 THE SHIPP (AND *or* &) STARR
719 H.H. (A) ¼ AT THE DOLPHIN TAVERN
720 T.H. (M) ¼ AT YE BLACK BVLL
721 A.F., T.H. ¼ 1651 AT THE CASTLE TAVERN
722 T.H. ¼ — —
723 ROBERT HALTON (E) ¼ Servant pouring coffee into man's cup
724 WILL HINTON ½ 1666 AT YE GOLDEN, fleece
724A R.K. (E) ¼ 1657 THE CASTLE
725 IOHN LVCAS (M) ½ AT THE DOLPHIN TAVERNE, dolphin and boar
725A I.P. (M) ¼? 'Golden ball'
726 R.R. (V) ¼ 1649 AT THE GOLDEN CROSS, shield of arms on cross £28
726A R.R. (M) ¼ 1664 — —
727 IOHN SWEETING ¼ Mercers' Arms
728 W.T. (K) ¼ AT THE LIVE VVLTER, vulture
729 W.T. (M) ¼ 1651 THE MERMAYDE TAVERN
730 M.W. (I) ¼ 1648 AT THE SEVEN STARS £35
731 M.W. (I) ¼ n.d. —
732 GAMA WHITTAKER ¼ AT YE, sugar-loaf, GROSER
732A STEPHEN WILKINSON ¼ 1657 AT YE 3 TVNS

Cousin Lane (Upper Thames Street)
733 DAN BVRRY (M) ¼ Gate, WOODMVNGR
734 IOHN MARTE ¼ Millstone
735 PETER TVLL (A) ¼ Plough, WOOD-MONGER £35

Covent Garden
736 WILLIAM CLIFTON (½) AT THE FLEECE £32
737 W.C. ¼ AT THE FLEECE TAVERNE £30
738 WILLIAM FARNCOMBE ¼ 1654 OYL MANE £30
739 G.G. (G) ¼ THE CROE KEYES TAVERN £30
740 W.L. (M) ¼ AT THE ROSE TAVERN £32
741 V.M. (M) ¼ AT THE ROSE AND CROWN
742 IOHN MINCHIN ½ 1664 Angel, BAKER, OB
742A —— ¼ 1652 ——
743 IOHN MORE ½ IN BRIDGE STREET, rose and crown
744 ELLEN PRICK ¼ '59 IN B(OW ST?), bush
745 W.S. ¼ '58 Bible, FEARE GOD HONOR YE KING
745A GEORGE THROCKMORTON (M) ½ IN BRIDGESTREET, tobacco-roll
746 ROBERT WHITE (E) ½ IN BRIDGES STREET, windmill

Cow Cross (St John Street)
746A G.A. (M) ¼
747 I.B. (M) ¼ 1653 THE DOGG AND BARE
747A Robert Bellson ½ Bell
748 FRANCIS BRAY ½ '66 3 fleurs-de-lis
749 RICHARD BVRCHMORE (M) ¼ Wheatsheaf
749A WILLAM BVRTON (M) ¼ AT THE BVTCHERS ARMES
750 WILLIAM CORDWELL (A) ¼ Daniel in lions' den (?)
750A THO FRIEND ½ Anchor
751 H.G. (M) ¼ AT THE 3 KINGS
752 I.G. (M) ¼ 1650 THE 3 DOVES
753 IOHN GOLBARNE (M) (½) AT THE WORLDS END
753A John Hall (A) ¼ 1656 3 figures
754 IOHN HAMMOND ¼ 1667 CHEES MONGER
755 PHILLIP HOCKER (M) ¼ 1664 Men ready to kill bull
756 ELIZABETH HODGKINS ½ '65 AT THE RED LYON
756A ROBERT LYFORD (E) ½ 1667 AT YE COPERS ARMES
757 T.M. (I) ¼ AT THE SIGNE OF THE LAST
758 IOHN MARTINE ½ 1666 AT YE RED CROSS
758A SARA NEAL ¼ 1664 CHANLER
759 WILLIAM RICHARDSON (H) ¼ Fruiterers' Arms
760 S. ¼ THE WHITE LION
761 IAMES WATKINS (I) ¼ AT THE CROWN
761A —— (I) ½ —
762 IOHN WOOD (G) ¼ AT THE, sugar-loaf, crescent between pistols
763 IOHN WORMWELL (S) ¼ Prince of Wales' feathers

Cow Lane (Smithfield)
764 IOHN BEARD (L) ¼ AT THE BVLL HEAD
765 IOHN COLLINS (A) ¼ 1657 Naked figure holding staff
765A RICHARD COLLINS (A) ½ AT YE CROWN TAVERN
766 ELIZ GODDARD ¼ AT THE DRAGON
767 IAMES HILL (M) ¼ AT THE, bull's head
768 WILLIAM HOLMS (A) ¼ AT THE PLOW
769 I.R. (S) ¼ AT THE SHIPE
770 R.S. (I) ¼ THE 3 COCKS
771 WILLIAM STRINGFELLOW ½ AT YE BVLL HEAD
772 C.T. (A) ¼ AT THE PLOW
773 T.T. (A) ¼ '58 AT THE RED CROS £28
774 W.T. (M) ¼ 1652 THE SHVGER LOFE
775 THOMAS TARAT ½ IN BOARS HEAD COVRT, Bakers' Arms
776 IOHN THOROWGOOD (R) ½ Spur with leathers
777 IOHN WERREN (S) ¼ Still

Coxe's Quay (Lower Thames Street)
778 CHRISTOPHER BOSTOCK (A) ½ 1669 AT COCKES KEY, cock and key. **Plate 2**

Cree Church Lane (Leadenhall Street)
779 R.B. (M) ½ THE OATE SHEAF, CHANDLER
780 I.C. (I) ¼ 1653 AT THE BVLL HEAD
781 IONATHAN CLEREDGE (I) ½ 1668 Bull's head
782 WILL CLARKE (A) ¼ CHANLER
782A WIL LVDINGTON (M) ¼ Cock
783 EDWARD SHRAWLEY (I) 1d 1669 AT YE CROWN £32
784 — SHRAWLY (I) ½ '66 —

Creed Lane (Ludgate Hill)
784A I.D. (E) ¼ AT THE DOGS HEAD
785 THOMAS GREEN (M) ½ AT YE THREE PIGEONS
786 THO NEWBERY (S) ½ 1669 CHEESMONGR

Cripplegate
787 ROBERT AMY (P) ¼ Grasshopper £38
788 THOMAS ASH(B *or* LE)Y ½ 1666 Crown
788A N.B. (I) ¼ AT THE TOBACCO ROLL, arms
789 WILL BARNES (M) ¼ OYLE SHOP
789A Samuel Benton ½ 1668 Mermaid
790 THO CORNEL (M) ¼ 1657 MILNNR
791 WILL CROSLAND ½ 1668 AT YE BLEW, bell
792 G.F. ¼ AT THE WHIT HYND BRVHOVS
793 IOHN FLETCHER (A) ½ 1669 GROCER NEXT DOOR TO YR SVN TAVERN. *Heart-shape*
794 THO GREENHILL (M) ¼ 3 birds £38
795 I.H. (E) ¼ AT THE SVNNE TAVERN £32
796 IAMES HAYDYE (S) ½ POVLTERER

797 ISAAC HODGKIN ½ '66 AT YE, sun
797A HENRY KINDON ¼ *Cheesmonger*
798 EDWARD PHIPPS (S) ½ AT THE, cock
799 IOB SARGEANT ¼ Harrow
800 THO SPENCER (P) ¼ 1658

Crooked Lane (Cannon Street)
801 THOMAS COLE ½ 1669 TALLOW CHANDLER £32
801A RICH IORDEN ¼ AT BLACK BVLL
802 THOMAS OGDEN ½ 1664 AT YE, swan
803 I.S. (A) ¼ AT THE 3 CRICKETS, 3 stools
804 IOSEPH SHELLEY (E) ¼ AT, fleur-de-lis

Cross-Key Court (London Wall)
805 GEORGE HIGGINSON (K) ½ Clothworkers' Arms

Crown Court (Drury Lane)
805A E.B. (I) ¼ Fleur-de-lis
806 *Thomas Burnham* ½. *Octagonal*
807 IOHN SPICER ½ 1667 Crown; lute £30

Crutched Friars (Mark Lane)
808 I.B. (M) ¼ AT THE BLACKE BVLL
809 W.B. (E) ¼ AT THE SHIPPE
809A MARY CROSBY ½ Cooks' Arms
810 THO GREENE (I) ½ '67 AT THE crossed keys £35
810A WILL GREENSMITH (D) ¼ Bird
811 I.K. (E) ¼ AT THE 3 TVN TAVERN
811A IOHN KENT ½ 3 tuns
812 HVMPHRY MILLINGTON ½ Horseshoe
813 T.P. (M) ¼ AT THE 3 TVNNES
813A THEOPHILVS PACE ½ 3 tuns
814 WILLIAM SARGANT ¼ Bunch of grapes, MEALMAN
815 PHILIP STARKEY (M) ¼ AT YE, Brewers' Arms £24
816 FRANCIS WOODWARD (E) ½ 1667 Man on horseback blowing horn

Curriers' Alley (Shoe Lane, Fleet Street)
816A T.B. (M) ¼ 1658 Dolphin
817 I.W. (A) ¼ AT THE BIRD IN HAND £32

Cursitor's Alley (Chancery Lane)
818 IOHN GALE (E) ¼ Sugar-loaf
819 RICHARD HILL (M) ¼ Man making candles
820 I.S. (E) ½ 1667 AT THE ROSE TAVERN
821 I.S. (E) ¼ '57 AT YE ROSE TAVERN
822 ANTHONY YEWEN (I) ½ Goat

Custom House Quay (Thames Street)
823 ARTHVR BALDWIN (I) ½
823A SHERLY BLADWORTH ½ Sugar-loaf, sun
824 IOSEPH DREW (M) ½ AT THE BLAK BOY
825 HENRY HALFORD (E) ½ Horse
825A IO LARGE (B) ¼ AT GOLDEN ANCOR
826 S.T. (E) ¼ AT THE, queen's bust, TAVERN £28
827 THOMAS WHITBREAD (E) ¼ Man making candles

Dean and Flower Street (Spitalfields)
828 IOHN CVRTIS (A) ¼ Gunner and cannon, tent in distance

Dice Quay (Lower Thames Street)
829 WILLIAM DEW (M) ½ 1668 Fleece
830 FRANCIS TVRRALL (A) ¼ Key between dice

Distaff Lane (Friday Street)
830A G.C. (M) ¼? 'Livery Hood'
831 HENRY KEATE (S) ¼ AT THE, woolpack
832 R.M. (D) ¼ 1652 AT THE DEATHES HEAD £25
833 RICH MASON (I) ¼ TALLOWE CHANDLER
834 IOH PENNOYER (A) ¼ AT YE, pelican feeding young
835 R.T. (A) ¼ 1657 THE BELL TAVERNE
836 I.V. (E) ¼ AT THE SVGER LOFE
837 THOMAS WATERSFEILD (M) ½ BAKER

Ditch Side (Shoreditch)
838 IOHN HAZARD ½ Anchor

Doctors' Commons
839 G.H. ¼ AT THE PAVLE HEAD, St Paul £35

Dowgate
840 THO BATT (H) ¼ GROCER AT THE SVGER LOF £32
841 WILL BRANDON (M) ½ AT YE HAVE, man throwing stick at cock, AT IT
842 WILLIAM BROWNE (M) ¼ 1659 Crooked billet
843 WILLIAM BVRGES ½ 1668 AT YE SWAN
844 ANN COX ¼ AT THE KINGS HEAD, bust of Chas. II
845 IAMES CROMEE (½) 1671 THE POPES HEAD. *Octagonal*
846 IOHN DRIVE (H) ½ 1667 AT THE RED LYON
847 WILL GVRNEY (M) ½ AT TALLOW CHANDLERS HALL, Tallowchandlers' Arms
848 IOHN HAKLY (?) ½ 1668 AT THE, tree
(THOMAS HARMAN: See Appendix, after no. 3543)
849 GILBERT HOVGH (A) ¼ AT THE CORNER HOVSE
850 S.P. 1d
851 S.P. 2d
852 S.P. 6d
853 SARAH PAGGAN ¼ 1652
854 IOHN QVARRINGTON ½ 1668 Crescent moon
855 *Michaell Sellers* ¼ 1664 AT YE, St George & dragon

856 IOHN SMITH ½ 1668 AT THE, 3 crowns

Drury Lane

857 IOHN BARNES ½ Sunflower, CHEES-MONGER £22
858 RICHARD BEDWELL ¼ 1656 Bell; 3 birds
859 RICHARD BRIDGMAN (M) ¼ 1659 St George & dragon
860 ANSELL CARTER (A) ½ 1666 AT YE GOLDEN FOX £25
861 IOHN CLARE ½ Cheese-knife
862 ANTHONY CLARKE (E) ½ 1666 AT YE, horseshoe
863 ROBERT DELVKE ¼ AT THE ANGELL £16
864 DAVID DEMONCI (M) ¼ AT YE, helmet
864A MARY DENNIS (½) 1664 Bear chained
865 IOHN DVBAN (M) ½ Arms of France
866 IOHN ELDRIDGE ½ 1667 AT THE, bird and crown £30
867 IOHN GRICE ½ 1668 IRONMONGER AT, 3 sugar-loaves, cross
867A GERMAN HALE ½ 1667 3 doves
868 ANTHONY HALL (W) ¼ Daggers crossed
869 EDWARD HARRISE ½ 1666 MEALMAN £28
870 THOMAS HAYTON ½ Negro's head; crown £30
870A ANTHONY HINE ½ Horse; frying pan over rose and crown
871 ANN HOW ¼ 1657 Fruiterers' Arms
871A IAMES HVTTEN (E) ¼ 1666 Crooked billet with chain
872 IOSEPH INMAN (½) 1668 AT THE TANKERD HOVSE
873 RICHARD IOHNSON (S) ¼ Bell £28
874 WALTER LEE (M) ¼ FORTVNE, Fortune standing in shell
875 ALS MARTIN ¼ 1658 Helmet
876 WILL NEAGVS (I) ½ IN WHITE HORS YARD, BACKER
877 ELIZ NORLEY ½ 1667 AGAINST YE PLEA HOVSE, horn
877A T.P. ¼ 1653. In *lead*
877B IAMES PARTRICH (F) ¼ 165(9?) Wheatsheaf
878 WILLIAM PATTESHALL ½ St George & dragon £32
878A IOHN PEARCE (M) ½ AT YE BLACK BEAR TAVERNE £35
879 T. PEETERS (E) ¼ Crown and anchor
879A C.R. (M) ¼? 'Bull'
879B R.R. (M) ¼ AT THE EAGLE AND CHILD
880 RICHARD RICH ½ Bird on sheaf of corn, CHANGER OF FARTHINGS, figure 2 each side of bird. **Plate 2** £28
880A —— ¼ —— no figure 2's
881 NAT RIKARD (A) ¼ AT THE 3 CRANES
882 I.S. (A) ¼ AT THE SPAROSNEST £32
883 IOHN STON (M) ¼ AT THE GEORG
883A A.T. (M) ¼? 'Blackamore's head'
884 GEORGE THOROWGOOD (F) ½ 1666 3 horses saddled and bridled
885 GABRIELL TRVMAN (T) ¼ Goat
886 THOMAS WILSON ¼ OVER AGAINST THE, sunflower £30
887 WILL WRIGHT ½ YE CORNER OF BLACKMOR STREET, phoenix £32

Duck Lane (Westminster)

888 I.B. (M) ¼ 1665 AT THE BLACK PRINC
889 G.H. (S) ¼ THE MAYDEN HEAD
890 FRANCIS HAVILAND ¼ 1658 Harrow
891 RICHARD SWADDON (M) ¼ 1654 £35

Duke's Place (Aldgate)

892 HENRY BLAGRAVE (S) ¼ 3 tobacco-pipes
893 EDWARD CHEVALL 1d 1668 AT THE LAST
894 IOHN EMPSON (A) ½ 1667 Coronet on beacon, NISI DOMINVS £38
895 THO TIBENHAM ½ 1664 AT YE BLEW, anchor
896 RICHARD TYLER ½ 1668 Ship

Durham Yard (Strand)

897 WILLIAM BRIDGER (E) ½ 1668 AT YE, fleur-de-lis
898 —— (E) ¼ 1663 AT —
899 GABRELL MARDEN (C) ¼ 1659 Arms £28

Eagle Street

900 RICHARD DIXON (M) ½ 1671

East Smithfield

901 W.A. (E) ¼ AT THE 2 DRA MEN £24
902 HVMPHERY ALVEY (M) ¼ AT, Coopers' Arms
903 EDW AVERY ½ IN SWAN ALLY, sword and buckler
904 PETTER BENNT (E) ¼ AT YE, angel
905 RICHARD BERRY (E) ¼ Child's cradle
906 RICHARD BRIGSTOCK (G) ¼ '66 Seven stars
907 NATHANIELL BVRBIDGE ½ 1666 Woolpack
908 R.C. (A) ¼ AT THE 3 SVGAR LOVES £22
909 ANDREAS CASSTART ½ '70 AT YE, castle and 3 keys
910 EDWARD CHAPMAN (M) ¼ Brewers' Arms
911 LAWRANCE CHILD (E) ¼ AT, shepherd and dog
912 RICHARD CHILD ½ 1669 AT YE ROSE
913 O. COPPING, I. NORTH ¼ 1649 Crescent moon, sugar-loaf; Tallowchandlers' Arms £32
914 THO CREAVEN (M) ¼ IN PARRET ALLY, sun
915 R.D. ¼ THE BVLL HEAD TAVERNE
916 IOHN DENNETT ½ Bell £32
917 IOHN DVNTON ½ Shears and crown

918 —— (A) ¼ —
919 A.E. (M) ¼ AT THE OLD PRINC
920 H.G. (S) ¼ AT THE SVGER LOFE, sugar-loaf between cloves
921 T.G. (A) ¼ AT THE WHITE HORSE
922 W.G. (K) ¼ NEXT TO THE RED LION, B.H.
922A W.G. (K) ½? 'Halfe Moon in the Court next to the Redd Lyon'
922B IONATHAN GREENE ½ 1669 AT, St George & dragon
923 C.H. (A) ¼ AT THE STAR TAVERN
924 H.H. (F) ¼ AT YE GOVLDEN DRVM
925 M.H. (E) ¼ AT THE BIRD IN HAND
926 R.H. (E) ¼ AT THE BLACK BARE
927 HVGH HERNE ½ Woolpack?
928 GEORGE HICKES (R) ¼ Swan
928A THOMAS HOWITT (L) ¼ Starfish
928B ARTHER HVNT ½ 1666 Tobacco-roll
929 I. HVTTON, G. IERARD ¼ Half-moon, stick of candles; wheatsheaf £28
930/1 IOHN IELLVS (G) ¼ 7 stars
932 IOHN LANE (I) ¼ AT THE, sun
933 IEFREY LANGHAM (A) ¼ MELEMAN
934 PETER LAVRENCE ¼ Key
935 EDW LEADER (M) ¼ Heart
936 R.M. (E) ¼ AT THE YARNE SHOPP, scales
937 S.M. (P) ¼ AT THE HORSE SHOOE
938 W.M. (R) ¼ NEXT DOR TO THE RED CROS
939 ELEN NORRICE ½ 1669 AT YE COW & CALF
940 G.P. (A) ¼ THE NEW QVEENES HEAD
941 I.P. (M) ¼ '59 NEXT THE MAREMAIDE
942 R.P. (E) ¼ AT THE WHIT CROOS
943 DIXY PAGE ½ 1667 AT YE ANCHOR AND MARRIN
943A WILLIAM PEVERELL (H) ½ 1666 AT THE, ship
944 IOHN REDE (K) ¼ 1658 Men carrying barrel
945 THOMAS ROBERTS ¼ Half-moon, stick of candles; Tallowchandlers' Arms £20
946 SALATHIELL ROLFE ½ AT YE, shepherd and dog
946A P.S. (E) ¼ AT THE 2 DRAMEN
947 WILLIAM SMITH (E) ¼ Swan with chain
948 HENRY STILLEMAN ½ Swan on coronet
949 R.T. (M) ¼ AT THE OLD PRINS, bust of ?Prince Maurice £35
950 W.T. (A) ¼ THE TALLO CHANLER
950A W.T. (E) ¼ 1651 AT THE FLVSHING, ships in harbour
950B W.T. (E) ¼ 1666 ——
951 RICHARD THOMAS ½ BROKER
952 ELIZABETH TICHBVRN ¼ Man making candles
953 H.V. (M) ¼ YE BVLL HEAD TAVERNE
953A SVSANA VAVGHAN ½ 1669
954 I.W. (A) ¼ THE BVLL HEAD TAVERNE
954A I.W. (E) ¼ 'Angel Taverne'
955 I.W. (E) ¼ AT THE LYNN TOWNE
956 IOHN WILLCIMOT (M) ¼ Maltese cross
957 WALTER WILLFORD ½ 1666 Tallowchandlers' Arms £28

Exchange and (Ex)Change Alley

958 THO BROWNING (S) ¼ Bust of Henry VIII £28
959 N.C. (A) ¼ AT THE SVNN TAVERN
960 THOMAS CORDEN (A) ½ AT YE GRASHOPPER
960A W.E. ¼ AT THE GLOBE TAVERN
961 T.H. (I) ¼ AT THE HALFE MOON
962 AVRTHOR STANLEY ½ 1666 View of Exchange £30
963 P.T. (A) ¼ THE ANTWERP TAVERN, view of Antwerp
963A S.W. (M) ¼ 'Globe Tavern'
964 C.Y. (W) ¼ AT THE SHIP TAVERN
965 (1d) *Coffee Tobacco Sherbet tea and Chocolat retal'd* Bust of Sultan Amurath full-face, MORAT etc. £32
966 (1d) — Amurath side-face, MORAT etc. £32
967 (1d) *Coffee Chocolat tea sherbett & tobac sould.* —— £35
968 *The Coffee house* (½) Turk's head, *Morat* £40
969 (½) AT THE GLOBE COFFE HOVSE

?Fairfax Court (Strand)

969A IOHN PETTIE ¼ 1666 Justice with sword and scales; ship

Falconer's Alley

970 IOHN TVRNER ½ 1668 Falcon armed, jessed and belted

Fashion Street (Spitalfields)

971 ROBERT BOSWORTH (A) ½ 1670 Lion
972 RICH NICHOLSON ½ Tobacco-roll £30

Fell Street (Cripplegate)

973 *Beniamin Lawrence ½ ye Success*, ship. *Octagonal*

Fenchurch Street

974 G.A. (A) ¼ AT THE HATCHYT
975 R.B. (E) ¼ THE SHIP TAVERNE
976 W.B. ¼ THE ANGELL TAVERN
977 IOHN BAKER ½ 3 tongues, OYLEMAN £32
978 HENRY BEEBEE ½ AT THE, 3 horsehoes
979 BEN BRANND ¼ GROCER
980 I.C. (M) ¼ AT THE STAR TAVERN
981 EMANVELL CONYERS ¼ Rose
982 EDWARD DAVIS ½ 1669 Piece of ordnance, GROCER
983 TOBIAS DAVIS ½ 1666 Man holding halberd
984 I.G. (A) ¼ AT THE WHEAT SHEFE £32
985 RALPHE GARNER (E) ¼ Wheatsheaf, bird

986 ROGER GROVE (E) ¼ 1663 Bear
987 T.H. (E) ¼ BAKER, YE KINGS ARMES
988 ANN HEATH ¼ AT THE FLOWER DE LVCE
989 W.K. (A) ¼ THE FOVNT(ANE *or* IN) TAVERN £35
989A WILLIAM MALE ½ AT THE, angel
990 IEROM MATHEW (T) ¼ Barrel
990A MARY MILLER ½ AT THE ANGEL
991 IOHN MORRIS ½ AT EXCHENG
992 I.N. (S) ¼ AT THE BLEW BORES HEAD
993 HOMFREY PHARO ½ 1664 Sugar-loaf
994 D.R. (M) ¼ AT THE MITETR £20
995 IAMES RVDGE (C) ¼ Ram's head
996 HENRY SEAWARD ½ 1668 Ram's head
997 AMBROSE SMITH (A) ¼ AT YE, fountain
998 FRANCIS TYLER ½ Woolpack, OYL MAN £24
999 FRANC—(E) ¼—OYL MAN £28
1000 IAMES WAGGONER ½ 1666 Man making candles
1001 IOHN YOVNG ½ Stag's head, STATIONER

Fetter Lane (Fleet Street)
1001A *J.B.* ¼ Falcon
1002 ANN BROWN ¼ '65 Tiger
1003 WILLIAM BVRMAN (I) ¼ Chequers
1003A ANN BYATT ¼ Lion
1003B I.C. ¼ AT, woolpack. In *pb*
1003C PERCIFVLL CHANDLER ½ 1667 AT YE, 3 fleurs-de-lis
1004 ROBERT COTTERILL ¼ Horse, *Cheesmonger*
1005 IOHN COTTON (K) ½ AT YE GOVLDEN LYON
1006 W.D. (E) ¼ Cock within hoop
1007 THOMAS DVTCH (I) ¼ Dog and ball £24
1007A — — (S) ½ 1668 —
1007B T.E. (K) ¼ THE WHITCROS TAVERN
1008 WILLIAM GARRETT (M) ½ 1667 Still and barrel
1009 — GARRET (K) ¼ Still and barrel
1010 HENRY GIBBON ¼ 1650 AT THE FALCON £25
1011 IAMES GOVLD (S) ¼ 1664 Cock in hoop
1011A W.H. ¼ 1657 WHITE CROSSE TAVERN
1011B GEORGE HARPER (M) ¼ Bear chained
1012 IOHN HIGGS (M) ¼ Man making candles
1013 THOMAS HILL ½ 1669 AT THE BLACK PRINCE, Indian holding spear
1013A R.I. (M) ¼ 1657 YE 3 GOVLDEN COCKES
1014 IOHN IVYE ½ 1670 Tree; man making candles
1015 G.L. (P) ¼ MAGPY YARD, falcon, HEEL MAKER
1016 ROBERT LANGBORNE (I) ¼ Falcon
1017 ROBERT LANGLEY (I) ¼ AT THE, falcon
1017A RICHARD NEWNHAM (R) ½ 1668 AT YE, rose
1018 THOMAS POSLET (A) ½ 1667
1019 ROBERT REDWAY ½ AT YE LION £25
1019A C.S. (M) ¼ WHIT CROS, cross with rose
1020 R.S. (M) ¼ AT THE GOOLLDEN LYON TAVERN
1021 IOHN SIMCOE ½ 1666 Sugar-loaf
1022 IOHN SMITH (K) ¼ 1654 Mermaid £18
1023 W.T. (A) ¼ AT THE SVGAR LOAFE
1024 ROBERT TOTHAKER (E) ¼ 1657 MEALMAN £32
1024A ROBERT VAVGHAN (E) ¼ Bear
1025 CLEMENT WILLCOCKS (E) ½ 1666 AT THE WHITE CROSS
1026 MARGRET YELVERTON ½ 1668 AT YE, cock
1026A ¼ Chequers. In *pb*

Field Lane (Holborn Bridge)
1027 PEET BECKFORD (F) ¼ AT THE GVY OF WORICK
1027A R.C. (E) ¼ 1653 AT THE GAY OF WARICK
1028 T.C. ¼ AT THE ROSE
1029 RICHARD EVANS (E) ½ '68 AT YE, rose and crown, TRIPEMAN
1030 GODFREY FOLIAMBE (H) ¼ 1664 COMFITT MAKER
1031 I.G. (A) ¼ AT THE GEORGE

Finch Lane (Cornhill)
1032 PHILLIP CROSSE (A) ½ AT YE IERSY CASTLE
1033 R.H. ¼ 1652 AT THE HORSE SHOOE, horse-shoe £32
1033A R.H. ¼ — — dove within horseshoe
1034 THOMAS OGDEN ¼ AT, bust, with globe and sceptre, TAVERNE
1035 THOMAS STVBS ½ 1669 Bull on horseshoe
1036 ROBERT WILLIAMS (M) ¼ Goat
1036A The Horse Shoe ¼. In *pb*

Finsbury
1037 ELENOR FLEEMIN ¼ Skull
1038 WILLIAM GODBEE 1d 1671 Horse and bell
1038A IANE GREENE ½ 1668 AT YE MANEGD HORSE
1039 IOHN HARCOVRT ½ 1668 AT YE BEL AND BLACK HORSE £30
1040 IOHN MARGROVE ½ 1667 3 fishes
1041 ROBERT NICHOLLS ½ 1668 AT YE DOG AND BEARE
1042 SAM NICKOLLE (E) ¼ Dogs dancing
1043 IOHN RVDVCK (E) ¼ Catherine wheel, WIER DRAWER
1044 WALTER WITHERS (A) ¼ Catherine wheel, THROYSTER

Fish Stocks
1044A IOHN THOMPSON ¼ Weavers' Arms; Fishmongers' Arms

Fleet Bridge
1045 W.B. (D) ¼ 1649 *or* '49 AT THE ROSE TAVERN £24
1046 S. BALL (S) ¼ AT YE BALL
1046A MORRIS BRIGSTOCK (M) ¼ Bricklayers' Arms
1047 THO CARTWRIGHT ¼ GOLDEN, windmill
1048 I.H. (G) ¼ THE KINGS ARMES
1048A GEORGE LEESON ¼ 1659
1049 T.S. (A) ¼ 1658 IN GEORGE YARD, Noah's ark and dove
1050 MATHEW SORE (S) ½ 1668 AT YE ROSE
1051 THO STROVD (I) ¼ AT THE 3, tongues
1052 WILL TOMKINS (W) ¼ 1657 Spread eagle
1053 WILL WALL (M) ¼ Merchant Taylors' Arms, CAPP MAKER £30
1054 HENRY WOODLEY ¼ 1657
1055 EDMOND WRATTEN ½ AT YE, Weavers' Arms

Fleet Ditch
1055A M.B. ¼ 1659 'At the Grammer School'

Fleet Lane
1056 IOH ABBOTT (P) ¼ AT YE BRIDGE, stick of candles
1056A *Henrey Allin* (M) ¼ *at the black lion*
1057 WIL DVGDALE ½ 1663 MEALE MAN, NEAR YE BRIDGE £28
1058 —— ½ 1664 ——
1059 SAMVELL GRIFFETH ¼ King's head, full-face
1060 IOHN HOWKINS (S) ¼
1061 S.O. (A) ¼ 1649 AT THE SHIP £28
1061A THO PINCKARD (M) ¼ '57 Still, barrel below
1062 HENRY WATERFALL (E) ½
1063 HENRY YEO ½ AT THE PLOVGH, 3 halters

Fleet Street and **Conduit**
1064 IOHN ASHTON (L) ¼ 1664 3 kings crowned
1065 E.B. ¼ AT YE THREE HATS
1066 F.B. (E) ½ 1665 Bear, TAVERNE
1067 THO BACKHOVSE ¼ Lion
1068 IOHN BRYAN (I) ½ 1667 Bull's head
1069 —— (M) ¼ 1656 AT THE, bull's head
1070 M.C. (A) ¼ AT THE SHVGER LOFE IN RAM ALLEY
1071 WILL CARTWRIGHT (E) ¼ Dragon
1072 *Robert Cole* ½ 1666 *at the*, man firing cannon, *In Hercules Pillars*
1073 THO CORDIN ½ AT THE WHITE HART, Grocers' Arms
1074 IAMES FARR ½ 1666 Rainbow £32
1075 N. FITZIEFERY (A) ¼ 1656 MILINER
1076 D.G. (S) ¼ AT THE CASTLE TAVERN
1077 ANDREW GRACE ¼ 1657 AT YE IERVSALEM, building
1078 WILLIAM HALSTED ½ AT THE, Grocers' Arms £20
1078A Thomas Hammond ¼?
1079 IOHN HANCOX ½ AT THE GOLDEN, angel, GROCER £30
1080 IO HARWARD ¼ AT 3 NVNS £32
1081 WILLIAM HEALEY (M) ½ 1668 AT THE, boar's head
1082 THOMAS HOPLEY (A) ¼ AT YE, Indian holding bow
1083 *William King* ½ 1664 *att ye*, crown, *In Hercules Pillers* £35
1084 IOHN LEIGH (M) ½ AT YE SINE OF YE TEMPLE
1085 ROBERT MARKHAM (E) 1d 1672 AT THE SEVEN STARS AGAINST ST DVNSTANS CHVRCH
1086 ROB — (E) 1d n.d. AT THE, 7 stars, AGAINST ST DVNSTONS CHVRCH
1087 WILLIAM MART ¼ Bust of queen
1087A —— (K) ½ CHANCEREY LANE END, bust of Henry VIII
1087B THOMAS MAYHEW (P) ¼ AT THE, 3 legs
1088 ED OLDHAM (P) ½ AT YE HERCVLES PILLERS
1089 H.P. ¼ AT 3 SQVIRRELLS
1090 I.P. (K) ¼ AT THE IERVSALEM, view of Jerusalem
1091 P.P. (S) ¼ AT THE HORNE TAVERN
1092 WILL PAGGET (E) ¼ AT THE MITER
1093 RO PEM(BLE *or* ELL) (E) ¼ IN RACKETT COVRT, bodice
1094 I.S. (I) ¼ AT THE INNER TEMPLE GATE, mortar with pestles £32
1095 I.S. (M) ¼ THE HERCVLVS PILLERS £38
1095A W.S. (A) ¼ AT THE RACKET
1096 IOHN SECOL (P) ¼ AT S DVNSTANS CHVRCH £25
1097 THO SEQVENCES ½ IN WHIT LYON COVRT
1097A IOHN SHARPE ¼ Mercers' Arms
1097B WILLIAM SOMMERS (K) ¼ WHITE LION COVRT, stag
1097C SAMVEL SPEED 1d 1667 AT YE FARRS, rainbow, COFFEE HOVS BETWEEN YE TEMPLE GATES
1097D H.T. (S) ¼? 'Cock'
1098 THO TICKNER (D) ¼ AT YE FETHERS
1099 THOMAS TISBERY (C) ¼ 1653 OLE MAN £32

1100 THOMAS TISBERY (C) ¼ Lion, OYL MAN
1101 I (*or* H?).W. (A) ¼ THE HORNE TAVEREN
1102 L.W., H.M. ¼ AT THE KINGS HEAD, bust of Henry VIII
1102A W.W. (M) ¼? 'Blew boare against Ramm Alley'
1103 WILL WARDE 1d AT THE VNICORNE £48
1104 LEWIS WILLSON ½ AT YE, sun, TAVERNE £25
1104A H.Y. (M) ¼ THE BVLL HEAD AT DVNSTONS CHVRCH

Fleet Yard
1105 THOMAS GREENE (M) ½ 1664 AT THE BARLY BROTH

Flemish Churchyard (St Katharine's)
1105A R.B. (E) ¼ THE SHVGER LOFE, sugar-loaf between cloves
1105B IOHN DAVIS (A) ¼ Baker's peels(?) crossed
1106 I.G. (I) ¼ THE LABOR IN VAYNE, women washing negro £28
1107 T.H. (D) ¼ AT THE GOATE £32

Fore Street (Cripplegate)
1108 I.B. ¼ AT THE TOBACO ROVLE
1108A THOMAS CHESHIRE ½ 1669 AT YE KINGS HEAD
1109 ISAAC ELLSWORTH ¼ AT YE, lion
1109A ISRAEL HOBS (M) ½ AT YE GOVDEN LYON
1109B RALPH PADGETT (E) ½ 1666
1110 THOMAS PAPWORTH (E) ¼ Lion £24
1110A IOH READING ¼ MEALMAN, NEXT YE SHIP
1111 CLEMENT SMITH ½ 1666 AT THE, dove
1112 THOMAS WHITE ¼ 1661 Tree £20
1113 SARAH WILLCOCKES ½ 1668 7 stars, MILENER

Foster Lane (Cheapside)
1114 LANCELOTT AYRES (M) ½ AT YE, rose
1115 ELLEN BILLING ½ AT YE DARK, female bust
1116 IOHN CHAMBERS (A) ¼ AT YE, woolpack £20
1117 M.D. (H) ¼ AT THE DAGAR AND PYE. Dagger with magpie on point; 3 cloves, crest above £35
1118 SAMVELL DAWSON ½ 1666 AT YE, nag's head
1119 RICHARD EAST ½ 1664 AT THE, stag's head
1120 IAMES FERNE (S) ¼ Bellows
1121 ROBERT GEARRARD (E) ½ AT YE RED LYON
1122 — GERARD (E) ¼ Lion
1123 MATHEW HOVLT ½ 1665 3 nuns
1124 EDWARD IARVES (I) ½ 1668 AT YE, sun £32
1125 ANTHONY POOLE ½ 1668 Nag's head, IRONMONGR £16
1125A IOHN ROWTHE ¼ Rose. In *pb*
1126 WILLIAM WADE (M) ½ n.d. AT THE DAGGER
1127 —— (M) ¼ 1661 AT, dagger
1128 IOHN WALLIS ¼ Lion on shield

Fox Lane (Ratcliff Highway)
1128A RICHARD LECHFORD (M) ¼ Sugar-loaf

Freeman's Lane
1129 (See *Southwark* 230)

Fresh Wharf (Billingsgate)
1130 T.D. (S) ¼ AT THE 3 MARRINERS £35

Friday Street (Cheapside)
1131 PHILLIP IORDAN (E) ½ 1669 AT YE BLAK BOY £28
1132 H.P. (E) ¼ AT Y WHIT HORS TAVRAN
1133 E.M. (M) ¼ '57 AT YE WHITE HORSE
1133A IOH RADCLIFFE ¼ Sword
1133B EDWARD SANDERS (M) ¼ A CHAND SHOP
1134 ANDREW VINCENT 1d '71 YE COFFEE HOVSE £28
1135 SAM WATSON ½ Hand pouring coffee into cup

Fuller's Rents (Holborn)
1136 WILLIAM BATHE (K) ½ '65 AT YE OXFORD ARMES
1137 *Edward Buttlor* ½ Royal oak
1137A N.E. (H) ¼ AT WARRINGTON BRIDGE
1138 GEORGE RYTHE ½ AT THE, angel crowned £35

Gander Lane
1139 ISABELL HOPPELLTON ½

Garden Alley (Clerkenwell)
1140 IOHN MEDOWCOVRT (E) ¼ IN ST IONESES
1141 IOHN OSBVRNE ½ '67 Fruiterers' Arms

Garlick Hill (Upper Thames Street)
1142 A.B. ¼ THE GRAHOVND TAVERN £20
1143 R.W. (S) ¼ AT THE COOKES ARMES
1144 I.R. ¼ 1655 AT THE HORSHOE

George Yard (Westminster)
1145 WILL ADKINES (A) ½ Queen's bust £22
1146 THOMAS COOKE (M) ¼ 1666 BAKER
1147 WIL OXTON ¼ St George & dragon, BREWER
1148 EDWARD PHIPPS (A) ½ Winged lion

Gibbon Street (Clare Market)
1148A IOHN HOTON (E) ½ Gridiron (?)

Giltspur Street (Newgate)
1149 D.B. ¼ AT THE MAIDEN HEAD
1150 SAMVEL BOTLEY (H) ¼ 3 nuns
1150A WILLIAM CARTER (E) ¼ 1657
1151 THOMAS HARRIS (A) ¼ Grocers' Arms
1152 RICHARD IOHNSON ¼ Mermaid
1152A IAMES MARCH ¼ PASTERY COOK, dolphin
1153 *Richard Patricke* ½ 1664 *att ye*, Turk's head
1154 IAMES STEPHENS ¼ AT YE, 3 nuns £28

Glasshouse Hall (Broad Street)
1155 1d Turk's head; ship, GOD PRESERVE NAVIGATION £38

Golden Lane (Barbican)
1155A IOHN ANDREWS ½ 1666 AT THE, pot of lilies
1156 WILL ARKESDEN (F) ½ 1668 Man and cat
1157 G.B. (W) ¼ AT THE VINE
1158 GEORGE BAISGROVE (I) ½ AT THE PLAY HOVS YARD, actor (?)
1159 WILL BARRETT (V) ½ AT THE BALL BREWHOVSE
1159A I.C. (S) ¼ AT THE HORNES
1160 DANIEL CHERRY (M) ¼ 1656 BREWER
1161 FREEMAN ELLIS (I) ¼ 1656 IN VINE COVRT
1162 SAMVELL EVANS ½ 1666 AT THE, chequers
1162A THOMAS FVLLOVE ½ 1667 AT 2, sugar-loaves
1163 D.G., W.B. ¼ 1657 AT THE BALL
1163A THO GRIMSHAW, THO READ ½ St Christopher carrying Jesus, BRE(?WERS?)
1164 B.H. (M) ¼ 1656 THE ANGEL AND PORTER £35
1165 RICHARD HVCKWELL (E) ¼
1166 THOMAS HVMPHRIES (E) ½ AT YE GEORGE £30
1167 WILLIAM IOHNSON (A) ¼ CHANDLER
1167A THO LOVDE (I) ¼ AT THE, Grocers' Arms
1168 IOHN MAXWELL (I) ¼ Dyers' Arms £28
1169 RICHARD PAWLEY (M) ½ AT THE 3 CVPPS, 3 cups £30
1170 —— (M) ½ — Grocers' Arms
1171 THOMAS PERROT (E) ¼ 1658 Sugar-loaves £22
1171A MARMADVKE ROGERS (E) ¼ Bird and hand
1172 IOHN SHARPE (S) ½ 1666 MEALEMAN £30
1172A ADAM SMITH (R) ¼ 1658 AT THE, globe
1173 *Will Sudbury* ½ AT THE COCK
1174 W.T. (A) ¼ AT THE WHITE SWAN £25
1175 MARGRET TVTTLESHAM ½ 1666 AT YE WORLDS END
1176 S.W. (S) ¼ 1653 AT THE ROBIN HOD
1176A IOHN WEBB (M) ½ 1668 PLAY HOVSE YARD, women drawing bucket from well
1177 WILLIAM WICKINGS ½ AT YE BREW HOVSE, gate with towers
1178 *Samuel Woodcock* (M) ½ 1669 Antlers
1179 ISAAC WYBVRD ½ '66 AT YE, crooked billet

Goodman's Yard (Whitechapel)
1180 WILLIAM BARTON (I) ½ 1667 AT YE RED, lion, shoe above
1180A WILLIAM HOWES (S) ¼ 1667
1181 THOMAS NORRIS (A) ¼ 1667 AT YE, guns crossed
1182 WILLIAM PRESCOTT (I) ½ 1668 AT YE, sugar-loaf
1183 HONEST NED SPENCER (E) ½ 1668 AT YE, tobacco-roll

Goose Lane (Bow)
1184 THO BAILY (E) ½ 1668 Lion
1184A WILLIAM LOVINGE (D) ¼ Lantern

Goswell Street
1185 IOHN BERRY ½ 1666 AT YE, horn
1186 IOHN BIGGS (I) ½ BAKER AT FRENCH ALLY END
1187 WILLIAM BRIANT (M) ½ '68 IN FRENCH ALLEY
1188 M.C. (A) ¼ AT THE BVTCHERS ARMES £30
1189 MICHAEL COPE (M) ½ Butchers' Arms
1190 SARAH CONY ½ 166?
1191 R.F. (A) ¼ AT YE WHIT LOYON
1191A T.G. (P) ¼ AT THE SHVGER LOFE
1192 THOMAS GILLMAN (A) ¼ Spade, CHANDLER
1193 ROBERT HAINES ½ Swan
1193A IACOB WEIGHT (S) ½ Shoe, LETHER CVTTER

Gracechurch Street
1194 IOHN ADAMES ½ 1668 Lion with anchor
1195 THOMAS ALLISON (A) ½ 1668 3 tuns
1196 W.B. (M) ¼ AT THE GEORGE
1197 L. CASHE (A) ¼ AT THE BORS HEAD £28
1198 ROBERT CARTER 1d 1668 AT YE WHITE, lion
1199 IAMES CHVRCHEY ½ 1670 AT THE, bell
1200 T.D., N.B. 1d NEW COFFEE HOVSE HALL, dog £48
1201 I.F. (S) ¼ 1650 THE RED LYON £30
1202 W.H. ¼ '53 BOVRES HEAD
1203 I.K. (E) ¼ THE 3 TVNN TAVERNE £22
1204 SAMVELL KING ¼ Man making candles; St George & dragon
1205 A.P. (M) ¼ AT THE RED LYON

1205A IOHN POTTS ½ 1669 Apothecaries' Arms
1206 IOHN ROMNEY (I) ¼ 1659 Blazing star
1207 DAVID VRRY ½ AT THE, plough
1207A MARTIN VERNON (A) ¼ '57 Plough
1208 T.W. (M) ¼ YE PEWTER PLATTER
1209 MICHAELL WARREN (A) ¼ Horseshoe
1210 WILLIAM WILLIAMS (F) ¼ Lion
1211 ½ AT THE SHIP TAVERNE, monogram

Gravel Lane (Houndsditch)
1212 ED DAY (M) ¼ 1666
1213 BEN STONES (I) ¼ 1666
1214 S. STRVGNELL (K) ¼ Stirrup

Gravel Lane (Ratcliffe Highway)
1215 IOHN ABBOT (E) ¼ Pewter measure
1216 WILLIAM ALLTHRVPP (H) ½ Sugar-loaf
1217 ESDRAS AMEREY ½ Spur
1218 — AMERY (I) ¼ —
1219 A.B. (M) ¼ AT THE SVNN
1220 MATTHEW BRIGGES (C) ¼ Stag
1221 THOMAS CAPON (B) ¼ Wheatsheaf
1222 GEORGE HVNTLEY (A) ¼ CHANLER
1223 T.H. ¼ AT THE SVGAR LOAFE
1223A H.L. ¼? 'Sugar Loafe'
1224 ED MEASEY ½ 1666 Sugar-loaf, COMFIT MAKER
1225 A.S. (M) ¼ AT THE BLEW ANKER
1226 IOHN WARD (A) ¼ AT THE, Commonwealth Arms
1227 I.W. (A) ¼ AT THE STATES ARM, Commonwealth Arms

Gray Friars (Newgate Street)
1228 GEORGE IONES (S) ½ Friar
1229 ANTHONY MOSLYE (E) ½ 1666 Rainbow
1230 RICHARD TART ½ Half-length figure filling coffee-cup £38
1231 FRANCIS SMALLEY (E) ¼ Friar
1232 IAMES WATERS (A) ¼ Friar. **Plate 2** £30

Gray's Inn Gate (Holborn)
1233 C.T. ½ GEORGE YARD, king's bust, full-face
1233A C.T. (E) ¼? 1659 'George Yard'
1234 IOSEPH HIGGS (A) ½ Fleur-de-lis and rose, CONFECTIONER
1235 IOHN IONES ½ Scales
1236 I.K. ¼ 3 fleurs-de-lis; scales
1237 WILLIAM PLACE ½ Man on horseback blowing horn, FOR POST LETTERS
1238 RICH SVTTON ½ AT YE MARMADE
1239 ELEANER WEAVER ½
1239A THO WOLLARSSTONE (M) ½ Carpenters' Arms

Gray's Inn Lane
1240 EDWARD BATTY (M) ¼ AT YE, spread eagle
1241 BENIAMIN BENNET (A) ¼ Cross
1241A FRANCIS BRAKES (M) ¼ '58 Mercers' Arms
1242 I.C. ¼ THE SWAN TAVERN
1242A P.C. (M) ¼ 1659
1243 W.C. (M) ¼ AT THE SWAN TAVERNE £32
1244 IAMES COLE (K) ½ PEICE BROKER
1245 IOHN COX ¼ 1664 AT YE SWAN TAVERN
1246 LYDIA DVNWELL ½ 1668 AT YE, oil-flask
1247 IOHN FARMER ½ Man making candles £30
1248 IOHN GILLMORE ½ Sugar-loaf, TALLOWCHANDLER
1248A THO GILMORE (M) ½ Sugar-loaf, TALLOWCHANDLER
1249 T.H. (M) ¼ THE C. TAVERNE, castle £28
1250 TIMOTHEY HALSEY (S) ¼ Man making candles
1251 THOMAS HODGHES (I) ½ Fleur-de-lis
1252 ROBERT KEMBLE ½ 1667 BAKER AT THE STARR £28
1252A IOHN READING ½ 1666
1253 IGNATIVS ROBINSON (M) ½ AT YE OLD, angel
1254 ROB STOCKTON ½ IN ROSE AND CROWN CORT, greyhound £32
1255 HVMPHREY WIGAN (B) ½ 1663 Harrow £32

Great Eastcheap
1256 I.B. (I) ¼ THE BORES HEAD TAVRNE
1256A THOMAS BVRROWS ½ AT THE, bear chained
1257 WILL CVRTIS ½ AT THE, ship
1258 H.N. ¼ AT THE HARTS HORNES
1259 IOHN SAPCOTT (E) 1d AT YE BORESHED TAVERNE
1260 WILLIAM TEW (B) ½ AT THE, unicorn, MEALMAN

Great Garden (St Katharine's)
1261 WILLIAM CHISHVLL ¼ Malt-shovel; shears
1262 IOHN MAYSEY (A) ¼ AT THE, Vintners' Arms
1263 IOHN WEDELL (K) ¼ AT THE, malt-shovel £30

Great Queen Street (Lincoln's Inn Fields)
1264 THOMAS GREENE (A) ½ AT YE, Queen's bust
1265 THOMAS HILL (F) ½ AT THE, harp
1266 THOMAS TANNER (M) ½ 1668 Horseshoe on anchor
1267 PHILIP WETHERELL (M) ½ '69 Apothecaries' Arms

Great Trinity Lane
1268/9 IOHN CO(X *or* CK) (R) ¼ Prince of Wales' feathers, cock

Green Dragon Court (Cow Lane)
1269A WILL HALL (I) ½ Bell, dragon

Green Yard (Leadenhall Street)
1270 HVMPHREY EEDES ½ AT THE, nag's head £25
1271 NATHANIELL HIGGINS ½ Butchers' Arms
1272 THOMAS LANE (M) ½ Lion
1273 FRANCIS LEONARD ¼ 2-headed eagle
1274 RICHARD NETTELTON ½ Bust of Chas. II £32
1275 WILL PAYNE ½ AT THE BLACK, bull £25
1275A (½?) EXCELLENT COFFIE

Green's Rents (Bride Lane)
1276 EDM IAMES (M) ¼ Sun; hat
1277 —— ¼ Sun; pestle and mortar
1278 W.W. (A) ¼ 3 leopards' faces, A SEACOALE SELLER
1279 WILL WARDE (A) ½ 1666 Weavers' Arms £35

Grocers' Alley (Poultry)
1280 IOSEPH HOWSON ¼ 1663 Founders' Arms; sugar-loaf
1281 THOMAS IOHNSON ½ 1666 Cock

Grub Street (Cripplegate)
1281A Marmaduke Bell ¼?
1281B IAMES BRANCH (E) ¼ 1664
1282 IOHN DAWSON ½ 1666 AT THE, rose and crown
1283 ROGER FOSSETT (M) ¼ Crane
1284 WALTER HADDON (E) ¼ AT THE 5 INKHORNS
1285 WILLIAM HATTON (M) ½ 1666 £32
1286 IOHN HENLEY ½ Pegasus; Innholders' Arms
1287 *George Hide* ¼ Tobacco-roll, half-moon, *Grocer*
1288 ABRAHAM IOHNSON (B) ¼ AT YE FRYING PAN
1289 THOMAS ORGHAR (A) ½ '67 CHANDLER
1290 ROBERT PEARCE ½ 1666 AT THE, arrow
1291 R.P. ¼ '57 AT YE BROADE ARROW
1291A EDWARD POTTER (S) ¼ AT THE CROVN
1292 IAMES ROBBINSON ½ AT YE FLYING HORSE
1293 WILLIAM TENNANT ½ AT YE NAKED BOY
1294 *Thomas Threlkeld* ½ AT YE WHITE LION, *Grocer*
1294A WALTER WINFEILD (F) ½ 1666
1295 SAM WRIGHT ½ 1669 Unicorn and crown, APOTHECARY

Guildhall
1296 THOMAS AILAY (E) ½ 1665 AT THE 3, tuns
1297 W.C. (A) ¼ AT THE WHIT LYON
1298 IOH MEARES (A) ¼ AT THE, lion
1299 ROBERT PEETE ½ 1669 Lion
1300 IOHN STOKES (A) ¼ Vintners' Arms
1301 WIL TILER (A) ¼ AT YE OFF(ICE?) BEHIND THE 3 TVNS
1301A ELIZ TVRNER ¼ BLACK HORS

Gunpowder Alley
1302 THOMAS ASKEW (M) (½) Blacksmiths' Arms

Gun Yard
1303 WILLIAM BLACKIE (E) ¼ Ship's gun £38

Gutter Lane (Cheapside)
1304 THOMAS FITZHVGH 1d AT YE GOLDEN ANCKOR £32
1304A T.G. (M) ¼ AT YE ADAM AND EV
1305 WILL GRAINGE (E) ½ 1669 AT YE HORNES & HORSHOOE
1306 EDWARD HILL (A) ½ AT YE CROWNE AND ANCKER
1307 B.N. (A) ¼ 1653 THE HAMER AND CROVN
1308 IOHN STANDEREN (R) ½ 1666 AT YE HARTS HORNS
1308A I.W. (I) ¼ 1657 WHEATSHEIF 3 PIDGONS
1308B RICHARD WITE (M) ¼ AT THE, Mercers' Arms

Half Moon Court (probably The Hermitage)
588 W.B. (H) ¼ 1648 AT THE HALFE MOON IN THE CORTE £35
589 S.M. (A) ¼ 1658 —

Hammon's Key
1309 ELIZABETH FELLSTED ½ 1667 AT YE, hen and chicks
1310 DOROTHY SELL ½ 1668 AT THE, hen and chicks
1311 IOHN SELL ¼ n.d. AT THE HEN AND CHICKINS, initials S.R.
1311A —— (R) ¼ 1659 —

Harp Alley (Shoreditch)
1312 HENRY BROWNE (I) ½ £25

Harp Lane
1313 RICHARD LOMAX (A) ¼ AT THE STARE, star

Hart Street (Covent Garden)
1314 GEORGE BROWNE ½ AT YE THRE, geese (?)

Harts Horn Court (Golding Lane)
1314A WILL IORDEN ½ Bunch of grapes

Hartshorn Lane (Charing Cross)
1314B W.B. ¼ Fleur-de-lis. In *pb*
1314C IOHN CROSMAN (A) ¼ 1662
1315 T.H. (M) ¼ THE M(AI *or* E)DEN HEAD
1315A RICHARD MAYBANK (M) ½ 1667 AT THE, antlers
1316 HENRY MORRELL (E) ½ 1667 AT YE LIME WHARF £35
1317 I.T. ¼ THE ANCHOR

Hatton Garden, Street and **Wall**
1318 IOHN BALL ½ 1666 AT THE, bust of Chas. II
1319 IOHN BARKER ½ 1668 AT THE BALL AND CAP
1320 FRA BRETT ¼ 1659 Lion
1321 *Joseph Kinge* ½ AT YE CROWN
1322 THOMAS LANE ½ AT THE GOLDEN, rose
1323 *Thomas Lane* ½ AT YE GOLDEN, bell
1324 REBECKA NEGVS ¼ 1657 Cock
1325 EDWARD NVTBY ½ '67 Hand holding bird
1326 — — (D) ¼ LEATHER CVTTER
1327 HENRY PANTON (R) ½ Mercers' Arms
1328 THOMAS PRENCE (M) ½ 3 sugar-loaves £30
1329 — BRENCE (M) ½ —
1330 RICHARD SHIPTON ½ AT THE STILL
1331 IOHN SLATER ½ 1668 AT YE EWE AND LAMBE
1331A MATTHIAS SPENCE (A) ¼ Wall
1332 EDWARD WARING ½ Whip

Haymarket
1333 HENRY BENGOVGH ½ AT YE GOATE AND BALL
1334 IOHN CROSBE (E) ¼ Half-moon (?), MEALEMAN
1335 *Simon Harney* (A) ¼ 1664
1336 NATHANIELL ROBINS ½ 1666 SEA COALE SELLER
1337 IAMES WARREN ½ 1664 Half-moon £32

Heares Street (?)
1337A Thomas Garrard ¼?

Helmet Court (Thames Street)
1338 S.B. (E) ¼ AT THE GEORGE
1339 IOHN HAWARD ½ St George & dragon

Henrietta Street (Covent Garden)
1340 CHARLES MORGAN (S) ½ Angel, GROCER
1341 E.W. (M) ¼ AT YE DOLPHIN

(The) Hermitage (Wapping)
1342 W.A. (E) ¼ KINGS HEAD TAVERNE £32
1343 S.H. (E) ¼ KINGS HEAD TAVERNE
1344 B.H. ¼? 1671 LYME WHARFE
1345 WILL HODGES (H) ½ AT THE GOLDEN, anchor
1346 WILLIAM KEDWARD ½ BAKER
1347 IOHN MAYHEW ½ 1666 GOVLDSMITH £40
1348 IOHN NEWELL ¼ Stick of candles; naked figure with bow and arrow
1348A S.W. (R) ¼ AT THE 3 CASTLES
1348B W.W. (I) ¼ 'Golden Anchor'

Hick's Hall (St John Street)
1348C ROGER NOWTLY ¼ 1668 Arms

High Timber Street (Upper Thames Street)
1349 THO ERWIN (S) ½ Plough, MEALMAN
1350 L.F. (F) ½ 3 tobacco pipes. *Octagonal* £55

High Street (? Aldgate)
1351 G.H. (A) ¼ NEXT TO THE CHEK KER TAVERNE, sugar-loaf £32

Hockley-in-the-Hole (Clerkenwell Green)
1352 WILLIAM COVERLEE (E) ½ Coopers' Arms
1353 GEORGE HALL (M) ¼ AT MOTHER REDCAPS
1354 ANN TRAVER (½) 1667 AT THE, flying horse; Coopers' Arms

Hogg Lane (St Giles's)
1355 IOHN BAVET (A) ¼ Horse and dog £35
1356 WILLIAM CREAKE (M) ¼ 1653
1356A M.G. (B) ¼ '57 AT YE 3 COVLTES

Holborn (Bars, Bridge, Conduit; High Holborn)
1357 DANIELL ANDREW ¼ 1659 Fishmongers' Arms
1358 BENIAMIN ASH ½ AT YE FOVNTA TAVERNE
1359 M.B. (D) ¼ 1658 AT THE THREE CVPS
1360 T.B. ¼ THE HENN AND CHICHENS £18
1361 GILES BAGGS (½) AT THE HAMER AND CROWN
1362 IOHN BALL ½ AT YE KINGS GATE
1363/4 *Samuel Ball* (M) ½ 1668 *at ye Kings gate*
1365 WILLIAM BARRETT ½ 1668 IN HAND YARD, hand
1365A ISAAC BAXTER (S) ½ AT YE ROYAL CEACH (= ketch) IN MIDLE ROW
1366 MATT BAYLY (T) ½ AT YE RED COW £25
1366A IOHN BEALE (H) ¼ St George & dragon, GROCER
1367 IAMES BENNETT (A) ½ Horseshoe b.s., CORNE CHNDLER £30
1368 W. BIRCH (A) ¼ AT THE WHITE HORSE, man on horseback £32
1369 — — (A) ¼ AT THE, horse saddled
1370 WILLIAM BLOW ½ AT YE KINGS ARMES
1371 IANE BOARDMAN ½ NEERE STAPLES INN, boats on river, city behind
1372 *William Boden* ½ 1669 AT YE ROSE & CROWN, *Grocer*

1373 (Probably misreading of 1375)
1374 ELIZABETH BOLD ½ 1666 CASTLE YARD, head
1375 ROBERT BOOTH ¼ Men with staves £30
1376 THO BOSTOCK ½ AT YE GOLDEN BALL
1377 RICHARD BROMFEILD (E) ¼ 1659 Merchant Taylors' Arms
1378 HENRY BROWNE (I) ½ 1659
1379 IOHN BROXON ½ 1668 NEAR KINGS GATE. Mermaid; key
1379A WILLIAM BROXON ¼ Sun; ? mermaid
1380 AVGVS BRYAN (A) ¼ AT THE GEORGE
1381 ANTHONY BVGGIN (M) (½) AT THE GLOBE TAVERN £32
1382 CHARLES BVRFORD (I) ¼ TALLOW CHANDLER
1382A EDWARD BVTLER (M) ¼ 1659 TVRN STILE, hand holding crown
1383 A.C. (E) ¼ *or* (½) AT THE SVN TAVERN £28
1384 T.C. ¼ AT THE MEAREMAID
1385 ROBERT CARTWRIGHT ½ AT THE, head of St Agnes, NEXT THAVIS INN
1386 THO CATTERALL ½ OYLMAN AT YE PID, bull, AGAINST ST ANDREWS CHVRCH
1387 MICHAELL CHAMBERS ½ 1666 IN THE MIDDLE ROW, lion
1387A CHRISTOPHER CHAPEL (D) ¼ Devil in stocks
1388 CLARVEATO ½ 1668 AT THE SVNN TAVERN
1389 EDMOND CLAY ½ '67 AT THE GOLDEN FALCON
1390 WILLIAM COBB ½ Sun
1391 EDW COLE ¼ AT YE CROWNE TAVERNE
1392 RICHARD CORNISH (M) (½) Castle
1392A IOHN COX (M) ½ 1666 AT BLEW, anchor, IN CASTLE YARD
1393 R.D. (E) ¼ AT THE GOVLDEN STILL
1394 WILLIAM DANCER ¼ 1659 Apple-tree
1395 THOMAS DAY ½ AT YE BLACK SWAN
1396 IOHN DEAKES (E) ¼ AT THE STARR
1397 (See *Dorset* 215)
1398 IOHN DRVRY ½ AT YE GOLDEN, horseshoe
1399 —— (A) ¼ AT GILDED. — £32
1400 IOHN DVRHAM ¼ AT THE, crown
1401 I.E. (M) ¼ AT YE KINGS HEAD, merchant's mark
1402 T.E. (T) ¼ AT THE GOVLDEN WREN
1403 HENRY EDWARDS ½ 1668 Dog, CORN CHANDLER
1404 O.F. ¼ THE FETHARES
1405 THOMAS FARMER (E) ½ 1668 BAKER
1406 EDWARD FORMAN ¼ Turnstile
1407 IOHN FRENCH ¼ Haberdashers' Arms
1408 BAPTIST FRERE (S) ¼ 1661 OYLEMAN £32
1409 H.G. (I) ¼ AT THE SWORD AND BALL
1410 IAMES GLADMAN (M) ¼ Bell
1411 THO GRESWELL (I) ¼ IN GEORGE YARD, St George & dragon
1412 DANIELL GREY ½ SALLVTATION TAVERNE
1413 E.H. (E) ¼ QVEENE HEAD TAVERNE, full-face Elizabeth I £35
1414 E.H. (S) ¼ 1651 AT THE GLOBE TAVERN
1415 H.H. (M) ¼ AT THE KINGS HEAD, Jas. I
1416 R.H. (A) (½) AT THE WHITE DRAGON, wyvern crest
1417 T.H. (E) ¼ AT THE TVRNE STILE TAVERN
1418 T.H. (M) ¼ 1648 AT THE 3 TVNS
1419 T.M. (E) ¼ AT THE 3 TVNS
1419A HENRY HANCREST (M) ½ Rose, CONFECTIONER
1420 DAVID HATTON (E) ½ AT YE YORK CITTY IN YE MIDLE ROW. City view. *Octagonal*
1421 NICHOLAS HAWETT (E) ¼ ON HOLBORNE HILL, 3 birds on wheatsheaf, MEALE MAN
1422 IOHN HILL (A) ¼ AT THE SVNN TAVERN
1423 ROBERT HOLMES ½ AT THE FETHARS £30
1424 ROB — ¼ —
1425 GEORGE HOPKINS ½ 1669 VINTNER, NEAR HATEN GARDEN, fountain
1426 IOHN HVNTER (E) ½ 1664 NEXT WARWICK HOVSE
1426A THOMAS HUSSEY ½ AT YE THREE, tuns (on shield), VINTNER
1427 ANTHONEY IOYCE (K) ¼ 3 stags
1428 I.K. ¼ AT THE RAVEN
1429 HENRY KING (M) ¼ Rose and crown
1430 IOHN LAMBE (M) ½ 1667 CONFECTIONER IN CASTLE YARD, lamb
1431 IAMES LATHAM (M) ½ AT THE, eagle and child, AGAINST YE MIDLE ROW
1432 (Probably same as 1449)
1433 RICHARD LLOYD (M) ½ AT THE POAPS HEAD
1434 EDMOND MANFORTH IVNIOR ½ NEXT STAPLE INN, armed man holding spear
1435 SIMON MARSHAL (M) ¼ VINE TAVERNE
1435A THOMAS MASON (S) ¼ 3 tuns
1436 WILL MIDDLEMORE (E) ¼ Prince of Wales' crest, plume
1437 IOHN MVRDOCK (B) ¼ Mercers' Arms
1438 HENRY MVSCVT (E) ½ AT YE COFFE HOVSE AGAINST BROOK HOVSE. *Heart-shape*

1439 DANIELL NALER ¼ 1662 3 stags, TALLOW CHANDLER
1440 IOHN NICHOLLS ½ BAKER OVER AGST KINGSGATE, 3 birds on wheatsheaf
1441 IOHN NORRIS ½ AT THE WEAPON CROSSTAKE TAVERN
1442 RICHARD ODBER ½ AT YE ROYALL CATCH, ship
1443 WILLIAM OVEROND (M) ½ 1668 AT YE, last, IN MIDDLE ROW
1444 T.P. (S) ¼ THE GOLDEN GRIFFIN TAVERN
1445 T.P. (T) ¼ AT THE GOVLDEN FAIKEN £30
1446 FRANCIS PAINE ¼ AT YE, globe
1447 SYMON PANNATE (M) ¼ Butchers' Arms
1447A ROBERT PANTON (M) ¼ Bust of Chas. I
1448 WILL PETTY (M) (½) AT YE YORKE CITTY IN MIDLEROW, view of city
1449 THO PIGETT ½ AT YE GOVLDEN, griffin, TAVERN
1449A GEORGE PVLLMAN (E) ½ 1666 AT YE GOLDEN ANKER
1450 MATHIAS PYTMAN (M) ¼ Soldiers £35
1451 FRANCIS POCHIN (E) ½ AT THE, bust of Eliz. I, TAVERN
1451A C.R. (B) ¼ AT THE 3 ARROWES
1451B T.R. (I) ¼ 165(7?) AT THE GLOBE TAVRN
1451C WALTER RAWLY (F) ¼ 1657
1452 THO RAYNER (E) ¼ AT KINGS GATE
1453 —— (E) ¼ '57— £32
1454 L.S. (C) ¼ 1652 AT THE RED LYON
1455 R.S. (E) ¼ 1653 AT THE FAVLCON
1456 T.S. (E) ¼ THE 3 SVGAR LOVES
1457 T.S. (M) ¼ 1651 AT THE FLEECE TAVERN £28
1458 ANN SAVNDERS ½ 1666 IN CASTLE YARD, hare
1459 EDMVND SCOTT ½ 1669 IN GEORG YARD, head of Duke of York
1460 THO SCVLTHORPE ½ BAKER IN GORGE YARD
1461 WILLIAM SHEERS ¼ 1656 Anchor
1462 RICHARD SHEPHEARD ½ 1666 3 horseshoes, CORNE CHANDLER
1463 RICHARD SHIPTON ½ AT THE STILL £28
1464 HVMPHRY SIMES ¼ 1658 Cavalier's boot; 3 pigeons (?)
1465 BARTHOLOMEW SIMONS ¼ 1654
1466 IOHN SKARVILL (I) ½ 1667 Man holding club, smoking pipe, DESTILLER
1466A GEORG SLATER (I) ½ AT YE BLEW, shoe sole, IN MIDLE ROW
1467 IOHN STEELE (S) ½ AT THE BLEW, boar's head
1468 NATHANI STRATTON (E) ¼ KINGSGATE, rose £32
1468A NATHAN SVTTON (I) ¼ Bell
1469 RICHARD TALBOT (A) ½ 1667 £30
1470 THOMAS TAWNY ½ 1668 AT THE, bust of king
1471 ROBERT THODY ½ 1667 AT YE, bust of Chas. II £28
1472 IOHN TIRION (I) ½ AT YE SVNN
1473 IOHN TVRNER (R) ¼ 1657 Stick of candles within crescent
1474 IOHN TWYNE (R) ¼ TOBACO ROWLE
1474A Roger Underwood ¼? George Yard
1475 RICHARD VNDERWOOD (E) ½ Hare, POVLTERER
1475A I.W. ¼ 1657 '3 torches'
1476 I.W. (H) ¼ THE FLEECE AND AT ROSE £25
1476A T.W. (S) ¼ AT THE BLACKE BOY
1477 RALPH WALEY (M) ¼ AT YE BLACK, bear
1478 GEORGE WALLIS ¼ 3 doves (?) £25
1479 RICH WARD (A) (½) TALLOW CHANDLER
1480 ROBERT WARNER ½ 1667 3 sugar-loaves
1481 IOHN WEEDON (A) ½ 1665 GROCER
1482 WILLIAM WHETSTON (I) ¼ 1653 Black boy £20
1483 GILES WHITHORNE ¼ MEALMAN
1484 ALLAN WILSON (½) AT YE FLECE TAVERN
1485 IOH WRIGHT (M) ¼ AT YE SPVR, MIDLE ROW
1486 MICHAEL(L) WRIGHT (E) ½ '67 AT THE BVLL HEAD
1487 SAVILL WRIGHT (A) ¼ IN COKE ALLEY, cock
1488 ¼ CROWNE & TOBACKO ROLL, Babington family Arms
1489 ½ 1666 Monogram of name William Boden, AT YE; key, GROSCER

Holiday Yard (Ludgate)
1490 THO HOLMES ½ 1669 Lion
1491 NATHA WASTALL (G) ¼ Magpie

Holles Street (Clare Market)
1492 FRANCIS ELLIS (M) ½ 3 tuns £22
1493 THOMAS SHVTTLEWOOD ½ AT YE, ball

Holywell Street (Strand)
1494 W.K. (M) ¼ AT THE 3 LIBARDS HEADS
1495 W.S. ¼ AT THE BODY MAKER, stays £30
1496 ROBER WOODCOKE (E) ¼ Woodcock

Honey Lane Market (Cheapside)
1497 CHA DANVERS (H) ½ 1670 AT YE ANCHOR

Horn Alley (? Aldersgate Street)
1497A Elizabeth Maund ½ 1667 3 morris-dancers

Hosier Lane (Smithfield)
1498 M.F. ¼ GOLDEN WINDMILL
1499 RICHARD LANGHORNE ½ AT YE, 3 crowns
1500 ANDREW LEAKE ½ AT YE, harrow £32
1501 RICHARD NORWOOD ½ 1668 Horse's head, SALTER
1502 I.P. (R) ¼ 1651 AT THE SHVGER LOFE

Houghton Street (Clare Market)
1503 WILLIAM IONAS (A) ½ '68 Ram's head
1504 WILL — (A) ¼ Greyhound's head

Houndsditch
1505 WILLIAM ACTON ¼ 1664 AT YE, ball (?); shears £25
1506 IOHN BARNES ½ 1669 COPER AT YE BLACK BVLL
1507 GILES BLY (B) ½ 1669 5 bells, hand-bell
1508 SARAH CLARKE ½ 1668 Croppers' shears
1509 PETER ESSINGTON ½ 1668 Rose and crown
1510 I.G. (A) ¼ 1649 AT THE BELL
1511 EDMOND GOODALE (A) ¼ AT YE, King's Arms £35
1512 L.H. (E) ¼ AT THE WHIT HORS £32
1513 SARY HIET ¼ AT WOLSAAK
1514 RICHARD HOLBROVGH ½ 1669 Hand holding pen
1515 ROBERT HOLLIS ½ AT YE SEVEN STARRS, 7 stars, hand holding pen
1516 IOH HVDSON (E) ¼ '64 BLACKMORS, head
1517/8 PHILLIP IEMMET (E) ¼ GOLDEN COCK £30
1519 IOHN LANGRISH ¼ Man making candles; flowers £28
1519A IOSE MASTER (I) ½ WINE COOPER
1520 IOHN MERRY (S) ¼ 1663 AT THE, beehive £30
1521 THOMAS NETTLETON ¼ Man making candles; woolpack
1522 E.P. (H) ¼ AT YE PRINCES ARMES
1523 I.P. (A) ¼ 1658 AT THE WHITE HORS
1524 IOHN PALMER (I) ¼ 1667 Anchor
1525 ABRAM PARRAT (I) ¼ 1654 Raven, BROWER
1526 WILLIAM RAWL(IN *or* NI)S ¼ 3 horseshoes; crooked billet £30
1526A THOMAS RAYNIE (A) ½ Sugar-loaf, CONFECTIONER
1527 SAMVELL SHAKMAPELL (E) ¼ 1660 3 birds £32
1528 G.T. (A) ¼ AT THE GOVLDEN LION
1529 M.T. (A) ¼ 1653 AT THE HAND AND PENN
1530 W.T. (M) ¼ 1664 AT THE SHEERS £24
1531 GEO WAPLES (A) ¼ YE OLD BVNCH, bunch of grapes £32
1532 THO WEBB (E) ½ 1669 AT THE NAGS HEAD

Huggin Lane (Wood Street, Cheapside)
1533 ROBERT RAVEN (K) ½ Raven
1534 ANTHONY WASHBVRN ½ 1670 AT YE, Feltmakers' Arms

(The) Inner Temple
1535 HVMFRY TOMLINSON (½) Gateway, MILINER

Ireland Gate (Blackfriars)
1536 WILLIAM OYLE (M) ¼ Shears

Irongate (St Katharine's)
1536A I.C.(M) ¼ 1651 THE FOVNTIN TAVERN
1537 R.C. (M) (½) 1664 Bust of Chas. II, full-face £35
1538 IOHN FREND (E) ¼ 1650 BREWER
1539 I.H. (M) ¼ 1648 AT THE COK
1540 DAVID KEMPE (A) ½ 1668 AT YE COCK. *Octagonal*
1541 —— (A) ½ 1669 —. *Octagonal*
1542 —— (A) ¼ n.d. AT THE, cock
1542A D.K. (A) ¼ 1651 AT THE COK
1543 H.M. (I) ¼ AT THE COK AND BVLL
1543A I.N. ¼?
1544 I.P. (E) ½ Grocers' Arms; monogram of name
1545 IOHN PATSTON (A) ¼ Monograms
1546 W.R. (H) ¼ Cock and bull
1547 IOHN RAMMAGE ½ AT THE, crown
1548 EDMON SMITH ½ Soldier blowing horn £35
1549 R.C. ¼ Bust of Chas. II; Arms

Ironmonger Lane (Cheapside)
1550 RICHARD ASKEW (A) ¼ Coffee-pot
1551 IOHN DAVENPORT ¼ Horse
1552 IAMES DOCKSI (E) ¼ Arms
1553 IOHN SNOW ¼ Bakers' Arms
1554 —— ¼ WHIT BAKER £35

Ivy Lane (Paternoster Row)
1555 SAMVELL GAINSFORD (M) ¼ Woolpack
1556 WILLIAM HEBB (I) ¼ 1664 Plasterers' Arms, initials W.I.B.
1557 WIL OSMAN ¼ Chequers, CORNE CHANLER £35
1558 IOHN SNOOKE (A) ¼ AT THE, sun (?), TAVERN
1559 H.W. (E) ¼ 1652 AT THE 3 CROVNS
1560 ¼ 1663 *att the coffee house*

Jamaica House
1560A W.P. (E) ½ 1668 *At the Jamaicoe House*, man on barrel holding bunch of grapes. *Octagonal*

Jerusalem Alley (Gracechurch Street)
1561 E.A. (E) ¼ View of Jerusalem
1562 I.B. (D) ¼ Boar's head, lemon in mouth
1563 IOHN BLISSE ½ 1666 AT YE BORES HED
1563A LAVRANCE CASH (A) ½ 1667 Boar's head
1564 ED CHENEY (A) ¼ AT THE SWAN
1565 THOMAS FISHER ½ 1666
1566 F.H. ¼ Swan

Jewin Street (Cripplegate)
1567 FRANCIS BACKHOVS ½ AT THE, bolt in tun. *Square*
1568 IOHN CROSS (A) ½ AT YE SVNN & RED CROSS
1569 I.D. (M) ¼ 1659 AT THE SVNN
1570 IOH DOVEFEILD ½ 1666 Sun; clouds
1571 HENRY DVNCOME (S) ¼ Heart and anchor, joined
1572 IOHN GOVLDLEY ½ 1669 CHEESMONGER
1573 GEORGE LANCASTER (A) ½ CARMAN
1574 ANTHONY LAWSON ½ 1666 AT YE WHITE LION
1574A THOMAS LINFORD (H) ½ 1667 Lion
1574B GEORGE LONGMAN (A) ½ SILKMAN
1575 IOHN NEWTON (M) ½ 1667 Saracen's head, GROCER
1576 ROBERT STANHOPP ½ 1667 AT THE, fleur-de-lis
1577 RANDOLPH WATSON ½ Boar's head
1578 THO WHITE (E) ¼ GROCER £32

King Street, Covent Garden
1579 IOHN MASSON (E) ¼ Helmet
1580 N.N. (S) ½ THE WHITE BEARE, bear and chain
1581 N.N. (S) ¼ — —
1582 N.N. (S) ¼ Bear and chain
1583 ANTHONY SMITH (E) ¼ Fox entering gateway

King Street, Wapping
1584 G.B. (M) ¼ AT THE DOLPHIN £25
1585 IOHN GODDIN (K) ¼ Bunch of grapes. **Plate 2** £30
1586 ISBELL IZARD ¼ 3 arrows
1587 R.L. (C) ¼ AT THE TRVMPET

King Street, Westminster
1588 IAM ABRAMS (D) ¼ Griffin's head, GLOVYAR
1589 ALLAN ADLINGTON (K) ½ '67 Goat
1590 S.B. ¼ 3 gloves; fleur-de-lis
1591 R.B. (K) ¼ '57 AT YE BALL
1592 THOMAS BAKER (F) ½ AT THE GREENE, dragon, star
1593 *Edward Barnard ½ at ye Dolphin*, dolphin, arm holding coffee-pot over cup £35
1593A IOHN BA . . . ON (E) ¼ AT Y, eagle
1594 T.C. (I) ¼ THE TRVMPET
1595 T.C. (M) ¼ Hart
1596 WILL CARTER (A) ¼ Angel
1597 WILL CLARKE (E) ¼ Queen's head
1598 C.D. (M) ¼ THE BELL TAVERN £25
1599 IOHN FVRNIS ½ Pewterers' Arms
1599A — — ½. In *pb*
1600 IOHN GASELY (E) ½ AT YE KINGS HED, bust of Chas. II
1601 WILL GEESE (E) ¼ AT YE GEES, 3 geese
1602 IOHN GENEW (F) ½ 1668 AT YE OLD RENISHE WINE HOVSE, vase of flowers
1603 CHISHALL HARMAN (M) ½ WHIT, lion
1604 WIL HAWKINS (H) ¼ Bull's head in coronet £32
1605 IOHN HVDSON ¼ (AT YE *or* IN) BRVRS YARD
1606 PHILLIP HVFFA ½ Bust of Chas. II
1607 SAMVELL IEFFERY (S) ¼
1608 G.B. (E) ¼ 1657 CROS KEYS
1609 THOMAS LEADBETTER (A) ½ 1668 Stag. *Octagonal* £55
1610 *Thomas Luntley* (M) ½ Anchor, *grocer*
1611 E.M. (A) ¼ 1651 Pestles and mortar £32
1612 DANIEL MACKADAM ½ 1668 AT THE, Butchers' Arms
1613 EDMOND MANGELL (A) ¼ Fleur-de-lis
1614 WIDDOW (K) MATHEW ¼ 1659 £22
1615 WILLIAM NETTLETON (K) ¼ Bull's head
1616 I.S. (M) ¼ 3 birds and wheatsheaf
1617 RICHARD SANGAR (M) ½ 1668 Negro's head
1618 THOMAS SHERWOOD (P) ¼ Hart
1619 NATH TVCKER (E) ¼ Unicorn
1620 E.W. (F) ¼ THE SVN TAVERN
1621 G.W. (H) ¼ YE BLACK DOGG, dog, flower
1622 I.W. (D) ¼ THE BORS HEAD £32
1623 IOSEPH WALKER (A) ¼ 1659
1624 THOMAS WALKER (M) ¼ MITER
1625 WILLIAM WATTS ¼ 1650 Cordwainers' Arms £20

Knight Rider Street (Doctor's Commons)
1626 G.G. (H) ¼ 1650 THE SWANN
1627 RICHARD HOBBS (I) ½ 1671 MEALMAN
1628 THOMAS HOVEDEN (A) ¼ Drapers' Arms
1628A R.S. (I) ¼? 'Crowne'

Lad Lane (Cheapside)
1628B E.A. (I) ¼ AT THE S IOHN BAPTIS HEAD
1629 IOHN MARSH ½ 1669 Hand holding coffee-pot over 3 cups on table
1630 S.W. ¼ AT THE SWAN WITH 2 NECKES

Lambeth Hill (Upper Thames Street)
1631 SAMVELL ANDREWES (E) ¼ Cock
1632 W.C. (E) ¼ YE KINGS HEAD TAVERN, full-face bust of Henry VII
1633 I.H. (E) ¼ 1651 AT THE GREEN DRAGON
1634 IOHN STANES ¼ 1664 Sugar-loaf
1635 I.T. (M) ¼ AT THE CASTELL
1636 (See *Surrey* 172A)

Lawrence Lane (Cheapside)
1637 CARLLILE (1d) 1671 Turk's head; monogram of name. **Plate 2** £50
1638 IOHN MASON (M) ¼ AT WHITE, hart
1639 LEONARD PARDE ¼ Stag
1640 I.S. ¼ AT THE CROS(E *or* S) KEYES £35
1640A T.S. (F) ¼ 1651 AT THE CROSSE KEYS

Leadenhall Street, Market and **Gate**
1641 I.A. (I) ¼ AT YE KINGS HEAD, bust of Jas. I with orb and sceptre
1642 I.A. (I) ¼ THE KINGS HEAD TAVERN, Jas. I with cap and feather
1643 IO AMYES (S) ¼ 3 arrows, OYLEMAN
1644 IOHN ALDER (A) ½ 1668 AT YE PEALE, baker's peel £20
1645 H.B. (M) ¼ AT THE GILT FRIIN PAN
1646 I.B. (E) ¼ YE PEWTER POT
1647 M.B. (F) ¼ AT THE PEY TAVERN, magpie within hoop
1648 IOHN BARNARD ¼ Nag's head
1649 IOHN BLAND (E) ¼ 1666 Horseshoe
1650 ROBERT BONNER (A) (½) AT THE, fountain
1651 IONE BRIMECOME ¼ 1658
1652 IOHN BROND ¼ GROCER AT TWO SVGER LOVES, Family Arms
1653 IOHN BROOKES (A) ¼ AT THE, ship
1653A IOHN BVCKLEY (M) ¼ Boar's head
1654 CORNELIVS CAGE (M) ¼ Nag's head
1655 IOHN CARTER ½ 1664 Lion and lamb
1656 ALLICE ONLEEY 1d 1668 AT THE BVLLS HEAD
1656A ELITIA COLE ½ 1667 AT THE, hen and 7 chicks
1657 IOHN CROWE (A) ¼ Anchor
1658 A.O. ¼ 1657 AT (THE *or* YE) BVLL HEAD
1659 GEORGE DANIELL ½ AT THE, Lion and lamb; hands, OB
1660 ROB DAVICE ¼ AT GOLDEN, ball
1660A W.E. (E) ¼ AT THE WHIT HART
1661 THOMAS EAST (M) ¼ 1666 Angel
1661A IANE EVENETT ½ 1666 Lion and lamb
1662 WILL FOSTER (D) ¼ Bull
1663 I.G. (K) ¼ THE NAGS HEAD TAVERN
1664 NATHANIEL(L) GARDNER ½ AT, unicorn, cock
1664A ANTHONY GLOVFER ¼ 1671 POVLTERER
1665 GEORGE GRIGMAN ½ AT THE, boy holding camel by rein
1666 R.H. (E) ¼ AT THE DERY MEAD, woman churning
1667 RIC HANSLOP ¼ AT YE, royal oak
1668 THOMAS HILL ½ 3 sugar-loaves, GROCER
1669 W.I. (S) ¼ AT THE RAVEN
1670 IOHNS ½ NEAR THE EAST INDIA HOVS, Turk's head
1671 IOHN KEMPSTER (E) ¼ Vase with flowers £30
1672 WILL KNOWLES (M) ½ AGST CREDE CH, 3 anchors
1672A H.M. ¼? 'Ironmongers Armes and Frying Pan'
1672B N.M. (A) ¼ AT THE BVRD IN HAND
1673 T.M. (B) ¼ AT THE GROCERS ARMES £28
1674 THO NORTH 1d 1669 AGIN YE EST INDIA HOVS, Turk's head £50
(A.O.: See 1658)
1675 M.O. (E) ¼ AT THE 7 STARS
1675A ROBERT ORPIN ½ AT THE men bowing (Salutation)
1675B IOHN OWEN (I) ½ AT YE OLD KINGS HEAD, bust of Chas. I (?)
1675C T.P. (E) ¼ IN THE HOOPE TAVERN
1676 W.P. (A) ¼ THE NAGS HEAD TAVERN(E)
1677 ROB PALMER ¼ AT WHITE, bell
1678 KATRIN PICK ¼ Butchers' Arms
1679 HEN QVELCH (I) ¼ Barrel, OYLMAN
1680 IOHN ROWLAND ½ 1669 Tallow-chandlers' Arms, MEALMAN
1681 EDWARD RVGBEY ½ 1668 AT THE, angel holding crown £30
1682 P.S. ¼ AT THE, hoop, AND 3, tuns
1683 R.S. (I) ¼ AT THE PLOVGH
1684 THOMAS SAWYER ½ 1668 Woman churning £32
1685 IOHN SCOTT ½ AT THE RED, lion
1686 — — (S) ¼ — —
1687 THOMAS SCOTT ½ AT THE RED, lion
1688 HENRY SMITH ¼ '57 Key £30
1689 PHILLIP STVB(B *or* BS) ½ AT YE HOOP AND 3, tuns
1689A IOHN STVRT (F) ¼ 1651 Stag, fleur-de-lis, MEALMAN
1690 G.T. (A) ¼ AT THE DOGE AND DVCK
1691 G.T. (E) ¼ THE GRAVE MORYES, bust of Prince Maurice of Nassau £30
1691A R.T. (A) ¼ 'Anchor and 2 Sugar loaves'
1692 CRISTOPHER TILLARD (A) ¼ Bust of Jas. I with hat
1693 WILLIAM VASTON ½ Man making candles
1694 IOSEPH VERE ¼ Nag's head
1695 I.W. (E) ¼ AT THE GEORGE £32

1696 I.W. (S) ¼ THE PRINCES ARMES
1697 W.W. (E) ¼ THE GRAVE MORYES
1698 IOHN WADDINGTON (I) ¼ King's Arms within garter and motto
1699 GEORGE WAIT ½ AT THE SIGNE OF YE EAST INDIA HOVSE, 3 saltires
1700 IOSEPH WEBB 1d 1668 Woman spinning, FLEXMAN; Spinning wheel
1700A —— 1d 1668 Spinning wheel b.s., FLEXMAN. In *copper* with centre inset of *brass*
1700B MICHAEL WELCH ½ BY CREEDCHVRCH, hart
1701 IOHN WONDE (E) ¼ Tree
1702 ¼ AT THE GOLDEN HART, heart, A SOPE SHOP £32
1703 ¼ THE BLACK HORSE, merchant's mark

Leather Lane (Holborn)
1704 W.G. (G) ¼ '57 AT YE WINDMILL BREWER

Lilypot Lane (Foster Lane)
1704A WILL COOPER (A) ¼ 1656 Sugar-loaf
1705 IOHN DOWSE (M) ¼ Drapers' Arms

Lime Street
1706 IOHN BIRD ½ 1668 AT PEWTERERS HALL, dove with olive branch
1706A V.P. (I) ¼ 1651 AT YE IACK OF NEWBVY, his bust

Lincoln's Inn Fields
1706B WILL IONES (K) ¼ Royal oak
1706C S.L. (E) ¼ 1657 Crown

Lincoln's Inn Gate
1707 RICHARD WINSPER (M) ¼

Little Britain (Aldersgate Street)
1708 S.A. (M) ¼ 1667 PEWTERER
1709 ZACHARY ALLEN (A) ¼ Still
1710 IOHN BERRIDGE (M) (½) '67 AT YE GOVLDE STILL
1711 IOHN COLLINES ¼ Breastplate
1712 THOMAS GASLEY ½ 1666 Bunch of grapes, GROCER
1713 H.H. (K) ¼ AT THE HARTE & BAL
1714 RAPHA HARFORD ¼ '58 Book; heart
1715 HENRY HAYNES ½ 1666
1716 RALPH HOLLAND (D) ¼ Arm holding anchor, crown above
1717 W.I. (E) ¼ 1650 AT THE GOVLDEN GLOBE
1718 DANIELL LANE ½ AT THE goat
1718A HESTER MICHELL ¼ 1656 Bunch of grapes
1718B DANIELL MIDWINTER (A) ½ Leathersellers' Arms, TALLOW CHANDLER
1719 R.P. (E) ¼ AT THE RED CROSE
1720 IOHN PAPWORTH ½ 1667 Horse
1721 GABRIELL PVLTENEY (M) ¼ '57 Crown
1722 FRANCIS TAYLOR (A) ¼ Angels supporting crown
1723 SAMVELL TORSHELL (D) ½ '67 GROCER
1724 —— (D) ¼ 1667 —
1725 THO WHITTINGHAM (B) ¼
1726 ROBERT WILMER (M) ¼ '63 Part of shoe, LETHER CVTTER £35
1727 DANIELL WRAY (I) ¼ '61 *Soap boyler*

Little Eastcheap
1728 IOHN BEALE (A) ¼ 1664 Crown
1729 EMANVELL GREEN (P) ½ AT YE KINGS HEAD, full face bust of Chas. II
1730 SAMVELL HALLVM (A) ¼ Crown
1731 I.R. (A) ¼ AT THE GLOBE
1732 IOHN ROLSTON (A) ¼ AT YE, Prince of Wales' crest
1733 RICH SESSIONS (A) ½ 1669 AT YE ANKER
1734 I.V. (S) ¼ AT THE RED LION

Little Queen Street
1735 A.T. (E) ¼ 1658 AT YE CORNER HOVSE

Little St Bartholomew's
1735A NOAH BANCKES ½ 1661 CHEESMONGR
1736 WILL BOLTON (A) ¼ AT THE, cock
1737 ROBERT DAWSON (I) ½ AT YE COCK
1738 S.I. ¼ 1652 THE COCKE
1739 ROBERT PEACOCK ½ AT YE, crescent; peacock

Little Tower Hill
1740 ROB ATKINSON (M) ¼ AT THE, stocking
1741 FRANCIS BVLFELL (A) ½ 1666 Fleece, sugar-loaf
1742 WILL BVRROVGH (M) ¼ Tobacco-roll between sugar-loaves
1743 WILLIAM CARTAR (R) ½ AT THE, lion
1744 RICHARD CLIFFON (S) ½
1745 I.D. ¼ 1656 AT THE BELL
1746 ELIZABETH GEOAGE ¼ AT, sugar-loaf
1747 IO IAKEMAN (K) ¼ Triskelis, YARNE SELLER
1748 THOMAS IEWETT ½ Hand holding pen
1748A WILLIAM MALLETR (K) ¼ 7 stars
1749 PHILLIP MAYFEILD ½ Boar
1749A SAMVELL MOREHOVSE (A) ½ Angel
1750 THOMAS PARKER ½ Coopers' Arms

Lolesworth Lane (? Spitalfields)
1751 THOMAS SPICAR (H) ¼ 1657

Lombard Street
1752 RICH GOODALL (A) ½ 3 swans
1753 T.H. (M) ½ AT YE SALVTATION £35
1754 ROBERT IONES ¼ AT THE PLOW
1755 IOHN ROLFE ¼ Hand holding glove

1756 I.S. (M) ¼ THE CARDENALLS CAP TAVERN
1757 WILLIAM SMITH ½ 1666 Royal oak
1758 (1d) AT YE 6 BELLS IN DOVE COVRT, 6 bells; dove with olive-branch £38

London Bridge
1759 T.C. (A) ¼ AT THE WHIT LYON
1759A NICHOLAS HARRISON ½ 1666 AT BLAK, bull
1760 EDWARD MVNS ½ 1668 AT THE SVGER LOAF £28
1761 C. TVNS (S) ¼ AT THE 3 BIBLES
1762 GEORGE WALLKER (A) ½ 1667 Rose
1763 IOH WELD ¼ '57 AT YE LYON

London Wall
1763A OLIVER ALIN (I) ¼ AT YE SLEDG, sledge drawn by horses passing building
1764 IO BENION ½ IN WHIT HORS YRD, NEER MORGAT, horse £28
1764A RANDOLPH BVCKLY ½ 1669 AT YE BALL
1765 HENRY CRANFIE (E) ¼ AT YE MAID HEAD
1766 GANNELL GANNELL (E) ¼ 1655 Fox, goose in mouth
1767 CHARLES GRIFFIN ½ 1668 NEARE BROAD STREETE, griffin
1768 GEORGE ITHELL ½ NEAR BROAD-STREET, Blacksmiths' Arms
1769 W.K. (E) ¼ 3 TVN ALLEY, bust of Jas. I
1770 THO LEE (M) ½ NEARE THE POST-ERNE GATE, cropper's shears
1771 T.S. (A) ¼ 1657 THE BELL, VINTENER
1772 HESTER TROTTER ¼ '67 AT YE, horse
1773 RICH TVCKER ½ 1666 NEAR CARPENTERS HALL, crown, D.O. above
1773A RICHARD WALLTER (½) AGAINST MOORGATE, Mercers' Arms; Clothworkers' Arms
1774 EDWARD WARING ½ Whip

Long Acre
1775 ROBERT ABBITS (A) ¼ 1659 Stocking
1776 IOHN ASKVGH (M) ¼ 1659 Man making candles £30
1777 ROBERT AVNGEIR (S) ¼ Griffin
1778 IAMES AYLARD ½ AT YE GLOBE TAVERN
1779 — AYLORD (E) ¼ AT THE, globe
1780 IAMES BARBEY (A) ¼ 1663 AT THE, 7 stars
1781 IOHN BARNES ½ 1664 AT THE VINE, WINE COOPER
1781A THOMAS BARNES (E) ½ 1666 Salters' Arms, OYLEMAN
1781B ANDREW BRODHVRST (M) ½ 1667 MILLINER
1782 MARGERET BROOKES ½ 1670 MILLINARE
1783 MARTHA CHVRCHER (M) ½ 1667
1784 —— (M) ¼ 1663
1784A M.C. (M) ¼ 1663 Kings' Arms, THE CROWN COMMANDS
1785 GABRIELL CRANNIDGE ½ 1666 Man making candles £20
1786 G.D. (D) ¼ 1656 AT THE SVGAR LOAFE £30
1786A IOHN DICKIT (M) ½ 1667 AT THE MAIDENHEAD
1787 WILL EDMONDS (M) ½ '67 AT YE GLOBE TAVERN
1788 RALPH ELRINGTON ¼ 1657 Still £28
1789 IOHN FOY (P) ¼ AT THE BLACK RAVEN
1790 R.H. AND MORGAN HIND ½ Hind, BREWERS
1790A RICHARD HARRISON (A) ¼ AT THE GLOAB
1790B ROBERT HIDE (M) ½ '67 AT THE CASTLE
1791 IOHN HORNE (I) ¼ Sheep standing on bone (?)
1792 HVGH IACKSON ½ AT THE GOLDEN LYON
1793 WILL IONES ½ 1664 AT THE GOVLDEN COCK
1794 DAVID LVMSDEN (D) ½ Kings' Arms
1795 BENIAMIN MASON (E) ½ 1666 £30
1795A WILL MERREDETH (E) ¼ 1664 AT YE, peacock
1796 WILLIAM NALER (E) ¼ 1654 AT THE VIRGINY
1796A ROBERT PARSONS (H) ½ 1666 MEALEMAN
1797 ISACK POSTE (E) ¼ YE WOSTED SHOP
1798 GEORGE PRIST (D) ¼ 1663 A SEMSTRS SHOP
1799 WILLIAM RALPH ½ 1667 GROCER £20
1800 WILL RALPHE (I) ¼ 1656 — £22
1801 RICHARD REDHILL (M) ¼ Man making candles £22
1802 IOHN SARES (I) ½ 1664 Harp, harrow £32
1803 ROBERT SKIPWITH (M) ½ 1666 Bunch of grapes
1804 EDWARD STANTON ¼ OYLEMAN
1805 IOHN WATSON (M) ½ 1669
1806 WILLIAM WHITEHALL (M) ¼ 1660 Cheese-knife
1806A ¼ SPRING WATER AT THE CONDVIT. Man carrying buckets; horse and cart with barrel

Long Alley (Finsbury)
1807 WILL ANDREWS (M) ¼ AT THE CROKED BILET
1808 MARY FVLWOOD ¼ Blazing star
1809 IOHN GREENHILL ½ 1671 3 tuns
1810 LAWRENCE IEFFERES ½ BAKER
1811 THO LEAWOOD (M) ½ Baker's peel, scales, BAKER
1812 W.M. (T) ¼ AT THE 3 HORS SHOWES

Long Ditch (Westminster)
1813 IOH DEVERELL (M) ¼ King's Arms
1814 IAMES LABAR (E) ¼ AT THE GRIFIN
1815 IOHN THROWLEY ¼ 1656 Harrow £30

Long Lane (Smithfield)
1816 IOHN BRADBVRY (I) ¼ Sun, crescent moon
1817 THO BVRR ¼ AT GREENE, dragon
1818 RAINBIRD DVGDALE ½ Wheatsheaf, 3 birds
1819 IOHN HAMMOND (A) ½ 1668 IN RAINEBOW COART
1820 HENRY HARWOOD (P) ½ 1667 Bull
1821 RICHARD HIGGINGS (I) ¼ '58 Lion
1822 I.M. (M) ¼ '57 AT WHITINGTONS CAT
1823 MOSES MAYHEW (E) ½ 1667 Stag
1824 CHRISTOPHER MILLER (E) ¼ YE HORNES
1825 THOMAS MORTON (M) ½ 1666 Grasshopper
1825A —— (M) ¼ n.d. AT THE GRASHOPER
1826 I.S. (S) ¼ 1656 AT THE ACORNE
1827 ROGER SEYMOR (E) ¼ Bell
1828 MATHIAS SHELDRAKE ¼ Sugar-loaf; tobacco-roll
1829 ROBART WILDBORE (M) ¼ AT YE, harp
1830 THOMAS YOVNG ½ 1668 AT THE HARP
1831 ¼ GOLDEN BALL, MEALE SHOPP

Lothbury
1832 EDWARD BRISCO (½) 1670 3 greyhounds
1833 THOMAS BROWNE (M) (½) OYLE SHOP, Weavers' Arms
1833A WILL CARTER (M) ½ 1669 COOKE AT THE MARTI NEECO
1834 IOH DOEGOOD (M) ¼ FOVNDERS ALLEY, bottle with handle
1835 R.R. (A) ¼ 1659 AT THE TVRKES HEAD
1836 IOHN ROSE (E) (½) IN TOKEN HOVS YARD, A CLOTH WORKER, sugar-loaf. **Plate 2** £35
1837 I.S. (½) AT THE WEST CVNTRY COFFE HOVSE £35
1838 AVERY TERRILL (M) ½ '69 COOKE AT YE GOLDEN FAVLCON
1839 IOHN VARNY (M) ¼ 1671 AT THE, bunch of grapes. *Octagonal*
1839A — VARNEY (M) ¼ '63 bunch of grapes
1840 MICHAEL WOLRICH ¼ 1656 Prince of Wales' crest £28

Love Lane (Billingsgate)
1841 W.L. (I) ¼ '57 KINGS HEAD POST HOVSE, bust of Jas. I
1842 IOHN MVRDINE (M) ¼ 1666 TALLOW CHANLER
1842A IOHN WHITTING ½ AT YE, bust of Jas. I; Apothecaries' Arms

Ludgate
1843 IOHN BENETT ½ GROCER
1843A T.E. (M) ¼ 'Hand and mouth'
1844 S.G. (H) ¼ 1652 THE MERMAIDE TAVERN
1845 I.H. (E) ¼ AT THE S IOHNS HEAD TAVERN £32
1846 RICHARD HAWKINS (½) AT THE, 3 tuns, TAVERNE £28
1847 THO HEATH (E) ½ AT THE GLOBE
1848 THOMAS HOLMDEN (A) ¼ Stag £30
1849 ANDREW HVNTER ½ 1665 Swan and ball
1850 M.N. (M) ¼ 1649 AT THE S IOHNS HEAD
1850A R.O. (M) ¼ AT THE MADEN HEAD, GROCER
1851 G.P. (G) ¼ AT THE DOGG TAVERN £32
1852 HENRY PAINE (A) ¼ AT THE DOGG TAVERN
1853 IOHN PINSON (1d) AT THE BELL SAVIGG. Turk's head; chequers £48
1854 THOMAS STROVD 1d COFFEE HOVSE, Turk's head; view of Ludgate
1855 IOSEPH SYLVESTER (E) ½ 1670 AT THE, frying-pan, IRONMONGER
1856 HENRY YOVNG (M) ¼ AT YE, Indian holding bow and arrow

Lutener Lane (later Charles Street, Drury Lane)
1857 IEAMS BEDFORD (P) ½ 1669 CHANDLER
1857A R.H. (E) ¼ 'Rose'
1858 THO IACKSON (I) ¼ AT YE, crescent moon

Lyon's Inn (Newcastle Street, Strand)
1859 R.S. ¼ AT THE WHITE HORSE

Maiden Lane (Covent Garden)
1860 ALLCOCK (½) Pegasus within wreath; Grocers' Arms, MEALEMAN
1861 IOHN ALLCOCK (E) ¼ MEALE MAN
1862 GEORGE BARTMAKER (E) ½ 1668 AT CAMDEN HOVSE, view of house
1863 IOHN DVCKWORTH (M) ¼ Legging
1864 T.K. (E) ¼ AT THE COCK £35
1865 ROBERT PACKWOOD ½ Heart
1865A IO SEDGWICK (M) ½ 1667 AT YE SIDER HOVSE, family Arms

Mark Lane (Fenchurch Street)
1866 IOSEPH ADAMS (E) ¼ AT YE, blazing star
1867 T.B. (P) ¼ AT THE FOX AND GOOSE £35
1868 WILLIAM CHAPMAN ½ 1669 AT YE STAR, star
1869 — — ¼ — Star
1869A DANIELL MILES ½ 1666 Coffee-pot
1870 MARGRY MOS ¼ 1653 Horse
1871 WILLIAM PARKAR (K) ½ 1669 3 tuns, OYLE MAN
1872 W. PAYNE (M) ¼ 1651 TAL CHANDLER
1873 WILLIAM PAYNE (C) ½ 1667 Man making candles
1873A THOMAS SHARP (I) ¼ 1666 AT YE, rose
1874 ALEXANDER STRINGER (M) ¼ 1666 Clothworkers' Arms
1875 IOSEPH TAYLOR ½ IN BLANCH APPLETON COVRT, Coopers' Arms

Market Place
(See St James's Market)

Market Street
1876 (See note to *Beds.* 73A)
1877/8 (Probably *Beds.* 73A, 73B)

Marlow's Rents
1879 A.B. ¼ THE CARPENTERS ARMS £35

Mary Maudlin's (Old Fish Street)
1880 EDWARD DODSON (M) ¼ Pitcher
1881 ROGER MIDLETON (E) ¼ 1664 Brewers' Arms
1882 HENRY RICHARDSON ½ AT THE, bear (?). *Octagonal*
1883 FRANCES WOOD ½ 1668 AT THE, David playing harp
1884 FRANCIS — (I) ¼ AT YE, Arms of Commonwealth

Maypole Alley
1885 GEORGE MEDDENS (E) ¼ 1663 COOK

Mercers' Street (Long Acre)
1886 THOMAS LVCKE (M) ½ 1666 BREWER £28
1887 STEPHEN TAGG ½ 1667 AT YE ANGELL

Mile End
1888 THOMAS ALLIN ½ 1668 AT YE, cock
1889 IOSEPH ALMOND (I) ½ 1668 AT YE SHIP £32
1890 IOHN AMPS ½ Grocers' Arms £32
1891 HENRY BARTLETT (E) ¼ 1658 Dolphin
1892 MATHEW BROWNE ½ 1667 Bakers' Arms
1893 WILLIAM CROSS (A) ¼ 1667 King's Arms
1894 ROGER NICKOLLES (A) ¼ AT YE OLD ROSE, Weavers' Arms
1894A — NICHOLS ¼ AT YE OVLD ROSE. —
1895 GEORGE SMITH (M) ¼ 1658 WEAVER £32
1896 WILLIAM STEWARD ½ 1667 Royal oak

Milford Lane (Strand)
1897 RICHARD ACTON ½ 1665 BY ST CLEMENTS CHVRCH, MARCHAL
1898 IOHN BVRGESSE ½ 1666 COALMAN £38
1899 ROBERT FARMER ½ 1668 Horseshoe, COLEMAN
1900 I.H. (A) ¼ AT THE GRAYHOVNDE

Milk Street (Cheapside)
1900A ROB BREARELEY (A) ¼ Ship
1901 ROBERT GARDINER (A) ¼ Moon, 7 stars
1901A ISACK HODGKIN (E) ¼ Sun
1902 W.I. (S) ¼ AT THE BOARES HEAD £30
1903 RICH(ARD) LVKEY ¼ Pump; Arms
1904 WILLIAM RIXON ½ AT THE RED COW £30
1904A IAMES ROSSE ¼ THE GOLDEN PLOVGH, Grocers' Arms

Millbank (Westminster)
1905 I.A. (A) ¼ Men carrying barrel
1906 RALPH FANCOTT (H) ¼ Robin Hood and Little John, WOOD MONGER
1907 RICHARD FISHER (S) ¼ Crooked billet, WOOD MONGER
1908 THOMAS MASCALL ½ Scales £35
1909 IOHN STANDBROOKE (E) ½ LYME MAN. **Plate 2** £35

(The) Minories (Aldgate)
1910 A.A. (I) ¼ 1651 AT THE TRVMPET
1910A C.A. (R) ¼ 'Fountaine Taverne'
1910B M.B. ¼ 3 tuns, THE PORTER AND CARR
1911 MARMADVKE BLVDDER (S) ¼ 1666 Indian holding arrow
1912 THOMAS BROWNE ¼ '59 Man driving horse and cart, WELCOM LVCK
1913 RICH BVRTON (M) ¼ 1666 AT THE, ship
1914 ADAM CROMBTON (E) ½ 1668 AT YE, windmill
1915 RICHARD CHVBB (S) ½ 1666 Ship £30
1916 RICHARD CLARKE (F) ½ 1668 AT THE, swan £28
1917 GEORGE COX (E) ¼ AT THE 2 COKS, man making candles
1917A HENRY COX (A) ¼ Horse
1918 THOMAS COX (I) ¼ St George & dragon, cock above
1919 MARY CRAGGE ¼ A MEALE SHOP
1920 R.E. (E) ¼ Sun, MEALEMAN
1921 I.F. (S) ¼ AT THE GOVLDEN ANKER
1922 TIMOTHY GARBERT ½ 1666 AT THE, fountain
1922A RAFE GILLAM (A) ¼ 1656 BAKER
1923 ARTHVR HANCOCK (A) ¼ Bell and wheel £35
1924 THO HANSON ¼ AT THE, still, AND SWAN
1925 RICHARD HARRIS (R) ½ AT YE SEV, sieve

1926 IOHN HERBERT (1d) AT THE, mortar and pestles £50
1927 IOHN HILL ½ 1669 AT YE GOVLDEN LION
1927A EDWARD HOVLT (M) ¼ Man on hobby horse
1928 CHRISTOPHER KEAINE (½) 1669 Fleur-de-lis and ball; monogram
1929 WILL KNIGHT (S) ¼ 1666 AT YE RED, lion
1930 G.L., I.C. ¼ YE BAGE OF NALES
1931 I.M. (E) ¼ AT THE HAND AND PEN
1932 L.M. (A) ¼ AT THE SWANN TAVERN
1932A MARY MINCHING 1d 1671 Woman spinning
1932B I.P. (A) ¼ 'Cammell'
1933 I.P. (S) ¼ 1655 AT THE 2 SMITHES. **Plate 2**
1934 W.P. (I) ¼ AT THE CAMMELL
1935 THOMAS PEIRSON (L) ¼ 1655 Man making candles £25
1936 CLEMENT PLVMSTED ½ Monogram of name, IRONMONGER
1937 IOHN ROPER ¼ Kings' Arms, IRONMONGER
1937A WILLIAM ROWSE (S) ¼ 1666 AT YE, anchor
1938 I.S. (A) ¼ 1659 AT THE PIY, magpie; muskets
1939 R.S. (A) ¼ 1653 AT HAWDON HOVS, 3 leopards' heads
1940 HENRY SADD, A COFFE HALFE PENNY, '66 Crowned rose; Turk's head £35
1941 EDWARD SAE (M) ¼ AT THE, lion
1942 THOMAS SANDON (M) ¼ 1667 AT YE, eagle and child
1942A HENRY SMITH (M) ¼ Merchant Taylors' Arms
1943 IOHN SMITH (M) ¼ MEALE MAN £30
1944 WILLIAM SMITH (S) ¼ 1659 Angel holding scroll
1945 ELENOR STONE ½ Name in monogram
1946 HENRY STONE (S) ¼ 1656 Eagle and child
1947 H.T. (I) ¼ AT THE 3 SVGAR LOFES
1948 MARY TAYLOR ¼ Unicorn
1949 ANTHONY TREVILLYON (S) ¼ Tobacco-roll
1950 THO WASHBOVRNE ¼ '6–(?) AT, 3 crowns; Grocers' Arms

Monkwell or **Mugwell Street** (Cripplegate)
1951 IACOB HICKMAN (S) ¼ 1660 AT WHITE, horse
1952 MOVNTAGVE MICHELL (A) ½

Monmouth Street
1952A RICH FRANCKES (A) ½ 1669 MEAL MAN AT YE, wheatsheaf

Moorfields
1952B EDWA BEECH (A) ¼ AT Y DVNKIRK, castle, NEW GATE
1953 *Isabella Bennett* ½ 1668 OVER AGAINST YE POPES HEAD
1954 SIMON BOND (A) ¼ 1666 AT THE GREEN HOVSE
1955 WILL BROWNLEY ½ 1666 AT THE, star £32
1956 G.C. ¼ AT THE BEARE £24
1957/8 H.C. (S) ¼ NEARE (BADLAM GAT *or* BEDLAM GATE), angel £20
1959 FRANCIS GIBSON ½ AT YE HERCVLES
1960 EDWARD GRANTE ½ NEARE YE BEARE, tobacco-roll
1960A C.H. (K) ¼ AT THE GOLDEN HIND, antelope
1961 R.H. (T) ½ THE CROSS DAGERS, horn
1961A IOHN HARECOVRT (M) ½ Cock
1962 MARY LACY ½ 1667 Female crest
1963 RICHARD MARTEN (M) ¼ Pope's bust, with triple crown
1963A THO MVDD ¼ Sugar-loaf with (?) upturned horseshoe; hen with chicks. GROCER. In *iron*(?)
1963B ¼ R.W. AT THE COK; G.C., bear
1964 HENRY YOVNG 1d NEARE BEDLAM GATE, still

Moorgate
1965 IOHN BAKER ½ 1667 AT YE WHITE SWAN
1966 IOHN CLARKE (B) ½ GROCER AT THE, boar, sugar-loaf
1967 OLIVER HOLMES (A) ¼ AT, wild boar £35
1968 PELHAM MORE ½ AT YE SONN & MORES HEAD £32
1969 I.N. (E) ¼ AT THE WEAVERS ARMES
1969A WILL PLIMPTON ½ 1669 Crossed keys; initials W.P., M.P.
1970 IOHN RANDALL (M) ½ 1666 View of Moorgate b.s. £28

Moor Lane (Cripplegate)
1971 P.C. (M) ¼ 1653 AT THE 3 FLOWER DE LVC
1972 IOHN CHAPMAN ½ 1671 AT THE, horse and cart
1973 IOHN DEARMER (S) ¼ 1664 AT YE, horseshoe
1973A WILLIAM LVND ½ Carpenters' Arms; David with harp
1974 ALEXANDER RVD ½ IN MAIDEN HEAD YARD, Plasterers' Arms
1974A WILLIAM SANDS ¼? AT YE, 3 pigeons
1975 WILL STOKES (E) ¼ BELL YARD, hammer crowned

1976 I.T. (A) ¼ IN MAIDENHEAD ALY, Coopers' Arms

Mouldmakers' Row (St Martin's Le Grand)
1976A I.K. (E) ¼?

Mutton Lane (Clerkenwell Green)
1977 EDWARD VSHER ½ 3 tuns; initials I.M.R.
1977A —— (F) ½ —
1978 IOHN GARDINER (A) ½ 1668 AT THE, crooked billet and shovel

New Cheapside (Moorfields)
1979 IOHN ANNISON ½ '68 AT YE WHALE BON £35
1980 HENRY AYRES ½ 3 lions
1981 ROB EWIN ½ A CAKE HOVSE, Prince of Wales' crest
1982 NEVELL HARWAR ¼ AT YE CIVET, cat, BAL & POWDER SHOP
1983 MYLES LETHERBARROW ½ 1670 Hart
1984 HENRY SOVCH (A) ½ 1668 Catherine-wheel
1985 SAMVELL WING ½ '67 AT YE FRYING PAN

New Crane (Wapping)
1986 WILLIAM DVSELL (M) ½ '68 AT THE, bust of queen with orb and sceptre
1987 H.G. ¼ AT THE GRENE DRAGON £35
1988 IOHN HEYWOOD ½ Wheatsheaf
1989 —— (E) ¼ 1664 —
1989A IOHN KNIGHT (E) ¼ Sugar-loaf
1990 CLEMT NIXON (B) ¼ Bunch of grapes
1991 EDWARD PRATT ½ Spread eagle £35
1992 I.R. (E) ¼ Wheatsheaf, MEAL MAN
1993 I.R. (M) ¼ AT THE QVEENS HED, bust of Eliz. I
1994 IOSEPH STENT ½ 1666 AT THE, wheatsheaf
1995 IA WATERS (E) ¼ 3 sugar-loaves joined, CHANDLER

New Exchange (Strand)
1996 ANNE CLARKE ½ AT THE, 3 crowns £35
1997 DANIELL CLARKE ½ AT THE, griffin £18
1998 THOMAZIN DVKE ½ Cordwainers' Arms
1999 IOHN HALL (A) ¼ Sun £25
1999A R.H. (P) ¼ AT THE TAVERN VNDER THE NEWE EXCHAINGE, view of Exchange
2000 FRA MOLSES (M) ¼ 1657
2000A F.M. (M) ¼ —
2001 R.P. ¼ YE WHIT LYON
2002 WALTER RANDELL ½ '64 Horseshoe £30
2003 IO RADCLIFFE ½
2004 IOSEPH SYLVESTER ½ 1667 Frying-pan, IRONMONGER
2005 ED THVRMAN (D) ¼ 1664 MEALMAN
2006 MARY TRAFFORD ½ Cordwainers' Arms

New Fish Street
2007 T.B. (M) ¼ THE KINGS HEAD TAVERN, bust of Henry VIII
2008 G.B. (E) ¼ '57 YE SWAN & BRIDGE, swan on London Bridge
2009 THO BLAGRAVE (I) ¼ KINGS HEAD, bust of Henry VIII
2010 I.C. (A) ¼ AT (THE *or* YE) HARROW IN(N)
2011 ROBERT CRADOCKE ¼ Bust of Henry VIII
2012 W.H. (A) ¼ AT THE MITER £30
2013 F.M. (M) ¼ THE BLACK SPRED EAGLE
2014 WILL NEWMAN ½ AT THE, anchor and cable £22
2015 T.P. (E) ¼ '57 YE SVN TAVERNE
2016 T.V. ¼ AT YE GRASHOPER

Newgate Market
2017 IEREMIAH ARNOLD (E) ¼ French horn; pig
2018 WILL BONNER (E) ½ 1670 Woman churning, CHEESMONGER
2018A EDMOND BVRY (M) ¼ Frying-pan
2019 T.F. (M) ¼ WHEATSHEAF AND 3 PI(DG *or* GE)ONS
2020 THOMAS FOX (A) ¼ AT THE FOX
2021 W.F. ¼ AT THE 3 TOBAKO PIPS
2022 C.H., E.S. ¼ AT YE 3 TVNNS TAVERN
2023 I.H. (I) ¼ AT YE GOLDEN PLOWE
2024 MARY HVRST ½ 1668 YE WHITE SWAN(N)
2025 —— ½ 1670 YE WHITE SWANN
2025A IOHN HYDE (M) ½ 1669 NEXT DORE TO YE ROSE TAVERN
2026 THOMAS ROGERS (S) ¼ Arms
2027 E.S. (A) ¼ AT YE ROSE TAVERNE
2028 RICHARD SKELSON (M) ½ IN ROSE ALEY, rose
2029 ROBERT SNESBY ¼ Bell
2029A C.T. (I) ¼ AT THE KINGS HEAD, Jas. I
2030 D.W. (E) ¼ THE FOX AND GOOSE £35
2031 EDMVND WARNER ½ 1666 POVTERER £35
2032 IOHN WIGHTMAN ½ 1670 View of Market

Newgate, Within and **Without**
2033 THOMAS ANDREWS ¼ Horseshoe and sugar-loaf £35
2034 IOSIAS ASKEW ¼ AT, horseshoe and &; sugar-loaf
2035 FRANCIS BVNDEN (F) ½ Keys crossed; IRONMON
2035A ROBERT CARRINGTON (I) ¼ Swan
2036 IOSEPH HOLLED (A) ¼ GROCER
2037 IOHN MOORE ½ 1669 AT THE GVY OF WARWICK. *Octagonal*
2038 RALPH PACKMAN (I) ¼ Merchant Taylors' Arms; hat

2039 W.R. (M) ¼ THE FOVNTANE TAVERN
2040 NICHOLAS ROYS ½ AT YE BLACK DOGG £35
2040A E. SWAN ¼ Swan; king enthroned, INN
2040B I.W. (M) ¼ AT THE WHIT BEARE. In *pb*
2041 WILL WALKER ½ 1666 Chafing-dish, IREMONGER
2042 MARY WINGFEILD ¼ Bear with chain
2043 ½ 1669 View of Newgate Prison, BELONGING TO YE CELLOR ON THE MASTERS SIDE

New King Street (Bloomsbury)
2044 THOMAS FOOTE ½ AT THE LEG
2045 IOHN HALL (M) ½ Kings' Arms*

New Palace Yard (Westminster)
2046 EDWARD GIBSON ¼ 1662 POTTER
2046A IOHN HARMON ¼ Maltese cross
2047 W.I. (A) ¼ 1649 Grocers' Arms
2048 W.R. (A) ¼ 1649 Grocers' Arms £30
2049 SIMON NORCOTT (S) ½ AT Y GOLDEN STARR
2050 THO PALLISER ½ 1666 Grocers' Arms; bust of Chas. II £32
2051 (Probably misreading of 2157)
2052 THO STONE (P) ¼ AT THE LEGG £30
2053 EDWARD WRITE (S) ½ AT YE BLVE, boar

New Queen Street
2053A PETER PENKETHMAN (I) ½ AT YE RED COW

New Street, Covent Garden
2054 THOMAS BEARDSWORTH (M) ½ 3 herrings on string
2054A ROBERT BROCK (A) ¼ 1656 Fleur-de-lis
2055 IAMES FOE (A) ¼ 1658 Tallowchandlers' Arms
2056 IOHN HIGGS (M) ½ 1668 Stick of candles
2056A THOMAS HOGGARD (M) ½ Griffin
2057 IOSEPH HOWARD (1d) 1671 COFEE HOVSE, hand pouring coffee into cup held by man, 3 pipes on table
2058 —— (1d) ——— 2 pipes on table
2059 DOROTHY HVLET ¼ 1663 Heart crowned
2059A IEREMIAH IVES (S) ¼ Haberdashers' Arms
2060 ABRAM LEWIS ½ WITNES MY NAME, CHANDLER
2061 SARAH — ½ ——
2061A THOMAS RVSSELL (E) ¼ Pot of flowers, POTMAN (?)
2062 IOHN SAVORY ¼ 1656 £28

* See also No.366 and St Giles-in-the-Fields

2063 RIC STEVENSON (½) 1658 CHESE MONGER
2063A EDWARD WADE (M) ¼ AT THE, key
2064 WILLIAM WILDING (A) ¼ Swan

New Street, ?Cripplegate
2064A ¼ 'Tobacco roll', Arms and B

New Street, Shoe Lane
2064B RANDAL BAKER ¼ Man making candles
2064C IOHN GOODE ½ 1669 Elephant and castle
2065 W.M. (E) ¼ Lion £32
2066 WALTER MANNING ½ 1664 Crooked billet
2066A IOHN YOVNG (M) ½ 1669 Haberdashers' Arms

Newton Street (? Holborn)
2067 IOHN BVSTION ¼ King's head; queen's head
2068 RALPH WINCKLES (M) ½ 1669 AT YE RED LYON

Nightingale Lane (East Smithfield)
2069 TIMOTHY BARKER ¼ Bakers' Arms
2070 IAMES CHAPPELL ¼ Chapel with spire, initials M.A.H.
2071 HENRY CRVMP (S) ¼ 1665 3 leopards
2071A T.G. (M) ¼ AT THE ROOSE, rose
2071B IOHN HALL (M) ¼ Wheatsheaf
2072 RICHARD IAMES ½ Hope holding anchor £32
2073 R.L. (E) ¼ AT THE COALE YARDE, arms*
2074 IOHN PARKER (S) ¼ MELE MAN
2075 IOHN WELCH (S) ¼ 1658 Swan
2076 ROB WIGINES (A) ¼ AT Y, Hope and anchor

Noble Street (Foster Lane)
2077 IOHN EAMES (E) ¼ 1659
2078 IOSEPH WELLS ½ 1665 AT THE TVNN

Northumberland Alley (Fenchurch Street)
2079 S.A. ½ 1667 AT THE KING DAVID
2080 T.B. (E) ¼ AT KING DAVID
2081 I.C. (E) ¼ AT THE FETHERS
2082 THOMAS KNIGHT (B) ¼ Scales

Norton Folgate
2083 W.A. (H) ¼ THE DOLPHIN IN LONGE ALEY
2084 G.B. (A) ¼ AT THE PLOW £30
2085 E.C. (S) ¼ AT THE RED LION
2086 B.H. (E) ¼ 1650 AT THE COCK
2087 I.H. (I) ¼ AT THE BLACK TALBVT
2088 IOHN HAMMOND (S) ¼ '68 Tobacco-roll, CHEESMONGER
2088A THOMAS HARGOOD (F) ½ AT THE, ?
2089 T.L. (I) ¼ AT THE TVN
2089A THOMAS LAMBE (I) ¼ Tun

* See also *Essex* 10

2090 ABRAHAM LE KEVX ¼ 3 tuns £25
2091/2 TRISTRAM MAY & HEN(RY) SELL ½ 1667 Lion, BREW(E *or* L)RS £28
2093 WILLIAM PAINE (I) ¼ AT YE, bluecoat boy £35

Oat Lane (Wood St)
2094 WILLIAM HORNE ½ 1671 Antlers

Old Bailey
2095 I.B. (E) ¼ Fleur-de-lis £30
2096 W.B. ¼ 1651 NEXT TO THE 3 CRANES TAVERN, SALTER
2097 EDWARD BACKER (I) ½ 1669 Crown
2098 I.C. ¼ AT THE ROSE
2099 ANN CLEAYTON ½ 1669
2100 P.E. (S) ¼ 1650 THE BLACK SPREAD EAGLE £30
2101 THOMAS EAVESON (P) ¼ Spread eagle
2102 GEORGE ETCHYS (H) ¼ Carpenters' Arms
2103 I.F. (I) ¼ AT THE 7 STARS £28
2104 T.F. (K) ¼ 1650 AT THE BLEW BELL £32
2105 I.G. (A) ¼ 1650 AT THE SWAN
2106 THOMAS HOSE (R) ½ AT THE, dove and olive-branch
2107 T.H. (K) ¼ AT THE CROWNE
2108 W.I. (E) ¼ '57 AT THE GEORGE
2109 A.K. (I) ¼ 1649 AT THE 3 CANDLESTICKS
2110 PHILLIPA KENN ¼ AT THE GEORGE
2110A SYMON LEE (A) ¼ AT YE LYON AND BALL
2111 M.N. ¼ THE GOVLDEN FAVLCON
2112 THOMAS PAVLSON (E) ¼ Spread eagle £28
2113 N.S. (E) ¼ AT THE LYON AND BALL £22
2114 A.S. (M) ¼ THE STAR AND CHANDLER
2115 HENREY SANDYS (F) ½ 1668 AT THE, angel
2116 RICHARD SVTTEN ½ AT YE KINGS, bust of Chas. II, TAVERN
2117 T.T. (B) ¼ AT YE SHIPE TAVERN, ship on *obv.*
2118 Similar but ship on *rev.*
2119 ROBERT TOWNSOND (A) ¼ Bust of a divine
2120 IOHN VERE (B) ¼ AT THE PLOW £32
2121 — — (M) ½ 1664 Plough, MEAL MAN
2122 T.W. ¼ MAN IN THE MOON, TAL CHANDLER
2123 ALCE WATES ¼ 3 pigeons

Old Barge House (Bucklersbury)
2124 IANE GVN(N) ¼ 1666 A MEAL SHOP
2124A THOMAS LISKE (A) ½ 1667 AT THE, antlers

Old Change (Cheapside)
2125 EDWARD ANDREWES (I) ¼ Rose and crown £32
2125A IOHN ASHBY ½ AT YE GOLDEN STILL
2126 I.B. (I) ¼ AT THE WORSTER ARMES, castle
2127 N.B. (I) ¼ AT THE WILLOW TREE £18
2128 EDWARD CHIPP (G) ¼ '59 Dragon
2129 EDMOND DOBSON ½ AT THE, Indian smoking
2130 IOHN ELLIOTT ¼ Rose and crown
2131 ANN FISHER ¼ 1664 Merchant Taylors' Arms
2132 IOHN GRIFEITH (M) ¼ Oil-jar
2132A GEORGE IMINGS (M) ¼ OYLEMAN
2132B RICHARD LIDGOVLD ½ 1669 BAKER
2133 IOHN LISLE (A) ½ AT THE 3, morris-dancers
2134 — — (A) ¼ AT YE 3 —
2134A H.P. ¼ AT THE BLACKE BOYE

Old Fish Street (Upper Thames Street)
2135 W.A. (R) ¼ THE KINGS HEAD TAVERN, full-face bust of Henry VII
2136 WIL BAGGOT ¼ Women washing negro ('Labour in Vain') £25
2137 EDWARD BETTERIS ½ Unicorn
2138 WILL GAY (M) ¼ AT YE FOX
2139 GEORGE HEARON ½ 1662 Fox £32
2140 IOHN HOWELL (K) ¼ Boar's head
2141–3 I.M. (A) ¼ AT THE SWAN TAVERN(E) £22
2144 W.M. (E) ½ AT THE CARDINAL WOOLSEY, HIS OB
2145 I.P. (E) ¼ AT CARDYNAL WOOLSEY
2145A WILLIAM ROBINSON ½ 1668 AT YE, castle
2146 E.S. (E) ¼ AT THE SHIPP TAVERN
2146A NICOLAS TOMPSON (E) ¼ Unicorn
2147 I.W. (M) ½ 1666 AT YE WILL SOMERS, figure of the jester to Henry VIII, OB

Old Jewry (Cheapside)
2148 ANDREW BLEACHLE (A) ¼ WHIT, hart
2149 S.L. (½) 1656
2150 IOHN MILLER (M) ¼ 1663 Game cock
2151 HENRY PELLING ½ 1668 AT THE, mitre £28
2152 RICHARD TYMMS ½ 1670 AT YE, three sugar-loaves, YE IEWRY
2153 Similar but with 3 in *obv.* field, OLD IEWRY
2154 THO WALKER (I) ½ 1666 AT YE SVGER LOF

Old Palace Yard (Westminster)
2155 IOHN GVY (E) ½ 1666 Human head on dish
2156 IOHN HARMAN (S) ½ AT THE, crooked billet
2157 THOMAS PEARSON (I) ½ Naked child

Old Street (St Luke's)
2158 ED(WARD) BVCKLEY ¼ 1652 WITE HART, BREWER

2159 R.D. (K) ¼ 1652 THE BELL BREWEHOVS
2160 IOHN FVLLERTON, IOHN SANDSBVRY ½ Anchor, chequered square £20
2161 THOMAS HEDGER (M) ½ 1668 Crooked billet
2162 R.L. (M) ¼ 1648 AT THE PRINCES ARMES, P.C.
2162A N.P., C.D. ¼ '64 THE BLAZING STARR BREW HOVSE, comet
2162B THOMAS PALMER ½ 1665 MEAL MAN
2162C John Parnell ¼?
2163 RICHARD PRENTIS ½ AT THE GEORGE
2164 MARY ROW ½ 1667 IN BLEW ANCKOR ALLY, tobacco-roll
2165 T.R. (E) ¼ THE DOGGS HEAD IN THE POTTE
2166 A.S. (E) ¼ AT THE BLACKE GACK, leathern pitcher
2167 ROBART SACKLER (S) ¼ AT THE BVLL
2168 IOHN SAVAGE (S) ¼ 1658 Comet
2169 EDWARD TAVENER ½ 1664 Goat's head £35
2170 IOHN TWISLETON (M) ¼ 1659 Steering-wheel
2171 THO WELLES, FRA LEONARD (½) THE BELL, tun; bell £30
2172 RICHARD YEATMAN ½ 1667 AT YE, hart, comet above

Orchard Street (Westminster)
2173 PETER CLESBY (E) ½ BLAK, horse

Pall Mall
2174 RICHARD ADAMS (I) ¼ AT THE, oak branch with acorns, TAVERN
2175 EDMVND BROWNE ½ (?166)8 AT THE ?, STRONG WATER MAN
2176 ROBERT GISBERNE (A) ½ 1667 PEWTERER
2176A EDWARD OWENES (G) ½ AT THE COCK
2177 RICHARD PINCK (M) ½ 1667 AT YE HERCVLES PILLERS
2178 MATHEW ROGERMAN (M) ½ '67 AT YE 2, pigeons

Pancras Lane (Queen Street, Cheapside)
2179 T.B. (S) ¼ AT THE NEW VIRGINNE, Indian smoking, holding tobacco-leaf

Panyer Alley (Paternoster Row)
2180 EDW FOSTER ½ LETHERSELER AT YE CORNER SHOPP, nag's head upon gridiron
2181 ROBERT HAYES ½ AT YE COFFE HOVSE
2182 HEN LACKE ¼ AKORNE

Parker's Lane (Drury Lane)
2183 HENRY DVNSCOMBE (I) ½ 1668 Man making candles £30
2184 EDWARD KING ½ AT THE, flagon
2185 W.K. WHITCOMBE ½ 1664 4 circles, BREWER
2186 W.K. — ¼ 1659 — —

Paternoster Row
2187 THOMAS ALLEN ½ 1664 Bust of queen with sceptre
2188 I.B. (D) ¼ THE CASTELL TAVERN £30
2189 S.B. (E) ¼ YE MEARMAYD TAVERN
2190 R.F. (I) ¼ THE MER MAYDE TAVERN
2190A IAMES PARIS ¼ Wicker cradle
2191 THO TATE ½ IN QVEENS HEAD COVRT, queen's head

Paul's Alley (Paternoster Row)
2192 IOHN BROOME (E) ¼ 1657 Harrow

Paul's Chain (St Paul's Churchyard)
2192A A.A. ¼ '57 AT YE CASTLE TAVERN
2193 WILLIAM ADKINSON (C) ¼ Apothecaries' Arms
2193A FRANCIS LASHE (?) (E) ¼ Rose
2194 THOMAS SWETTINGHAM ½ Castle
2194A GREGORY WALKLATE (M) ¼ Lion
2195 EDW WOODWARD (A) ¼ Daggers crossed, COOKE
2195A EDWARD — (A) ½ Swords crossed

Paul's Wharf (Upper Thames Street)
2196 M.B. (M) ½ AT YE NEXT BOAT, boat with three men £35
2197 ABRAHAM CHITTY ½ 1669 AT YE BELL BREW HOVS. *Octagonal* £45
2198 I.H. 6d THE BALL
2199 I.H. 3d —
2199A I.H. 1d —
2200 D.T. (I) ¼ THE FRIEN PAN IN BEL YARD

Peerpool Lane (Gray's Inn Lane)
2201 HVM ASMORE ½ BAKER
2202 IOHN BAKER (F) ¼ 1664 Sugar-loaf
2203 WILLIAM COVLSON (A) Sheaf of corn
2204 IOHN DAVISON (A) ½ Unicorn
2205 THOMAS GALE (I) ¼ Shoemaker fitting woman with shoe
2206 IOHN HIND AND THO GWILYM ½ King's head, full face, BREWERS £25

Peter Street (= Denzell Street, Clare Market)
2207 IOHN GRAY ½ 1667 AT MOTH SHIPTON

(Great) Peter Street (Westminster)
2207A MICHAEL ARNOLD ¼ Merchant's mark (?), BREW
2207B W.C. (S) ¼ Monogram (?), BREWER
2208 G.R. (M) ¼ AT THE DAGER
2209 R.Y. (R) ¼ AT THE KINGS HEAD, bust of Jas. I

Petticoat Lane (Whitechapel)
2210 IOHN BICKCEM ½ '68 AT THE, bust of Chas. II
2211 WILL BOLTON (K) ½ AT YE BLACK BEL, CHANDLR
2212 R.D. (E) ¼ AT THE WHIT LYON
2213 DANIELL DEBOVRCK ½ Hand holding bird
2214 ANTHONY FINCH (S) ¼ 5 ink-horns
2215 S.H. (A) ¼ NEARE THE SHEARES
2215A RICHARD HIGGINS ½ 1668
2215B EDMOND HILLER (S) ¼ Lion
2216 SAMVELL KENT (S) ¼ Crescent
2216A W.M. (B) ¼ (?) 'Rose and Crowne'
2217 RALPH MARKLAND ½ 1667 AT YE RED CROSS
2218 IEFERY WALLETT (M) ¼ Lion
2219 GRAVES WEAVER ¼ AT YE, wicker cradle
2220 CHRISTOPHER WELDON ½ 1667 AT YE, half-moon
2221 HENRY WHITE ¼ '57 HART

Petty France (Bishopsgate)
2222 IOHN BARNES (S) ¼ Carpenters' Arms, CHANDLER £22
2223 THO CLAROE ½ IN MORE FEILDS, man making candles
2224 SAM HVNT (E) ¼ 1670 AT YE BALL
2225 WILLIAM RACK (I) ¼ '66 AT YE, Indian holding dart £28

Petty France (Westminster)
2226 NICHOLAS SHERMAN (M) ¼ WHIT HALL, tall building with gate £38
2227 WILL SMITH (M) ¼ King's head in oak tree
2228 I.T. (S) ¼ AT THE SAVL, Saul on ground, horse nearby £25

Philpot Lane (Fenchurch Street)
2229 SAMVELL HEWSON (A) ½ 1668 Wheatsheaf
2230 LAWRENCE LANCASTER (S) ¼ 1655
2231 WILL MOSELY (R) ½ 1667 IN MOSELIES COVRT, Half-figure of St Hugh
2232 ROBERT NEVELL (A) ¼ Leathersellers' Arms
2233 R.B. (S) ¼ AT THE SVGAR LOAFE

Piccadilly
2234 ROBERT BEARD (I) (½) 1662
2235 R.B. (I) ¼ Mermaids
2235A RICHARD BVLL (M) ¼ Bull, MERCER
2235B F.C. (I) ¼ '58 AT YE HAYCART AND 3 HORSES
2236 WILLIAM FLINDELL (M) ¼ '58 Mercers' Arms
2237 EDW GILLNEY (H) ¼ AT YE, 3 horseshoes
2237A RICHARD GORSE ½ 1671 GROCER
2238 RICHARD GROOME ½ 1665 Crown and anchor
2239 WILLIAM HILL (I) ¼ 1670
2240 ABBET(T) NEVELL (A) ¼ 1657 Rectangle £35
2241 W.P. (E) ¼ '57 Blacksmiths' Arms
2242 IOH(N) PALMER (M) ¼ '57 YE GEORGE
2243 RICHARD THORP ½ 1666 GROCER £35
2244 IOHN VAVGHAN (A) ½ 1668 AT THE, still, fire beneath
2245 INO — (A) ¼ AT YE, Still, fire beneath
2246 WILL VESEY (S) ½ AT THE GARDEN HOVSE, Fruiterers' Arms
2247 IOH WALKER (S) ¼ '59 SVGAR LOAFE

Pie Corner (Smithfield)
2248 ADAM EVERELL ¼ Horseshoe
2249 FRANCIS HARRIS (M) ½ BAKER £28
2249A E.L. ¼? 'Sr. John Oldcastle'
2250 IOHN MARSTON ½ n.d. Half-moon, 7 stars, string of candles, TALLOW CHANDLER £30
2251 — — (D) ¼ '59 — — — —
2252 SAM PARKINS (M) ½ MEALMAN
2253 STEPHEN WIL(L)COCKS ½ BREWHOVSE, Antlers

Pissing Alley
2253A THO GELDING (M) ¼ NEARE PAVLS, woolpack
2253B RICHARD HIGGS (S) (½) Woolpack
2254 DANIELL HILLS (C) ¼ Rose and crown
2255 FRANCIS WOOD (A) ¼ 1664 AT YE, bust of Chas. II

Pope's Head Alley (Cornhill)
2256 IOHN SAWYER (F) ¼ Pope's bust

Popping's Alley (Poppin's Court, Fleet Street)
2257 SIMON PENYCOTT (D) ¼ GREEN, dragon

Porter's Quay
2258 W.H. (E) ¼ THE REDE HOVSE
2259 RICH SMITH ½ AT THE RED HOVSE

Postern Gate (Cripplegate)
2260 KATHERIN BRANDON ½ '71 Ball suspended
2261 D.C. ¼ AT THE YEARNE SHOPP, bell £35
2262 WILL CHARLWOOD ¼ Woman churning
2263 R.D. (E) ¼ AT THE BLV BORE
2264 ALEX HARWOOD (A) ¼ Cheesemonger's knife £32
2265 RICHARD HAWES (E) ¼ Dragon
2266 W.M. ¼ THE CASTEL TAVERN
2267 ROB MILLS (E) ¼ Turnstile
2268 THO RAWLENSON ½ DISTILLER
2269 ROBERT SARRESON (E) ¼ Postern-gate
2270 ROBERT WILLIAMS ½ 1666 Four areas railed round, planted with trees

Postern Street
2271 HVGH LOOE (E) ½ 1666 AT YE WHITE, hart £28

Poultry

2272 IAMES BAINES ¼ 1659 AT THE, sugar-loaf, 3 tobacco-rolls

2273 T.D. (E) ¼ AT THE ROSE TAVERN

2274 HENRY DIXON ¼ 1660 Arms; sun on heraldic wreath

2275 THOMAS DYOTT ½ AT THE ROSE TAVERN

2276 THE EXCHANGE TAVERN ½ 1668 View of Royal Exchange

2277 W.K. ¼ 1651 THE EXCHANGE TAVERN, view of Royal Exchange £38

2278 GEORGE TWINE ½ 1665 3 cranes standing £28

Princes Street

2279 RALPH DRAPER ½ AT THE, Blacksmiths' Arms

2279A WALTER MORTON ½ 1663(?) Still

2280 THOMAS SNELLING ½ Bakers' Arms, OYLMAN

2281 IOHN RIXON ½ AT THE SVN

Pudding Lane (Lower Thames Street)

2282 B.A. (W) ½ 1668 AT THE MAYDEN HEADE £32

2283 B.A. (W) ¼ 1657 AT YE MAYDENHEADE £32

2283A ROBART GOODSPEED ¼ Cooks' Arms; cross. In *pb*

2284 IOHN HANDS (M) ¼ 1664 3 sugar-loaves

2285 W.P. (I) ¼ AT THE BLACKE BVLL

2285A THO SELL (E) ½ AT YE SPANIL DOG & 3, hats

2286 ¼ 1657 AT YE MAYDEN HEADE

Puddle Dock (Blackfriars)

2287 THO BAKER (A) (½) 1659 AT THE, Prince of Wales' feathers £30

2288 R.C. ¼ 1660 KINGS COLLEDG

2289 FRANCIS ELWOOD (L?) ¼ Cock?

2289A HVMPHRY FRITH (K) ½ 1668 AT YE, rose and crown

2290 THOMAS GVY (A) ½ 1668 AT YE FEATHERS

2291 ROBERT HALE (M) ½ 1662 CHANDLER £25

2292 SAMVEL HARRIS ½ 1669 Tallowchandlers' Arms

2293 BENIAMEN HOWE (E) ½ St. George & dragon

2294 ELIZABETH IORDEN ½ 1669 AT YE STILL

2294A FOVLKE LACEY (I) ½ 1668 Anchor and wheatsheaf

2294B IOHN LAWRANCE ½ 1663 BAKER

2295 IOHN OSMAN (M) ½ 1664

2296 IOHN ROGERS ½ AT YE WHITE SWAN

2297 R.S. 1d AT THE BREW HOVSE, City Arms

2297A R.S. ¼ — Wheatsheaf; barrel

2297B WILL WEST ½ AT YE GREEN DRAGON

Queenhithe (Upper Thames Street)

2298 THOMAS BAKER (I) ½ 1668 Sugar-loaf

2299 RICHARD BRIGGS (A) ½ 1660 Fishmongers' Arms £32

2300 ROBERT CANHAM (I) ½ 1669 Rose and crown; Coopers' Arms

2300A IOSIAS COOPER (½) 1658 Ship; anchor, AD SV CROS

2301 B.F. (M) ¼ AT THE NOBLE GARTER, 3 fishes

2302 ROBERT FEILD (A) ½ 1667 AT YE NAKED BOY

2303 BARTHOLLOMEW FISH ½ 1667 3 fishes £24

2304 D.G. (M) ¼ 1652 THE ROSE

2305 HENRY GIFFORD (M) ½ 1668 Ironmongers' Arms; bell

2306 BARTHOLOMEW HESTER (A) ¼ Fletchers' Arms

2307 SAMVEL LONGE (M) ¼ 1655 Naked boy holding boar's head

2308 —— (M) ¼ 1657 — £35

2309 IOHN NEALE (A) ½ Axe

2310 ROBERT SKRINE (½) AT THE BVLL, Ironmongers' Arms £38

2311 PEARCIVALL STEVENSON (E) ½ Rose and crown

2312 HENREY TATVM (F) ¼ Heart, BAKER £32

2313 THOMAS WHELDALE (M) (½) AT YE BEL

2314 QVEENS HEAD TAVERN ¼ 1662

Queen Street (Cheapside)

2315 IOHN CANNON (S) (½) Bust of Queen Catherine £35

2316 WILL CLERKE ½ 1669 AT YE, cock and bottle

2317 THOMAS EDDENBVRRO (A) ¼ Fruiterers' Arms

2318 WILL(I)AM HOLMS (A) ¼ AT THE PLOW £30

2319 ROBERT MOSS (F) ¼ Tallowchandlers' Arms, MEALMAN

2320 EDWARD NORTHEN (E) ¼ Crown

2321 IOHN WHEELER ½ AT IACK OF NEWBERYS

Ram Alley (Fleet Street)
(See under Fleet Street)

Ratcliff Cross

2322 W.B. (E) ¼ AT THE SHIPP TAVERN £22

2323 IOHN BAKER (R) ½ 1668 AT YE, Prince of Wales' feathers

2324 WILL BAKER ½ AT LITLE WHIT HORS £28

2325 IOSEPH BROCKE ½ Man's coat, COATE SELER £32

2325A GEORGE BVLMOR (E) ½ 1666 Castle

2325B —— (E) ¼ 1658 —

2326 PHILLIP BVRGES (A) ½ 1667 Merchant-Taylors' Arms
2326A T.C. (A) ¼? '3 flowerdeluces'
2327 ROBERT ELLIS ½ 1668 3 men standing round globe
2328 ALEXANDER HARWOOD (A) ¼ Cheese-knife between 3 stars
2328A NICHOLAS HAYMAN (A) ½ 1666 Man with telescope (?)
2328B ANN HOW ½ 1667
2329 RANDOLPH HVFF (M) ½ 1667 AT THE, royal oak £32
2329A FRANCIS IONES ½ 1668 Fish
2330 IOHN MARCH (M) ¼ THE SWN, swan £28
2331 WILLIAM NVNN (A) ½ AT THE BEL INN
2331A WALTER ONIONES ½ 1667 Bell
2332 IOHN SIMONS (A) ½ 1666 Flagon
2333 T.W. (M) ¼ GALY, galley
2333A YE GALY ½ Galley
2334 LAZARVS WEEDEN ½ AT YE WHARF, Bakers' Arms; horse and cart

Ratcliff (Highway)
2335 A.A. (S) ¼ 1649 AT THE RED LYON
2336 WILL ARCHER ½ AT THE COFFEE HOVSE
2337 H.B. (D) ¼ THE WHEAT SHEAF AND SVGER LOFE £32
2337A H.B. (D) ½ THE WHEAT SHEAF AND SVGER LOAFE
2338 R.B. (A) ¼ 1662 AT THE GOLDEN BALL
2339 *Francis Beame* (S) ¼ 1666
2339A IOHN BERRIDG (M) ½ 1666 AT THE RED COW
2340 IOHN BISHOPP (M) ¼ 1656 3 sugar-loaves £28
2341 FRANCIS BVLL (A) ¼ 1656 Bust of Henry VIII
2342 THOMAS BYLE (S) ½ 1666 Bust of Henry VIII, ALE MAN
2343 W.C. (M) ¼ AT THE PLOWE
2344 THOMAS CAPON (B) ¼ Wheatsheaf
2344A IOHN CLARKE (S) ¼ AT THE, rose crowned
2344B RICHARD DAFT (H) ½ 1664 Oblong box (?)
2345 *George Dam* ½ 1669 *at ye Rose Brew house*
2345A ROBERT DAVERS (A) ¼ AT YE, Weavers' Arms
2346 IOHN FLY ½ 1669 Distillers' Arms, DISSTILER
2346A ROBERT GOODMAN (M) ½? NEW MARKET, 3 tuns
2346B IAMES GOODWYN ½ Ship and gun
2347 R.H. (I) ¼ THE SHIP TAVERN
2348 WILLIAM HANES (M) ¼ 1664
2349 EDMOND HOLT ½ 1668 AT THE SHIP
2350 GEORGE HVTCHINSON (B) ¼ Bull's head, TAVERNE
2350A EDWARD IEAFFERIS (I) ¼ AT YE, 3 foxes
2351 IOHN KNOT (S) ½ 1666
2352 IOANE LAW ¼ AT YE KEY
2353 THO LEADER ½ 1667 Whale, 3 harpoons, SOPE MAKER
2354 M.M. (M) ¼ THE BRICKLERS ARMES
2355 IOHN MATHEWS ½ Bull's head
2356 IOHN MAYOR (H) ½ NEARE NEW GRAVELL LANE
2357 THOMAS MOREGRAVE (M) ¼ 1668
2358 THOMAS MVNN. . . (M) ¼ 1653
2358A WILLIAM NEALE ½ 1668 AT YE, crown
2359 GRACE PESTELL ½ IN FIGG TREE YARD, mortar and pestle
2360 IAMES PRICKE ½ '68 AT YE STILL
2361 ROBERT ROOKE (D) ½ 1666 NEARE THE SCOOLE HOVSE, rook £35
2362 MARY RVSSELL ½ 1669 Article of dress, SLOPSELLER
2363 I.S. (B) ¼ 1653 AT THE ROSE TAVERN
2364 N.S. ¼ THE SHIPP
2365 IASPER SKACHAR ½ 1667 AT THE, bust of Chas. II, TAVERN
2366 THO SORELL ½ AT RED LYON TAVERN
2367 RICH STILES ½ 1666 AT YE WHITE, lion £28
2368 ROBERT STRANKE ¼ Bull
2369 W.T.(A) ¼ AT THE GVNN
2370 IOHN TRICKER (E) ¼ IN BLEW GATE FEILD, Tallowchandlers' Arms
2371 N.V. (E) ¼ 1651 AT THE BLACK BOAY £28
2372 THOMAS WADLAND ½ 1668 Ship; still
2372A NICH WATTS ½ AGAINST THE SCOOLE HOVSE
2373 IEAMES WEST (E.M.) ¼ Bellows

Redcross Street (Cripplegate)
2374 THOMAS BALLETT (A) ¼ AT YE, mermaid
2375 ISAAC BENNETT (E) ½ AT YE GOLDEN, lion
2376 MARGRET BRANDRED ½ 1668 Bible
2377 BALDWIN DAVIS ½ 1666 Salters' Arms, TALLOW CHANDLER
2378 —— ¼ TALLOW CHANDLER
2379 T. DICKENSON ½ 1666 AT THE SVNN £35
2380 EDW DOBSON (A) ¼ AT YE, stick of candles (?)
2381 ARON EDWARDS ½ 1669 AT YE BAL OVER AGAINST IEWEN STREET
2382 *Phillip Ferrers, Barrett Gurdon* ½
2383 *Robert Gifford* ½ Castle and Arms of Worcester
2384 ALEXANDER HANKIN (M) ¼ Turk's head

2385 THOMAS HOLLOWAY ½ 1666 AT YE, bust of Jas. I
2386 *Nich Jackson* ½ WHITE BEAR
2387 CHRIS PIERSON (M) ¼ 3 suns
2387A ROBERT PRICHARD (R) ¼ Skinners' Arms
2387B RICHARD TREDLY (A) ½ AT YE CROWN
2387C F.W. ¼ THE RED CROSS TAVERN
2388 OLIVER WALLIS (I) ¼ 1667 Dog eating from pot £32
2389 THO WHITLE ¼ 1657 CORNER BEECH LANE, baluster measure

Redmead Lane (Wapping)
2390 MATHEW DAVIS ¼ IN FRYERS COVRT NERE THE HERMITAG

Rood Lane (Fenchurch Street)
2391 WILLIAM COVLSON (M) ¼ Horseshoe
2392 DANIELL LYNDALL (I) ¼ Arms

Rose Lane
2393 IOHN ATWOOD ½ THE MAN (IN *or* AT) THE WOOD

Rosemary Lane (Whitechapel)
2394 IOHN BAYLE ½ AT THE 7 STARS
2395 ROBERT CARPENTER (K) ½ 1668 Blacksmiths' Arms, crest
2396 RICHARD COOLES ½ 1669 Lion
2397 HENRY CRISPE (M) ¼ Pipes crossed, tobacco-roll
2398 SAM CRISP (M) ¼ Still, CHEESEMONGER
2399 ROBERT CRYER (S) ½ Bust of Chas. II, PASTRY COOK
2399A N.D. (I) ¼ AT THE FALCON
2400 PH DOE ¼ ON ARMETAGE BRIGE, wheatsheaf; plough £32
2401 WILLIAM EVERED (E) ½ 1669 AT YE WHIT HORSE
2402 —— ¼ 1667 Horse
2403 ED FLOWERS (M) ¼ AT TH(E), bunch of grapes
2404 FRANCIS GILSTRAPE (E) ¼ 3 rabbits (?)
2405 IA GODFREY ¼ 1662 Rose, IRON MONGER
2406 R.H. ¼ AT THE FALCON
2407 IOHN HARRISON ½ 1667 Arched crown
2407A —— ½ 1666 —
2407B WILLIAM HILL (E) ¼ 1667
2408 RICHARD LANE (H) ½ 1670 AT THE 3, tuns
2409 HENERY LOFT ¼ Fishmongers' Arms
2410 F.M. (M) ¼ AT THE WHIT SWAN
2410A EDMVND MEARE (L) ½ 1670 AT THE, angel
2411 WILL MINSHEW ¼ '59 Plough; still £32
2412 DANIEL PEASE ¼ 1656 Man making candles
2413 EDWARD READE (T) ¼ Fruiterers' Arms
2413A WILLIAM SKINNER (A) ¼ 1671
2414 STEPHEN SMITH (M) ¼ AT TOWER HILL
2415 T.T. (M) ¼ AT THE 3 PIDGONS
2416 WILLIAM TAYLOR (M) ½ 1668 Sun, BREWER
2417 C.W. (F) ¼ AT THE PLOW
2418 N.W. (A) ¼ AT THE RED LYON
2419 ROBERT WHITBOVRNE (E) ½ 1668 AT, sugar-loaf, star

Rotten Row (Aldersgate Street)
2420 RICHARD CVPMAN ½ 1666 AT THE, 2 brewers

Round Court (Strand)
2421 THO ALLATT (E) ½ AGAINST YE NEW EXCHAING, man carrying sack, shovel, CHANDLER £30
2422 IOH AYSHLE(Y *or* E) (P) ¼ AT YE 3 PIGEONS
2423 NICHO CABRITT (E) ½ Man making candles
2424 EDWARD CRAWLEY (E) ¼ Royal oak £32
2425 HENRY ROCKET (E) ½ Cock crowing
2426 WILLIAM LANDER ½ 1664 Man making candles £28
2427 WILL LAVNDER (F) ¼ Man making candles £25
2428 HENRY MVN? (K) ½ Eagle
2429 HENRY PACKETT (K) ½ Spread eagle
2429A IOH SHERRED (A) ¼ 3 horseshoes

Russell Street (Covent Garden)
2430 IOHN ASHTON (L) ½ AT THE, Fruiterers' Arms
2431 TIMOTHY CHILD ½ AT YE COFFE HOVSE £35
2431A THOMAS EVSTIS (A) ½ Queen's bust
2432 C.G. (E) ¼ AT YE VNICORNE
2433 IOHN HATTEN (D) ¼ Prince of Wales' feathers £35
2434 MARY LONG ½ Rose on stalk £38
2434A IAMES MAGNES ½ Horse, STA(C *or* T)IONER
2435 PHILIP REILLEY (E) ¼ Ship, OYLEMAN
2436 THO SNELL ½ 1669 GROCER
2437 PET SPITSER ½ Turk's head
2437A W. THOMPSON ¼
2438 HVMPHRY VAGHAN (R) ¼ Goat

Sabs Key
2438A IOHN GOODAKER (E) ¼ Chequers

Saffron Hill (Holborn Hill)
2439 ROBERT BANKES (E) ¼ 1657

2439A THO GIBBS (L) ½ 1667 AT YE NEW ENGLAND, ship, 2 boats
2440 IOHN IONES 1d 1672 OVRE AGANIST THE CASTLE
2441 GEORGE MASON ½ 1668. In *pb*
2442 WILLIAM ORCHARD (E) ¼ 1660 Harp
2443 G.P. (A) ¼ AT THE 2 BREWERS
2443A WILLIAM PARLAR (E) ½ AT THE, Joiners' Arms

St Alban's Street (St James's)
2444 GEORG CARTER ½ AT YE ST ALBAN, St. Alban standing near altar
2444A *John Hill* ½ 1668 Girl milking goat. *Octagonal*

St Anne's Lane (Aldersgate Street)
2445 MATHEW HANSCOMBE (A) ¼ '58 Sugar-loaf
2446 IOHN HARRIS (M) ½ 1671 Mermaid
2446A IOHN PERROT (A) ½ 1671 TOBACONIST
2447 NICH STRAINGE (½) '69 AT YE COFFEE HOVSE
2448 IOHN TAYLER ¼ Ape playing bagpipes; spectacles
2449 B.W. (E) ¼ AT YE S(IG *or* Y)NE OF YE MEARE MAID

St Benet's Hill (Thames Street)
2450 MATHEW TVNSTALE 1d AT THE HARROW £48

St Bride's
2451 WILLIAM NORSE (½) COFFEE HOVSE

St Clement's (Strand)
2452 RICH CHIDLEY (R) ½ 1666 NEARE NEW MARKETT, tobacco-roll £25
2453/4 (See after 2477)
2455 T.F. (A) ¼ AT THE 3 TVNNES
2455A THO FOX ½ 1669 NEAR LVMBER STREET, 3 foxes
2456 RIC FVLLER ¼ 1657 NEARE LYONS IN, half-moon
2457 EDWARD GEERY (L) ½ 1667 BROKER
2458 IA GOLES (D) ¼ WHITE HORSE
2459 LEWIS HARRINDINE (B) ½ LACE SHOP, artichoke
2459A *Samuell Haw* ½ 1670 *att the*, hand holding vine spray. *Octagonal*
2460 PHILIP IOHNSON ½ 1665 AT THE, paschal lamb
2461 *Abraham Jorden* ½ 1664 at ye, Turk's head
2462 (See after 2477)
2463/4 GEO LAVRANCE (M) ¼ 1668 Wheatsheaf, MEAL
2465 LAWRANCE LEWES (I) ½ 1668 MERCER £28
2465A WORRALL MAYO ½ AT THE, angel
2466 E.N. (A) ¼ AT THE KINGS HEAD, bust of Henry VIII
2467 I.P. (A) ¼ THE CASTEL TAVERN
2468 I.P. ¼ —
2469 I.P. ¼ THE CASTELL TAVERNE, DAINES instead of CHVRCHYARD £32
2470 I.P. (I) ¼ THE CASTEL TAVERN
2471 T.S. ¼ '57 YE ANGEL
2472 W.S. (E) ½ YE COFFEE HOVSE
2473 W.S. (M) ¼ AT THE WHIT LYON
2474 IOHN SMIT (I) ¼ WT OVT TEMPLE BAR, dog
2475 IOHN SMITH (W) ¼ AT, St George & dragon
2476 THO SPRINGALL ½ AT THE, castle
2477 FRANCES WALKER ¼ Crowned ring round arrows piercing heart

St Clement's Lane (Eastcheap)*
2453 THO CLARK (S) ¼ 3 neat's tongues
2454 CHRISTOPHER DANBROOK ½ Hand pouring coffee into cup
2462 M.K. (A) ¼ AT THE SHIP £35

St Dunstan's in the East
2478 T.C. (C) ¼ 1649 THE LOCK AND SHEERS†
2479 ANTHONY PARSLOV (E) ¼ Horse-shoe £35

St George's Lane
2480 SAMVEL BOVERY (A) ¼ AT YE, man examining foot

St Giles in the Fields
2481 NATHANIELL ABBOT (R) ¼ 1659 DIS(S)TILLER
2482 E.B. ¼ AT THE BLACKE BOY £24
2483 WALT BIGG ¼ AT THE BEL £24
2483A RICHARD BIGGS ¼ Bear; tree (? vine)
2484 EDWARD BONVS (E) ¼ RED COW
2484A WILLIAM BOOTEY (S) ¼ Men carrying barrel
2485 IAMES BRICKILL ¼ 1663 MEALE MAN
2486 THO BRODWAY (A) ¼ AT FOVNTAN LAN END, hand holding pineapple
2487 IOHN BVTLER (E) ½ 1670 Castle
2488 E.C. ¼ AT THE HELMET
2489 WILL COLLINES (E) (½) Arms, BREWER
2490 ROBERT DERDS (I) ½ 1666 MEALEMAN £32
2490A MARMEDVKE DORREL ½ 1668 AT DVKES HEAD, bust of James, Duke of York
2490B THO GIRLINGTON (R) IN NEW STREET, Arms
2491 THOMAS GREENE (M) ¼ Bear with chain
2492 E.H. (E) ¼ AT THE WHEAT SHEIFE
2493 I.H. ¼ THE TALOW CHANDLER £32

* Others of the tokens listed under *St Clement's* (Strand) may possibly belong here
† Usually (? always) overstruck by *Uncertain* 72

2494 NAT HARDING ¼ GROSER
2495 ROBERT HITCHAM (D) ½ 1670 Crown
2496 WILL HORNE (H) ¼ AT YE HORNES
2497 ROBERT HVLLCVP (M) ¼ Cat
2498 DANYELL IAMES (M) ¼ 1657 Ship
2498A G.L. (R) ¼ AT THE ROSE BRVHOVS
2499 I.L. (B) ¼ '57 YE EAGLE & CHILD
2500 SAMVELL MARSTONE (M) ½ 1666 AT YE, bottle, ON YE CAVSEY
2500A RALPH MORE (P) ¼ Half-moon
2501 WILL MORECOOT ¼ '57 Man with hat and sash; Farriers' Arms
2501A H.N., F.W. ¼ COCK & PIE BREWHOVS
2502 ROBERT NEW (E) ¼ 1652 Tallowchandlers' Arms £32
2502A ROBERT PANTON ¼ '57 Fountain (?)
2503 ELIZABETH PEARCE ½ '63 3 pigeons £25
2504 HENRY POWELL ½ 1662 CHEESMONGER £25
2504A WILLIAM POWELL (B) ¼ Drapers' Arms, VPHOLSTER
2504B WILL RAYNER (I) ¼ 1657
2505 IOHN REDDELL (R) ¼ AT YE ROSE, CHVRCH STREETE
2506 I.S. (M) ¼ YE SWAN & WHIT HART
2506A WILLIAM SEEL (I) ½ 1663 Cross pattée
2507 ROBERT STARKY (A) ½ Dog
2508 IA WAGSTAF ½ 1669 NEAR YE WHITE HART
2509 IOHN SLADE ½ 1668 MID(DI *or* EL)L ROW, 3 barrels and sugar-loaf
2510 THOMAS TARLTON (E) ¼ Bull
2511 IOHN WETHERED ½ Swan, TALLOW CHAN
2512 PHILIP WETHRELL (I) ¼ 3 lions £32
2513 IOHN WOODMAN ½ 1665 AT THE, raven, CHESESMONGER
2514 THO WOOLLAMS (I) ½ IN NEW KING STREET, 3 brushes
2514A WILL . . . ½ NEW KING STR, bull (?)

(Great) St Helen's (Bishopsgate)
2515 *Hugh Adderley* ½ 1666 Dolphin
2516 R.S. (E) ¼ AT THE RED LYON

St James's (Westminster)
2517 RICH BARRETT (A) ¼ 1665 Cheese-taster, CHANLER £24
2517A ANN BLAKE ½ 1671 CHANDLER
2518 RICHARD CHANCE (A) ¼ AT, fleece, TAVERN
2519 ROGER GODFREY (E) ½ AT YE DVCHES OF YORK
2519A M.H. (A) ¼? 'Rose Taverne'
2520 T.H. (M) ¼ 1649
2521 T.H. (M) ¼ n.d.
2522 IOSEPH LARKE ¼ Grocers' Arms
2522A EDWARD LLOYD (M) ½ Building, SVTTLER TO HIS MAIESTIES GARD OF FOOT
2523 R.M. ¼ 1650 Arms, THE SVTLER
2523A R.N. (M) ¼ 'Glove'
2524 WILL SLIDD (I) ½ Bust of Duke of Albemarle (?), SVTLER TO YE GVARD £32
2525 EDWARD SMITH ½ AT YE POETS HEAD £35
2526 DAVID THOMAS (I) ¼ 1663 Crown and anchor

St James's Market
2527 RICHARD ATHY ½ 1668 Fleur-de-lis. *Octagonal* £45
2528 SARAH AVSTIN ½ AT THE GREEN MAN
2529 LAVRANCE BALL (E) ½ '64 Bakers' Arms £28
2529A IOHN BOTTOM ½ TALLOW CHANDLER
2530 IOHN DICKENSON (½) 1669 Sugar-loaf; rose
2531 FRANCIS DORINGTON (A) ¼ Hart
2532 W.F. (I) ¼ AT THE OLD MAN, 'Old Parr's' head £35
2532A ROB GEALE (?) ½ 1670 GROSER AT THE, sugar-loaf
2533 I.H. (M) ½ 1670 THE WHITE HORSE
2534 IOHN HOOKE (A) ¼ Cheese-taster
2535/6 THOMAS IENN(IN)GS (E) ¼ Man making candles £30
2537 ANN KANES ½ 1667 MILLINER
2538 NICHOLAS KEEVE ½ 1668 Rose £22
2539 *Mark Lawn* ½ 1667 Plough, *Fishmonger*
2540 THO PAGITT ½ 1669 Woman churning, CHEESMONGER
2541 IOSEPH PARSONS (F) ½ 1666 AT THE SINE OF YE PARSON GREENE
2542 ANDREW PORTER (E) ½ 1670 Butchers' Arms £32
2543 EDWARD PERSMORE (E) ¼ Vase of flowers
2544 GEORGE ROSE ½ GROCER AT YE, rose
2545 BVRBAGE SALTER ½ AT YE, rose and crown
2546 I.T. (E) ¼ AT THE SOP BOX IN THE M.P. (= Market Place)
2547 ELIZABETH TOWNESEND ½ 1666 Market place
2548 HENRY WEAVER (S) ¼ '65 Ship
2549 — — (S) ¼ '66 —
2550 ½ 1666 AT THE QVEENS HEAD

St Johns Court, Lane, and **Street** (Clerkenwell)
2551 T.A. (M) ¼ AT THE BIRD IN HAND £28
2552 CHRISTOPHER ALLEN (E) ¼ 1664 AT, sugar-loaves
2552A EDW BAGLEY ½ 1668 AT YE THACHT HOVSE
2553 IOB BANWELL (E) ¼ 1658 Dragon

2554 THOMAS BENNETT ½ 1668 Rose and crown
2555 IOHN BROTHERTON (M) ¼ Bell
2556 R.C. ¼ 1666 AT THE BELL
2557 GEORGE COLDWELL ½ Mitre, POTTER
2558 FRANCIS CHICHOE (E) ¼ 1663 Tree
2559 *John Dodson* ½ 1667 £22
2560 ISACK ELLISTON (H) ¼ AT YE 3 ELMES
2561 ROGER FINCH (E) ¼ 1659 AT THE, fleur-de-lis
2562 A.G. ¼ THE RED BVLL
2562A E.G. ¼? 'Grocers' Armes'
2563 THOMAS GALE ¼ 1666 AT THE, queen's head
2564 IOHN GARNER ¼ Globe b.s.
2565 IOHN GAZELEY (E) ¼ AT YE, cock; sugar-loaf
2566 (Probably same as 2557)
2567 GEORGE GRADEN (M) ½ 1668 AT YE FOX
2568 IONATHAN GRAST (F) ¼ '57 CHEISE MONGER
2569 ALICE GROVE ¼ 1659 Still
2570 ROGER HART (E) ¼ AT THE, bust of Eliz. I
2571 WILLIAM HILL ½ 1666 AT THE POPES HEAD
2572 HENRY HOTCHDALE ½ AT THE, windmill, BREW HOVSE
2572A I.L. (M) ¼ 'Miter Taverne'
2573 I.M. (E) ¼ THE PEWTER PLA, platter
2574 EDMVND MANNING ½ '71 AT YE, tobacco-roll
2575 EDWARD MIDWINTER ½ AT THE, bust of Chas. II, TAVERN £32
2576 IAMES PENNINGTON (S) ½ 1667 Crossed keys, GROCER
2577 THOMAS PRESTWOOD ½ 1668 Salters' Arms
2578 IOHN RADBVRNE ½ 1668 GROCER AT YE SOLDIER £32
2579 E.S. (A) ¼ AT THE OLFA TREE, olive-tree £22
2580 THOS SAYLE (S) ½ AT YE WHITE BEARE, SALTER
2581 GEORGE SCAVINTON (E) ¼ Stick of candles
2582 —— (A) ¼ —
2583 IOHN SHORE ½ AT THE CROOKED BILLET
2584 IAM SMITH (M) ¼ Horse and groom, SOPEBOYLR
2585 IOHN TIMBERLAKE (E) ¼ Musket-rest
2585A ANN VARNY ¼ AT THE WHITE SWAN
2586 T.W. (A) ¼ AT THE VNICORNE
2587 THO WATTS ½ AT THE BLEW ANCHOR
2588 THOMAS WILKINSON ½ 1667 AT, bear
2589 ½ AT YE, VNYCORNE BREWHOVS

St Katharine's (Tower)
2590 IAMES ALLEN (M) ¼ 1665
2591 ROBERT ASKE ¼ Crown, SALTER £20
2592 R.B. (S) ¼ THE KINGES HEAD, bust of Henry VIII
2593 W.B. (A) ¼ AT THE BLACKE BOY
2594 *Edward Belitha* ½ 1669 *Grocer*
2595 ROBERT BLACKBVRN ½ Fishmongers' Arms
2596 RICHARD BRYAN (M) ½ 1667 £18
2597 WILLIAM BVTLER (I) ¼ Sugar-loaves, GROSER £15
2598 —— (I) ¼ Grocers' Arms, GROSER
2599 I.C. (A) ¼ THE SWORD AND DAGER
2600 I.C. (S) ¼ AT THE BLEW BELL
2601 T.C. (I) ¼ AT THE LEE HOY, boat
2602 IOHN CHEQVRIGHT (S) ½ 1669 Bell
2603 FRANCIS CLARKE ½ 3 tobacco-rolls
2604 IAMES COOPER (A) ½ 1668 AT THE, rose and crown. *Octagonal* £50
2605 IOHN COVLTON (A) ½ 1667 Globe
2605A —— ½ 1670 Globe; bust of Chas. II
2606 IOHN CVRTIS (F) ¼ Wheatsheaf
2607 I.D. (A) ¼ AT THE 2 DRAY MEN
2608 T.D. (A) ¼ AT THE 2 DRAY MEN
2609 IOHN EDWARDS (M) (½) Wheatsheaf
2610 RICHARD GILBVRT ½ St George & dragon
2611 I.H. (A) ¼ AT THE COOPERS ARMS
2612 I.H. (K) ¼ 1659 AT THE BLACK SWAN
2613 IOHN HAWARD ½ IN HELMET COVRT, St George & dragon
2614 IOHN HEAWARD (M) ¼ SPECTELE MAKER
2615 MARKE HEYNES ½ Coopers' Arms £22
2616 THOMAS HOCK WELL (B) ¼ Horse and cart £35
2616A THO HOPE ¼ 1659 AT THE, ?
2617 *Thomas Houlcroft* (M) ¼ 1665 BY YE CAGE £24
2618 IOHN IARVIS (M) ¼ 1653 Arms, BAKER
2618A M.L. ½ 1669 AT THE FLVSHING RIVER, ship
2619 R.L. (D) ¼ THE 3 TOBACCO PIPES
2620 T.L. (E) ¼ THE 3 TOBACCO ROVLS
2621 THOMAS LACY ½ 1669 St George & dragon
2622 EDWARD LOLESENE ¼ Key
2622A E.M. (M) ¼ AT THE MARLL POT
2623 E.N. (A) ¼ THE PLVM OF FETHERS
2623A I.P. (E) ¼? 'Feathers'
2624 IOHN PERREY ¼ 1669 NEARE YE BARE BREW HOVSE
2625 HENRY ROWE ½ Bakers' Arms, MEALEMAN
2625A I.S. (M) ¼ AT THE ROYALL OKE
2626 WILLIAM STANION (½) Gridiron; sugar-loaf
2627 DANIEL STVTSBERY (E) ½ '68 WINE COOPR
2628 R.T. ¼ 1649 AT THE BLEW BELL, 3 birds
2629 GILBERT TAYLER ½ Archer £32

2629A IACOB VANDEBOCK (M) ¼
2630 W.W. (S) ¼ 1653 AT THE DEARY MADE
2630A BRIGET WHITE ¼ Dolphin
2631 IOHN WHITHORNE (S) ¼ Woman churning, CHESMVNGER
2632 BRIAN WEAVER ¼ Tobacco-roll

St Martin's-in-the-Fields
2633 PETER ALSOP (R) ½ BROKER
2635 WILL FOORD ½ '68 AT YE CROOK BILLET
2637 IAMES HOPKINS (T) ½ 1668 AT YE HARROW £35
2638 IOHN LADD (A) ½ NEARE CHVRCH

St Martin's Le Grand (Aldersgate)
2634 THOMAS ELY ½ Castle gateway
2636 IOHN FVLLERTON ¼ 3 horseshoes £30
2639 IOH BOVDEN (E) ½ Leg in boot
2640 IOHN CORNE (C) ¼ Lady's shoe
2641 THO DOWNES (A) ¼ Fleur-de-lis
2642 E.F. (A) ¼ THE BLACK MORES HEAD
2643 GEORGE GOSNELL (H) ¼ 1664 Windmill, spread eagle
2644 T.H. ¼ AT YE CROSSE KEYES
2645 *Edward Haile* ¼ 1664 Bust of Jas. I
2646 WILLIAM HOLDEN ½ AT YE, man in moon
2647 HENRY HVGGINES (E) ½ Crooked billet
2648 *Thomas Jackson* 1d IN KINGS HEAD COVRT, hand pouring coffee into one of two cups on table
2648A IOSEPH LEE ½ AT YE BLACK, 2-headed eagle
2649 T.M. (A) ¼ THE SONNE
2650 MATT MARRIOTT ½ AT THE KINGS HEAD, Chas. II £32
2650A WILL MASON (A) ¼ Hand holding bird
2651 RICHARD MOSES ½ AT, 2 keys crossed
2652 I.P. (S) ¼ THE DAGGER IN NEW RENTS
2652A WILL PORTER (H) ¼ 1658 Mortar and pestle
2653 R.R. (E) ¼ DOGS HEAD IN THE POT
2654 SAMVEL(L) RICKARDS ¼ 1666 3 harps around sun £32
2655 R.S. (M) ¼ THE HAROW
2656 W.S. (A) ¼ IN THE BORDE(D or T) ENTRY, Drapers' Arms £30
2657 WILLIAM SOLMON ½ IN THE NEW RENTS, lamb and flag
2658 T.T. (A) ¼ THE HAROW
2659 RALPH THOMPSON ½ AT THE, men wrestling
2660 GEORGE THORNE ¼ Ship
2660A N.W. (E) ¼ AT THE HOLEY LAME
2660B IOHN WALLER (I) ½ '64 Angel £35
2661 EDWARD WHITE (M) ½ '69 AT THE, rose and crown
2662 COR WHITEING ½ 1669 DISTILLER
2663 IOS WILSON (M) ½ 1669 Last, CHANDLER

St Martin's Lane (Westminster)
2664 THO ARMITAGE (I) ¼ Lion £12
2665 IOSIAS ASKE (H) ½ YE OKE, tree, SALTER
2666 IOHN BERIMAN ¼ 1657 AT THE, sugar-loaf
2666A WILL BVCKLAND (I) ¼ '58 Boar
2667 I.C. (S) ¼ AT THE BLEW BELL
2668 WILLIAM CARTER (K) ¼ Crown, sceptres
2669 THOMAS DIMBLEBY ¼ HABERDASHER
2670 I.G. (D) ¼ YE QVEENES ARMES TAVERN
2671 GEORGE GVNTHORPE ½ 1667 Man making candles
2671A I.H. ¼ THE PLOW, GOD SPEED YE PLOW
2672 E.I. ¼ 1657 AT YE CROSS KEYS
2672A THOMAS IENINGS (E) ¼ Man making candles
2672B IO LOVELL (A) "2/1" AT THE KINGS ARMES, VINTNER
2673 RICHARD LYNE (E) ¼ Billet
2673A R.N. ¼ Facing bust of (?) James I. In *pb*
2674 W.N. (M) ¼ AT THE TOBACCO RO
2674A ROWLAND OAKELY (C) ¼ '57 Man making candles
2675 WILL ROBINSON ½ 1667 AT YE GOVLDEN, anchor
2676 IOHN ROBOTTOM ½ 1667 AT YE FLEESE TAVERN £20
2676A MARTIN SNELLINGE (E) ¼ Vase of flowers
2677 IAM SVPPLE (M) ¼ AT GOL, fleece
2677A AMY SVTTON ¼ Shepherd and dog
2678 NICHOLAS TOMLINSON (M) ½ '68 Bell
2678A WILLIAM WEBB ½ 1667 AT YE COVLT AND CRADLE, colt in cradle
2679 IOHN WICKS (½) '66 BAKER £30
2680 IOHN WILLIAMS ½ 1667 THE KINGS CHAIRMAN, AT YE BALCONY. *Rev.* legend in 6 lines. *Octagonal*
2681 —— ½——— *rev.* legend in 7 lines. *Round* £32
2682 RICHARD WILLSON (I) ¼ 1657 MEALEMAN £30
2683 (Female issuer) ½ THE WILSHIRE SHEPARD, shepherd and dog

St Mary at Hill (Billingsgate)
2684 SARAH EDWARDS ½ 1669 Salters' Arms. *Octagonal*
2685 IAMES GALATLY ½ 1668 AT YE, 3 castles. *Octagonal* £50
2686 WILLIAM HALL (K) ½ 1668 AT YE KINGS, Arms

2687 IOHN HIVE (D) ½ 1667 AT THE, beehive
2688 THOMAS HVNTE (S) ¼ AT YE, Salters' Arms
2689 WILL LAFTON (S) ¼ MEAL MAN
2690 EDMOND LAWRENCE ½ Fishmongers' Arms
2691 — — (E) ¼ —
2692 MARGRET NORTH ½ 1668 Ship. *Octagonal*
2693 T.T. (M) ¼ 1651 AT THE 3 TONS TAVERN

St Mary Axe (Leadenhall Street)
2694 MARY DELL ¼ 1657 Bell
2694A W.H. (E) ¼ '58 THE BLACK BOAY

St Mary Friars (Fleet Street)
2694B THOMAS ISLEY (S) ¼ AT THE, swan

St Michael's Alley (Cornhill)
2695 STEPHEN HAYWARD, GEO BACKLER ½ *At the ould Coffee house, formerly Bomans*

St Michael's Churchyard (Cornhill)
2695A IOHNS ½ Turk (?), pouring coffee from pot to cup (?)

St Michael's Lane (Thames Street)
2696 THOMAS NVTT ½ NEER THE OLD SWAN, dolphin

St Nicholas Lane (Lombard Street)
2697 I.B. (K) ¼ AT THE BEL
2698 FRANCIS DODSWORTH ½ Lion
2699 IOHN SPINKE (E) ¼ 1657 Wheatsheaf

St Nicholas Shambles (now Newgate Street)
2700 ION ASPINALL (½) Swan, castle
2700A IOHN BVLLOCK (M) ¼ AT THE, sugar-loaf
2701 P.B. (M) ¼ AT THE FLYING HORSE
2702 T.B. (E) ¼ THE READ CROSE
2703 A.C. (E) ¼ AT THE RED LYON
2704 L.D. (I) ¼ AT THE HARROW
2705 T.E. (A) ¼ THE READ BVLL
2705A IOHN FAREL (A) ¼ Bull's head
2706 I.H. (M) ¼ 1649 AT THE SWANN £25
2707 RICHARD HVRST ½ AT THE, swan
2708 IOHN HARPER ½ AT THE, tun
2709 IOSEPH LARKE ¼ Grocers' Arms
2710 I.M. (S) ¼ AT THE BVCHERS ARMES
2711 MATHEW MARIOTT (S) ¼ Crowned bust with sceptre
2712/3 E.S. (A) ¼ THE TALLOW C(A)HANDLER
2714 G.S. (E) ¼ YE RED BVLL
2715 IOH TADPOLE (M) ¼ 1656 HABERDR

St Paul's Churchyard
2716 E.C. ¼ AT THE 3 TVNN TAVERNE £22
2717 W.C. (E) ½ AT THE SAMPSON, Samson and lion
2718 W.C. (A) ¼ AT THE SAMSON. —
2719 GILES CALVERT (E) ¼ AT THE, spread eagle, WEST END
2720 IOHN DICKENSON ¼ Sugar-loaf
2721 IOHN DORMER ¼ '58 AT YE, rose and crown, WEST END
2722 I.B. (S) ¼ n.d. FEATHERS TAVERNE, WESTEND S. PAVLS
2722A I.B. (S) ¼ '58 — —
2723 I.B. (S) ¼ n.d. — IN PAVLS CHVRCHYARD
2723A THO CHESTER ¼ AT THE, 3 sugar-loaves
2724 GEORG GREEN ¼ AT TH, anchor
2725 F.H. ¼ AT ST PETER AND ST PAVLE. St Peter with keys; St Paul with sword
2726 R.H. ¼ AT THE BELL TAVERN
2727 S.H. (M) ¼ THE TOBACCO ROWLE £32
2728 IOHN MILLER ¼ AT THE, windmill; Prince of Wales' feathers, EAST END
2729 IOHN WEBSTER (M) ¼ 1663 AT YE ALMON TREE
2729A MICHAEL WILKINSON (I) ¼ '58 View of St Pauls, SVTLER
2730 (1d) THE COFFE HOVSE AT THE WEST END, Turk's head

St Paul's Market
2730A A.G. ¼ BRANCH IN HAND

St Peter's Lane
2730B PRISSILLA THORNHILL ½ 1668 NEAR HIXES HAL, Haberdashers' Arms

St Swithin's Lane (Lombard Street)
2731 I.C. ½ 1666 AT THE MEALE SHOPP
2732 SAMWELL CLARKE ¼ Shepherd, dog
2732A IOSEPH CLEEVE (E) ¼ Gate, BAKER
2733 WM EMET ½ Bull, bear, horse. **Plate 2** £35
2733A I.G. (M) ¼ Lion
2733B ROB LANGHORNE (E) ¼ Bust of Henry VIII

St Thomas Apostle (near Thames Street)
2734 W.B. (A) ¼ 1649 AT THE GEORGE
2735 IOHN MATHEW ½ 1669 Sugar-loaf
2736 H.R. (M) ¼ Bust of priest
2737 GEORGE SPENCER (A) ½ SILK DIER

Salisbury Court (Fleet Street)
2738 RICHARD BVRMBY (M) ¼ Tallow-chandlers' Arms
2739 WILL HARVEY (A) ¼ AT YE CATT
2740 1d THE SVNNE DYALL, flower £50

Saltpetre Yard
2741 W.B. (E) ¼ 1653 AT THE COCK

(The) Savoy (Strand)
2742 R.D. (M) ¼ AT THE VINCORNE, unicorn £30
2742A WILLIAM HAYTER ½ AT THE, goat

2742B RICHARD HVLL (H) ¼ Unicorn
2743 RICHARD LAWTON ½ '67 AT YE BEL AND 3 CRANES
2744 WILL(IAM) LYNE (E) ¼ AT YE 3 CRANES
2744A T.M. (B) ¼ In *pb*
2745 IOSEPH MAN ½ 1667 Sunflower and sun, OYLMAN
2746 IOHN PEEK (S) ¼ Castle, COOKE
2747 HANNA PVTTNAM ¼ AT THE, unicorn
2748 H.T. (M) ¼ THE ROSE AND CROWNE
2749 P.T. (S) ¼ 1653 THE SVTLER £30

Scalding Alley (Poultry)
2750 IOHN LANSDELL ½ Hand pouring coffee into cup
2750A — — ½? AT YE POST HOVSE COFFIE HOVSE
2751 FRANCIS RVSSELL (E) ¼ '57 Clothworkers' Arms
2751A WIDOW THVRRITON ¼. In *pb*

Schoolhouse Lane (Ratcliff)
2752 G.R. (A) ¼ THE COOPERS ARMES
2753 PERCIVALL TOWLE (T) ½ 1668 BAKER
2754 NICH WATTS (A) ½ Hand holding scissors and curling-irons

Seacole Lane (Snow Hill)
2755 GEORGE BARKER (A) ½ '66 AT YE, 3 tuns
2756 *Samuell Chappell* ¼ 1671 Goldsmiths' Arms
2756A GILES HONE (D) ½ '68 AT THE PVMP, Arms
2757 IOHN MEREIFEILD (M) ¼ Blacksmiths' Arms
2758 RICH WEST (S) ¼ 1662 AT RED, cross

Seething Lane (Great Tower Street)
2758A ANN BABINGTON ½ Crown
2759 RALPH BONNICK (I) ½ '68 AT YE BLACK DOG
2760 EDWARD RADCLIFFE (M) ½ 1667 AT THE PIDE DOG £28
2761 THOMAS RIVERS (I) ¼ Grocers' Arms £30
2762 WILLIAM VASTON ¼ Man making candles

Sentry Gate (The Sanctuary, Westminster)
2763 THOMAS FOVNTAYNE ¼ Fountain
2764 WILLIAM GARWAY (A) ½ 1666 Still £32
2764A W.L. ½ 1668 AT THE GREAT SENTERY, man making candles

Sharp's Alley (Cow Cross)
2765 GEORG ADAMS (M) ¼ 1657
2766 IOHN EVERETT (B) ½ 1667 3 horses
2767 G.F. (M) ¼ 1657 AT THE 3 LYONS £25
2768 THO FARR (M) ¼ 1670 Rose
2769 FRANCIS OLIVER ½ 1667 Leathersellers' Arms
2770 IONATHAN REDOCK (E) ¼ 1663

Sharp's Alley (Leadenhall Street)
2771 F.R. (G) ¼ AT THE SHIP

Sherborne Lane (Lombard Street)
2772 RICH THOMSON ¼ Indian with bow and arrow

Ship Yard (Temple Bar)
2773 *J.D.* ½ Ship
2774 R.G. ½ Guy of Warwick holding spear with boar's head, and sword
2775 IOHN REYNOLDS ½ 1666 Fox carrying goose, COOKE

Shire Lane (Temple Bar)
2776 I.D. (E) ¼ Harp
2777 *J.D.* (*W*) ½ 1666
2778 L.H. ¼ AT THE FRENCH TAVERN, French horn
2779 L.H. ¼ HORNE TAVERN
2780 I.M. (I) ¼ AT THE RED LION
2781 IOHN PARRETT ½ 1667 AT THE SWORD AND BVCKLER £16
2781A *Jerom Powell* ½ *Tobacconist*
2782 E. REYNOLD ½ 1666 AT THE, harp, AND THE, fox £28
2783 *Will Richardson* ½ 1667 £22
2784 THO SKELTON (M) ¼ 3 arrows, MEALMAN
2785 THOMAS SMITH (E) ½ 1667 Anchor
2786 MARGARET TOMSON ¼ Arms
2787 SAMVELL WATERS (L) ½ 3 birds, one on cornsheaf

Shoe Lane (Fleet Street)
2788 IOHN BARKSDALE (A) ¼ Indian smoking
2789 IOHN BRIGHTMAN (I) ¼ Cross
2790 IEREMY BVSHER (S) ¼ SMOKER AT YE, sugar-loaf
2791 ANN CATSTREE ¼ AT YE 5 BELLS
2792 SAMVELL CLEVER (M) ¼ AT COCK, PITT COVRT
2792A IOHN FOX (A) ¼ AT YE GEORG
2793 R.G. ¼ 1659 AT FOVNTAINE CORT GATE
2793A M. H(ickin?) ¼ 'Plough'
2793B ELIZABETH HART ½ 1663 AT THE, 5 bells
2794 ROBERT HISCOCK ½ 1666 AT THE, last
2794A THOMAS HOWLDIN (C) ¼ Man carrying sack
2795 WILLIAM IOHNSON (S) ½ AT YE, bust, IMORTAL BEN
2796 CHARLES LANGWORTH ½ BEHIND THE WINDMILL, tree
2797 ANN LAWRENCE ¼ 1662
2797A RICHARD LOVE (D) ¼ AT THE PLOW

2798 MANSFIELDS COFFEE HOVSE (1d) BY PROVIDENCE, coffee-cups, pipes
2799 ELIZABETH MAYNE ½ 1668 Merchant Taylors' Arms. *Octagonal*
2800 GEORGE MINTMAN (½) Raven
2800A IAMES OLIVER (M) ¼ Shears
2801 IOHN PAYNE (D) ½ 1669 MEALEMAN
2802 I.K. (H) ¼ 1657 Crown, PASTRY COOKE
2803 NICHOLES ROW (½) 1669 Lion; hammer, crown
2804 THOMAS SEELE (A) ¼ Tobacco-roll
2805 IAMES SMITH ¼ 5 bells
2806 IOHN THRAPSON (S) ¼ 1653
2807 AMOS WINCH (M) ½ Bust of Jas. I
2808 (1d) 1672 BEN IOHNSONS HEAD
2809 1d ATT THE CROSE KEYES

Shoemaker Row (Blackfriars)
2809A M.N. ¼ 1664 Boot

Shoreditch
2810 L.B. (I) ¼ AT THE 3 TVNES IN HOLOWEL COART
2811 T.B. (I) ¼ AT THE HORS SHEW
2812 EDMOND BANNISTER (E) ½ 1668 IN HOLLOWAY LANE, lion
2813 IOHN CHAPMAN (A) ¼ Windmill
2813A IOHN CROSLEY (E) ¼ 1665 Rabbit
2814 RICHARD DREW (M) ¼ 1663
2815 I.E. (S) ¼ AT THE FAVLKON
2816 WILLIAM FELLOWES (E) ½ AT THE, stag
2817 IOHN FERRER (R) ¼ St. George & dragon
2818 THOMAS GATELEY (A) ¼ 1664 Bear
2819 WILLIAM GILLAM ½ AT THE IEAN SHORE, Jane Shore and Edward IV
2820 E.H. (E) ¼ 1656 AT THE CROS DAGERS
2820A ROBERT HILL ¼ 1667 AT YE, unicorn
2821 RICHARD HOVLDER ½ 1669 Press, PATTIN MAKER
2822 WILLIAM HVLL ½ AT YE ROYAL CHARLES, ship
2823 DEBORAH IOHNSON ¼ 1664 AT IANE SHORE
2824 HENRYE IORDEN (A) ¼ TALLOW CHANDLER
2825 ROBERT LEAKE ½ 1668 AT THE, man making candles, within crescent moon
2826 FRANCIS MVSTER ¼?
2827 S.P. ¼ 1652 THE ROSE AND CROWNE £30
2828 IOHN PARSON ½ 1668 Gridiron
2829 C.R. ¼ 1657 AT SVN
2830 N.S. (L) ¼ 1656 AT THE CROWN
2831 N.S. (L) ¼ 1657 —
2831A P.S. ¼ 1652 AT THE OLD SWAN
2832 IOHN TRIMNELL (I) ¼ 1657 Stag
2833 FRANCIS TVNSTEED (E) ½ 1668 Man making candles
2834 H.W. (M) ¼ 1656 THE HARTIECHOAKE
2834A EDWARD WALKER (M) ¼ OF HOLYWELL COVRT, saint
2835 ROGER WARE ½ 1667 Kings' Arms
2836 IOHN WOODESON ½ 1669 Plough

Silver Street (Wood Street, Cheapside)
2837 IOHN LAVRENCE (S) ½ 1665. **Plate 2**
2838 —LAWRANCE (S) ¼ 1659 £28

(West) Smithfield
2839 THO ALLDRIDGE (M) ½ AT THE CATORN WHEEL, Catherine wheel £28
2840 SIMON BERRY (E) ½ 1664 Bakers' Arms
2841 FRANCIS BLECHINDEN ½ 1666 AT THE, goat, TAVERN
2842 IOSEPH BROOKES ½ Crown
2843 LIONELL BVFKINE (½) 1666 AT THE, 3 roses, NEER CLOTH FAIRE GATE
2844 —— (½) 1669 —— NEER CLOTHE FAIRE GATE
2845 FRANCIS BVRTON (C) ½ 1668 AT YE BLACK, bear with chain
2845A FRANCES — (C) ¼ AT, bear with chain
2846 IAMES BYARD (E) ½ 1666 AT THE 3, sugar-loaves £30
2847 C.C. (M) ½ 1664 AT THE HARTS HORNS, THE COFFE HOVS
2848 I.C. (A) ¼ AT THE CROVN TAVERN
2848A S.C. ¼ THE ANTLOP TAVERN
2849 W.C. (I) ¼ CONFECTIONER AT YE, stag's head
2849A FRANCIS CLIPSHAM ¼ Bunch of grapes
2849B IO COGGS (S) ½ 1668 NEAR YE HARTS HORNES, CHANDLER
2850 ROBERT CONAWAY (E) ¼ Still
2851 RICHARD CVNSTABLE (E) ½ 1667 Heart
2852 RICH CONSTABLE (F) ¼ Heart
2852A R.D. ¼ THE BVLL HEAD TAVERN
2853 R.D. (I) ¼ THE WHIT HART TAVERN £32
2854 FREEMAN FANN ½ 1669 AT YE PVRSE
2855 *Robert Fletcher* ½ 1666
2855A IOHN GOVLDINGE ½ 1668 Man and lion
2856 SAMVELL GRAVES ½ 1669 AT THE, Tallowchandlers' Arms
2857 —— (I) ¼ 1657 St. George & dragon
2858 T.H. (D) ¼ AT THE GEORGE INN
2859 RIC HARPER (A) ¼ AT THE HARP
2860 THEO HOTHERSALE (E) ¼ Stag
2861 THO HATTON ½ 1664 ANTILOP, BIBIS VINVM SALVTA
2862 *Euodias Inman* ½ *Gouldsmith*
2863 EDWARD IZATT (I) ½ 1668 AT YE, greyhound

2863A THO IONES (E) ¼ '59 AT THE, Paschal lamb
2863B THO KEM ½ NEXT THE RAM, GROCER
2864 R.M. (E) ¼ ATT THE ROSE INN
2865 I.M. (T) ¼ THE QVEENE HEAD TAVERN, bust of Elizabeth I
2866 IAMES MARCH ½ AT THE, dolphin; negro's head
2867 IOHN MERIEFIELD (M) ½ 1669 AT YE, ? female head
2868 IOHN MILES ½ 1669 AT YE, swan, TAVERN
2869 TYMOTHEY NEWBEY (A) ¼ Dolphin
2870 G.P. (A) ¼ THE NEW QVEENES HEAD, Elizabeth I
2870A WILLIAM PAGE ½ 1666 Man making candles
2871 RICHARD PEMBLE (E) ¼ Frying pan
2872 IOHN PHILIPSON (I) ½ 1667 Hand holding sceptre and crown, IRONMONGER
2872A IOHN PORTER (M) ¼ AT THE, horse
2873 IOHN REEVE ½ Bull and still
2874 I.S. ¼ '57 THE BLACKE BVLL
2875 P.S. (E) ¼ '58 YE COACH & HORSES
2876 IOH SAWYER ¼ AT YE NAGS HEAD, still
2877 KATHREN SELLAM ¼ 3 tuns
2878 IAMES SHERL(E)Y ½ AT THE KINGS ARMES
2878A ABRAHAM SMITH (M) ¼ Ship
2878B GEORGE SMITH ½ CHEESMONGER OVER AGAINST YE SHIPPENS (= sheep pens)
2879 THOMAS TAYLOR (A) ½ '67 AT THE, coach and horses with driver
2880 IEFFER(E)Y THOMAS ½ GROCER OVER AGAINST YE SHIPPENS £32
2881 IOHN WARREN ¼ '58 Anchor, GROCER
2882 THO WATSON ½ GROCER VPPON YE PAVED STONS, NEARE COW LANE
2883 CHARLES WHITE (M) ½ AT YE RED LION
2884 THO WHITE (E) ½ AT YE BLACKMORES HEAD, HIS OB £35
2885 WALTER WILLEC ½ Tallowchandlers' Arms
2885A EDWARD WOODWARD (A) ½ Crossed swords. *Heart-shape*

Smithfield Bars, and **Without Bars**

2885B THO ADAMS (A) ¼ Butchers' Arms
2886 T.B. (H) ¼ CVMFIT MAKER, angel
2887 IOHN BAKER (K) ½ 1669 Pole-axes crossed, BVTCHER
2888 IOHN BOND (M) ½ AT THE BVLLS HEAD £22
2889 IOSEPH COLLINS ½ AT THE 3, sugar-loaves
2890 FRANCIS CLIPSHAM ½ AT THE, bunch of grapes
2890A —— ¼ Bunch of grapes
2890B ROBERT CVRD (S) ½ FISHMONGER
2891 ROBERT CVRTIS ½ 1669 Fleur-de-lis £30
2892 THOMAS FELL (I) ½ '67 AT YE ANGELL
2893 GODFREY FOLIAMBE ½ 1666 AT YE GOLDEN, angel, CONFECTIONR £28
2894 ROBERT PITT (E) ½ 3 tuns
2895 RICHARD RICHMOND ½ 1667 AT YE, Indian holding arrow £35
2896/7 SALOMON SIBLEY (K) ¼ Cage
2898 THO STREAM (M) ¼ Boar's head, GROCER

Snow Hill

2898A RAPHE ABBOTT ¼ AT THE HOLY LAM
2899 RICH AYNSWORTH ½ 1669 AT THE STILL
2900 E.B. (E) ¼ 1649 AT THE COK
2901 GABRIEL BONNER (D) ¼ Grocers' Arms
2902 A.C. (M) ¼ Weathercock on spire, APOTHECARY
2903 GEORGE FOSSON ½ AT THE FOVNTAIN TAV
2904 (Same as 3501)
2904A IOSEPH HIDE ½ 1669 IN GREENE DRAGON
2905 THO HITCHCOCK (E) ¼ AT STARR
2905A THOMAS LAWRANCE ¼ AT THE TALBOT
2905B R.N. (E) ¼ 1656 AT THE COK
2906 R.N. (T) ¼ 1660 AT THE COK
2907 BARACK NORMAN (A) ¼ Naked boy holding cup, CHEESM
2908 THO PVLTENEY (M) ¼ '57 AT YE BALL
2909 ALEXANDER PRESTON ¼ *3 Gloves*
2910 ALLEN SARTAN (E) ¼ Tobacco-rolls
2910A FRAN STAMAR (M) ¼ BLACK LION
2911 L.W. ¼ AT THE LION AND LAMBE £32
2912 IOHN WEST ½ 1668 TINMAN AT THE CROWNE

Soho

2913 IOHN BROWNE (E) ¼ 1664 Pelican and young, MEALMAN
2914 EDMVN MOLLTON (C) ¼ AT YE CHEKER
2915 THOMAS RODGERS ½ 1667 Dog baiting bull
2915A P.S. (I) ¼?

Somers Quay (Lower Thames Street)

2916 STEPHEN LOCK (A) ½ '68 Queen's head
2917 IOHN MICHELL 1d Tilt-boat, passengers and boatmen. *Octagonal*
2918 AILL(I *or* Y)S PASCALL 1d AT YE QVEENS HEAD

2919 IOHN SIMMONS (H) ½ 1666 Still, fire beneath £22
2920 M. ¼ SWAN WITH 2 NECKS
2921 M. ¼ — BOS ALLE

Southampton Buildings (Holborn)
2922 I. CLEAVER ¼ 1658 AGNST YE ARCH, Grocers' Arms
2923 F.G. (E) ¼ YE PVRPLE LYON
2924 GEORGE IVSTIS (R) ¼ Bakers' Arms
2925 THO KENCIE ½ Crown £35
2926 SVSAN KIDDER (B) ¼ 1658 SEMSTER
2927 SIMONE OSGOOD (M) ¼ MEALE MAN
2928 IOHN WILKINSON (E) ¼ WHIT, lion
2928A NICHOLAS YATES ½ Bakers' Arms

Spitalfields
2929 NATHANIEL BARRS ½ 1669 AT YE, maypole
2930 W.C. (M) ¼ AT YE BALL AND RAVEN
2931 RICHARD MIDLATON (I) ½ 1667 3 tuns £30
2932 (Same as 972)
2933 IOHN ORMES (E) ¼ AT THE RED LYON £32
2934 IOHN SAMMON (P) ½ Salmon, bowl
2935 ROB WALLEY (S) ½ BREWER AT THE FOVNTAINE £30
2936 RALPH WILKES ½ AT THE, Turk holding coffee-cup £32
2937 —— (R) (½) —— COFFIE MAN

Spittlegate
2938 T.A. (S) ¼ AT THE KINGS HEAD, bust of Chas. I
2938A ROGER IVES (I) ¼ 1667 Harp

Sprusens Island (Wapping) (now Prusom Street)
2938B T.H. (A) ¼ THE SIGNE OF THE COCK

Stable Yard (Westminster)
2939 ROGER KENYON (A) ½ 1666 King's Arms. **Plate 2**
2940 I.N. (I) ¼ AT THE WHITE HORSE £25

Staining Lane (Wood Street, Cheapside)
2941 IONATHAN MAREFEILD (M) ¼ Royal oak
2942 I.T. (T) ¼ THE HAND AND SHEERS

Stanhope Street (Clare Market)
2943 ROBERT COLLINS ¼ Lion
2944 H.H. (E) ¼ 1657 AT ST HVGHES BONES
2945 I.K. (A) ¼ Keys crossed; dog and duck
2946 IOHN RVFFIN ¼ Man making candles
2947 THO SCARDEFEILD (E) ¼ Man making candles (?)

Star Alley
2948 PHILLIP WILKINSON (I) ¼ BAKER

Steelyard Hall (Thames Street)
2949 RICHARD DERNELLY (S) ¼ 1661

Stocks Market
2950 EDWARD BARRETT (1d) Arms
2950A I.C. (M) ¼? 'Drapers Armes'

Stool Lane
2951 ARTHAR BROOKE (A) ¼ AT YE RED LYON

Strand
2952 SAM ALLATT ½ AGAINST IVEY BRIDG, queen's head, IRONMONGER
2952A IOHN ALLISON ¼ AT THE GATE
2952B IOSEPH ASHNVRST (S) ½ AT YE COCK, cock and jug
2953 RICH ASHWIN (E) ½ NEAR SVMERSET HOVSE, 3 sugar-loaves; maypole
2954 R.B. (M) ¼ '57 YE GOLDEN LYON AND SVN
2954A W.B. ¼? 'Swann'
2955 MATTHIAS BOWMAN ½ 1667 Escalop-shell
2956 IOHN BROMLEY ½ 1666 NEARE YORKE HOVSE, soap-box
2957 ISAAC BROWNE (E) ¼ NEERE CHARING CROSS, rose and crowne
2958 A.C. ¼ AT YE KINGS HEAD TAVERN, bust of Henry VIII
2959 I.C. (E) ¼ AT THE ANGELL, angel holding scroll
2960 I.C. (M) ¼ 1657 AT YE CROS KEYES, COOKE
2961 ROBT CHAMBERLAINE (I) ½ AT YE MAYPOLE, maypole, sugar-loaf, 3 cloves
2962 NAT CHILD ½ NEAR YE MAY POAL, boar's head pierced by 3 arrows £32
2963 PHILLIP COMPLIN ½ 1666 AT THE, maypole, building, DISTILER £30
2964 WILLIAM CONSTABLE ½ 1664 Prince of Wales' feathers
2965 GEORGE CRAFTES (A) ½ 1666 AT THE SVN
2966 ELLES CRISPE ½ 1669 AT YE BLACK BOY £24
2966A SIMON CROSSE (A) ¼ AT MAYPOLE, sun
2967 I.D. ¼ 1653 AT THE AXE
2968 I.D. (K) ¼ AT YE HALFE MOONE TAVERN, half-moon and bunch of grapes
2969 THO DAY ½ Branch, TALLOW CHANDLER £32
2970 IOHN DOLLEN (D) ½ POVLTERER BY YE MAYPOLE, bell with maypole through it
2971 IOHN DVTTON ½ Head of Henry VIII; NEARE YE, maypole
2972 WILLIAM ELKINGTON (S) ¼ AT YE, bell, TAVERN
2973 ROBERT FAWCETT (E) ½ 1666 A MEALE MAN

2974 NICHOLAS FITZ IEOFFERY ½ Sunflower, MILLINER
2975 E.G. ¼ THE LOBSTER AT THE MAIPOLE £22
2976 RICH GEORGE ¼ 1664 AT BREWERS YARD END, St. George & dragon; cock and flagon
2977 CHARLES GIBBON ¼ Dragon
2978 ANTHONY GOLDSTON ¼ Female bust; 4 cloves, CONFECTIONER
2979 FRANC GROVE (E) ¼ AT WHIT, swan, AGAINST SOMERSET HOVSE
2980 C.H. ¼ THE WHITE HARTE BREWHOVSE
2981 E.H. ¼ 1657 THE FOVNTAINE TAVERNE
2982 RICH HARABEN ¼ 1661 GROSER AT EAGLES COVRT £30
2983 ST HARRISE ½ IRONMONGER AT THE, lobster, AGAINST YE, maypole and building
2983A W. Hayter ¼?
2984 WILL HORSLEY ½ 1667 CHEES-MONGER NEARE YORK HOVS
2985 THOMAS HVNT ½ 1666 9 rolls of bread £18
2986 F.I. (M) ¼ AT THE GOLDE LYON TAVERN £32
2986A G.I. (E) ¼? 'Fountain Tavern'
2987 R.I. (M) ¼ AT YE GRAY HOWND TAVERNE
2988 IEREMIAH IVES ½ 1666 AT THE, Kings' Arms, CHEESMONGER £32
2989 FRAN IEFFERY (A) ½ THE GOLDEN, lion, BY YORK HOVS
2989A THOMAS KIRBYE (D) ¼ 5 bells, VINTNER
2990 I.L. (A) ¼ NERE CHERING CROS
2991 R.L. ¼ 1657 AT YE ONE BELL
2992 R.L. (M) ¼ NEARE SOMERSET H £30
2993 THO LANGTON (D) ¼ AT YE MITER
2994 GEORGE LANGFORD (S) ¼ AT EXCETER, city view £20
2995 *Richard Lyone* ½ Lion pouring from coffee-pot into cup
2996 S.M. (S) ¼ Press
2996A ANTHONY MOREING ½ BREWER AT YE WHITE HART
2997 IAMES MOREY ¼ 1656 AT YE WHIT HART
2998 L.P. (E) ¼ AT THE SALVTATION TAVERNE
2999 IOHN PERRIS ½ 1666 AT THE HARE £32
3000 WILLIAM PHLIS (E) ¼ Arms, BAKER
3001 EDWARD PRICE ½ AT YE MITER & ROSE TAVERNE
3002 B.R. (A) ¼ 1656 AT THE HARPE £32
3003 EDWARD ROBERTS ½ GROCER NEAR YORK HOVSE, Drapers' Arms £32
3004 IACOB ROBIN (E) ½ AT PRINCE RVPERTS HEAD
3005 THO ROGERS ¼ 1658 MEALE MAN
3006 CALIXT RVST ¼ 1655 Apothecaries' crest (rhinoceros); pot of lilies
3007 G.S. (M) ¼ 1657 AT YE 3 SVGAR LOAVES
3008 *Thomas Salisbury* ½ NERE CHARING CROS, 3 falcons on perch
3009 GEORGE SMITH ½ AGAINST YORK HOVSE AT YE, crown
3010 —— (A) ¼ 1658 GROCR
3011 CHARLES STVRTON ¼ AT THE SWAN
3012 RICHARD SVMPTER (E) ¼ 1664 Greyhound £22
3013 E.T. (E) ¼ AT THE ANCKER
3014 IOHN TWISLETON ½ AT YE, building
3015 *Robert Ward* ¼ 1664 Bottle, GLAS SELLER
3016 IOHN WILLIAMS (E) ½ AT YE CROWN, VINTNER
3017 LE WILLSON ½ 1666 AT THE, bust of Henry VIII, TAVERN
3018 1d 1665 AT THE CANARY HOVSE, wreath of vine-leaves £40

Strand Bridge
3019 I.B. (I) ¼ AT YE GREENE MAN
3019A I.B. (M) ¼ AT Y RED BVLL
3020 IOHN BROMLEY ½ 1666 Barber's soap-box
3021 WILL BRVNSLEY ½ AT LILLYS HOVS, clock-face and hands
3022 LAWRENCE GIFFORD (E) ¼ Patten-Makers' Arms
3023 I.H. ¼ AT THE BLACK BVLL £25
3024 WILLIAM IEFFERSON ½ Hand-barrow
3025 C.S. ¼ AT THE 2 SVGER LOFES
3026 IOHN STATIONER (G) ½ '69 YE GOLDEN BALL £28
3027 THOMAS WILLIAMS ½ Goat, COAL SELR £30

Sun Court (Petticoat Lane, Whitechapel)
3027A A.C. ¼? 'Sunn'

Swan Alley (Ludgate Hill)
3027B ION WATTS (S) ¼ 1659 BAKER

Swan Alley (St John Street, Clerkenwell)
3027C A. HARRIS 1d AT Y WORCESTER-SHIRE HOVSE, Arms of Worcester

Swan Street
3027D 1d THE RED BALL, Roman numerals around sun's rays

Sweeting's Rents (Cornhill)
3027E IOHN BOOTH ½ 1666 Bell
3028 THO CHVB (M) Lion, YE COOKE
3029 (½) THE SVLTANESS A COFFEE HOVSE, arms £38

Temple Bar

3030 EDWARD APTHORP ¼ 3 sugar-loaves £28
3031 I.B. (A) ¼ AT S DVNSTANS TAVERN
3032 IOHN BATTELL (D) ¼ AT LION TAVERN
3033 T.B. (S) ¼ THE HAND AND HOALY BVSH AT S.C. (= St. Clements)
3034 GEORGE BRYAN ½ AT YE, sugar-loaf
3035 — BRYAR ½ — sugar-loaf between G.B.
3036 IOHN BVTLER ½ Lion, FRV(I)TERER
3037 H.C. (M) ¼ 1655 THE COCK ALE HOVSE
3038 R.C. (M) ¼ AT THE GREEN CVSHEN, cushion
3039 NICHOLAS COTTON ¼ Dragon
3040 THOMAS DENMAN ½ AT THE KINGS HEAD, plough
3041 IAM GOVER (K) ¼ 1657 Gate, APOTHECAR
3042 IOSEPH GVRNEI (I) ¼ AT THE, man making candles, within crescent
3043 I.H ¼ AT THE LAMBE TAVERN(E)
3044 R.H. (E) ¼ AT THE ROSE TAVERN
3045 T.H. ¼ AT THE MAN IN THE MOON £32
3046 HVGH HALL (E) ½ 1666 AT YWHITHART
3046A — HALLE ½ — AT THE WHIT HART
3047 IOSEPH HAST (M) ¼ Dragon, OYLMAN
3048 THOMAS HAWARD ½ 1666 Heart crowned
3049 S.I. (A) ¼ AT THE GOLDEN FLEECE, fleece on *obv.*
3050 S.I. (A) ¼ AT YE GOLDEN FLEECE, fleece on *rev.*
3051 IOHN IAMES (K) ¼ Horse, sun
3051A GORGE IENNINGS (M) ¼ Cow suckling calf
3052 I.K. (M) ¼ AT THE CROWNE
3053 I.L. (K) ¼ AT THE WHIT HORSE, horse, sun above
3054 (Probably same as 173)
3055 IOHN LAWTON (I) ¼ The Baptist's head on charger
3056 WILLIAM LOVINGE (D) ½ AT THE, Baptist's head on charger
3056A E.M. (H) ¼ 'Swann'
3057 I.M. (E) ¼ AT THE GOVLDEN LOCK, door-lock £20
3058 ROBART MATHEWS (M) ¼ Plough
3058A R.M. (M) ¼ THE PAVLSGRAVE HEAD
(*William Morrison* see Appendix after no. 3543)
3059 I.P. ¼ AT THE WINDE MILL. **Plate 2** £35
3060 RICHARD PARROT (I) ¼ Lion
3061 G.R. (B) ¼ 1650 THE ELEVANT, elephant, castle on back
3062 I.R. (D) ¼ THE PAVLSGRAVE HEAD £22
3063 R.R. (S) ¼ THE TALLOW C(H *or* AR) ANDLER
3064 IOHN RADFORD (E) ½ '68 AT YE GOVLDEN, spectacles
3065 D.S. ½ THE PALSGRAV HEAD TAVERN
3066 W.S. (M) ¼ 1649 AT THE SHIP £13
3067 IOHN SPICER ½ 1666 AT YE SVGER, 3 sugar-loaves
3068 IOSEPH SPICER ½ 1666 AT YE 3 SVGER, loaves
3069 FRANCIS STONE ¼ MEAL MAN
3070 RICHARD TAYLER (A) ½
3071 I.W. (S) ¼ AT THE D AND DVNSTANS, St. Dunstan pulling devil's nose with tongs
3072 W.W. (M) ¼ AT THE DOLPHIN £25
3073 THOMAS WASTCOATE ½ IN STAR COVRT, star

Tenter Alley (Little Moorfields)

3074 I.S. (S) ¼ Pelican feeding young

Thames Street

3075 G.A. ¼ AT THE WHITE BARE, GROCER £30
3076 H.A. ¼ AT THE 3 GOATS HEAD
3077 G.B. (K) ¼ AT THE SHVGER LOFE, Grocers' Arms
3078 I.B. (S) ¼ AT THE ADAM AND EVE
3079 T.B. (E) ¼ THE NAG(G)S HEAD TAVERN(E) £25
3080 ROBERT BAYNES (S) ½ 1668 AT THE, boar and 3 horseshoes £20
3081 ROGER BAYNES (I) ¼ GOLDEN, horseshoe £24
3082 IAMES BEECH ½ 1666 SWAN ALLY AT YE FOOT OF GARLICK HILL
3083 EDWARD BLAKE (H) ¼ Fortress or ship with men
3084 RICHARD BROWNE (R) (½) 1659 THREE QVEENES
3084A R.C. (A) ¼ 1653 AT THE MAREMAID
3084B MATHEW CARR (M) ½ '69 AT YE ROSE TAVERN AT YE OVLD SWAN
3085 BENIAMIN CLARKE ½ NEARE YE OLD SWAN, plough
3085A ¼ 'of the Plough neare Ould Swan'
3086 IOHN CLARKE (A) ¼ Woodmongers' Arms, WOODMONG
3087 WILL DOD (E) ¼ AT YE WHITE LYON WHARFE, lion
3088 A.E. ¼ AT THE STAR
3089 A.E. (E) ¼ AT THE SVGGAR LOFE
3090 I.E. (A) ¼ AT THE FLING HORS, winged horse
3091 THOMAS ELKIN (E) ½ 1667 AT THE, cock and magpie
3092 RICHARD EVANS (E) 1d AT THE OLD SWAN, view of London, near bridge £60
3093 —— (S) ½ AT YE OVLD, swan
3094 IOH EWER ¼ 1658 AGAINST WICKEN KEY, king's head

3095 WILL FIELD (S) (½) AT THE, lobster, NEERE QVEEN HITH LON £25
3096 M.G. (M) ¼ AT TO TOBACO ROWLES
3096A ROBERT GOLDSON (S) ¼ NEARE BLEED STR HILL, phoenix
3097 T.H. (I) AT THE HALFE MOON AT RAPHS KEY
3098 W.H. (K) ¼ AT (THE) BVLL HEAD, bull's head; sun, hand
3098A WILL HADDOW (½?) AT YE ADAM & EVE. In *pb*
3099 IOHN HARDIE ½ 1668 AT THE, bunch of grapes in hoop, BY DOV GATE
3100 IAMES HAWKINS (V) ¼ AT LYON KEY, lion and key
3100A ROB HELLOW (E) ½ AT YE BAYNORDS CASTL, CHANLR
3101 IOHN HEMING (R) ¼ Greyhound £30
3102 IOHN HINDE ½ 1668 BAKER NEAR QVEENE HITH GATE £28
3103 F.I. (S) ¼ AT THE LION
3104 IO IOHNSON ½ 1669 IN BRICKHILL LANE, vixen
3105 *Edward Jones* ½ 1668 *over against the Custome House*, King's Arms £32
3106 IOHN IONES ½ 1666 AT DIERS HAL, bull £30
3107 A.K. (E) ¼ AT THE SVGGAR LOFE
3108 M.M. (P) ¼ AT THE BLEW ANCOR
3109 WILLIAM MASLIN ½ 1663 Bear with staff. **Plate 2** £30
3110 HVMPHREY MIDELLMOR (E) ½ '68 AGST TRIGSTAIRES, King's Arms
3111 HENRY MORTON (V) ¼ AT YE, crossed swords
3112 P.N. ¼ AT THE, horseshoe, NERE THE OLD SWAN GROSER
3113 ROBERT NORIS (M) ¼ GLOVER
3114 P. NVCE (N) ¼ 1652 AT THE BLACK BELL £22
3115 EDWARD OAKES (G) ¼ AT BENETS CASTLE, windmill
3116 ROWLAND OWEN (A) ½ 3 kings
3116A W.P. (M) ¼ THE 3 TVNNES TAVERN
3117 STEPHEN PHIPPS ½ '59 AT THE, swords crossed
3118 F.R. (E) ¼ 1651 THE LYON AND KEY £25
3119 S.S. (D) ¼ 1657 THE QVEENS HEAD, Elizabeth I £32
3120 ROB SELMAN (M) ¼ KINGS HEAD
3121 RICH SEWELL (S) ¼ AT THE PINKE, ship
3122 RICHARD SPIRE (I) ¼ Initials in hoop
3123 WILLIAM STEERE (K) ¼ 7 stars
3124 OBADIAH SVRRIDGE (A) ½ 1668 IN ANGELL ALLY, angel
3125 W.T. (E) ¼ AT THE RED LYON IN THE OLD SWAN
3126 B.W. (E) ¼ AT THE CROSE BVLETS
3127 I.W. (E) ¼ AT THE PRINCES ARMS, P.C.
3128 IOHN WICKES (M) ¼ BAKER, FRYER LANE
3129 R.W. (M) ¼ AT THE BLACK(E) SWAN
3130 SARAH WOOD ½ 1669 AT THE, male bust, cap on head, and wheatsheaf £32
3131 IOSEPH WORWOOD ½ 1669 Helmet
3132 WILL YEELES ½ AT GOLDEN BALL £30

Thieving Lane (Westminster)
3133 IOHN BROWNE (A) ¼ AT THE GRIFIN

Threadneedle Street
3134 W.A. (F) ¼ AT THE 2 WRASLERS
3135 THO BLAGRAVE ½ AT YE, crown, TAVERN £35
3135A THOMAS BVRDET (M) ¼ AT, Fleur-de-lis
3136 WILL GOODWIN ½ AT YE, King's Arms, TAVERN
3137 B.P. ¼ AT YE KINGS ARMES TAVER
3138 WM STONYER ½ AGT YE FRENCH CHVCH, Turk's head £35

Three Colt Alley (Cinnamon Street, near Wapping Docks)
3139 T.O. (M) ¼ 1653 AT THE BELL £32

Three Cranes Wharf (Thames Street)*
3140 ROB IACKSON (I) ¼ AT YE RED, portcullis £32
3141 EDWARD NORMAN (S) ¼ AT YE, fox carrying crane
3141A EDWARD PEMBERTON ¼ 1670 Shield with 3 buckets
3142 EDWARD PINCHON (K) ¼ Arms

Three Fox Court (Long Lane, Smithfield)
3142A RICH DREW ½ 3 foxes; crescent moon

Three Leg Alley (Fetter Lane)
3143 IOHN ROWLAND (G) ¼ 1663 Sun crowned

Three Leg Court (Whitecross Street)
3144 IASPER COOPER (A) ½ King's head

Three Nuns Alley (Threadneedle Street)
3145 CORNELIVS GLOVER 1d NEAR YE OLD POST HOVS, TRVSSMAKER, horseman blowing horn. *Copper* with piece of *brass* in centre
3146 RICHARD KEN (E) ½ 3 nuns
3147 THOMAS LOWE (M) ¼ 3 nuns
3147A CHAR WELLENS ½ 3 nuns

Throgmorton Street
3148 ROBERT CHARLES (I) ¼ AT YE, nag's head

* See also Appendix after no. 3543

3149 IOBE SARGEANT 1d COOKE AT THE, stag

Tilt Yard (Westminster)
3150 RICHARD WASHBOVRNE (A) ½ 1666 AT THE, bust of Duke of Albemarle, SVTTLER £22

Tothill Fields
3151 WILL CRASKEES (A) ¼ IOYNER

Tothill Street (Westminster)
3152 W.A. (E) ¼ AT THE HORES SHOW £15
3152A E.B. (A) ¼ YE KATHERN WHEELE TAVERN
3153 IOANE BARTLITT ¼ WHITE HART £18
3153A — BARTLETT ½ 1669 Scales
3154/5 ROBERT BLACKDEN (I) ¼ 3 birds £32
3156 M.C. ¼ AT THE WHEAT SHEAF £28
3157 ANDREW CARTER ½ BELL
3158 ROGER COOKE ¼ THE EAGLE AND CHILD, CHANLER
3159 *William Done* (A) ½ 1668 *at the fleece*
3160 I.F. (I) ¼ AT THE 3 PIDGENS £28
3161 R.F. (A) ¼ 1651 THE CROWNE £14
3161A T.F. (I) ¼ AT THE SVGAR LOFE
3162 MICHAELL FIDSALL (S) ¼ Arms
3163 RALPH FIRBANCKE (E) ¼ Hart
3164 E.H. (K) ¼ '57 YE GOVLDEN FLEECE
3165 IOHN HARISON ¼ AT THE BLACK LYON £22
3166 PAVL HEATH (A) ¼ BAKER £30
3167 THO HVCCHINES ¼ Tobacco-roll
3168 *Henry Hurly* (E) ½ 1668 AT YE BAG OF NAILS, bag of nails, hammer
3169 M.L. ¼ '57 AT THE LYON £28
3169A R.M. (S) ¼ AT THE GROCERS ARMES
3170 W.M. (I) ¼ AGAINST THE CHAPEL, fox
3171 IAMES MILLER (M) ¼ Fleur-de-lis, TALOW CHANDLER
3172 IOHN RIX ¼ 1655 Rose and crown
3173 EDMVND TANNER (E) ½ 1668 AT YE GOLDEN BALL
3174 WILL WADLY (A) ¼ AT, greyhound
3175 WIL WADLEY ¼ GOLDEN LYON

(The) Tower
3176 MORGAN COWARNE ½ Rose and crown £25
3177 PHILLIP GARDENER ¼ 1652 Naked boy astride barrel; child seated, holding cornstalks and sickle £25

Tower Ditch
3178 PAVL BADCOCK ½ 1669 Ship
3179 WILLIAM BREND (B) ¼ 3 harts
3180 PHILLIP IACOB (A) ¼ Harrow £32
3181 WILLIAM LANGLEY (H) ¼ 1666 Oar
3182 WILLIAM LILLYSTONE ½ 1667 Mercers' Arms £32
3183 IOHN MVRRE (E) ¼ AT THE RED LION
3183A THOMAS ROLLE ¼ 3 bales; crossed rapiers
3184 G.S. (M) ¼ AT THE RED LYON
3184A EDWARD SANDS (I) ¼ 1655 Crossed trumpets
3184B ¼? '3 conyes and cross daggers'

Tower Dock, Stairs and **Wharf**
3185 M.C. (H) ¼ THE ROSE AND CROWN
3186 A.S. ¼ AT THE GOLDEN ANKER
3187 D.G. (M) ¼ AT THE 3 TVNNS
3188 T.K. (D) ¼ THE BLEW ANKER £25
3189 G.P. (A) ¼ AT THE 3 MARINERS £30
3190 RICHARD STONE (E) ¼ BAKARE £28
3191 TIMOTHY STEPHENSON ½ 1664 OLD, rose
3192 IOHN WATERS (E) ½ 1669 AT YE COCK. *Octagonal*

(Great) Tower Hill
3192A C.A. (R) ¼ THE HORSHOW TAVERN
3193 GEORGE ALLSOP ½ Ship's gun
3194 THOMAS CLARKE (A) ½ 1667 AT THE, Indian holding dart
3195 HENRY COLEMAN (E) (½) 1666 AT THE VICTVALL OFFICE, arms £24
3195A L.D. (E) ¼ AT GOVDON PELLICAN
3195B IOHN DAIVIS (A) ¼ TRY THE BOVL
3195C WILLIAM DVRBVRN ½ Rose
3196 RICHARD EVSDEN ¼ King's head b.s.
3196A E.F., S.F. ¼ HERE THE POSTERNE, jackboot
3197 IA GODFREY ¼ 1662 Rose, IRONMONGER
3198 THO HOGSFLESH ½ COOPER IN THE STILL YARD. *Octagonal*
3198A W.P. ¼ AT THE BLACKE BOYE
3199 CLEMENT PLVMSTED (M) ¼ 1666 Horseshoe
3199A Antho Ringwood ¼?
3199B ROBERT SEWILL ½ Chequers
3200 GEORGE TAYLOR ¼ 1651 BAKER
3201 T.W. (D) ¼ 1649 AT THE ANGEL TAVERNE
3202 IOHN WELLS (S) ¼ BACKER

Tower Street
3203 G.A. (D) ¼ AT THE GREHOVND
3204 T.B. (E) ¼ AT THE SALVT ATION TAVERNE
3205 BENEDICK BAREFOOTE (A) ¼ Crossed keys
3206 RALPH BVTCHER (A) ¼ 1664 3 sugar-loaves
3207 R.C. ¼ 1659 AT THE BLACK SWAN
3207A MARY CHILD ¼ 1666 Grocers' Arms
3208 WILLIAM COX (M) ¼ AT THE, king's head
3209 EDWARD DRAYNER (A) ¼ King's head
3210 STEPHEN EARLE ½ 1666 Grocers' Arms
3211 RICHARD FINCH (I) ¼ Wheatsheaf

3212 IOHN GOSLING ¼ 1658 3 cauliflowers (?)
3213 A.H. (E) ¼ AT THE BLEW HELMET
3213A RICHARD HARISON ½ 1666 AT THE COFFE HOVSE
3213B WILL HIRTT (P) ¼ AT SWAN. Grocers' Arms
3213C S.L. (A) ¼ AT THE GOLDEN HELMET
3214 E.M. (M) ¼ 1658 AT THE HORSHOW
3215 T.M. (A) ¼ THE WHITE LYON TAVERNE
3216 THOMAS MILLS ¼ 1666 Bust of Chas. II
3217 ROBERT PARKER ½ Rose
3218 WILLIAM PEAKE (M) ½ 1667 AT YE WHIT SWAN
3219 *Samuell Remnant* ¼ 1666 Swan
3220 P.S. (M) ¼ 1648 AT THE KING(E)S HEAD £28
3220A R.S. (C) ¼ 1657 AT THE FRYING PAN, Ironmongers' Arms
3220B CHRIS SAMWORTH ¼ Bishop's mitre
3221 THOMAS SATTERTHWAITE (E) ½ 1667 Arms of Colchester
3222 WILLIAM SHEARS, A COFFEE PENNY, 1669
3223 THO STEELE (M) ¼ CHANDLER
3224 THOMAS TAYLOR ½ Star; arrow
3224A RICHARD VTHWAY (L) ½ AT THE, C.R. crowned, TAVERNE
3225 R.W. (E) ¼ 1650 THE DOLPHIN TAVERN, dolphin and bear
3226 W.W. (M) ¼ AT THE ROSE TAVERN

Tower Royal (Watling Street)
3227 *Tho Scarlett his Coffee Penny*, Turk's head £50
3228 W SHAW (E) (½?) AT THE COFFEE HOVSE

Trinity Lane (Bread Street)
3229 THO BVTLER (E) ¼ AT THE ANGEL
3230 THOMAS CLAYTON ½ 1668 AT (THE *or* YE), Prince of Wales' feathers
3231 MARY HANSON ½ 1668 AT YE PETER AND PAVL, St. Peter with keys, St Paul with sword
3232 IOANNE LANGDELL ½ 1666 Anchor £32
3233 IOHN MILLIST (E) ¼ BAKER £28
3234 MARY STRINGAR ½ 1669 Hand pouring from coffee-pot into one of two cups, on table with tobacco-pipes

Trump Alley (Lawrence Lane)
3235 IOSEPH SCOTT (I) ¼ Bugle-horn

Turnagain Lane (Snow Hill)
3236 IOHN DVNMORE (R) ¼ AT YE, hart's horns
3237 RICHARD FLEWDE (E) ½ Bricklayers' Arms

Turnmill Street (Clerkenwell)
3238 IOHN ATKINSON (I) ¼ Hercules with club and staff
3239 H.B. (A) ¼ AT THE BLACK SPRED EAGEL
3240 H.B. (H) ¼ AT DAGGER ALLEY, dagger
3241 R.B. (R) ¼ PINDAR OF WAKE FEILD
3242/3 EDWARD B(E)AKER & SIMON SOVLE ¼ Camel?
3244 GEORGE BEDFORDE (E) ¼ Portcullis
3244A THOMAS BIGNALL ½ 1669 Tobacco-roll
3245 SIMON COOKE (R) ¼ 1651 Cock
3246 THOMAS CROSS (G) ¼ Women scrubbing negro, CHANDLR
3247 EDWARD DEWHORRE (M) ½ Blacksmiths' Arms
3248 WILLIAM DINN (R) ¼ AT YE, bust of Chas. II
3249 IAMES FOWKES (A) ½ 1666
3250 I. GANT (E) ¼ 1652 AT THE TVNN £30
3251 T.L. (I) ¼ AT THE LABER IN VANE, women washing negro
3251A I.M. ¼ AT THE CHRISTPHER, St Christopher
3252 ISAAC MARTIN (K) ½ 1667
3253 IOHN MAYHEW (I) ½ St George & dragon
3254 WILL MAYHEW (M) ¼ 1664 AT YE BLACK, lion
3255 CHRISTOPH NVTTALL (M) ¼ Fleur-de-lis
3256 THO PALMER (I) ¼ AT YE, bell
3257 IOHN PLANNER ½ AT THE, brewers carrying barrel
3258 IOHN VARNEY (M) ¼ Spectacles, MEALMAN

Turnstile (Holborn)
3259 R.A. (C) ¼ THE 3 SVGER LVES
3260 RICHARD ARKELL (E) ½ Hand holding sunflower; sun issuing from cloud
3260A W. Bailey ¼?
3261 ISBELL BARRAT ½ 1664 AT YE ORINGE, tree
3261A EDWARD BVTLER (M) ¼ 1659 Hand holding crown
3262 MARTHA CHAPMAN ¼
3263 PETER LENARD (M) ½ Queen's bust
3264 ROWLAND STINTON ½ 1665 AT THE, turnstile

Vere Street (Clare Market)
3264A WILLIAM BRVCE (D) ¼ Arms
3265 W.C. (S) ¼ 1652 AT THE FETHERS
3266 THOMAS MICHEL (M) ¼
3267 ANNE SINBR . . . LE (?) ½ '67 GOVLDEN, lion, TAVERN
3267A IOHN STAGGSTILLE (E) ¼ Stag

Vine Court (Custom House)
3268 R. MACHIN (I) ½ Rose and crown
3269 IOHN SMITH (R) ¼ Chequers

Vinegar Yard
3270 HENRY RICHMAN (E) ¼ 3 horseshoes

Walbrook
3270A HEN AYNSCOMBE (E) 1d IVST AGAINST WOLL CHVRCH MARKET
3271 WILLIAM FROST 1d AT THE GLOVB £42
3271A IONATHAN SMITH ½ 1669 Lamp with flambeaux, OYLEMAN
3271B GEORGE WHEELER (R) ½ 1668 Joiners' Arms

Waneforth Street
3272 IOHN MILNER ½ 1666 Prince of Wales' feathers; sugar-loaf

Wapping (Dock, New and **Old Stairs, Wall)**
3273 MATHEW AWSTAN (E) ¼ Boy holding pipe
3273A G.B. (M) ¼ AT THE DOLPHIN
3274 I.B. (D) ¼ AT THE FISHMONGERS ARMES
3275 I.B. (I) ¼ '58 THE BLOW ANKER
3276 ARON BARLOW ½ AT THE, Indian holding arrow
3277 BENIAMIN BARNES ½ Samson slaying lion £32
3278 RICHARD BOONE (M) ½
3279 ISAAC BOVLES (A) ½ VPON THE GREEN BANCK, building
3280 THOMAS BREMREDGE ½ 1666 Fish-hook, packing-needle
3281 ROBT BRISTOW (M) ¼ Pewterers' Arms, CHESMVNGR
3281A E. Brooke ¼?
3282 IOHN BROVGHTON (M) ¼ 1650 AT, globe
3283 WILLIAM BVTCHER ½ 1666 Swan
3284 I.C. (I) ¼ AT THE FLOVR DELVS, fleur-de-lis £25
3285 GEORG CARPENTER (M) ¼ MELLMAN £18
3285A GORG CARPENTR (S) ¼ MELL MAN
3286 IOHN CARTER (H) ¼ AT YE, smiths working at anvil
3287 IOHN CITREE ½ AT THE DOLPHIN
3288 IOHN CLARKE (E) ½ 1668 AT THE MAN IN YE MOON, man standing in crescent moon, tobacco-rolls over head. *Octagonal* £38
3289 I.C. (M) ¼ AT THE MAN IN THE MOONE £30
3290 ANDREW COLEMAN ½ AT THE COCK £16
3291 MARKE COLLINS (M) ½ 1666 AT YE, 3 wheatsheaves
3292 ANN CVRTIS ¼ 1654 Stocking
3293 — — ¼ 1658 —
3294 T. DRY (E) ¼ 1650 AT THE 3 SVGER LOAES £14
3295 L.E. (E) ¼ '59 AT YE COPPENHAGEN, arms, on castle gateway
3295A THOMAS F . . CH (M) ¼ NEERE WAPPING CHAPPILL
3296 EDWARD FISH ¼ AT THE SVNN £22
3297 HENRY FORMAN ½ 1668 AT EXECVTION DOCKE BREWHOVSE £24
3298 HANNA FROST ¼ 1666 Hen and chicks
3299 WILLIAM FRY ½ Sugar-loaf
3300 WIL — ¼ — AT THE SVGGAR LOFE
3301 W. GAVNT (E) ¼ 1652 AT THE MAN IN THE MOVN. **Plate 2** £20
3302 ROGER GOODE ½ Tobacco-roll within half-moon
3303 THOMAS GOONOL (K) ½ 1666
3303A WILLIAM GRIGREY (E) ½ 1667 IN WEL ALY, angel
3304 H.H. (B) ¼ 1648 AT THE GVNN TAVERN, cannon and 3 fleurs-de-lis
3305 IOHN HARLING (A) ½ 1667 TOBACCONIS
3306 IOSEPH HARRIS ½ '68 MEALMAN
3307 THOMAS HARRIS (E) ½ 1669 AT THE GOLDEN BALL
3308 THOMAS HEWS (K) ¼ AT THE GOLDEN STILL £25
3309 WILLIAM HEWES ¼ AT THE SHIP TAVERN £28
3310 IOHN HOLLAND (I) ½ 1668 AT YE GREENE BANCK, horseshoe. *Octagonal* £45
3311 ED HOLSTEAD (A) ¼ AT THE, bull baited by dog
3312 WILLIAM HOPKINS (V) ¼ 1659 Leathersellers' Arms
3313 DANIELL HOWES (G) ¼ 165(3?) 3 birds
3314 RALPH HVDSON ¼ Grocers' Arms
3315 RICHARD HVNNING ½ Pear tree
3315A PHILLIP IOHNSON (A) ¼ 1666 AT YE, pelican feeding young
3315B IEREMIAH KINGE (S) ¼ CHANDLER
3316 EDWARD LAMB (E) ¼ 1658 Flagon
3316A IOHN LANSDOWNE ¼ IN COCKE ROW
3317 T.M. ¼ AT THE BVLL TAVERN
3318 W. MAIOH (H) ¼ GROCER
3319 THOMAS MILLS (E) ¼ 1664 AT YE, pelican feeding young
3320 WILL NODES (E) ¼ AT THE WHIT BEARE
3321 FRANCES NORES ¼ 1653 Bunch of grapes
3321A G.P. (E) ¼ AT YE OVLD WHIET LION
3321B *John Packman* (E) ¼ *at ye Greene Bancke*, woman holding anchor. *Octagonal*
3322 FRANCIS PALMER (M) ½ 1667 Pelican in nest, man nearby £32
3323 ROBERT PARSONS ½ IN WELL ALY, dolphin
3324 IOHN PASHALAER (S) ¼ NERE WAPING CHAPEL
3325 THOMAS PEIRCE (M) ¼ Shears £30
3326 G. PERCY ¼ BAKER £24

3326A AVGVSTINE PETRVS ¼ Demi-lion on crown, CHEESMONGER
3327 ANTHONY PHILLIPS (A) ½ 1668 Fleur-de-lis
3328 —— (A) ¼ n.d. —
3329 ARTHVR PHILLPOT (M) ½ 1667 IN COCKE ALLEY
3330 BENIAMIN POOLE ½ AT THE EXECVTION DOCK BREWHOWS
3331 ROGER PRICE (I) ¼ AT THE BLACK BOY £22
3332 WILLIAM PROCTER (K) ½ 1669 Indian smoking
3333 E.R. (M) ¼ AT THE WHITE BEARE
3333A F.R. ¼ AT THE DOLPHIN IN WELL ALLEY
3333B TIMOTHY RAMAN (E) ½ 1668 AT YE, black jack
3334 WILLIAM REDDING (I) ¼ 1663 Sugar-loaf suspended by ring
3335 IOHN RE(D)WOOD ½ AT THE ROYAL OKE
3336 FRANCIS RICHARDSON ½ '66 AT, leg, SOPE MAN £30
3337 HVGH ROWCLIFFE (A) ½ 1667 Sugar-loaf
3338 I.S. (E) ¼ 1650 AT THE SHIP TAVERNE
3339 M.S. (A) ¼ 1651 AT THE PLOW
3340 R.S. (I) ¼ 1667 AT THE TOBACKO ROLE
3341 IOH SHAW (E) ¼ AT EXECVTION DOCK, King's Arms
3342 IOHN SLATER ½ Windmill, MEALMAN
3343 ANN (SARESCOCK *or* STARESTOCK) ½ Plough
3344 FARLEY STEVENSON (I) ½ AT THE, castle
3345 IOHN TAYLER (E) ¼ Hand holding shears, TAYLER
3346 WILLIAM TAYLER (A) ¼ 1658 3 wheatsheaves
3346A THOMAS THEKESTON (R) ½ 1668 AT THE ONE TON
3347 E.V. (M) ¼ AT THE 3 DETHES HEDES
3348 DAN VOS (E) ¼ AT YE SHIPP A GOVLDEN CROSS
3349 (Probably same as 3350)
3350 R.W. (E) ¼ 1655 AT THE SWAN TAVERN
3351 IAMES WAKEFEILD ½ 1667 AT THE FORTVNE TAVERN, Fortune on globe, holding veil
3351A NATHANIELL WARNER (I) ½ '69 AT THE, queen's head
3351B IAMES WATERS ½ 1670 AT YE 3 SVGER LO(F *or* O)ES
3352 FRANCIS WINTERBVRN (M) ¼ IN GOVN ALEY, bunch of grapes
3353 EDWARD WILLDEE (E) ½ AT YE WATERMANS ARMS
3354 SAMVELL WISEMAN (F) ¼ AT, nag's head
3355 RICHARD WOOSLEY (I) ¼ 1665 BAKER

(The King's) Wardrobe (Doctors' Commons)
3356 EDWARD DENNIS ½ 1666 Sugar-loaf
3357 W.H. ¼ 1653 HEMP; FLAX. AT THE WARDROBE IS WORKE FOR THE POORE
3358 RICH LEVIS (M) ¼ Sugar-loaf

Warwick Lane (Newgate Street)
3359 ANDREW ATKINS ½ 1664 Bakers' Arms
3360 T.C. (M) ¼ 1657 AT YE CROWNE
3361 MATHEW GEORGE ½ AT THE CROWNE
3362 EDWARD IONES ½ 166(3?) AT YE GEORG, St. George & dragon
3362A —— ½ '63 AT THE, St George & dragon
3363 *Richard Lyon* ½ Lion with coffee-pot
3363A H.W. ¼ AT THE BLACK SWAN

Water Lane (Tower Street)
3363B RALPH BEST 1d?*
3364 ROBERT BRETT (P) (½) AT THE CROWN
3365 AVGVSTINE DAVIES (B) ½ Anchor
3366 E.S. (S) ¼ Crowned bust with sceptre
3367 I.S. (A) ¼ 1658 AT THE GVNN
3367A WILLIAM SPVR (I) ¼ AT THE PLOW
3368 H.T. (P) (½) Crowned bust with sceptre

Watling Street
3369 THOMAS COOPER ½ 1668 AT THE, negro's head
3370 IOHN HAMMOND ¼ Dog, GROC
3370A NICHOLAS HAYTOR (E) ¼ Leg
3371 THOMAS KITCHINMAN (A) ½ AT THE GVILD HALL
3371A WILL & SAM WEBB ¼ BELL

Wellclose Stile
3372 IOHN BEWER ½ Fruiterers' Arms

Wentworth Street (Petticoat Lane)
3373 WILL EXEL (A) ¼ BY YE ANTWERP, city view
3374 IOHN HAM (M) ¼ Cross
3375 EDWARD HOLTON ½ 1668 AT YE BLACK, horse. *Heart-shape* £135
3376 R.W. (E) ¼ AT THE SHVGER LOAFE

Westbury Street (now Quaker Street, Spitalfields)
3376A DAVID COVNCELL (R) ¼ Castle

West Harding Street
3376B S.G. ¼ 'Chandler'
3376C ISAAC HADLEY (A) ¼ 5 bells

* Known only with an Ipswich farthing (*Suffolk* 158) struck over it

Westminster
(All tokens bearing only the name Westminster, together with a few showing miscellaneous localities therein, were listed by Williamson under Middlesex, q.v.)

Wheeler Street (Spitalfields)
3377 THOMAS BOYDEN (A) ½ 1669 AT THE, bust of Chas. II
3378 ALEXANDER BYRCHET ½ Horse saddled and bridled
3379 IAMES GRIMES (A) ¼ Indian smoking pipe
3380 THOMAS LOLE (M) ¼ AT THE, sugar-loaf
3381 MARTIN RIDGIN (M) ¼ Gate
3382 WALTER SHALLER (H) ¼ Mercers' Arms
3383 W.W. (E) ¼ AT THE TARLETON, figure of the clown/actor

Whitechapel
3384 RICHARD AYSTIN (I) ¼ 1656 Half-moon
(I.B. ¼: see 3421)
3384A T.B. (M) ¼? 'Eluphant'
3385 THOMAS BAKER ½ 1668 Merchant's mark, CHEESMONGER
3386 WILL BALET (M) ¼ WHIT BARE, SALTER
3387 WILLIAM BECKITT (A) ¼ '58 Pie-crust (?)
3388 IOHN BELL (E) ¼ 1656 Prince of Wales' feathers
3389 ERASMVS BISH ¼ Bell; Arms, BELLMAN
3390 ISAAC BLISSETT (H) ¼ 1667 AT PEACOCK ALLY GATE, peacock
3391 SOLOMON BONNER (S) ¼ Founders' Arms
3392 EDWARD BYRCHETT (I) ¼ Joiners' Arms
3393 R.C. (I) ¼ 1650 AT THE 7 STARES (= stars) £25
3394 S.C. (E) ¼ 1658 AT THE SVNN TAVERNE
3394A IOHN CARTER ¼ Horseshoe; still, GROCER
3395 IOHN CASE (E) ¼ 1656 3 fleurs-de-lis
3395A RICHARD CAVE ½ AT THE, Cordwainers' Arms
3396 MARGARET CHARWELL ½ 1666 IN HAROW ALLY, royal oak
3397 WILL CHVDLEY ¼ Still; tobacco-roll, GROCER
3398 WILL CLAPTON (I) ¼ COCK AND HORSES
3399 RICHARD CLARKE (E) ¼ Shoulder of mutton
3400 RICHARD CVLLINGTON (A) ½ AT THE RED LION. *Octagonal*
3401 ROWLAND CVNEY (H) ¼ Man within moon
3402 I.D. (A) ¼ AT THE STILL
3403 EDWARD DALTON ¼ Patten; bell
3404 I.F. (E) ¼ THE TOBACKE ROVLD AND HOOP
3404A I.F. (E) ¼ 1658 AT THE SVN TAVERNE
3405 IO FARGISON ½ 1669 AT YE BLEW LYON
3406 BEN FELTON ½ 1669 AT YE SWAN & CROWN
3407 WILLIAM FOORD (M) ½ '68 AT YE BLAK LYON
3408 WILLIAM FRELAND (M) ¼ Drapers Arms
3409 RICHARD GREENE ½ 1670 Bakers' Arms
3410 THOMAS GROCOCKE ½ AT YE SPRED EAGLE TAVERN
3411 F.H. ¼ 1656 AT THE OLD PRISON
3412 H.H. (I) ¼ AT THE BLACK BOYES
3413 IOHN HARIS (A) ¼ AT THE ROS
3413A THOMAS HEPWORTH ¼ 3 cloves, CHANDLER
3414 SAM HINCKS ½ 1669 AT YE BAG OF NAILS
3415 P.I. ¼ 1650 AT THE NAGGES HEAD
3415A RICH IENINGS (G) ¼ AT, crossed keys
3415B I. Kinder ¼
3416 R.L. (E) ¼ AT THE SWAN BRWHOWES
3417 T.L. (M) ¼ AT THE WHITE LION
3418 NATH LITTLEFORD ¼ 3 balls
3419 HENRY NAPTON ¼ 1667 Duke of York's head
3420 GEORGE PERKENS ¼ AT YE 3 CVPS
3421 I.B. (S) ¼ THE MOSES AND AARON
3421A IOHN READ (I) ½ 1671 Tulip
3422 ELIZABETH ROSE ½ Rose; basket, 3 pestles (?)
3423 IOHN SKINNER ½ 1668 Plough, 3 birds, APOTHECARY
3424 E.T. (E) ¼ AT THE QVEENS ARMES, griffin
3424A P.T. ¼ 1660 AT THE NAGGES HEAD
3425 T.T. (R) ¼ 1656 THE SVNN TAVERN
3426 HVMPHREY TARREN (S) ¼ 3 tuns
3427 (Same as 640)
3428 ISAAC WEEKES (M) ¼ Cow
3429 MARGARET WEST ¼ Hour-glass
3430 IOHN WOOD (E) ¼ AT YE GOLDEN LEG
3431 CHRISTOPHER WORTH (A) ¼ Hen and chicks
3431A I.(?).(?) ¼ AT THE WINN MILL

Whitecross Street (Cripplegate)
3432 IOHN ALTHAM (I) ¼ Comb(?), B. (= bodice?) MAKAR £30
3433 WILLIAM AMBROSE (A) ½ AT THE, still, roll above
3433A WILL AMY ¼ GROCER
3434 DALLINGTON AYRES (E) ¼ Ball suspended
3435 G.B. (M) ¼ A CHANLER £25
3436 R.B. (I) ¼ THE BEARE AND RAGET STAF
3437 RICHARD BALLDWIN (E) ½ Windmill

3438 NATH BINGHAM (M) ½ IN RED LION COVRT, lion
3439 DAVID BREEATT (S) ½ 1668 Sugar-loaf, tobacco-roll
3439A THOMAS BVRT (M) ½ AT YE GRASHOPE
3440 T.C. ½ AT THE PECOCKE BRVHOVSE
3440A IOHN CLEMENT (O) ½ 1666
3441 WILLIAM COOPER (E) ¼ Hart
3441A RICHARD COVTLEY (D) ½ St. George & dragon
3441B ESTER CRAWLEY ¼
3442 I.D. (I) ¼ AT THE GLOVERS ARMES
3443 FRANCIS DOVE ½ 1669 TALLOW CHANDLER £32
3443A WILL DOVGHTY (C) ¼ THE WHITE, rose
3444 RICHARD EAST ½ AT THE, stag's head
3444A SAMVELL EMERSON (I) ½ AT YE, 3 tuns
3445 ROBERT ETHERIDGE (M) ½ 1666
3446 I.F. ¼ AT THE RED LION
3447 KATHEREN FEILDING ½
3448 IAMES FRANCIS ½ Lion, SALTER
3448A THO FRITH (D) ¼ AT YE GORGE
3448B T.G. ¼ 1657 AT YE VEARE SHO, jackboot
3449 T.G. (M) ¼ XTOPHER BREWHOVSE, St. Christopher carrying Jesus
3449A IOHN GARDINER (A) ½ 1668 OYLEMAN. *Octagonal*
3449B ROBERD GIFFORD ½ 1667 Turk's head
3450 THOMAS GRANBROO ½ 1667 Bell
3451 IOHN GRAY ½ Crown, WINE COOPER £32
3452 BENIAMIN HANDCOCKE ½ AT YE, cross on steps
3453 IOHN HARRISON (M) ½ 1665 Fountain
3454 — — (M) ¼ n.d. —
3455 SAMVELL IAMES (E) ½ '67 AT THE, soap-box
3456 — — (E) ½ n.d. — —
3457 EDMVND LANGTON ½ Coopers' Arms
3458 GEORGE LESCAILLET ½ NERE YE, bust of Chas. II, full-face
3459 EDWARD LEWIS ½ Flesh-pot, IRON-MONGER
3460 GEORGE LOWE (M) ½ 1667
3461 IOSEPH MAXSVM (M) ¼ Peacock
3462 ROBERT MILLEN ¼
3463 IOHN MVLLOCKE (A) ½ 1666 Dog with glove in mouth
3464 W.P. (A) ¼ AT THE BLEW ANKER
3465 DANIELL PAGE (A) ¼ AT WHITE, swan
3466 IOHN PERRY (A) ¼ CHESMONGR
3467 I.S. (S) ¼ AT THE CHILDS COATE £30
3467A I.S. (S) ¼ AT YE GOLDEN KEY
3468 T.S. (I) ¼ WHITE CROSS TAVERN £28
3469 W.S. (V) ¼ THE GOVLDEN ANCHOR
3470 MICHAELL SAYER (E) ¼ Dragon £32
3471 WILLIAM SKINER (I) ½ 1669 AT THE, cock and bottle
3471A RICHARD SMITH ¼ 1661
3472 THOMAS SMITH ½ '65 AT THE, chequers
3473 I.W. (A) ¼ Merchant-Taylors' Arms, TALLOE CHANDLER
3473A NICHOLVS WARE (M) ½ AT YE LIONS HEAD
3473B RICHARD WEB ½ CHEESMONGER
3473C R. Webley ½
3474 EDWARD WEBSTER ½ 1666 BREWER

Whitefriars

3475 IOHN CLAY ½ 1667 Horse and cart, WOODMONGER
3476 RICHARD FARSHAL (K) ¼ AT YE, wheatsheaf, BAKER
3477 ISAAC GVRDEN (I) ¼ IN WATER MANS LANE, rose and crown
3478 GOVIN GOVLDEGAY (A) ¼ WOOD MONGER
3478A I.H. (E) ¼? 'Boote Royall'
3479 ROBERT HANCOCK (I) Hand, cock £32
3480 IEREMIAH HORNE ½ 1664 Wheatsheaf
3481 EDWARD LIGHTMAKER (S) ¼ 3 goats' heads, BREWER
3482 ANN MATHEW ¼ AT THE LIME WHARFE, wheatsheaf
3482A ANTHONY MOREING ½ BREWER
3483 PETER SAYVE (M) ¼ Weavers' Arms
3484 EDWARD SMART (M) ¼ AT THE, bull's head
3485 THOMAS STOTESBERY (A) ¼ St. George & dragon
3486 WILLIAM WHITE (I) ½ BREWER
3487 I.Y. (A) ¼ 1657 THE DARKE HOVSE

Whitehall

3487A WILLIAM (?PINNYR?) ½ 1666
3488 RICHARD ROBERT (D) ¼ 3 greyhounds
3489 E.T. (E) ¼ AT THE QVEENS ARMS, dragon

White Hart Yard (Strand)

3489A ANN BARRET ¼ 3 birds
3490 PUILLIP CARTERETT (S) ½ 1666 Crown £30
3491 THOMAS CLATWORTHY ½ 1666 AT THE, crooked billet £28
3492 IOHN PEARSON (A) ½ Windmill, packhorse, MEALMAN
3493 IOHN SYMONDS (M) ¼ 1663 AT THE, crown, TAVERN
3494 HVMPHRY VAVGHAN ½ 1666 Man carrying sack

3495 IOHN WILLIAMS (E) ½ AT YE CROWN
3495A ¼? '3 goates heads and last'

White Horse Street (Ratcliff)
3496 ROTHRICK DIMINSDALE (A) ½ 1668 Rose
3497 THOMAS RAILTON ¼ Wheatsheaf; scales, BAKER £28
3498 ROBERT WELLS ½ 1666 Royal oak

Wild Street (Lincoln's Inn Fields)
3498A WILLIAM LOCKER (E) ¼ Axe
3499 IOHN SHERWINN (E) ¼ Swan crowned

Windmill Court (Snow Hill)
3500 NATHANILL BVRT (A) ¼ Windmill £40
3501 I.G. (I) ¼ 1657 Windmill
3502 I.T. (W) ¼ Windmill

Winford Street
3503 L.D. (T) ¼ AT THE KATTERN WHIL

(Great and **Little) Wood Street** (Cheapside)
3504 R.A. (M) ¼ 1650 THE CASTELL TAVERN
3505 IO ALMOND (I) ¼ AT THE, cannon and balls
3506 IOHN BELL (A) ¼ 1663 Bell
3507 BENIAMIN BOVLTBY ½ 1666 AT THE, Soapmakers' Arms
3508 WILL BVSBY (A) ½ 1666 Croppers' shears
3509 I.C. (H) ¼ 1651 AT THE COCK
3510 PHILLIP CLARKE (A) ¼ Sugar-loaf
3511 RICHARD CLARK (½) AT THE, winged horse
3512 IOHN COCK (R) ½ Crossed keys
3513 RALPH COMBS (E) ½ '68 AT YE SHEARS
3514 EDMVND COOPER (M) ¼ '64 Spur
3514A THOMAS COOPER ½ 1670 Bell on signboard
3515 IAMES CORNWALL ½ 1670 AT YE CROS KEYES
3516 THOMAS CROVCH ½ Palfrey, GROCER
3517 T.D. ¼ AT THE FLESE, fleece
3517A SAMVELL DRAYGATE ½ AT THE, wheelbarrow
3518 PHILLIP FERRERS ½ AT YE, 7 stars
3519 M.F. (A) ¼ AT THE EAGLE AND CHILD
3519A MICKAELL FRANCIS (A) ¼ Bell
3520 IOHN GIBSON (M) ¼ Salters' Arms
3521 ELIZABETH GRACE ½ 1668 Dolphin
3522 IOHN GRICE (G) ¼ Soap-box
3523 THOMAS HALFORD ½ 1669 Sheaf of corn
3524 WILLIAM HAYES ½ '64 Frying-pan, IRONMONGER
3525 R.M. (R) ¼ AT THE ROSE
3526 R.M. (T) ¼ THE HENN AND CHICKENS
3527/8 W.P. (E) ¼ AT (YE *or* THE) MITER TAVERNE
3529 IAS RAGDALL ¼ Man making candles
3530 FRANCIS PLOMER ½ 1666 Barber's soap-box £35
3531 IOHN STANDEVEN (R) ¼ 3 crowns
3532 IOHN WELLS (I) ¼ AT THE, King's Arms
3533 THOMAS WOODWARD ¼ Grocers' Arms
3534 (1d) AT THE MITER AND ROSE

Woolchurch Market (now Mansion House)
3535 HVGH LVMBARD (I) 1d 1670 AT THE, Prince of Wales' crest and motto £42
3536 HENRY WYBERT (S) 1d 1671 POVLTERER £42

Woolstaple (Westminster)
3537 WILLIAM BAYLIE (A) ½ Rose, other flowers £28
3538 WILLIAM FROST (S) ¼ Sword
3539 IOHN NEWMAN (A) ½ WHITE, lion
3540 ROBERT WILLIAMS (M) ¼ Cross

Wych Street (Strand)
3541 OSWALD FOORD ½ 1666 AT THE, bust of queen
3542 ROBERT GREENE (A) ¼ NERE NEW INN GATE
3543 ROBERT LEE ½ AT YE, eagle and child, AGAINST NEW INN
3543A S.P. (I) ¼ AT YE RED COW
3543B IOHN SHAW (M) ½ AT YE LYON RAMPANT

Uncertain Locality
3543C IOH SANDIVEAR (H?) ½ AT YE ROVND HOVSE NEARE THE FALCON, Bricklayers' Arms*

* Possibly the Round House in Love Lane, office for the Kentish daily post from 1661

APPENDIX

Large tokens of leather, lead or pewter and copper, of different style from the rest of the series

1 EDWARD BVRFORD NEAR *ye* 3 CRANES, bird and tree. In *pb*
2 COATES & BIDDLE AT 3 CRANES, arms with cock crest. In *pb*
3 CHAPTER COFFE HOVSE, mitre and stars, 4 below. In *leather*
4 CHAPTER COFFEE HOVS, crown, mitre and stars, 3 below. In *leather*, letters and device gilt
5 CHAPTER COFFE HOVSE, mitre, 2. In *leather*
6 Similar, but no figure. In *pb* (Perhaps a seal or die, as all letters are reversed)
6A Similar. In *leather*
7 D. I. W. ELLIS 1650; wyvern, birds' feet. In *leather*
8 THOMAS HARMAN AT THE CHEQVER INN DOWGATE. In *pb*
9 IOHN HVNTER AT THE 3 CRANES, arms, stag's head crest. In *leather*
10 THOMAS LVCAS, men saluting. In *Æ*

11 *William Morrison Temple Bar, 3. Diamond-shape*, in Æ, letters incuse

12 I.R. In *leather*

13 ROBINS IN OLD IEWRY, 3 above. In *leather*

13A — — — — 4 above. In *leather*

14 SAM TOWERS BEHIND THE ROY EXCHA, HIS TOKEN FOR 2 PEN. In *leather*

15 *union in cornhill*, 4 sideways. In *leather*

Middlesex

(See also *London*: apart from those of the City of London, most of the remaining tokens listed there belong strictly to the old County of Middlesex)

New tokens recorded from *SNC*, Mar. and May 1901, Aug. 1908; Oct. 1948; Aug. 1949; *NC*, 1902; W. Gilbert 'Unpublished . . .' (see under Cambridgeshire); A. Heal (from *Notes and Queries*: see under London); the Carthew collection (*SCMB*, Mar. 1946); *SCMB*, June 1949; *Hammersmith Historical Record*, Oct. 1959; 'The Robert Owen Token of Bromley-by-Bow' (*SCMB*, Oct. 1961); and *SCA* 51, 16 Apr. 1986.

See also George Berry, 'The Chelsea College Farthing' (*Coins and Medals*, Oct. 1974) and *Taverns* . . . (see under London); and Philip D. Greenall, 'The Lady of the Hampstead Halfpenny' (*Camden History Review*, 5, 1977).

Believed entirely unpublished: 21C, 23A, 44B, 95A, 110A, 119A, 132A, 169A, 172A, 186A, 190A, 211B, 213A.

Minimum price for unvalued tokens: £40

Acton

1 THOMAS BVLLMVR (M) ¼ 1664 Bust of Chas. II £32
2 ANNE FINCH, HIS ½ 1667 AT YE, cock
3 *Gervase Lawson* ½ 1667 St. George & dragon £28
4 IOHN MVNN (G) ½ 1668 Man making candles. *Octagonal* £32
5 —— (I) ¼ TALLOWE CHANDLAR
6 THOMAS SEXSTON (E) ¼ CHANLER £45
7 JAMES WILSON (E) ½ 1669 Thistle £30

Bow

8 RALPH ALEXANDER ½ Wheatsheaf, MEALMAN £45
9 GEORGE AYLIFFE ½ 1667 AT WHIT, bear
10 IOHN HANSCOMBE (S) ½ 1666 AT THE KINGS HEAD £28
11 WILL MEARES (M) ¼ 1658 AT YE, 3 tuns £24
11A HENRY MILFORD (Probably *Devon* 33B)
12 EDWARD ROBERTES (I) ¼ Saracen's head £48
12A OLIVER WAKE ½ 1669 Men rowing boat(?)

Brentford (New and Old)

13 W.C. (M) ¼ AT THE KINGS ARMES £20
14 IOHN ERING (M) ½ 1669 Grocers' Arms £22
15 THOMAS HOBBS (I) ½ AT YE, wyvern
16 L.I. (E) ¼ CHANDLER £18
17 LVKE IVORY (E) ¼ CHANDR, BRENTFORD £18
18 Similar but OLD BRENTFORD
19, 20 IOHN MOORE (M) ¼ 1651 £12
21 EDWARD SWIFT ½ 1668 Drapers' Arms £25
21A RICHARD WATERMAN (K) ¼ 1667

Bromley-by-Bow

21B ROBERT OWEN ½ 1668 AT THE SHIP
21C ROB — (E) ¼ n.d. AT YE SHIP

Chelsea

22 CHELSEY COLLEDGE ¼ 1667 View of College
23 *Henry Butts* ½ 1667 Greyhound £25
23A GEORGE CLOPTON (A) ¼ SVTLER IN CHELSEY COLLEDGE, building
24 P.L. (M) ¼ 1657 AT THE CROWNE
25 DANIELL DALTON (E) ¼ IN CHELSEY COLLEGE, building £50
26 WILLIAM FREEMAN ½ 1667 VICTVALLER £42
27 *Thomas Munden* ½ 1666 Prince of Wales' feathers £25
28 IOHN STAMFORTH (M) ¼ AT CHELSEY COLLEDGE, building £35
29 ADRIAN WESTERBAN ½ 1667 AT YE PRINC OF ORANGE

Chiswick

30 WILLIAM BOND (S) ½ 1666 £16
31 GEORGE BROWN (V) ½ 1668 £22
32 —— (V) ½ n.d. GROCR
33 IOHN COKE ½ 1670 BVCHER £20

34 IOSEPH GASQVOYNE (S) ¼ 1658 £20
35 IOHN HOBBS ¼ 1658 £15
36 GYLES PIERCE ¼ £22
37 WILLIAM SMEETH (E) ¼ £28

Clapton
38 I.G. (I) ¼ AT THE FLOWER DE LVC

Cranford
39 WILLIAM ALLEN (S) ½ 1669 Cross £50

Ealing
40 IAMES LEWIS (A) ½ 1666

Edgware
40A MICHAELL SHEPARD ¼ '64 Man making candles; initials R.E.D. £40

Edmonton
41 IOHN BROWNE (S) ¼ 1653 Sugar-loaf £55
42 EDWARD CLARKE (M) ½ '68 AT SOVTH STREET, Fishmongers' Arms
43 RICE IONES ½ 1666
44 ALEXSANDER KING ¼ 1665
44A THO SANDERSON (A) ½ AT YE, bell; HIS OB
44B THOMAS SVMPTER (E) ½ 1665 AT THE, bell; HIS OB
44C IOHN TABARAHAM ¼ 1668 AT, fleur-de-lis; Blacksmiths' Arms

Enfield
45 RICHARD IOSEPH (M) ½ AT YE RED, lion crowned £55
46 EDWARD NEALE (E) ¼ 1668 Turkey
47 EDWARD WILLMOTE (A) ¼ 1656 Drapers' Arms

Finchley
48 WILLIAM HIDE (E) ¼ 1665 Full-faced bust
49 THOMAS GRACE ½ 1670 Gamecock £55

Fulham
50 *John Fox* ½ 1666 Anchor £17
51 BENET HAMON (V) ¼ 1650 Wheatsheaf £40
52 F.S. (S) ¼ 1656 THIS WAS THE KINGES ARMES. **Plate 2** £32
53 MATHEW HARWELL (M) ¼ NEAR THE FERY, man rowing boat £60
54 FRANCIS STVTSBERY ½ AT THE, King's Arms £30

Hackney
55 T.B. (A) ¼ 1651 AT THE TAVERN, cock
56 IOHN BRAINE ½ 1667 AT YE GREEN, man holding club £25
57 I.C. (H) ¼ 1656 AT THE PIE TAVERNE, magpie £45
58 IOHN DAVIS (E) ¼ 1667
59 RICHARD IENNINGS (M) ½ 1668 Man rowing boat £45
60 ANN NICKOLLS ½ 1668 AT YE WHITE, hart; IN MARE STREET
61 I.P. (M) ¼ AT THE MAREMAID TAVERNE £25
62 WILLIAM PERRY (L) ½ 1669 £40
63 WILLIAM PROCTER (S) ½ Holy lamb, BREWER £45
63A RICHARD RAWLINSON (E) ¼ 1663 Bust of Eliz. I
64 WILLIAM TWISSELL (A) ¼ 1656 CHANLER

Hammersmith
65 E.B. (S) ¼ AT THE HALFE MOONE, BAKER £22
66 THOMAS CASSELL ½ 1667 £28
67 IOHN CIPPIS (I) ½ 1668 Brewers' Arms £38
68 WILLIAM HARDING (M) ½ 1667 3 horseshoes £20
69 ALICE KIRTON ½ 1668 £42
70 ELIAS HIRONS ¼ 1667 Hand from cloud holding bird, MILLENER £30
71 FRANCES TAERREY (M) ¼ BAKER
72 WILLIAM RENOLDS (R) ½ AT YE, anchor; Weavers' Arms £45
73 IOHN RICHARSON (E) ½ '68 Still £35
74 WILLIAM SIMONDS (A) ½ 1668 Still
75 RICHARD TERREY (I) ¼ Watermens' Arms £22
76 FRANCIS WATTS (E) ¼ Flower £38
76A THOMAS WORNOM (A) ¼ Bell
77 ADAM WRIGHT (M) ½ 1668 £22

Hampstead
78 RICHARD BAZELL (D) ½ 1670 AT THE WELL
79 *Thomas Leddell* (B) ½ 1669 Queen's head
80 DOROTHY RIPPIN ½ 1669 AT THE WELL

Hampton Court
81 *John Drewry* (D) ½ *at the Toye. Heart-shape*
82 — *Druree* (D) (½) *at ye Toye. Heart-shape*

Hampton (Town)
83 SAM BRATHERICK ½ 1669 AT YE BEL, Vintners' Arms £40

Hampton Wick
84 IOHN HARRIS (A) ½ AT YE WHIT, hart. *Square*
85 RICHARD RANCE (I) ½ '66 £38

Harmondsworth
86 RICHARD WATES ½ '69 3 hammers £40

Harrow-on-the-Hill
87 (See *Beds.* 50)
88 IOHN MILLGATE (E) ½ Anchor £38
89 NATHANIELL PAGE (I) (½) Grocers' Arms £45

Hendon
90 IOHN ALLIN (E) ½ 1669
91 IOHN GREENE (M) ¼ 1666 MALTMAN £55

Heston
92 THOMAS BELINGER ¼ 1657 Horse £35

Highgate
93 PHILIP ALLEN (A) ½ 1667 CHANDLER £50
94 THOMAS CHILDE (S) ½ 1670 Sugar-loaf
95 EDWARD CVTLER ½ 1668 AT YE GATE HOVSE £40
95A WILLIAM FENN (A) ½ 1669 AT YE FAVLCN. *Octagonal*
96 WILLIAM FISHER (S) ½ 1669 AT THE ANGELL £45
97 IOHN HILTON (I) ½ 1669 COACHMAN. *Octagonal*
98 WILLIAM PROCKTER ½ 1668 AT YE RED LYON £38

Holloway
99 *John Backster* (R) ½ 1667 *att the mother Read Capp* £45
100 NICHO HOLBROOKE ½ AT THE GREEN MAN, man with staff on shoulder leading dogs

Hounslow
100A ABRAHAM BONIFEILD (L) ½ CHANDLER
101 HENRY CLEAVER ½ Still, POST MASTER £32
102 MATTHEW GARNATT ½ 1668 AT YE RED LYON £24

Hoxton
103 MARGARET KING ½ 1668 AT THE, sun £35
104 GRACE PHILLIPS ½ Prince of Wales' feathers. *Heart-shape*
105 EZEK TANNER ½ 1668 AT THE WHIT HOVSE. *Diamond-shape*

Isleworth
106 IOHN BANESTER (E) ¼ £42
107 IOHN BENGOVN ½ AT YE ROSE & CROWN £45
108 RICHARD LANSBROVGH ½ 1669 Oars £25
109 —LANSBROV (F) ¼ n.d.— £35
110 RICHARD LARCHIN (A) ¼ Eagle and child
110A RICH — ½ 1672 — AT YE EGLE AND CHILD
111 GEORGE AND SVSAN PAGE ½ 1666 Grocers' Arms £16
112 THOMAS POCOCK (S) ½ 1666 3 shuttles £25
113 L.S. (E) ¼ 1657 AT THE BELL £38
114 ABRAHAM SHEWEL ½ 1666 AT YE, bell £25
115 SIMON SVTTON (M) ½ 1669 Vintners' Arms

Islington
116 CHRISTOPHER BVSBEE ½ 1668 AT YE WHIT LYON
117 ROBERT ECCLESTON (I) ¼ 1658 Sun
118 RICHARD GAYTON (S) ½ 1669 Horseshoe
119 WILLIAM GEARING ½ AT YE, old man holding bow and arrow, globe on back
119A IAMES HILLS (D) ½ AT THE MERMAID
120 EDWARD HOLLINGWORTH (M) ½ AT YE RED COW
120A T.I. (M) ¼? 'Catherine wheele'
121 IOANE KETTLE ½ 1667 Salters' Arms
122 ABRAHAM MEKCOM (I) ½ Blacksmiths' Arms £45
123 GEORGE MERRY (I) ½ 1666 Prince of Wales' feathers, coronet
124 ROBERT PEIR(CE?) (M) ½ 1667 CONFECTIONER
125 FRANCES POTTS (M) ¼ 1663 Rose and crown
125A WILL SAVIDG (E) ½ 1670 AT YE PECOCK
126 RALPH STEENE (E) ¼ Stag
127 IOHN VERE (M) ½ AT YE FRYING PAN, MEALMAN £42
128 ROBERT WILKINSON (I) ½ Chequered square

Kensington
129 *Randolph Cobbett* ½ 1666 Lion £20
130 ROBERT DAVENPORTE (M) ½ Plough, GOD SPEED THE PLOW
131 THOMAS ROBERTS (E) ¼ 1664 Sugar-loaf £22
132 PETER SAMMON (S) ½ 1667 AT YE, talbot £22

Kingsland
132A WILLIAM MASKELL (E) ¼ 1657 King's(?) Arms
133 IOHN PERRY (E) ¼ 1663 Chequers

Knightsbridge
134 RICHARD LONDON (M) ½ 1668 AT YE GOVLDEN, lion. *Octagonal*

Limehouse
135 WILLIAM BANES (E) ¼ Stocking £24
136 NICHOLAS BLAY (I) ½ 1668 BAKER
137 WILLIAM BRADSHAW (E) ¼ BAKER £28
138 EDMOND DOBSON ½ 1667 £22
139 I.H. (G) ¼ AT THE HOOP TAVERN, bunch of grapes within hoop
140 ANN HARLOW ½ £30
141 ISACK HICKMAN (E) ½ Woman churning, CHEES MONGER £35
142 SAMVELL KEINTON (I) ¼ BAKER £20
143 NICOLAS LATCH ½ Lion £24
144 MARGRET LVCAS ¼ 1663 Brewers' Arms £24
145 THOMAS MARTIN ½ AT YE ANKER £40
146 IOHN NEWCOMB (T) ¼ 1657 Ball
147 EDWARD PAGE (S) ¼ Wheatsheaf
148 IOHN RAILTON (E) ¼ 1658 BAKER £22
149 EDMOND RIVERS (C) ½ MEALMAN AT DICKSHORE, wheatsheaf with 3 birds £45
150 DOROTHY SMART ½ 1667 £32
151 FRANC(E)S ZACACY (E) ¼ Wheatsheaf, BREWER £32

London
152 (A pattern piece)

Mimms
153 IOHN COOPER (M) ½ 1669 Blazing star £40
154 RICHARD HODSDON ½ 1669 Bull. *Heart-shape*
155 RICHARD MASONN (M) ½ 1667 AT THE, crossed keys, INNKEEPER

Newington Green
156/7 I.W. (M) ¼ AT THE GREEN DRAGON

Northall
158/9 (See *Bucks.* 106A, 106B)

Paddington
160 THOMAS FITTER (D) ½ 1668 AT THE BELL

Parsons Green
161 *William Kempe* ½ £25
161A WILL KEMP (Same as *Surrey* 210)

Pinner
162 RALPH PAGE (I) ½ 1667 Hand holding bird £45

Ponders End
163 THOMAS BENNETT (B) ¼ 1664 £55
163A —— (B) ¼ 1659

Poplar
164 IOHN BVRDEN (S) ½ 1653 MEALE, LIVING IN POPLER £40
164A IOHN CLIFTON (D) ¼ 1669 Merchant-Taylors' Arms
165 M.F. (S) ¼ THE FALCON AND HORSE SHOOE
166 THOMAS HARRICE (I) ¼ 1666 Trumpet £38
167 IOSEPH HVNT ½ 1668 Haberdashers' Arms £45
168 ELIZABETH MOREING ¼ 1669

Potters Bar
168A WILL CLARKE ½ 1667 AT YE RED LYON

Potton
169 (See *Beds.* 81)

Shadwell
169A STEAVIN ALLEN (E) ½ 1668 Axe
170 IOHN ANNIS ½ 1667 NEAR COALE STAIRS, lion £20
171 N.B. (E) ¼ AT THE SWAN WITH 2 NECKS £32
171A RIC BLACKMAN (E) ¼ ATT, crossed guns
171B ELIZABETH BLAKE ¼ Star
172 W.C. (D) ¼ 1650 AT THE WHIT HART IN FOXES LANE
172A IOHN COLE ¼ 1653 AT COLE STARES
173 GREGORY COOKE ½ 1666 Head, Prince of Wales' feathers £25
174 THO COOKE ½ 1665 AT MOROCKA HEAD, Turk's head £25
175 THO COOKE ½ '64 AT YE GOVLDEN, griffin £30
176 THO DARRELL (M) ¼ AT BELL WHARFE
176A FRANCIS DIER (E) ½ AT COALE STAIRS
177 MATHEW DODSLEY (R) ¼ 1658 Bear with chain
178 L.E. (S) ¼ AT THE WORLDS END, 3 men holding astronomical instruments, around globe £25
179 IOHN FALL (I) ½ IN FOXES LANE
180 ELLINOR GANDOR ½ 1667 Goose £32
181 G.H. (E) ¼ 1650 AT THE HAND GVN, cannon
182 EDWARD HILLSYE (P) ¼ Cooks' Arms £25
183 IOHN HOBART (I) ½ 1667 Haberdashers' Arms
184 WILLIAM HOBBS ½ Crossed oars
185 ELIZ IELLVS ½ NEER BLACK CATT £22
186 HESTER KILLSBE ½ '68 AT THE, King's Arms, IN FOXSES LANE
186A WILLIAM LYFE ¼ 3 sugar-loaves
187 BENIAMIN MILLER ½ 1666 Windmill £30
188 E.N. (S) ¼ 1657 THE SONNE TAVERNE
188A H.P. ¼ 1662 MEALEMAN
189 T.P. (F) ¼ 1653 AT THE CROWN £25
190 MICHAELL PARKES (E) ¼ Noah's ark, dove above £30
190A —— (M) ¼ ——
191 IOHN PERKINS (T) ¼ AT THE, angel
192 WILLIAM POWES (E) ¼ Wheatsheaf £22
193 IOHN PLATER ½ '65 Cheese-knife, CHEESMONGES £25
194 IOHN PVLLING (S) ¼ Coopers' Arms
194A I.R. (A) ¼ AT THE NOAHS ARKE
195 IOSEPH RECORD (M) ½ 1666 French horn beneath rainbow
196 RICHARD SELWIN (A) ¼ 1659 CHANDLER (?)
196A RICH — (E) ½ CHANDLER AT, griffin
197 IOH SHACKSPEERE ½ ROAP WALK, Mercers' Arms
197A —— ¼ 1662
198 ED SKOILES (A) ¼ AGAINST BALIS WHARF, boar standing on fish £28
199 HENREY SMITH (A) ¼ 1658 Stocking £18
200 SIMON SNOW ½ AT YE GREEN MAN AND STILL £24
201 NICH THORY (S) ¼ Greyhound, CHANDLER
201A NICHOLAS — (S) ½ 166(6?) Dog or ape
202 ELIAS VNGLE (E) ¼ Scales £30
203 E.W. (E) ¼ Ship, YE SPEAKER FRIGAT £28
204 GEORGE WASTILL ½ 1667 Noah's ark
205 ANDREW WELCH ½ Breast-plate, AT YE SIGN YE PLAT
205A ROBERT WELCH ½ 1668 Glove

Staines
206 IOHN BARNTT (V) ¼ 1653 Swan flapping wings £28
206A RICHARD BARNATT (E) ¼ Bakers' Arms, MALLSTER
207 ABRAHAM BONIFEILD (L) ½ 1669 £25
208 WILLIAM COOKE (H) ½ AT THE GEORGE INN £25
209 THOMAS COLE (B) ½ 1670 AT THE SWAN
210 MARY KNOWLES ¼ AT YE FETHERS £35
211 IOHN PERKINS (M) (½) 1667 AT THE, ship

Stepney
211A ROBERT BECKITT (I) ½ 1668 IN WHITE STREET, horse. *Heart-shape*
211B THOMAS CVFF (A) ½ AT THE BREWERS ARMS

Stoke Newington
212 IOHN BALL 1d AT THE BOARDED HOVSE, men saluting £32
213 (More likely *Kent* 437A)
213A IOHN VSHER (A) ¼ Sun

Tottenham
214 NICHOLAS CVTT ¼ 1666 £40
215 SARAH HOYLES ¼ 1665 Rose and crown £45
216 EDWARD MAYCOCK ½ AT THE, 2 rabbits
217 CHRISTOPHER MILLER (S) ¼ 1666 £40

Turnham Green
218 IOHN HOLLAND ½ 1669 AT YE PACK HORS £55
219 FRANCIS SMITH (M) ½ 1669 Shears
220 IAMES YORKE ½ 1669 Cock on bell £45

Twickenham
221 WILLIAM EBVRN (M) ¼ 1665 £45
222 ABRAHAM SHEARS (L) ½ 1669 King's Arms
223 IOHN WILLIAMS ½ 1669 Prince of Wales' feathers £35

Uxbridge
224 MICHAELL CROSIER ½ Ironmongers' Arms £32
225 ANNE ENGELFEILD ½ 1668 Millrind? £24
226 ANN — ¼ 1664 — £28
227 THOMAS EVENS (A) ¼ Sugar-loaf £42
228 Z(E *or* A)CHARIAH GODWIN (I) ½ 1667 Blacksmiths' Arms £30
229/30 WILL(IAM) GVNN (M) ¼ AT YE 3 PYES, 3 magpies £28
231 IOHN GVRNEY ½ 1670 Chevron between 3 martlets
232 LVKE IAMES (A) ¼ Hart £30
232A EDMVND NICHOLAS (E) ¼ '58 CHANDLER
233 IOHN REEVE (E) ½ 1669 AT THE CHECKER £30
234 IOHN TAYLER (D) ½ 1666 3 swans £25
235 THOMAS TAYLER (E) ¼
236 IOHN TRIPLET (A) ½ AT YE EAGLE AND CHILD £25

Walham Green
237 RICHARD PROSSER (E) ½ CLOTHMAN £45

Westminster
238 E.A. ¼ THE 3 TVNNS AT THE ABY GATE
239 P.G. ¼ '59 Crowned rose £25
240 NEHE ARNOLD (E) ¼ BREWR IN CHAP STREET £25
241 I.B. (M) ¼ AT THE SARASONS HEAD, GROCER £18
242 ROBERT DANCE (S) ½ '67 IN STRVTON GROVND, eagle and child £32
243 ROBERT FRANCKLIN (A) ¼ GROCER
244 IOHN FROST (M) ¼ IN YE BOWLIN ALLY, anchor; chevron between 3 faggots
244A — — (M) ¼ — anchor
245 RALPH FVLLER (F) ¼ IN S ANS STREET, scales £14
246 IOHN HVDSON ¼ IN BRVTTS YARD KING STREET, Woolmongers' Arms
247 F.H. (A) ¼ 1659 AT THE BROKEN CROSS, heart £12
248 W.H. (A) ¼ 16?? AT YE DOGG TAVERN
249 (See *London* 1615)
250 (See *London* 2521)
251 T.M. (M) ¼ YE ROSE TAVERN
252 R.P. (I) ¼ '57 AT YE MITER TAVERN
253 ARTHOR PRYOR ½ 1667 £20
253A EDWARD ROMAN (E) ½ 1671 IN THE BOVLING ALLEY
254 *Mary Statham* (½) 1664 IN CABIDGE LANE, scales
255 WILLIAM LONGE (I) ¼ 1659 Arms, WOOD MVNGER

Whetstone
256 IOHN BOMEN ½ Sheaf of barley
257 ELIZABETH HOARE ¼ 1665 £45

Willesden
258 NICHOLAS NECKALL ¼ 1670 Anchor and cable £40
259 (See *Leics.* 13)

Norfolk

New tokens recorded from W. Gilbert, 'Unpublished . . .' (see under Cambridgeshire); R. Sharman, 'More Unpublished . . .' (see under London); Michael Mitchiner and Anne Skinner, 'English Tokens, *c.* 1425 to 1672' (*BNJ*, 1984); the Cornell Collection (sold at Christie's, 18 Feb. 1986); and *SCA* 51, 16 Apr. 1986.

Believed entirely unpublished: 11A, 13A.

Minimum price for unvalued tokens: £42

Aldborough
1 (Probably *Suffolk* 1)

Aldeby
2 PHILLIP ROBATS (M) ¼ Lion, 3 stars

Ashby
3, 4 (See *Leics.* 7, 8)

Aylsham
5 THOMAS EMPSON (A) ¼ 1665 GROCER
6 IAPHERY FLAXMAN (A) ¼ 1664 St. George & dragon
7 (Probably misreading of 104)
8 LANSALET THEXTON ¼ 1666 GROCER £40
9, 9* WILLIAM WATTS (M) ¼ Bull £38
10 (Probably *Kent* 277)

Bawdeswell
11 THOMAS BOWRNE (E) ¼ 1667 Ram

Blakeney (?)
11A IAMES WILSON ½ 1668 Woolpack

Brancaster
12 WILLIAM RIX (C) ¼ 1667 Blacksmiths' Arms

Burnham Market
13 IOHN TVCKE (M) ¼ Sugar-loaf £30
13A —— (M) ¼ 1660 —
14 MARTIN TVCKE ¼ Blacksmiths' Arms
15 (Probably *Essex* C49)

Caister
16/7 (See *Lincs.* 52, 51)

Carleton
18 (Probably *Yorks.* 59)

Cley-next-the-Sea
19 Town ¼ HOVLT HONDRED, Anchor; horseshoe £25
20 RICHARD SHAWE (M) ½ 1667 Man making candles £32
21 IOHN WILCH ¼ AT THE GEORGE £32

Creake, South
22 WILL SWALLOW ¼ 1667 Jug

Cromer
23 (Probably misreading of 24)
24 RICHARD BENNET (A) ¼ 1665 Lion
24A —— (A) ¼ 1664
25 ROBERT DRAKE ¼ Lion in shield
26 MARGRET MANGLE (M) ¼ 1666 Tree

Diss
27 Town ¼ 1669 Town Arms, crest £10
28/8* THOMAS BVRTON ¼ Ironmongers' Arms £18

Downham Market
28A H.I. ¼ 1652 Heart, crossed arrows. In *pb*
29 WILL RAY (A) ¼ 1666 Mercers' Arms £22
30 ION TROTT (E) ¼ Horseshoe £38

East Dereham
31 PETER BARKER (M) ¼ 1656 Grocers' Arms £35
32 THO BLYFER (A) ¼ DRAPER £40
33 HENREY BODDY (S) ¼ GROCER
34 IOHN HALCOTT (C) ¼ Bow and arrow
35 THOMAS IESSVP ¼ 1660 Grocers' Arms
36 —— ¼ n.d. — GRO
37 IOHN MARSHALL (E) ¼ '71 Eagle and child
37A THOMAS MOORE ¼ Tobacco pipes
38 FRANCIS WALLER ¼ Grocers' Arms; scales £45

East Harling
39 IOHN HILTON ¼ 1660 3 doves
39A THOMAS YOVNG ¼ Grocers' Arms

Emneth
40 GEORG WHYTING ¼ 1660 Grocers' Arms £50

Fakenham
41 (See *Hants.* 64)
42 EDMOND PECKONER ¼ 1667 Merchant Taylors' Arms, GROCR £28

43 ROBERT SHELDRAKE ¼ 1667 Apothecaries' Arms £48
44 WILLIAM SHILDRACK ¼ 1657 £32

Fordham

45 IOHN BADCOCK ¼ 1667 Grocers' Arms £45

Forncett St. Peter

46 ROBERT PLOWMAN (M) ½ 1668

Foulsham

47 IOHN ATTHILL (M) ¼ GROCER
48 EDWARD BENN (R) ¼ 1668 MERCER £38

Harleston

49, 50 STE(PH *or* V)EN FREEMAN ¼ 1666 Drapers' Arms £28
51/2 CLEARE SHEWE(L *or* LL) ¼ 1656 Grocers' Arms £14
53 — SHEWELL ¼ 1666 —

Hilgay

54 IOHN DEY ¼ 1664 Grocers' Arms

Hingham

55 EDWARD BALDWIN (E) ¼ 1668 Haberdashers' Arms £50
56 WILLIAM RIX (A) ¼ 1659 GROSER £40

Holt

57 DANIEL ROLL ¼ 1666 Mortar £55
58 FRANCIS SHAWE (P) ¼ 1658 Man making candles

Litcham

59 THOMAS FELTWELL ¼ AT YE BVLL
60 WILLIAM PEARSON ¼ GROSER

Loddon

61 HENRY BVRROVGH ¼ 1667 Grocers' Arms £38

Ludham

62 ROBERT WHITE ¼ GROCER

Lynn Regis (King's Lynn)

63/4 Town ¼ 1668 Town Arms £8
65 — ¼ 1669 — £9
66 ROBERT ALLEN (M) ¼ 1668 COOPER
67 EDWARD BILLINGES (E) ¼ 1656 Apothecaries' Arms £20
68 — — (E) ¼ 1662 — £28
69 ALEXANDER BINGHAM ¼ '66 Bust of Chas. II £18
69* — — ¼ '68 —
70 IOSEPH BRABAN (M) ¼ 1666 Stocking, HOSYER £15
71 IOSEPH BREBON ¼ 1657 Initials W.B., E.G. £28
72 GYLES BRIDGMAN (S) ¼ Family Arms £22
73 GILES — (S) ¼ 1650 £14
74 HILEARD BROWN (K) ¼ 1654 Grocers' Arms £32
75 IOHN BROWNE ¼ GROCER
76 ROBERT BVLL (B) ¼ AT THE BACKRS ARMS
77 IOHN CLAY (S) ¼ 1664 Tallowchandlers' Arms
78 (Probably misreading of 79)
79 E.D. ¼ 1660 IN LATH STREETE
80 THOMAS DENMAN (I) ¼ 1665 Tallowchandlers' Arms £25
81 ROBERT FRAVNCES ¼ Apothecaries' Arms
82 SETH GARRARD (M) ¼ 1652 GROCER £14
83 IOHN GREENE ¼ GROCER
84 THOMAS HARWICK ¼ MERCER £20
85 WILL HATFEILD (A) ¼ 1666 Tallowchandlers' Arms £20
86 IEREMIAH HOVELL ½ 1666 Man holding cross £25
87 IOHN HOWARD (D) ¼ 1660 Hand holding shears
88 REBECKAH HOWLETT ¼ Plume of feathers £20
89 ROBERT LEAK (M) ¼ Rose, WOLL COMER
90 BRYAN MIDLETVN (M) ¼ Merchant Taylors' Arms £30
91 WILLIAM PRESTON (B) ¼ Upholsterers' Arms, VPHOLSTER £20
92 EDMOND QVASH ¼ 1667 Anchor
93 MATTHEW RICHERS (A) ¼ 1665 GROCER
94 MATHEW — (A) ¼ 1667 Grocers' Arms
95 IOHN RINGSTEAD (F) ¼ 1658 CHANDLER £28
96 RICHARD ROBERTS (G) ¼ 1660 £35
97 SAMVEL ROBINSON ¼ 1660 3 stags' heads
98 IOHN SALTER (S) ¼ 1666 BAKER
99 WILLIAM SHARPE ½ 1668 Bakers' Arms £25
100 ROBERT THETFORD (M) ¼ '67 GROCER
101 EDWARD TILSON ¼ 1668 Bakers' Arms £35
102/2* N.W. (R) ¼ Grocers' Arms £13
103 RICHARD WOLTERTON ¼ 1656 Shuttle £14

Marsham

104 (Probably *Yorks.* 232)

Massingham

105 THO CHILDERHOVSE ¼ 1657

Mendham

106 (see *Suffolk* 242A)

Mileham

107 FRANCIS LADLY (C) ¼ 1666 £40

Narborough

108 (Probably misreading of *Yorks.* 300)

New Buckenham

109 FRANCIS WATTS ¼ 1657 Grocers' Arms £50
110 THO YOVNGMAN ¼ 1667 GROCER

Northwold

111 WILLIAM RVSSELL (R) ¼ GROSER

Norwich

112–4 IOHN ATWOOD (K) ¼ £18

115 IAMES A(V *or* R)BREE (M) ¼ 1667 £28
116 MICHAELL BAKER (A) ¼ 1667 £25
117 IAMES BARTON (E) ¼ 1667 Fruiterers' Arms
118 VIOLET BENTON (R) ¼ 1664 Key £22
119 NICHOLAS BILHAM ¼ Grocers' Arms £25
120/1 IOHN BLAND (M) ¼ Stocking £28
122 PEETER BLOFELD ¼ Grocers' Arms £15
123/4 AVGVSTINE BRIDGS ¼ Cock, GROCER £14
125 IAMES BROCKDEN (R) ¼ 1664 Castle £14
126 ROBERT BROWN (A) ¼ Merchant Taylors' Arms £22
127 IOHN BROWNE (S) ¼ 1657 Swan
128 EDWARD BVXTON (A) ¼ 1653 Grocers' Arms £13
129 EDMVND CAMOND ¼ GROCER
130 IAMES CASTILL (I) ¼ 1664 Woolcomb £16
131 — CASTLE (I) ¼ 1662
132 ROBERT CLAYTON ¼ 1663 IRONMONGER £16
133 WILLIAM COOPER ¼ 1662 Bust of Chas. II; rose £28
134 ISAAC COWPER (E) ¼ Trowel, BRICK LAYER £32
135 PEETER DEALE (A) ¼ 1664 Helmet £16
136/7 ABRAHAM DERRIX (I) ¼ 1665 Fleece £22
138 IAMES DOVER ¼ 1667
139 ROBERT DVGLAS (D) ¼ Swords crossed, CVTTLER £18
140 FRANCIS ELMER (G) ¼ 1667 3 foxes
141 ROBERT EMPEROR (E) ¼ Sword £20
142 THOMAS FERRIER ¼ 1664 Heart on anchor £22
143 THOMAS FLATMAN ¼ 1664 £22
144 RICHARD FREEMAN ¼ 1657 Dove with olive branch £25
145 L. GOODWYN ¼ 1660 CONFECTIONER AT THE GOLDEN CAMELL £25
146 THOMAS GREENE (S) ¼ 1658 Grocers' Arms
147 BENIAMEN GREENWOOD (E) ¼ 1667 Grocers' Arms
148 ELIZ HALFKNIGHT ¼ 1667 Dyers' Arms £20
149 GEORGE HALL ¼ 1664 Grocers' Arms £15
150 THOMAS HANSE (E) ¼ 1664 Anchor £20
151 EDWARD HARDING (A) ¼ GROCER £22
152 BLYTH HATTON ¼ Rose £20
153 HENRY HOLBEY (G) ¼ 1659 NEAR REDWELL, hand holding sword £30
154 NATHANAELL HOWLET ¼ City Arms, WOSD WEAVER
155/6 IOHN HVTTON (E) ¼ 1657 Triskelis £20
157 EDWARD HYRNE (M) ¼ GROCER £13
158 A.L. ¼ 1661 Leg, AT YE POST OFFICE £32
159–61 T.L. (D) ¼ 1653 IN S ANDREWES PARRICH £16
162 THOMAS LACEY (S) ¼ 1667 Keys crossed £28
163 WILLIAM LAMBERT (A) ¼ GROCER £18
164 IOHN LAWRENCE, L. GOODWIN ¼ 1658 7 stars £22
165 IOHN LEVERINGTON (V) ¼ £35
166 THOMAS LINSTEAD ¼ 1659 GROSER £15
167 THOMAS LONG (A) ¼1657 Grocers' Arms £38
168 IOHN MAYES (E) ¼ 1667 Man making candles
169 ANTHO MINGAY ¼ Man leading camel £22
170/1 WILL MONY (E) ¼ LION LANE, lion £16
172 RICHARD MORANT ¼ Shuttles, neck whisk
173 FRACIS MORLY ¼ Grocers' Arms £15
174/4* ANN MVNFORD ¼ Grocers' Arms £18
175 GEORGE MVNFORD ¼ 1657 Merchant's mark; Grocers' Arms £20
176 THOMAS NEWMAN ¼ Grocers' Arms £20
177 ELIAS NORGATS (E) 1660 Demi-man holding sceptre £25
178 IOHN OSBORN ¼ GROCER £22
179 IOHN PARKER (E) ¼ 1665 Sheep £18
180 WILLIAM PARMENTER (S) ¼ 1654 Grocers' Arms £22
181 ISAAC PEARCIVALE (I) ¼ 1667 Tree £16
182 WILL PLAYFORD (A) ¼
183 WILLIAM PRICE (S) ¼ 1662 £28
184 DANIELL PYCROFT ¼ Grocers' Arms £20
185 THOMAS RANDOLL (E) ¼ Bakers' Arms £22
186 AGVSTINE RAYLEY ¼ 1662 Grocers' Arms
187 THOMOS RAYNER ¼ 1653 Grocers' Arms £12
188 — — ¼ 1655 —
189 CHARLES REEVE ¼ 1664 £17
190–3 GEORGE REEVE (R) ¼ Grocers' Arms £12
194 WILL ROBINSON (E) ¼ 1662 Man in moon
195/6 IOHN SHEPPARD ¼ 1659 £22
197/8 HENRY SIDNOR (I) ¼ 1659 Greyhound £20
199 — — (I) ¼ 1667 Tallowchandlers' Arms
200/1 IONATHAN SNOWDEN (E) ¼ 1660 Grocers' Arms
202 MATHEW SOVLTER (B) ¼ OATMEALE MAKER
203 SPENDLOVE ¼ 1667 Merchant's mark; Grocers' Arms, GROCER £22
204 SAMVELL STARLIN ¼ 1664 3 rabbits £25
205 IOHN TABOR (M) ¼ 1663 Spade £18
206/7 ROBERT THARROLD ¼ GROCER £14
208 WILLIAM THVRTON (M) ¼ 1665 £32
209 BENIAMIN TOFT (E) ¼ 1664 Grocers' Arms £18
210 DANEL TOFT (E) ¼ 1653 GROCER £30
211 ROBERT TOMPSON ¼ 1652 Portcullis
212/3 IERIMY VYN ¼ ANNO 1657 Grocers' Arms £14
214 — IVYN ¼ — — —
215 IOHN WARD (E) ¼ 1667 Woolpack
216 THOMAS WARNE (I) ¼ 1662
217 THOMAS WARREN ¼ Grocers' Arms £15
218 THO WELD (C) ¼ 1657 HATTER

219 WILLIAM WITHERLEY ¼ Grocers' Arms
220/1 NICHOLAS WITHERS (F) ¼ 1658 £35
222 EDWARD WOODYARD (M) ¼ 1656 Sugar-loaf, 2 cloves, GROC
223 THOMAS WORMALL (I) ¼ 1662
224 WILL YOVNGEST ¼ Woolcomb £20
225 City ¼ 1667 City Arms £7
226/7 — ¼ 1668 — £8
228 — ¼ 1670 — £9
229 S.A. ¼? 1654 S. AVGVSTINES PARISH
230 (Pattern piece?)

Outwell

231 WILLIAM BAYLEY (K) ¼ 1667 Grocers' Arms
232 FRANCES BOYCE (M) ¼ 1664 Scales £45
233 STEPHEN CLARKE (M) ¼ Bell

Pulham Market (St Mary)

234 THOMAS FLATMAN ¼ 1664 PVLHAM MARKET £45
234A — — ¼ — PVLHAM ST MARY
235 HEN THEOBALD ¼ Hart wounded by arrow, DRAPER £35

Rudham

236 IOHN PEARSON ¼ 1667 Mercers' Arms

Shipdham

237 NICHOLAS GOLDING (S) ¼ Ship

Snettisham

238 FRANCIS CASTING ¼ '64 Grocers' Arms

Stoke

239 IOHN HVBBARD (E) ¼ GROCER £28

Stowbridge

240 THO CASE ½ '69 Keys crossed; bridge £25
241 IOHN PRATT ½ 1668 Bridge £28

(Long) Stratton

242 ROBERT BAYLY (E) ¼ 1654 DRAPER £28
243 (See *Cornwall* 94)

Swaffham

244 THOMAS CANNON (M) ¼ 1658 Family Arms and crest £25
245 — — (M) ¼ 1667 — £25
246 EDWARD CASE (E) ¼ Man smoking, tobacco under arm
247 THOMAS DAWSON (S) ¼ 1659 Keys crossed £40
248 ROBERT DENTON (A) ¼ 1660 Stick of candles
249 IOHN HOOKER ¼
250 — — ¼ 1667 Grocers' Arms

Swanton Abbott

251 WILLIAM COOPER ¼ Bust of Chas. II; rose

Swanton Novers

252 IAMES NAILOR (A) ½ 1667 £45
253 — NAYLOR (A) ½ 1671

Thetford

254 WILLIAM FLANNER (M) ¼ 1669 £18
255 WORMLY HETHERSET ¼ Grocers' Arms
256 FRANCIS HOWLETT ¼ 1668 Woolpack £22
257 EDWARD MOORE (F) ¼ 1668 Mercers' Arms £38
258 IOHN WAYMOND ¼ 1659 Grocers' Arms £45

Thornham

259 STEPHEN TVCKE (M) ½ 1667 Cross

Upwell

260 WILLIAM BOYCE (S) ¼ 1664 3 doves
261 (Probably misreading of 262)
262 IAMES BRONLES (I) ¼ 1664 Brewers' Arms
263 THOMAS NVRISH (A) ¼ 1664 Crown
264 THOMAS ROBINSON (A) ½ 1668 Keys crossed £40
265 SAMVELL VINCENT ¼ 1664 Mercers' Arms

Walsham, North

266 IOHN COOKE (M) ¼ Mercers' Arms £32
267 THOMAS MOORE ¼ Grocers' Arms
268 PETER RICHARDSON (M) ¼ '57 Duke of Norfolk's Arms £35
269 THOMAS RVDDOCKE ¼ Drapers' Arms £42
270 IOSEPH WASEY ¼ Mercers' Arms

Walsingham

271 BENIAMIN RVDKIN (S) ½ ANNO DOM 1669 BRAZIER £40
272 WILL FRAMINGHAM ¼ Rose
273 IOHN PARTINGTON ½ n.d. Haberdashers' Arms
274 — — ¼ — — £32
275 — — ¼ 1668 Scales

Watton

276 CHRISTOPHER HEY (M) ¼ MERCER £30

Wells

277 RICHARD MANSVAR ¼ Mercers' Arms £35

Wilton

278 THOMAS CLARK ¼ 1664 Weavers' Arms
279 (Probably *Wilts*. 268A)
280 (See *Wilts*. 268B)
281 FRANCIS WACE ¼ 1658 Swords crossed; Drapers' Arms £30

Wymondham

282 IOHN BVRRELL (E) ¼ Drapers' Arms
283 ANTHONY LOCK ¼ Grocers' Arms £38

Yarmouth

284/5 Borough ¼ 1667 Borough Arms, FOR THE VSE OF THE POOR(E) £8
286 — ¼ 1669 — FOR THE VSE OF THE POOR £9
287–90 IOHN AMES (I) ¼ 1652 Man making candles £11

291 IOHN ARNOLD (M) ¼ Bunch of grapes
291A FRANCIS BELL (M) ¼ Drum
292/3 BENIAMIN BARKER ¼ 1662 £16
294–6 WILLIAM BATCH ¼ Wheatsheaf £18
297/8 WILLIAM BATEMAN ¼ 1656 Merchant's mark; bugle horn £11
299 —— ¼ 1667 —— £22
300 EDMVND BEDDINGFILD (M) ¼ Sheaf of arrows £18
301 THOMAS BRADFORD ¼ n.d. 7 stars
302 —— ¼ 1655 —
303/4 WILLIAM BRATIN *or* BRETTON (R) ¼ Baker £25
305 IOHN CONDLEY (M) ¼ Merchant's mark, MARCHANT £20
306/7 IOSEPH COOPER (F) ¼ 1656 MARCHANT £20
308–11 CHRISTO COZ(E *or* I)NS *or* CHRIST(R) COZENS (A) ¼ Grocer £15
312 RICHARD CRAFFORD (D) ¼ '59 Teasel £28
313 THOMAS CRANE (I) ¼ 1665 Crane
314 IOHN CVRTIS ¼ 1662 Men saluting, BAKER £22
315 THOMAS DAWSON (M) ¼ 1667 Hand holding compasses £38
316–8 IOHN EMPEROR ¼ 1664 £25
319 RICHARD FLAXMAN (M) ¼ '57 3 goats' heads
320 THOMAS GODFRAY ¼ Griffin £22
321 (See *Suffolk* 292A)
322/3 THO(V)MAS HERING ¼ Holdfasts crossed £18
324 IOHN HOOKE (I) ¼ Tobacco-roll £38
325/6 WILLIAM LINCOLNE (I) ¼ 1652 Grocers' Arms £16
327 SAMVELL MANTHORP (I) ¼ 3 sugar-loaves
328 THOMAS MOVLTON (H) ¼ 1667
329 REBEKKA MVRRIL ¼ Bakers' Arms
330 IONAS NEAVE (E) ¼ 1659 Anchor £35
331 —— (E) ¼ 1661 Dolphin
332/3 EDWARD OWNER ¼ GROCER £18
334 EDWARD PETERSON (M) ¼ Face in sun £25
335 HENRY POTTER (S) ¼ '67 Griffin
336 THOMAS RICHMVND ¼ 1654 £30
337 FRANCS SHIPDHAM ¼ Dolphin
338 GEORGE SPILMAN (E) ¼ Man-at-arms £22
339 MICHALL TILLES (A) ¼ 1666 Grocers' Arms £28
340–2 STEPHEN TRACEY (A) ¼ Lion £15
343 CLEMENT TROTTER (S) ¼ 1653 Ship £25
344/5 BENIAMIN WALLER (A) ¼ 1658 £14
346 BENIAMIN WAL(L)TON (A) ¼ 1654 Anchor £16
347 — WALLTON (A) ¼ 1666 — £18
348 ROGER WATERS ¼ Family Arms £30
349 THOMAS WATERS (E) ¼ 1656 Stocking
350/1 GABRIELL WOODRIFE *or* WOODROOFFE ¼ Grocers' Arms £12
352 WILLIAM WOORTS (D) ¼ Dove with olive-branch, HOSYER £42
353 (A ticket or check or trial piece?)

Northamptonshire

Major reference: W.C. Wells, *Seventeenth Century Tokens of Northamptonshire* (London, 1914), and *Addenda et Corrigenda* to this (London, 1915). (Both works previously published in *BNJ*, 1909–14). 4 plates; updating and revision of 'Williamson', notes on the issuers, and much background information. See also Wells' notes in *SNC*, Sep./Oct. 1924.

Further new tokens recorded from *BNJ*, 1920; Faulkner collection (sold at Glendining's, 21 May 1940); and J. G. Milne, 'The Browne Willis Cabinet' (*BNJ*, 1951).

Minimum price for unvalued tokens: £50

Ashley
1 IOHN GRANGER ½ 1668 3 awls?

Aynhoe
2 THOMAS NORRIS ½ Lion £22
3 PETER PRVCE (M) ½ 1668 AT THE BEL £30

Barnwell St Andrew's
4 SAMVELL WRIGHT (S) ½ 1667

Bowden
5 (See *Leics.* 14)

Bozeat
6 WILLIAM GLOVER ½ 1668

Brackley
7 BARTHOLOMEW ATTOW ¼ Bell, DRAPER £32
8 CONNOWAY RANDS ½ 1671 Sugar-loaf £40
9 CONAWAY RAND ¼ n.d. Lion
10 MARY SKILDEN ½ 1665 AT THE SVN
11 IOHN STOAKES ½ 1670 3 cloves £32
12 ROBERT WILKINS (E) ½ Bust of Chas. II £40
13 WILLIAM WILLIAMS ½ 1670 AT YE RED LYON

Brampton Magna
13A THOMAS SMITH ½ 1668 £40

Brigstock
14 THO ALLEN ¼ Grocers' Arms, CHANDLER

Bulwick
15 WILLIAM WATTS (M) ½ 1669 Swan £25

Corby
16 (See *Lincs.* 54)
16A William Rigby ¼ 1658

Daventry
17 EDWARD ARNOLD ¼ 1667 Grocers' Arms
18 HENRY BASSETT ¼ Chain; Grocers' Arms
19, 20 RICHARD FARMOR ¼ Grocers' Arms; man holding bush ("Dane" with "tree") £42
21 ZACHEVS FREEMAN (½) BOOK SELLER
22 THOMAS GRVBB ¼ Candle b.s.
23 WILLIAM HEALY ½ Fruiterers' Arms; crowned rose

Doddington
23A IOHN IOHNSON (probably *Cambs.* 98)

Duddington
24 (Probably *Kent* 196A)

Geddington
25 IONATH ROWLETT ¼ 1654
26 IONATHN — ¼ 1657 £45
27 IONATH — ¼ 1664
28 THOMAS WALLIS ¼ Grocers' Arms; sugar-loaf

Grendon
29 THOMAS GAWTHERNE (E) ¼ Cordwainers' Arms £50

(West) Haddon
30 (Misreading of 31)
31 ELISHA ALMEY ½ Grocers' Arms £35
31A — ALLMEY (A) ¼ 1663 —

Harringworth
32/3 THO BEARLY (A) ½ THE PACK SADLE A CARIER *or* THE PACK SADEL A CAROR £25

Hartwell
34 WILLIAM CHVRCH (A) ½ 1666 Scales £35

Higham Ferrers
35 IOHN CHETLE ½ 1667 Stick of candles £35
36 HENRY CHETTLE ¼ Stick of candles
37 THOMAS IVDD (H) ¼ '56 Arms

38 (Misreading of 39)
39 GILBERT NEGVS (E) ½ 1669 Blacksmiths' Arms £28
40 (Probably misreading of another token)
41 TWYFORD WORTHINGTON (½) 1656 Goat crest £22
42 (Probably misreading of 41)

Ixworth
43 (See *Suffolk* 201)

Kettering
44 IOHN FOX ¼ 1664 Grocers' Arms £42
45 IOHN LADDS (A) ¼ 1664 £50
45A —— (A) ¼ 1657
45B IOSEPH SPAROW (E) ¼ CHANDLER
46 THOMAS WEBB ¼ Mercers' Arms £30

Kilsby
47 IOHN BVRGIS (M) ½ 1670 MERCER £40

King's Cliffe
48 OVERSEERS ½ Crown; fleur-de-lis £20
49 IANE BROWNE ½ 1660 Date on *obv.* £25
50 —— ¼ ——
51 —— ½ — Date on *rev.*
52 (Misreading of 51)
53 THOMAS LAW ¼ 1659 Grocers' Arms; scales
54 (Misreading of 55)
55 THOMAS LAW ¼ 1665 on *obv.*, 1659 on *rev.* £25

Lamport
56–8 (See *Som.* 177A, 175A, 177)

Lowick
59 LEWES SVLCH ½ 1666 Hart £35

Lutton
60 (Misreading of 61)
61 MATHEW GOSTON (M) ¼ Packhorse, LO

Mears Ashby
61A PAVL GROVE ¼ 1662 Scales

Moulton
62/3 IOHN PERYN ¼ Scales £24

Northampton
64/6 (Misreadings of 65)
65 RICHARD ALCOVT (M) ½ 1667 AT YE ONE PIGEON £50
67 EDWARD COOPER (E) ¼ 1654 Rose £48
68 THOMAS COOPER (E) ¼ 1652 Ironmongers' Arms £22
69 —— (E) ¼ 1668— £22
70 G.E. (E) ¼ AT THE WHIT HIND
71 IOHN LABRAM (S) ¼ IN THE DRAPERE, sugar-loaf £35
72 (Probably same as 71)
73 SAMVEL POOEL ¼ Holy lamb £35
74 S.R., town ¼ Castle gateway; lions† £14
75 I.S., town ¼ ——† £15
76–8 (Probably same as 75)
79, 80 I.S. (D) ¼ 1651 BIRD STREETE, scales £15
81/2 (Same as 79, 80)
83 I.S. (M) ¼ 1650 AT THE GEORGE £32
84 I.T., town ¼ 1660 Castle gateway; lions, CHAMBERLAINE† £50
85 IOHN TWIGDEN (½) 1666 Glove, CREDE SED CAVE* £28
86/7 ANCHOR WILLDINGE (A) ¼ Anchor, MERCER £16

Oundle
88 FEEFEES ½ Talbot; griffin £17
89 Town ½ 1669 Talbot b.s. FOR THE VSE OF THE POOR £22
90 IOHN AVDLEY ½ 1669 Still, TOBACCONIST £40
91 MATHEW AVSTIN ¼ Fleur-de-lis £32
92 NATH BROWING ¼ 1659 Holy lamb, CHANDLER £30
92A IOHN CLEMENT (M) ¼ 1664 TOBACONIST
93 HENRY COLDWEL (E) ¼ HABADASHER
94 IOHN EATON ¼ Grocers' Arms £30
95 WILL FILBRIGG ¼ 1658 Arms and crest, LINEN DRAPER £25
96 LAWRANCE HAVTON ¼ 1664 Man making candles £25
97 WILLIAM HVLL ¼ Haberdashers' Arms
98 MATHEW HVNT ¼ 1657 £30
99 WILLIAM IAMES ¼ 1663 3 cloves, CHANDLER
100 DANIEL MAVLEY ¼ 1657 6 cloves in shield; dove with olive branch, CHANDLER £22
101 IOHN PASHLER ¼ 1668 CHANDLER £22
102 RICH STEVENSON ¼ Grocers' Arms, CHANDLER £50
103 WILLM TERREWFST (K) ¼ Merchant Taylors' Arms £35

Peterborough
104 *Ouerseers* ½ 1669 Crossed swords between 4 crosses. *Octagonal* £25
105 (Misreading of 106)
106/7 *towne Bailife* ½ 1670 Crossed swords between 4 crosses. *Octagonal.* **Plate 3** £18
108 ROBERT ANDREWES ¼ Bakers' Arms
109 R.B. ¼ AT YE, clasped book; FEARE GOD HONOR THE KING
110 IOHN BLVDWICK ¼ 3 cloves

* Also known in silver; these and other base metal restrikes on heavy flans were probably of 18th cent. manufacture
† Although only of farthing size, nos. 75 and 84 were in fact issued to pass current as halfpennies. No. 74, issued as a farthing in 1653, was re-valued at a halfpenny two years later.

111 RICHARD BVRTON ½ 1668 Clasped book
112 IOHN BVTLER (E) ¼ 1664 Grocers' Arms £38
113 ROB(A *or* E)RT CARYER ¼ Pelican feeding young £38
114 (Misreading of 113)
115 IOHN CAWTHORNE ¼ Bakers' Arms £45
116 ROBERT DANYELL ½ 1668 Grocers' Arms £32
117 (Probably misreading of 118)
118 THO DILLINGHAM ¼ Tobacco-roll
119/20 IOHN FRENCH (F) ¼ DRAPER £32
121 (Same as 122)
122 GEORGE HAMERTON (M) ½ 1667 Grocers' Arms £32
123 —— (M) ¼ n.d. —
124 NICHOLAS HARDY ¼ Pipes, tobacco-roll
125 ALCE HARVEY ¼ 1659 AT THE, clasped book
126 (Probably misreading of 127)
127 MARGRET KEMPE ¼ 1664 £30
128 (Misreading of 129)
129 MATHEW KNOWLES ¼ Portcullis
130 IONE MANISTRY ½ 1668 £20
131 FRA(N)CIS MORTIMER ¼ Stocking
132 THOMAS SECHELL (A) ¼ Grocers' Arms
133 (Misreading of 134)
134 THOMAS SHINN ½ 1667 Grocers' Arms
135 THO SHINNE ¼ n.d. —
136 GEO SLYE ¼ Bakers' Arms
137 IAMES TALER ½ 1669 Cordwainers' Arms. **Plate 3** £20
138 RICHARD TOMPSON ½ 1668 £17
139 WILLIAM WELLS ¼ Grocers' Arms £32

Paulerspury
140 THOMAS RATCLIF (E) ¼ 1666 Scales

Potterspury
141 THOMAS SAVL ½ 1668 Falcon £30

Rockingham
142 SAMVELL PEAKE ½ 1668 Grocers' Arms

Rothwell
143 THOMAS BEBEE ½ BAKER
143A —— (M) ¼ —
144 IOHN COLLIER (M) ¼ 1658 3 cloves
145 WILLIAM DODSON ½ 1666 Mercers' Arms £30
145A WILLIAM MASON (A) ½ 1666
146 IOHN PONDER (D) ½ 1664 *Ob* £28
147 —— (D) ¼ 1655 Stick of candles £25

Rushden
148 GEORGE CARTER (E) ½ 1666 St. George & dragon £30

Stamford Baron
149 MILES HODGSON ¼ Falcon; woolpack
150 —— ¼ '67 ——

(King's) Sutton
151 EDMVND CHANDLER (E) ½ 1666 £28

Thingdon (now **Finedon**)
152 AMERICA BAGERLEY ½ 1669 Oak tree. *Heart-shape* £180
153 (See *Staffs.* 72C)

Thrapston
154 IOHN HVNT ¼ Man making candles
155 EDMOND PALMER ¼ '68 BAKR
156 WILLIAM WILLMOT ¼ 1666 Swan £22

Towcester
157/8 WILLIAM BELL ½ DYER £16
159 THOMAS CLARKE ½ 1669 Drapers' Arms £20
160 ——(A) ¼ n.d. — (not in shield) £25
161 (Misreading of 160)
162 RICHARD FARMER (E) ¼ Talbot
163 CHARLES GORE ½ 1663 Family Arms £25
164 THOMAS HARRIS (M) ½ 1668 Basket £30
165 *Pattricke Herron* ½ Arms. *Octagonal* £45
166 WILL HOWES ¼ 1670 Fleur-de-lis, MERCER
167 IOHN KINGSTON (½) 1666 Scales, MERCER £22
168 —— (G) ¼ Grocers' Arms, MERCER £45
169 GEORGE WAPLE ½ 1667 Mercers' Arms £20

Weedon
170 THOMAS MARRIOTT (F) ¼ 1657 Grocers' Arms
171 MARTIN PA(R *or* C)KER (M) ¼ 1652 Grocers' Arms £55

Weldon
172 WILLIAM RESBY ½ 1668 Man making candles

Wansford
173 GEORGE BOSEMAN ¼ 1663 Sugar-loaf £25

Welford
174 WILL WICKES ½ '69 St. George & dragon. *Heart-shape*

Wellingborough
175 RICHARD MANINGTON (M) ½ '65 £28
176 WILLIAM SEER (E) ¼ 1655 Scales £16
177 HENRY SMITH ¼ 3 cloves, bell £18
178 IOHN WORTHINGTON ½ 1668 Sun; crescent £18

Whittlebury
179 HENRY DOLTON (M) ½ 1669 Shovel (?)

Northumberland

See H. Hird, 'Northumberland Seventeenth Century Tokens' (*Transactions of the Yorkshire Numismatic Society*, 2nd Series, Vol. I pt. I, 1951). Two varieties of Williamson's descriptions, numbers of specimens noted, and illustration of a Newcastle farthing in lead which is probably a 20th century concoction.

Minimum price: £200

Newcastle

1 CHARLES BARKER, GABRILL FVLTHORP ¼ Mercers' Arms
2 WILLIAM BLACKETT ¼ Family Arms; Merchant Adventurers' Arms, MARCHANT
3 ANTHONY DOBSON ¼ Bust of Chas. II
4 IOHN GAVSTELL (I) ¼ Fleece
5 WILLIAM HVTCHINSON ¼ 1660 Castle; merchant's mark
6 WILL LONDON ¼ Town arms
7 HENRY SLINGER ¼ 1664
8 EDWARD SPENCER (P) ¼ Mercers' Arms
9 HENRY TOMPSON (E) ¼ Castle
10 IOHN THOMAS (M) ¼ 1659 3 standing figures

Nottinghamshire

Major reference: Peter Preston-Morley and Harry Pegg, 'A Revised Survey of the Seventeenth-Century Tokens of Nottinghamshire' (*BNJ*, 1981). 8 plates; updating and revision of 'Williamson', notes on some issuers, detailed classification of the tokens, locations of specimens, numbers examined, notes on some late 19th cent. forgeries, and an analysis of most that have been on the market, and when, since 1890. The most comprehensive of the county revisions so far.

Minimum price for unvalued tokens: £55

Bingham
1 EDWARD BANBVRY ½
2 THOMAS MARKHAM ½ 1669 CHANDLER

Blyth
3 THOMAS BVCKE (A) ½ 1666 Stag, MERCER
4 HENRY CARIER (R) (½) Eagle, MERCER

Brinsley
5 ROBERT HORESLEY ½ 1669 BLACK SMITH

Collingham (North)
6 THOMAS RIDGE ½ 1664 Grocers' Arms, MERCER £32
7 MARY SCRIMSHAW ½ Mercers' Arms

Cossall
8 AMBROSE COVPER ½ 1657 MERCER
9 (See *Essex* 78)
9A RICHARD SADLER ½ 1665 Mercers' Arms

Laneham
10 *Mary Adlington ½. Octagonal* £100

Mansfield
11 PEETER BROWNE ½ 1664 Blacksmiths' Arms
12 ROBERT CLEGGE (A) ¼ 1659 Apothecaries' Arms
13 SAMVELL HAVLTON ½ 1664 Bakers' Arms £45
14 HENRY HEATH ½ 1671 AT THE, talbot
15 WILLIAM HVRST ½ 1667 Packhorse, CARIER £32
16 WILLIAM POYZOR (K) ¼ 1659 Swan
17 — — ½ 1671 — £55
18 (Misreading of 17)
19 GREGORY SYLVESTER ½ 1666 Mercers' Arms £50
20 EDWARD SOVTHWORTH ½ Ironmongers' Arms
21/2 IOHN WIL(LD *or* DE) (A) (½) 1666 Grocers' Arms £42
23 FRANCIS WILSON ½ 1664 Tallowchandlers' Arms £55
24 — — ½ 1667 —
25 — — ½ 1668 — £55
26 ROBERT WOOD ½ 1667 Hat with feather £38

Mansfield Woodhouse
27 (Misreading of 28)
28 RICHARD LEWIS ½ Horse saddled and bridled £65

Newark
29 MATHEW ALVEY ½ 1664 Grocers' Arms, MERCER £50
30 CHRISTO BVRNETT ½ '68 SADLER £35
31 HENRY CAM ½ 1666 APOTHECARY, initials H.G. £60
32 IOSHVA CLARKE ½ 1666 Grocers' Arms MERCER £32
33 DENIS COOLING ½ 1666 AN APOTHECARY
34 IOHN FEATLEY ¼ 1658 Mercers' Arms
35 IOHN GERTON (E) ¼ 1659 Ironmongers' Arms
36 WILL GLOVER (A) ½ 1664 CHANDLER £40
37 THO GODDARD ½ 1669 BLACKSMITH AT YE GOLDEN, horseshoe
38 WILLIAM GRANT ¼ 1657 Mercers' Arms £55
39 HENRY LAMBE ½ 1667 NOE WANT WHERE THESE ARE £38
40 MATHEW NEWHAM ¼ 1657 Mercers' Arms £32
41 RICHARD SHIPMAN ½ MERCER
42 FRANCES WHITON ¼ 1659 Ironmongers' Arms
43 WILLIAM WHITTON ½ 1668 IRON MONGER
44/5 BENI(AMIN *or* MAN) WILSON ¼ 1657 Mercers' Arms £50
46 CHRISTOPHER WILSON ¼ 1659 Mercers' Arms £45
47 IOSEPH WILSON ¼ 1657 Mercers' Arms
48 ROBERT WILLSON (E) ¼ MERCER £40
49 — WILSON ½ 1667 —
50 *William Wilson* ½ MERCER

Nottingham
51 *Chamberlains* ½ 1669 Town arms £18

52/3 IOHN BERRIDGE (½) APOTHECARY
54/5 IOHN BLVNT ½ AT THE WEEKE (DERROSS, BAKER *or day Cross Baker*)* £55
56 SAMVELL BLACKWELL ½ 1667 Lion
57 (Misreading of 56)
58–61 THOMAS B(V *or* A)RROWES (½) Burr over rose; castle* £22
62 — BVRROWES ½ 1667 Wild boar £40
63 GEORGE BORZOWES, SALATHYELL GROVES ½ 1669 Cordwainers' Arms
64 THO COCKINGE (½) CHANDLER £42
65 ROBERT CRAMTON ½ Apothecaries' Arms £55
66/7 THOMAS DODSLEY (S) (½) Wheatsheaf £35
68 IOSHVA ELLISON ½ 1666 Ram, sword £55
69 THO FRANCE, SAMVEL BLACKWELL ½ 1666 Drapers' Arms
70 THOMAS FRANCE (T) (½) CVTLER
71/2 HVGH FARNWORTH (I) (½) Wheatsheaf £30
73 STE GARNER ½ Town Arms, TOVLMAN* £50
74 SAM GARNER (½) APOTHECARY £42
75 STEVEN GARNER (½) Rhinoceros, APOTHECARY £45
76 THOMAS GREATON ½ BREWER
77 (Misreading of 76)
78 THO GREENE (M) (½) AT THE BLACK HORSE, Ironmongers' Arms £55
79 WILLIAM GREENE ½ 1669 Knife, SHOOMAKER
80 CHRISTOPHER HALL (S) ¼
81 (Misreading of 90)
82 IOHN HART (E) ½ 1665 Heart, CHANDLER
83 *John Hart* (E) ½ *Chandler*, TAKE THESE THAT WIL ILE CHANGE THEM STIL. *Octagonal*
84 ROGER HAWKSLY ½ 1666 Merchant Taylors' Arms
85 WILLIAM HEBB ½ 1667 Tallowchandlers' Arms
86 IOSHVA HILL ½ 1667 Unicorn
87 IOH HODGES (E) ½ Ironmongers' Arms £50
88 IOHN HOVITT ½ 1667 Swan £45
89 IOSEPH INNOCENT ½ 1667 Apothecaries' Arms £38
90 IOHN MICHELL, ROB HARRYSON ½ Tallowchandlers' Arms; Distillers' Arms
91 W.N. ½ 1667 Angel, MEALE AND SALT £55

* Copies are known (late 19th cent.) of crude style

92 IOHN PARKER (M) ¼ Apothecaries' Arms
93 — — (M) (½) —
94 BENIAMIN RICKARDS (½) Apothecaries' Arms
95 ROBERT ROTHERAM ½ 1667 Salters' Arms £28
96 IONATHAN SIMPSON (M) (½) SADLER
97 SAM SMITH (½) APOTHECARY
98 SAMVEL — ½ 1667 Rhinoceros, APOTHECA
99 — — ½ 1664 Apothecaries' Arms
100 — — (½) n.d. —
101 THOMAS TOPLADY (S) (½) 1671 DRAPER
102 HENRY TRVMAN ½ 1664 Apothecaries' Arms
103 IOHN TREWMAN ½ 1669 Royal oak; sword
104 RICHARD TVRPIN (½) Tree trunk, 3 doves, CHANDLER
105 ED WHITE ½ 1666 Goat's head
106 ROBERT WINTER (½) 1667 Arms, CHANDLER
107 EDWARD WRIGHT ½ '67 Fleur-de-lis, MILLINER
108 IOSEPH WRIGHT (½) 3 bells
109 GERVAS WYLDE (F) (½) Family Arms
110 GARVAS — (F) ½

Retford (East)

111 PETER BOOTH (½) Falcon; merchant's mark
111A WILLIAM BVNBIE ¼ CHANDLER
112 IOHN CHAPMAN ½ 1666 Mercers' Arms
113 WILLIAM HALL (A) ½ 1668
114 WILLIAM MOODY (A) (½) 1666 BAKER
114A WILLIAM SCROOPP ½ 1669 Family Arms
115 *William Smith* (E) ½ *Milliner. Heart-shape*

Southwell

116 GREGORY SILVESTER, WILLIAM LEAVER (½) 1664 £40

Sutton-cum-Lound

116A WILLIAM SPVR (M) ½ AT YE, spur

Tuxford

117 WILLIAM READE (A) ½ SHOOMAKR
118 FRAN STRVTT ½ 1669 Grocers' Arms, MERCER £48

Worksop

119 IOSEPH FLECHER (K) ½ Apothecaries' Arms £50
120 THOMAS LEE (F) ¼ 1666 Grocers' Arms
121 RICH RVTTER (A) ½ 1664 Mercers' Arms

Oxfordshire

Major references: E. T. Leeds, *Oxford Tradesmen's Tokens* (Oxford, 1923). Covers the City issues; has additions and amendments to 'Williamson' and full notes on most issuers.

J. G. Milne (Editor), *Catalogue of Oxfordshire Seventeenth Century Tokens* (Oxford, 1935). Covers the rest of the county; 16 plates; updating and revision of 'Williamson', notes on most issuers and classification of specimens in the Ashmolean and British Museums.

Further new tokens recorded from the Lowsley collection (sold at Sotheby's, 3/4 May 1899); and *BNJ*, 1978.

See also J. L. Short, 'An Oxfordshire Token Reclaimed' (*TCSB*, vol. 1 no. 7, Oct. 1972); and George Berry, 'Tokens of Early Clockmakers' and 'Three Tennis Court Tokens of Oxford' (*Coins and Medals*, June and July 1977, respectively).

Believed entirely unpublished: 230A, 230B.

Minimum price for unvalued tokens: £45

Adderbury
1 THO AVSTIN (M) ½ 1669 AT THE RED LYON £40
2 HENRY HVNT (E) ¼ 1656 Crown £25

Bampton
3 SIMON BASSETT (E) ½ 1669 Phoenix in flames £25
4 WALTER LARDNER (M) ½ Man making candles £30
5 IOHN TVLL (R) ¼ 1656 Mercers' Arms £25

Banbury
6 IOHN ALLINGTON ¼ 1666 APOTHECARY £30
7 MATHEW ANSLEY ¼ Sugar-loaf £30
8 THOMAS DEKELL (E) ¼ Horseshoe
9 IOHN HALL (E) ¼ 1666 2-headed eagle £38
10, 11 BEN(IAMEN) HIBBERDINE (A) ¼ APOTHECARY £28
12 WILLIAM MANDER (E) ¼ 1656 Man making candles £28
13 T.P. (I) ½ Roll of cloth, MERCER
14 MANASSES PLVMTON (B) ¼ 1653 Fruiterers' Arms
14A MANASLES — (B) ¼ — Tree
15 THOMAS PYM (I) ¼ 1664 Roll of cloth
16 GEORGE ROBINS ½ 1669 MERCER £25
17 (Probably misreading of 16)
18 W.S. (I) ¼ 1650 AT THE VNICORNE
19 HENRY SMITH ½ 1668 IRONMONGR £30
20 —— (M) ¼ 1656 IRONMONGER £28
21 MATHEW SMITH (S) ½ 1669 Fruiterers' Arms on *rev.*, GARDNER £28
22 Similar but design on *obv.*
23 THOMAS SVTTON ½ 1666 AT THE RAINDEAR £15
24 IOHN VIVERS (E) ½ 1652 Mercers' Arms £42
25 NATHANIEL VIVERS ½ 1668 Fruiterers' Arms
26 IAMES WAGSTAFE (M) ¼ 1651 Fleur-de-lis £30
27 IOHN WAGSTAFFE (A) ¼ Mercers' Arms
28 WILLIAM WAGSTAFFE (M) ½ Fleur-de-lis
29, 31 (Probably misreading of 30)
30 IOHN WELCHMAN (M) ¼ 1663 APOTHECARY
32 NATHANIELL WHEATLY (M) ¼ 1664 Mercers' Arms £28

Burford
33 RICH BARTHOLOMEW (F) ¼ 1669 £38
34 IOHN HVSE ½ 1670 Scissors. *Heart-shape*
35 IOHN KNIGHT (S) ¼ 1656 Eagle and child £35
36 (Same as 49)
(See also 46 to 54)

Bicester
37 IOHN BORROWS ¼ IRON MONGER £32
38 THOMAS BVRGES (M) 1665 ¼ Pewterers' Arms £30
39 GABRIELL BVRROWES ¼ IRONMONGER £30
40 THOMAS CLEMENE ¼ Grocers' Arms, DRAPER
41 — CLEMENTS ¼ Drapers' Arms. — £30

42 WILL HVDSON (S) ½ 1669 Axes crossed £32
43 WILL STEVENS (F) ½ 1669 3 crowns. *Heart-shape.* **Plate 3**
44 FRANCES WALL (B) ½ 1669 3 bakers' peels. *Octagonal* £70
45 IOHN WARRY (M) ½ 1668 3 pipes. *Heart-shape* £120

Burford (continued from no. 36)
46 Borough ¼ 1669 Lion £18
46A As last, but in *pb*
47 E. C. ¼ 1653 AT THE 3 SHVGER LOVES £25
48 THOMAS MATHEWS (E) ¼ AT THE BEARE £20
49 LEONARD MILLS ¼ 1669 Horse and waggon, WAGONNER
50 IOHN PAYTON ½ 1669 Merchant's mark
51 IOH — ¼ 1666 Talbot, CLOTHYER £38
52 IOHN SINDRIY (E) ¼ 1653 Grocers' Arms £22
53 R.V. (A) ¼ 1652 AT THE GEORGE
54 CHARLES YATE (H) ¼ 1664 3 gates £22

Charlbury
54A ROBERT BROOKES ¼ 1665 Man making candles £45

Chinnor
55 THO BECKLY (S) ¼ 3 leopards' heads £32
56 WILIAM GOLDFINCH (E) ¼ 1662 Arms £28
56A L.W. (M) ¼ 1659

Chipping Norton
57 IOH CORNISH (K) (½) Arms of Oxford
58 — — (K) ¼ — £30
59 MICHAELL CORNISH (E) ¼ Arms £30
60 IOSEPH DAVIS (E) ¼ Roll of cloth £25
61 WILLIAM DISTON (M) ½ 1666 Hart £18
62 — — (M) ¼ — —
63 DAVID DIX (S) ½ 1664 £28
64 SAMVEL FARMER (E) ¼ Apothecaries' Arms. **Plate 3** £28
65 HENRY FAWLER (H) ½ 1669 Falcon £28
66 — — (H) ¼ Falcon with bells and jesses £22
67 MATHIAS TROVT (A) ¼ Fish
68 RICHARD GROVES (E) ¼ 1659 Man standing under tree £28
69 — — (E) ¼ 1663 —
70 E.R. (D) ½ 1668 Tobacco-roll, hand holding chopper over tobacco-leaf, pipes crossed. *Heart-shape* £120
71 EDMOND ROWLRIGHT (D) ¼ Lion £22
72 PHILLIPP WISDOME (K) ½ 1670 £38

Cornwell
73 (Probably *Cornwall* 106)
74 (See *Cornwall* 61)

Cropredy
75 MARGRET KING ¼ 1664 Grocers' Arms

Culham
76 (See *Middx.* 53)
77 IOHN WELLS ¼ AT THE HORS SHOOE £35

Deddington
78 SAMVELL BELCHER (B) ¼ 1668 Apothecaries' Arms £30
79 IOHN ELKINGTON ½ 1667 Pegasus £28
80 MICHAEL ELKINTON ½ 1668 AT YE VNICORNE £28
81 ANN MAKEPACE ¼ Eagle and child, MERCER £32
82 THOMAS NVTT ¼ 1653 MERCER £30

Dorchester
82A THOMAS APPLEGAT (E) ½ '69 AT YE CROWN £25
83 WILLIAM BROCK ¼ Grocers' Arms £17
84 — — (M) AND ROBERT COVLDRY ¼ £17
84A RICH FELLOWS (S) ¼ 1660 3 sugar-loaves

Duns Tew
85 THOMAS BARRET ½ 1669 Packhorse pannier, CARRIER £40
86 THO — (M) ¼ n.d. — CARRER £45

Enstone
86A THOMAS NEWMAN ½ 1669 Talbot £45

Ewelme
87 WILLIAM IONES ½ 1669 Crown

Finstock
88 EDWARD GARDNER (K) ¼ 1666 Hart £20

Great Tew
89, 90 IOHN ALEXANDER (A) ¼ BAKER £45

Henley
91 CORPORATION ½ Cloud with rays over ducal coronet £20
92 — ¼ — £20
93 WILL ATKINS (M) ¼ Catherine wheel
94 GEORGE DAMSELL (A) ¼ '68 Drapers Arms
95 RICHARD FOWLER ¼ 1668 Corset £38
96 AMBROS FREEMAN ¼ Grocers' Arms £25
96A IOHN HARRIS ¼ Griffin
97 IOHN HATHAWAY (D) ½ 1668 Man driving carriage and horses
98 IOHN HODGSHENS (K) ¼ Scissors
99 ROBERT RAINSFORD (A) ¼ Pot of lilies
100 WILLIAM ROBINSON ½ 1668 Dolphin, FISHMONGER. **Plate 3** £28
101 SETH SMITH (I) Arms of Oxford £42
102 EDWARD STEAVENS ¼ Barber-Surgeons' Arms
102A — STEVENS ¼ —. In *pb*
103 ROBERT SVRY ¼ Hart £42
104 THOMAS WICKINS (F) ¼ Stick of candles £38

Hook Norton

105 IAMES BEALE (M) ¼ Roll of cloth, MERCER £25
106 —— (M) ½ 1668 ——
107 RICHARD PARCKS (E) ½ 1666 IREMONGER £18

Nettlebed

108 DAVIDE GASQVON ½ AT YE BVLL £42
109 TIMOTHY HOLDING ½ 1669 AT YE WHIT HART £28

Northleigh

110 WILLIAM AND ANN MASON ½ Initials in heart £22
110A ———— ½ WA in heart, M above £32

Oxford

111/2 THE MAYOR ¼ 1652 City Arms £7
113 EDWARD APPLEBEE (I) ¼ TALLOW CHANDLER £20
114 THO APPLEBEE (S) ¼ Family Arms, MALLIA CADREENE £15
115 WILLIAM APPLEBEE (A) ¼ 1666 Man making candles £25
116 WILLIAM BALEY ¼ AT THE MORTER AND PEST £28
117 IOHN BARRETT (F) ¼ 1666 Moon and 7 stars £25
118 IOHN BETTS (E) ¼ Flaming star, TAYLOR NEER EAST GATE £25
119 MICHAEL BIRD (½) 1668 Cock, WATCHMAKER £22
120 GEORGE BISHOP (S) ¼ 1668 CVTLER £15
121 IOH BISHOP ¼ 1657 Looking glass, AT YE GVILT £22
122 IOHN — ¼ 1663 — AT THE GILT £28
123 IOH — ¼ 1669 MILENER, LOOKING GLAS £25
124 HVMPHRY BODICOTT ¼ VINTENER. **Plate 3** £15
125 IOHN BOWE(LL *or* L) ¼ 1657 MERCER, SVGAR LOFE £12
126 THOMAS BVRNHAM (I) ¼ AT YE TENIS COVRT, tennis racquet £25
127 THOMAS BVTLER (M) ¼ AT YE RACKIT & BALL £38
128 RICHARD CARTER ¼ BRVER £15
129 THOMAS COMBES ¼ NEARE THE EAST GATE, Grocers' Arms £10
130 RICHARD CONY (M) ½ 1666 AT ST. MARYS
131 WILLIAM CORNISH (E) ¼ 1658 MERCER £17
132 NICHOLAS DANIELL ¼ 1657 BAKER
133 THOMAS DENNIS (A) ¼ 1652 AT THE 3 KINGS. **Plate 3** £28
134 RICHARD ELY (A) ¼ AT THE 3 SAMMONS £16
135 IOHN FOX (S) ¼ AT THE FOX AND GOOSE £20
136 RICH GOODE ¼ 1670 Man making candles £25
137 ANTHONY HALL (A) ¼ AT THE, mermaid, VINTNER. **Plate 3** £20
138 IOSEPH HANSON ¼ 1670 Leathersellers' Arms and crest, GLOVER £28
139/40 THOMAS HARRISON (A) ¼ 3 eagles, FOR NECESARY CH(A *or* E)NG £17
141 THO HIGGS (M) ¼ MERCER AT 3 BLACK BIRDS £28
141A —— (M) (½) — £28
142 OLIFFE HIN(D *or* DE) ¼ 1657 MERC(E)R £15
143 — HIND ¼ 1666 MERCR £20
144 LEWIS HINE ¼ 1666 Grocers' Arms £18
145 THOMAS HVNSDON ¼ 1666 Weavers' Arms £12
146 EDWARD HVNT ¼ AT THE TVRLE GATE £15
147 WILL HVNTLEY ¼ 1670 Woolpack, RVG MAKER
147A THOMAS HV..EY (I) ¼ AT THE BEARE
148 SETH IRELAND ¼ AT THE GOVLDING KEY. Key; heart £18
149 IOHN IOHNSON (M) ¼ 1666 Pot of lilies
150 LAWRANCE KING ¼ GLOVER £17
151 *Joseph Knibb ¼ Clockmaker* £35
152 HVGH LAMBE ¼ 1668 HOSIER £16
153 ALCE LANT ¼ 1667 Last £32
154 ARTHVR MADLE (S) ¼ 1666 CHANDLER £35
155 ARTHER MADEL (S) ¼ 1667 £28
156 WILL MORRELL (A) ¼ AT YE CROWNE £14
156A —— (A) (½) —
157 (Probably misreading of 158)
158 NICH ORVM ¼ 1659 FISHMONGER £10
159 ANN PEIRSON ¼ 1669 Scissors £17
160 RICHARD PONT (E) ¼ 1668 Vintners' Arms £14
161 WILLIAM POTTER (A) ¼ APOTHECARY £25
162 DANIELL PRINCE (K) ¼ 1667 Duke of York's bust; mace £28
163 EDWARD PRINCE (E) ¼ CHANDLER £20
164 SAMSON RAVLINS (M) ¼ AT THE SALMON £25
165 WILL ROBINSON (M) ¼ 1668 GOVLDSMITH £25
166 IOHN RYLAND (A) ¼ 1659 Baker's peel £15
167 LAWRENCE SHORT (E) ¼ (NER *or* NEARE) NEW COLLEDG, hand holding coffee-pot, filling cup. **Plate 3** £17
168 IOHN S(H)OVCH ¼ 1657 Fan, MILLENER £16
169 RICHARD SOVCH ¼ Hen and chicks, MILLINER £18
170 EDWARD SPENCER ¼ CHANDLER £22
171 THOMAS STEVENSON (A) ¼ 1664 Upholsterers' Arms £18
171A IOHN STRINGER ¼ 1670 Saddle with stirrups
172 IOHN TEY ¼ AT THE ANGELL £14
173 IOHN TOLDERVEY ¼ 1660 Arms, MILLINER £20

174 WILLIAM TONGE (I) ¼ 1657 SKINER £32
175 —TONGVE (G) ¼ 1661 Cordwainers' Arms £16
176 (Probably misreading of 175)
177 WILL TVRNER (E) ¼ St. George & dragon £28
178 ANN TVRTON ¼ 1657 Ironmongers' Arms £25
179 RICH TVRTON (M) ¼ 1668 Ironmongers' Arms £16
180 WILL WALKER ¼ Hand holding bird, AT THE BVRD AND HAND £25
181 WILLIAM WALKER ¼—MERCER £25
181A WILLIAM WALKER (M) ¼ 1668 Stag*
182 SAMVELL WALLIS (A) ¼ Tobacco-roll
183/4 ROB(ERT) WHITE ¼ 1657 SILK(E) WE(A)VER £15
185 THO WILLIAMS ¼ AT YE SPECTACLES £35
186 ROBERT WILSON ¼ Merchant's mark, BREWER
187 THOMAS WOOD (M) ¼ 1652 Racquet, VINTNER £30
188 EDMVND WRIGGLYSWORTH ¼ 1652 AT NORTH GATE £16

Stokenchurch

189 GEORGE CVBBIDGE (A) ½ 1669 Scissors £35

Shipton-under-Wychwood

190 IOH WELLS (D) ¼ Grocers' Arms £35

Thame

191 RICHARD ADKINS (S) ¼ 1669 Grocers' Arms £35
192 WILLIAM ADKENS ½ 1669 THE BLACKE LION
193 RVTH AERIS ¼ £16
194 DOROTHY BVRGIS ¼ 1669 Lion £25
195 IOHN BVRGES ¼ 1653 Unicorn £18
196 WILL COPE (I, A) ¼ GROCER £22
197 ROBERT CREWES (F) ¼ 1668 Stick of candles £18
198 IOHN DANIELL (R) ¼ 1669 HATER £25
199 IOHN GVRDON ¼ 1657 £20
200 IOHN HARRIS ¼ AT THE READ LYON £15
201 RICHARD HEARNE ¼ 1669 Drapers' Arms £25
202 HVGH HESTER ¼ 1657 Grocers' Arms £18
203 WILLIAM IEMET (I) ¼ 1669 Plumed hat
204 EDWARD LEAVER (I) ¼ Merchant Taylors' Arms £28
205 RICHARD (*or* RICH) RASTELL ¼ Mercers' Arms £20
206 WILLIAM TRIPP (E) ¼ CHANDLER £15
207 MATHEW WATTERS ¼ MERCER £20
208 ISAAC WEEKES ½ 1667 Tree, GARDENER

Wardington

209 RICHARD SHORT ½ Grocers' Arms, MERCER £28
210 R. SHORT ¼— £38

* Different issuer to 180/1

Watlington

211 IOHN COCKEE (E) ¼ 1664 Anchor £25
212 ROBERT COGELL ½ 1669 Horseshoe
213 IOHN COCKY (E) ¼ 1663
214 MARY GREENDOWN ¼ '67 Bust of Chas. II £22
215 THO GREENDOWN ½ 1664 Vintner's bush; sugar-loaf £40
216 THOMAS GREENDOVNE ¼ 1659 Sugar-loaf; vintner's bush
217 RICHARD HAINES (M) ¼ Grocers' Arms £28
218 RICHARD HARRIS (E) ¼ Roll of cloth £25
219 ROBERT HAYNES (D) ¼ 1664 Mercers' Arms £42
220 NICHOLAS LANKFORD (G) ¼ Cleaver, knife £42
220A —LANGFORD (G) ½ 1670 Man with poleaxe over bull's head
221 MARY NASH ½ 1669 Mercers' Arms £20
222 RICHARD SEELEY (A) ¼ Rose crowned £25

Wheatley

223 THOMAS TEMPLE (E) ¼ Mortar and pestle £50

Witney

224 RICHARD ASHFIELD (M) ¼ Fleece, CLOTHIER £30
225 THOMAS BRICE (I) ½ Shuttle £30
226 WILLIAM CHAMBERLIN (I) ½ 1666 £38
227 THO COLLIER ¼ Fleece, CLOTHIER £38
228 RICHARD DVTTON ½ '68 Clothworkers' Arms, CLOTHER £40
229 THOMAS DVTTON ¼ Merchant's mark; woolpack £30
230 WILLIAM FITCHETT (E) ½ 1671 £25
230A —— (E) ½ — Woolpack
230B —— (E) ½ 1667
231 IOHN GARDINER (E) ½ 1669 Shuttles £22
232 LEONARD GOODE (I) ¼ 1657 Bakers' Arms £25
233 THO GREGORY (I) ¼ 1664 Tallowchandlers' Arms £28
234 WILLIAM HEARN (I) ¼ AT THE WHITE SWAN £17
235 —— (I) ¼ 1668 AT YE SWAN
236 ANDREW HOLLAWAY ¼ 1659 Hands clasped, CLOTHYER £20
237 —— ¼ 1666 ——
238 IO IORDEN (G) ¼ Merchant's mark £25
239 PETER KATTE (A) ½ 1670 AT THE 3 LIBBETS HEADS £42
240 IOHN PALMER (A) ¼ 1656 Woolpack £40
241 WILLIAM AND MARY SANDERS ½. **Plate 3** £20
242 PAVL SMITH (S) ¼ 1656 DRAPER £35
243 THOMAS WARD ½ 1668 AT YE, Tallowchandlers' Arms £28
244 RALPH WERGE (M) ¼ 1653 Mercers' Arms £22

245 ANDREW WHITE SENIOR (M) ½ 1667 Initials on woolpack £25
246 ROBERT WILLY SENIOR (P) ½
247 IOHN YOVNG (A) ¼ 1655 Man making candles £14

Woodstock

248 ALEXANDER IOHNSONS (I) ¼ 1652 Grocers' Arms £28
249 T.P. ¼ 1653 AT THE 3 CVPPS £32
250 THOMAS SPARROW (A) ¼ 1654
251 THOMAS WOODARD ¼ Grocers' Arms, GROCER £30
252 —WOODWARD ¼— £42

Wootton

253 (See *Glos.* 226A)
253A IOHN WYATT (P) ½ 1670 Man shoeing horse

Rutland

New tokens recorded from J. Young (see under Leicestershire); and *BNJ*, 1927.

See also *SNC*, June 1913.

Believed entirely unpublished: 1B.

Minimum price for unvalued tokens: £75

Caldecott

1A RICHARD HILL ½ 1668

Exton

1B THOMAS EDMONDS (I) ¼ Arms

Langham

1 IOHN HOMES ¼ 1658 Tallowchandlers' Arms

Liddington

2 HENRY SEWELL ½ 1669

(North) Luffenham

3 THOMAS GOODMAN ¼ '57 Man making candles

4 THOMAS HVNTT ¼ Fleur-de-lis, NORTH LVFFENHAM

5 Similar but LVFFINHAM (no NORTH)

Oakham

6 IOSHVA CHARLSWORTH (A) ¼ Ironmongers' Arms

7 IONATHAN FISHER (S) ¼ Man making candles

8 RICH MATTHEW AND IOHN POTTERILL ½ Family Arms £22

9 SAMVELL REEVE ¼ 1655 AT THE BELL £55

Uppingham

10 PETER BARRIFFE ½ 1668 Drapers' Arms. *Heart-shape* £200

11 THOMAS BVTLER ¼ Family Arms

12 HENRY CLIPSAM (M) ¼ 1657 Grocers' Arms £50

13 EDMOND FARBECK *or* FARBECKE ¼ Tobacco-roll £65

14 ELIZABETH GOODWIN ¼ 1666 Spinning-wheel

15 GEORGE GREENE ¼ 1666 Scissors

16 IOHN HVLL (M) ¼ 1666 CHANDLER

17 RICHARD MVNTVN ¼ Fleur-de-lis

17A IAMES SMITH ¼ Grocers' Arms

Shropshire

(Salop)

New tokens recorded from the Macfadyen collection (sold at Sotheby's, 15 July 1907); Faulkner collection (sold at Glendining's, 21 May 1940); *SNC*, Jan. 1949 and Apr. 1968; Glendining's sale, 17 Nov. 1977.

Believed entirely unpublished: 11B, 32A.

Minimum price for unvalued tokens: £75

Bishop's Castle

1 IEREMY AMBLER ¼ Family Arms
2 RICHARD AMBLER ½ 1670 APOTHC, SQVARE DEALING. *Square*
2A SAM AVNSHAM ¼ 1664 Arms
3 WILLIAM MALL (L) ¼ Lion
4 THOMAS MASON ½ 1670. *Heart-shape*
5 EDWARD WOLLASTON IVNIOR ½ 1670 Family Arms £65
6 EDWARD WOLLASTON ¼ Castle

Bridgnorth

7 THE CHAMBERLINS ½ 1665 Castle £45
8, 9 THE CHAMBERLAYNES ¼ Castle; portcullis £70
10 SYMON BEAVCHAMP ¼ Drapers' Arms
11 IOHN HIGGINS (C) ¼ Grocers' Arms
11A — —, RALPH SHARETT LVDLOW ¼
11B RICHARD SING ¼ Boat (?), AT THE CAVE
12 THO WHEELER (M) ¼ Mercers' Arms

Broseley

13 RICHARD CROMPTON ½ 1664
14 WILLIAM OKES ½ 1669 Royal oak £55

Church Stretton

14A ANN PHILLIPPS ½ 1666
15 IOHN PHILLIPS (A) ¼

Coman Hill

15A ROBERT BLOONER (M) ½ 1666 £65
15B — — (M) ½ n.d.

(Market) Drayton

16 (Probably misreading of 17)
17 IN HALES ¼ 1664 Merchant Taylors' Arms
18 IOHN COX (I) ½ 1668
19 THOMAS NICHOLL ½ 1670 Apothecaries' Arms
20 MATTHIAS THVRSTON, RICHARD CHAMBERLYN ½ 1669 £75

Ellesmere

21 THOMAS COOKE (M) ½ 1666
21A ROBERT HIGGINSON (A) ½ 1666
22 EDWARD RENOLDS ½ MERCER

Hodnet

23 THOMAS ANNKER ½ 1665 Mercers' Arms

Ludlow

24 RICHARD BEBB ¼ Man smoking, IRON MONGER
25 IOHN BOWDLER ½ 1664 MERCER £28
26 IOHN BRIGHT ½ 1669 3 cloves, MERCER
27 EDWARD DAVIES (?) ½ 1669 APOTHECARY
28 TAMBERLAINE DAVIES ½ 1669 Mercers' Arms, MERCER £65
29 TAMBERLAYN — (M) ¼ Mercers' Arms
30 BLANCH HACKLVIT ½ 1669 Goat's head, axe
31 GEORGE HAVGHTON ½ 1666 Castle
32 — — ½ 1669 — MERCER £70
32A THOMAS HINTON (A) ½ 1669 Bakers' Arms
32B Richard Hitchcott ½
33 WALTER IONES (M) ½ Mercers' Arms
34 EDWARD MIELS (M) ½ 1663
35 — — (M) ½ 1665
36 IOHN PEARCE ¼ 1656 Ironmongers' Arms
37 WILL RIC(K *or* H)ARDS ¼ 1656 Haberdashers' Arms
38 RALPH SHARETT (M) ¼ Bakers' Arms
39 CHARLES VALLE (E) ½ 1669 Royal oak. *Octagonal*

Madeley Market

40 IOHN HOLLAND ½ 1667 Pickaxe
41 (? Later striking of *obv.* of 42)
42 EDWARD LEWIS ½ 1669 Collier's pick between roses, MADELY WOOD YEILDS COLE THATS GOOD
43 LAWRENCE WELLINGTON ½ 1669 Ironmongers' Arms £75

Much Wenlock
44 HENRY BLAKE AND WILLIAM EVANS ½
45 THOMAS OWSLEY ¼ MERC

Newport
46 THOMAS CHALONER (M) ½
47 SAMVELL CLARKE ½ 1666 Mercers' Arms £65
48 SAMVELL DOWNTON ½ 1669 Mercers' Arms
49 ROBERT HVDDELL (M) ½ 1666
49A —— (M) ½ 1670
50 (See *Hants*. 109)
51 ARTHVR ROWE (E) ¼ 1658 Beehive, bees £60
51A WILLIAM ROWE (M) ¼ Beehive £35
52 (See *Bucks*. 105A)
53 THOMAS YOVNGE IVNIER ¼ Mercers' Arms £45
54 (Probably misreading of 53)

Oldbury
55 OLIVER ROVND ½ 1663 St. George & dragon

Oswestry
56 HVGH EDWARDS 1d 1669 Shoe. **Plate 3** £30
57 RICHARD EDWARDS 1d 1668 Wool-bag
58 PHILLIP ELLICE ¼ Tobacco-roll
59 IOHN IONES 1d 1666 Sword, pistol £60
60 RICHARD PAYNE (M) ½ MERCER
61 —— 1d 1667 Mortar and pestle £70
62 ARTHER WARD 1d 1668 Pheon £70

Poston
63 (See *Lincs*. 16A)

Prees
64 RICHARD MADELEY ½ 1666 Mercers' Arms

Shifnal
65 ARTHVR MANWARING ½ 1664 Mercers' Arms £55

Shrewsbury
66 (Probably misreading of 67)
67 THOMAS ACHELLEY 1d 1671 Wheatsheaf; fleur-de-lis. *Octagonal*
68 PETER BAKER (E) ½ Lion, DISTILER AND GROCER. *Heart-shape*
69 IOSEPH BENYON (E) 1d 1669 Wheatsheaf; scales. *Octagonal*
69A As last but on *round* flan
70 IOSEPH BENYON ½ Scales; wheatsheaf
71 IOHN BRIGDELL ½ 1667 CHANDLER £42
72 EDMOND CLARKE ¼ Town Arms
73 SAMVELL CONEY 1d 1669 Star, INKEEPER
74 ROBERT DAVIES ¼ Mercers' Arms
75 WILLIAM HARRISON ½ 1666 Stationers' Arms
76 BENIAMIN HINDE ¼ Town Arms £45
77 IOHN HOLLIER ½ 1668 MERCER
78 SAMVELL MACHEN (H) ½ BAKER £60
79 PETAR MACHEN 1d 1669 BAKER. *Octagonal*
80 THOMAS MEYRICHE ¼ 1663 Vintners' Arms
81 THO MEYRICKE ½ —— £55
82 IOHN MILLINGTON (M) ½ 1664 Bakers' Arms £30
83 IOHN MILLARD ½ 1667 A DISTILLER
84 CONSTANTINE OVERTON ½ 1663 Cordwainers' Arms £32
85 SAMVELL RIDGEWAY ½ 1671 Grocers' Arms
86 OWEN ROBERTS ½ 1666 Wheatsheaf £55
87 IOB SELBY ½ 1667 DISTILLER
88 THOMAS STVDLEY (E) 1d
89 IOHN THOMAS ¼ 1660 MERCER
90 WILLIAM THOMAS ½ 1666 MERCER £55
91 MICHAELL WILDING ½ 1664 Mercers' Arms £65
92 — WILDINGE (I) ¼ n.d. — MERCER
93 IOSHVA WILLIS ½ Town Arms, MERCER
94 —— ½ Grocers' Arms. In *brass*, with centre of *copper*

Wellington
95 ANDREW SOCKETT ½ 1666 MERCER
96 STEPHEN WRIGHT ½ 1668 Greyhound, MERCER. **Plate 3** £70

Wem
97 WILLIAM ALANSON ½ 1666 —
98 IOHN CHETTWOOD ½ Drapers' Arms, MERCER
99 THOMAS IEBB ¼ Mercers' Arms
99A — IEBBE ½ 1666 —
100 SAMVELL ROYCROFT ½ 1665 Ironmongers' Arms
101 IOHN SHENTON ½ 1666 Arms, MERCER
102 SAMVEL SMITH ¼ 3 greyhounds, MERCER
103 —— ½ ——

Whitchurch
104 IOHN BATHOWE ½ '66 Tallowchandlers' Arms
105 PHILIP AND MARY BROOK ½ St. George & dragon
106 EDW NEWTON, HVMPHRY ROWLY (½) Mercers' Arms
107 HVMPHREY ROWLEY 1d 1669 Ship. *Octagonal*
107A THOMAS SHAW 1d 1671 Crown, CHANDLER
107B IOHN SIMCOCK ½ 1665 Grocers' Arms

Somerset

Major reference: H. St. G. Gray and H. Symonds, 'Somerset Trade Tokens XVII Century: New Types and Varieties and Corrections of former Lists' (*Proceedings of the Somersetshire Archaeological and Natural History Society*, vol. LXI, 1915). With notes on a few issuers.

Further new tokens recorded from the Carthew collection (*SCMB*, Mar. 1946); and *SNC*, Jan 1949.

See also S. Sydenham, *Bath Token Issues of the 17th Century* (Bath, 1905): many notes on the issuers; 'Taunton Tokens of the 17th Century' (*Proceedings of the Somerset Antiquarian and Natural History Society*, 1911); and J. Stevens Cox, *The Ilchester Mint and Ilchester Trade Tokens* (Ilchester Historical Monographs, no. 3, 1948).

Believed entirely unpublished: 3A, 178A.

Minimum price for unvalued tokens: £45

Ashcott
1 RICHARD MILLES ¼ 1666 2-headed eagle £42

Axbridge
2 WILLIAM HOPKINS ¼ 1656 Fleur-de-lis £30
3 IOHN TVTHILL (D) ¼ 1669 AT YE, angel
3A — TVTHILE ¼ 1652

Batcombe
4 STEPHEN PARSONS (I) ¼ HOSIR

Bath
5 City ¼ 1659 City Arms (not on shield) £28
5A — ¼ City Arms. In *pb*
6 — ¼ 1670 City Arms (on shield). **Plate 3** £8
7 RICHARD ABBOTT ¼ MERCER
8 BENIAMIN BABER (E) ¼ Drapers' Arms
8* — — (E) ¼ 1669 —
9 GEORGE BAKER (E) ¼ 1669 YE, Clothworkers' Arms
10 RICHARD BIGGES (H) ¼ MERCER £32
10A AMBROSE BISHOP (M) ¼ 1669 Cog wheel
11 IAMES BVRTON ¼ Mercers' Arms
12 IOHN BVSH (A) ¼ 1656 MERCER £28
12A — — (A) ¼ 1658 —
13 HENERY CHAPMAN ¼ Sun, QVONDAM ESQVIRE £40
14 (Probably misreading of 13)
15 WALTER CHAPMAN (A) ¼ MERCER £22
16 IOHN CLARKE (A) ¼ 1655 MERCER £42
17 *Richard Collins* (E) ¼ 1669 *A Clothier*
18 IOHN FISHER (I) ¼ Arms (3 fishes)
19 ROBERT FISHER (E) ¼ 1652 MERCER
20 IOHN FOORDE (O) ¼ 1666 Cordwainers' Arms
21 PRISCILLA HECKES ¼ 1665 AT YE 3 SWANS
22 RICHARD HORLER (S) ¼ 1664 Tallowchandlers' Arms
23 *William Landicke* (A) ¼ 1669 3 tuns
24 WILLIAM MARDEN (A) ¼ SILK WEAVER
25 IOHN MASTERS (E) ¼ AT WHIT, hart
26/7 IOHN PEARCE (I) ¼ 1652 MERCER £15
28 ROBERT PENNY (I) ¼ MERCER £38
29 RICHARD PITCHER (A) ¼ 1667 Hat with feathers
30 FRANCIS RANCE (E) ¼ 1659 Mermaid £30
31 IOHN REED (B) ¼ 1656 Mermaid
32 GEO REVE (M) ¼ 1658 GOLDSMITH
33 THOMAS SALMON ¼ 1667 Clasped book b.s. £40
34 WILLIAM SMITH (I) ¼ 1666 Shears £32
35 IOHN SWALLOW (S) ¼ 1669 YE, swallow
36 EDWARD WHITE (I) ¼ 1655 MERCER

Batheaston
37 RICHARD HARFORD (I) ¼ 1667 Mermaid
38 IAMES PEARCE (I) ¼ MERCER
39 ELDAD WALTERS (M) ¼ Merchant's mark

Beckington
39A WILL BOYNE ¼ 1657 Grocers' Arms, CHANDL
40/1 RICH GILES ¼ 1666 *or* '66 Merchant's mark
42 IOHN HORLER ¼ Haberdashers' Arms £38
43 NIC THRING ¼ 1658 Rose, CLOTHIER
44 N.T. ¼ 1670 Rose, GLORY BE VNTO THE KING

Bishops Hull
45 WILLIAM BARBER (F) ¼

45A WILLIAM BARBER (B) ¼

Bradford
46 WILL SERLE (E) ¼ 1659

Brent
47 SIMON SHIPARD ½ 1669 Scythes crossed; roll of bread

Bridgwater
48 Town ¼ 1666 Town Arms £12
49 — ¼ — — with flags on outer towers of castle £10
50 — ¼ n.d. Town Arms £25
51 ALEXANDER ATKINS (A) ¼ 1654
52 ALEXAND — (A) ¼ 1656
53 IOHN BONE ¼ 1666 Hand holding woolcomb
54 IOHN CRAPP (I) ¼ 1659
55 WILLIAM CRAPP (M) ¼ 1670 £16
56 ED DAWES (A) ¼ 1657 BRASIER
57 IOSEPH FRANKLIN IVNR ¼ 1666 Woolcomb
58 WILLIAM GOODRIDGE (I) ¼ 1669 Ship £28
59 ROBERT HAVILAND (L) ¼ Merchant's mark £30
60 — — (L) ¼ 1652 —
61 IOHN HVNT (S) ¼ 1651
62 IOH(N) LINTON (E) ¼ Salters' Arms
63 IOHN — (E) ¼ 1656 — £45
64 — — (E) ¼ 1658 —
65 — — (E) ¼ 1659 —
66 WILL PAGE (E) ¼ 1669 £35
67 IOHN PALMER (A) ¼ 1664 Drapers' Arms
68 EDMOND PETTITT (I) ¼ 1654
69 CHRISTOPHER ROBERTS (F) ¼ 1664 Covered cup
70 IOHN ROGERS (T) ¼ 1669 AGAINST THE HIGH CROSS, Family Arms £18
71 IAMES SAFFORDE (E) ¼ 1652 £35
72 WILLIAM SEALY ¼ 1652 £22
73 — — — ¼ 1654 £16
74 WILLIAM SERLLAND ¼ 1654

Bruton
75 Town ¼ 1669 Tun; bridge £22
76 IAMES BRAYNE (E) ¼ 1659
77 ROBERT LVDWELL ¼ Grocers' Arms, MERCER £40
77A — — ¼ — (no MERCER)

Cannington
78 EDWARD COALES (M) ¼ 2-headed eagle

Carey Land
79 WILLIAM IRELAND (K) ¼ 1660 Paschal lamb

Castle Cary
80/1 EDWARD RVS(S)E (M) ¼ 1666 £55

Chard
82 BVRROVGH ¼ 1669 Plant between birds, MADE BY YE PORTRIFF FOR YE POORE £30
83 Town ¼ 1671 Initials I.H. £25
84 HVMPHRY ABLE (M) A BRASSE HALFE PENNY, Family Arms £50
85 GEORGE BARTLY (A) ¼ Roll of bread £42
86 WILLIAM BVRIDG (A) ¼ 1665 Scissors
87 IOHN CHAPMAN ¼ 3 cloves
88 — — ½ Scales
89 P.I. ¼ Rose crowned, RECEIVE THE CROWN IN EVERY TOWN
90 IOHN LEGG (A) ¼ 1660 Shears
91 ROGER LOCK (A) ¼ 3 cloves
92 ABRAHAM MASON (E) ¼ BOOKSELLER
93 HENRY MILLS (H) ¼ 1668 Pegasus, SADLER
94 WILLIAM SAYER (S) ¼ Woolpack
95 — — (S) ¼ 1660 —
96 HENRY SELDRED (I) ¼ Woolcomb
97 ROBERT SWEET (S) ¼ 1667 Mercers' Arms
98 IOHN WAY ¼ Hat with feather £32
99 PETER WAY (S) ¼ Rose
100 THOMAS WILLIAMS (M) ¼ 1656 St. George & dragon £45
104 ANNE ADKINS ¼ 3 cloves

Cheddar
101 IOHN GARDNER (I) ¼ 1652 Man making candles

Cheddon
102 GEORGE WORRALL (K) ¼ 1666 Crown

Creech
103 ROBERT BOBBETT ¼ '60 Spade £40

Crewkerne
104 (See under Chard)
105 WILLIAM BENNET ¼ 1666 Lion
106 ROGER BREWER (R) ¼ 1668 Lion £40
107 EDWARD COSSENES ¼ 1670 Haberdashers' Arms £35
108 WILL COSENS (M) ¼ Bird above scales, skull
109 IOHN GRENWAY (I) ¼ Family Arms £14
110 IOHN IAMES (T) ¼ 1666 Mortar and pestle
111 IOHN SHIRE (A) ¼ 1666 £45

Croscombe
112 GEORGE BLINDMAN ¼ 1668
113 — BLINMAN ¼ 1656 £32
114 IAMES CVTTING (I) ¼ Weavers' Arms
115 IAMES GEORGE (I) ¼ 1666 St. George & dragon £28
116 ONESIPHORVS LVFFE ¼ 1666 Rose crowned £30
117 ANTHONY PLIMTON ¼ 1656 Talbot with chain £38

Crowcombe
118 F.H. ¼ Hill family Arms

Doulting
119 THOMAS HODGES (A) ¼ 1665 Hammer and pincers, crossed

Dulverton
120 NICH CRASE ½ 1669 MERCER
121 THOMAS HEARNE ¼ 1664 Scales

East Coker
122 IOHN GYLES ¼ Dog pursuing hare

Evercreech
123 ROBERT HAYES ¼ HOSIER £60

Freshford
124 IOHN CVRLE SENIOR (I) ¼ 1663 Bell £20
125 IOHN CVRLE IVNIOR ¼ 1666 Family Arms £20
126 PEETER FISHER ¼ 1669 Lion

Frome
127, 127* Town ¼ 1670 £18
128 RICHARD BVRLTON ¼ Haberdashers' Arms
129 HENRY MARCHANT ¼ 1654 £32
130 —— ¼ 1661
131 —— ¼ 1664
132 WILL PAINE ¼ 1669 MERCER
133 IOHN SANDERS ¼ 1671 Stocking £25
134 THOMAS TVRNER (M) ¼ Merchant's mark
135/6 ROBART WHITCHVRCH ¼ 1651 Mercers' Arms £28
137 SAMVEL WHITCHVRCH ¼ Mercers' Arms £32
138 WILLIAM WHITCHVRCH ¼ 1651 Grocers' Arms

Glastonbury
139 *William Allwoode Senior* ¼ Stocking
140 WILLIAM TRICKY ¼ 1656 Bust of bishop, BISHOP
141 GEORGE CARY (A) ¼ '68 HOSIER £28
142 WILLIAM COOPER ½ 1666 House
143 —— ¼ 1668 G within knot; house £25
144 MARY DAY ¼ 1668 King's Arms £35
145 THOMAS DENHAM ¼ 1666 AT YE, crown £45
146 RICHARD EDWELL (A) ¼ 1668 Ship
147 HENRY GVTCH (A) ¼ 1666 Glastonbury Thorn, MERCER
148 —— (A) ¼ 1653 —— £28
149 SIDRICKE HANCOCKE (M) ¼ Chequers
150 IAMES HOPKINS ¼ 1656 Mercers' Arms £25
151 —— ¼ 1666 —
152 NICHOLAS HOPKINS ¼ DRAPR
153 HENRY MABSON ¼ (M) 1666 HOSIER £35
153A —— (M) ½ HOSIER
154 THOMAS ROODE (I) ¼ 1668 Hart
155 CHRISTOPHER SVMMER ¼ HOSIER
156 PETER WEST (M) ¼ Hand, DRAPER £28
156A —— ¼ 1652 Rose
342 WILLIAM GODFREY ?¼ 1668

Godney
156B ANNE ORGAINER ½ 1665

Henstridge
157 RICH HVSON (M) ¼ Grocers' Arms, MERCER £35

Holton
158 WILLIAM IARMAN (D) ¼ Mermaid

Ilchester
159 YE BAYLIFF OF YE BVRROV (½) Town Arms £38
160 IOHN LOCKIER ¼ 1657 MERCER
161 — LOCKYER (M) ¼ 1658 Star and crescent
162 SAMVELL SCOT (D) ¼ 1668 3 cloves
163 GEORGE SMITH ¼ 1668 Mercers' Arms

Ilminster
164 Town ¼ Swords crossed between T.P.; Stocking between T.S. £38
165 THOMAS CARTER (M) ¼ Shears
166 WILLIAM CROSSE ¼ Hart
167 —— (I) ¼ 1658
168/9 ROBERT HORWOOD (M) ¼ Scales, CHANDLER £38
170 ALICE ROW *or* RAW ¼ 1664 St. George & dragon
171 ABRAHAM RICE ¼ 1668
172 NATHANIEL WEBB (H) ½ Family Arms

Kilmersdon
173 WILLIAM FOSTER ¼ 1669 Family Arms £60

Kilve
174 CHARLLS MICHELL ¼ 1670 Initials M.E. £35

Langport
175 PORTREEVE ¼ 1667 Portcullis between I.M. £18
175A IOHN BROWNING (M) ¼ St. George & dragon
176 IOHN BVSH (M) ¼ 1667
177 IOHN WEECH ¼ Haberdashers' Arms
177A —— ¼ Mercers' Arms

Lullington
178 IAMES BRADFORD (M) ¼ Merchant's mark
178A As last but in *tin-plated Æ*

Lydeard St Lawrence
179 IOHN DAW ¼ 1671 Mercers' Arms

Martock
180 HVMPHRY ELLIOTT ¼ 1664

Mells
181 WILLIAM CORNISH ¼ 1651 Salters' Arms, MERCER
182 IOHN GVING ¼ Cock, hand under; hand

182A RICHARD MORE (I) ¼ 1670
183 EDWARD OBORNE ¼ 1667 Heart £60

Midsomer Norton
183A IOSEPH HORLER ¼ 1659

Milborne Port
184 ROBERT PLVCKNETT ?¼

Milverton
185 GILES KING ¼ Croppers' shears; teazle brush
186 IOHN NEWTON (M) ¼ Mortar and pestle, MERCER

Minehead
187 Town ¼ 1668 Ship; woolpack. THE POORES FARTHINGE £20
188 (See *Wilts.* 247)
189 RICHARD CROCKFORD (E) ¼ Warship
190 SAMVEL CROCKFORD ¼ 1654 Scales b.s. £20
191 IOHN STREETE (M) ¼ 1666 Axe
192 ROBERT VGDEN (M) ¼ 1666 AT YE, 2-headed hammer £35
193 —— (M) ¼ n.d. 2-headed hammer

Montacute
194 IANE BLATCHFORD (H) ¼ Mortar and pestles
195 IOHN CLOTHER (M) ¼ 1655 Unicorn
196 — CLOTHIER (D) ¼ Harp

Nether Stowey
197 IOHN HOOPPER (G) ¼ Mortar and pestles
198 WILLIAM PATEY (A) ¼ Fleur-de-lis £35

North Petherton
199 THO HOOPER (M) ¼ 1668 Tallowchandlers' Arms
200 EDMVND IEFERIS (M) ¼ Man making candles
201 THO LOVEDER (A) ¼ 1657 £38

Nunney
202 GEORGE ASHE ¼ 1652 Mercers' Arms

Petherton
203 WILL CHAPPEL (I) ¼ Woolcomb

Rode
204 DAVID IEFRES ¼ 1664 Barrel
205 RICHARD TVCKER ¼ 1670 Hat with feather; wreath
206 WILLIAM WHITCHVRCH (S) ¼ 1668 Woolpack

Shepton Mallet
207 RICHARD BARNARD (M) ¼ £45
208 WILL BROWNE ¼ Merchant's mark, HOSIER £30
209 IOHN BYRTT (M) ¼ 1665 Merchant's mark £40
210 WILLIAM IAMES (I) ¼ 1667 £32
211 THO PAR(F *or* E)IT ¼ 1652 CHANDLER £20
212 THOMAS WESTLY (E) ¼ 1664

Somerton
213 IEROM CHVRCHEY (M) ¼ 1652 Church £30
214 THOMAS HARBIN (A) ¼ 1658 £38
215 IAMES PATEY (S) ¼ '63 Nag's head £42

South Cadbury
216 SAMVELL WILLS (I) ¼ 1666 Bust of Chas. II

South Petherton
217 EDMOND ANSTIE (A) ¼ 1668 Crescent moon
218 IOHN WILLY (D) ¼ 3 sugar-loaves £28
219 WILLIAM WINTAR (E) ¼ Family Arms

Spaxton
220 IOHN CHICK (E) ¼ Clothworkers' Arms

Staplegrove
221/2 IOHN VICKRY ½ 1664 Woolcomb £40

Stogumber
222A IOHN PHILLIPS (C) ¼ RED LION

Stogursey
223 THOMAS ECLESTONE (E) ¼ 1665 Tailor's iron (?)
224 WILLIAM EXON (M) ¼ 1664 Scissors £45
225 RICH WICKHAM (G) ¼ Axe

Taunton
226 Town ¼ Castle; tun £45
227 CONSTABLES ¼ 1667 T and tun; castle. Rose between 2 dots above T £8
228 — ¼ ——— 3 dots above T £12
229 — ¼ ——— 2 dots above T £9
230 — ¼ ——— No dots above T £10
231 (230 overstruck on *Herts.* 126)
232 THOMAS ANDREWS (I) ¼ Woolpack
233 — ANDROSSE ½ 1666 — £24
234 THOMAS ASH (L) ¼ 1664 3 trees
235 IOHN BARTON (M) ¼ 1666 Rose crowned
236 SAMVE BINDEN (S) ¼ Scales
237/8 IOHN BOBBETT (A) ¼ Bag, CAR(Y *or* RI)ER £28
238A THOMAS BVRRIDGE (E) ¼ 1663 Rose
239 THOMAS CARPENTER (A) ¼ Soldier
240 WILLIAM CHACE (E) ¼ 1662 Unicorn
241 —— (E) ¼ n.d. —
242 CHRISTOPHER COOKE (R) ¼ 1667 Grapes £38
243 WILLIAM CORICKE (I) ¼ 1655 Shuttle
244 —— (I) ¼ 1657 —
245 IOHN CORNISH (D) ¼ 1655 Horse
246/7 ABRAHAM CROCKER (P) ¼ 1666 Weavers' Arms £14
248 EDWARD DAWLEY (T) ¼ IAMES, Woolcomb
249 HENRY DVNSCOMBE (A) ¼ 1654 Hand holding wool card £32

250 ROGER GALE (E) ¼ 1652 Grocers' Arms
251 MATTHEW GAYLARD (A) ¼ 1666 Hand holding woolcomb. **Plate 3** £22
252 IOHN GLYDE (M) ¼ 7 stars
253 HVGH GRAYE (A) ¼ 1666 Woolpack £20
254 ROBART GRAY (K) ¼ 1659 Cauldron
255 ROBERT — (K) ¼ Woman making candles
256 ANDREW GREGGORY (M) ¼ 1655 Globe £30
257 IEFFERY GROVE (R) ¼ 1664 DEANE, Clothworkers' Arms £32
258 MARTIN HOSSHAM (I) ¼ 1655 Catherine wheel £25
259 ROGER HOW (C) ¼ 1653 £28
260/1 THOMAS (L *or* I)OVDELL ¼ Cock, MERCER £42
262 — LOWDELL (I) ¼ 1658 — —
263 IOSEPH MABER (M) ¼ 1664 Clothworkers' Arms £32
263A As last but in *pb*
264 IOHN MEREDITH ¼ 1666 Castle £42
265 — MERIDITH (A) ¼ n.d. MERCER £38
266 ROBERT MIDLETON (E) ¼ MAGDALEN, crown £35
267 MATHEW MVNDAY (W) ¼ Woolcomb
268 THOMAS MVNDEN (E) ¼ Tun and T £40
269 TOBIAS OSBORNE (S) ¼ 1666 Fountain £40
270 PETER PARRY ¼ 1654 Hart, CLOTHWORK
271 THO PEARCE (E) ¼ 1664 AT YE WHITE LYON
272/3 ANDREW PITTS (A) ¼ 1652 Tobacco-roll
274 IAMES PITTS (A) ¼ 1661 Shears
275 — — (A) ¼ '63 —
276 IOHN POWEL (D) ¼ AT THE RED LYON
277 IOHN RADFORD (E) ¼ 1653 Hand holding pen
278 ANTHNEY REYNOLDS (A) ¼ 1652 Bell
279 IOHN SATCHELL (M) ¼ 1655 Castle
280 ROBERT SMITH (E) ¼ 1665 Shears
281 RICHARD SNOW (F) ¼ 1655 Catherine wheel £45
282 IOHN SPRAKE (G) ¼ Scales £28
283 IOHN TAMPSON (I) ¼ 1654
284 R.P. (E) ¼ 1655 AT THE 3 WIDDOWS £40
285 HENRY TANNER (A) ¼ 1664 DEEN
285A — — (A) ¼ — DEANE, Haberdashers' Arms
286 STEAPHEN TIMEWELL (E) ¼ Hat and feather
287 ROBERT TOMPSON (E) ¼ Croppers' shears £35
288 GEORGE TREAGLE (F) ¼ Open book £32
289 IOHN TVBB (E) ¼ 1666 £24
290 HENERY YOVNG ¼ AT THE ANGEL, MERC

Wallcombe
291 (See *Herts.* 199A)

Wellington
292/3 OVERSEERS ½ 1666 FOR THE BENEFIT OF THE POORE £38
294 GEORGE BICKNELL (P) ¼ Croppers' shears
295 GEORGE FOWLER ½ 1666 Croppers' shears
296 THOMAS MARSH (M) ¼ Scales
297 CRISTOPHER SAMFORD (A) ¼ Grocers' Arms £35
298 NICHOLAS TROCKE ¼ 1665 Woolpack
299 (See *Salop* 96)

Wells
300 City ¼ 1657 City Arms £12
301 — ¼ '69 —; crown £8
302 WILLIAM ANDREWS ¼ 1651 £25
303 — — ¼ Mercers' Arms
303A W.A. ¼ 1651 —
303B RICHARD ATWELL ¼ 1669 Sugar-loaf
304 IOHN DAVIDGE ¼ 1652 £32
305 MATHEW IRISH ¼ 1656
306 IAMES MIDLEHAM ¼ 1666 Stick of candles £40
307 WILLIAM PHELLPES ¼ 1668 Holy lamb
308 WILLIAM SMITH ¼ 1652
309 TRISTRAM TOWSE ¼ 1655
310 ROBERT WARMALL ¼ 1664 £17
311 — WARMER ¼ 1660

Weston
312 (Probably *Herts.* 224C)
313 THOMAS HANCOCKE ¼ 1656 Cock; hand
314 WILL PAGE (E) ¼ St. George & dragon

West Pennard
315 GEORGE AMOR (A) ¼ '68 Dove with olive branch

White Ball
316 IOHN SMITH (E) ¼ 1666

Wilton
317 RICHARD ANRASSE (I) ¼ 4 lozenges
318 — — (I) ½ 1666 —

Wincanton
319 WILLIAM IVY (E) ¼ 1659 7 stars
320 IOHN KE(V *or* N)ES ¼ Squirrel
321 BEN LEWES (M) ¼ 1667 AT YE BLACK, lion £50
322 IOHN ROGERS ¼ 1652 MERCER £50

Winscombe
323 (See *Glos.* 212)

Wiveliscombe
324 IOHN MICHELL (M) ¼ Heart
325 AMOS STOCKER (M) ¼ Laureate head

Yeovil
326 PORTREEVE OF THE BVRROVGH (½) 1668 Crown £12
327 — (½) 1669 — £14

328 CHRIST ALLEMBRIDGE (M) ¼ 1656 Pipe, tobacco-roll £25
329 IOHN BANCK(E)S (E) ¼
330 IOHN BOONE (A) ¼ Hand
331 NATHANIELL CARYE (A) ¼ 1652 Angel £25
332 IOSEPH CLARKE (I) ¼ AT THE, mermaid £35
333 IOHN COSBEY ¼ 1667 AT THE, shears
334 WILLIAM DANIELL (M) ¼ 1653 3 cloves £40
335 IOHN HAYNE (D) ¼ Lion
335A —— (D) ¼ 1652 —
336 PHILLIP HAYNES ¼ 1655 Dove with olive branch £25
337 GEORGE MOORE (E) ¼ £32
338 RICHARD MOORE (D) ¼ 1668 Hart £30
339/40 AMBROSE SEWARD (A) ¼ Cross pattée £28

Dorset and Somerset

341 (Same as *Dorset* 169)

Glastonbury (contd.)

342 (See after 156A)

Southwark

(Borough, formerly in Surrey, now part of London)

New tokens recorded from *NC*, 1902; *SNC*, Jun. 1907 and Feb. to Apr. 1949; Macfadyen collection (sold at Sotheby's, 15 July 1907); Glendining's sale, 25 Sep. 1907; Hodgkin collection (sold at Sotheby's, 22 Apr. 1914); W. Gilbert, 'Unpublished . . .' (see under Cambridgeshire); A. Heal (from *Notes and Queries*: see under London); J. G. Milne, 'The Browne Willis Cabinet' (*BNJ*, 1951); *TCSB*, vol. 2 no. 9, Sep. 1975; *SCMB*, Aug. 1980; R. Sharman, 'Unpublished . . .' and 'More Unpublished . . .' (see under London); and *SCA* 51, 16 Apr. 1986.

See also William Rendle, *Old Southwark and its People* (1878); Rendle and Norman, *The Inns of Old Southwark* (1888); and G. Berry, *Taverns . . .* (see under London).

Believed entirely unpublished: 17C, 31A, 36A, 42A, 43A, 53A, 56A, 101A, B, 110A, 114A, 152A, 159A, 161A, 192A, 193A, 200A, 202A, 213A, 226A, 227A, 229A, 232A, 275A, 281A, 289A, 303A, 306A, 322A, B, 330A, 346A, 359A, 378A, 379A, 393A, 397A, 409A, 440A, 461A, 464A, 475A.

Minimum price for unvalued tokens: £35

Borough issues without specific locality

1 R.A. (I) ¼ AT THE SWAN WITH 2 NECKS £25
2 SAM ABERY ¼ CHESMOVNGER £22
(A.B. (I) ¼: See 289)
3 I.B. (A) ¼ 1648 AT THE WHIT BVLL HEAD £32
4 I.B. (M) ¼ 1651 AT THE 3 COVLTS £32
5 T.B. (K) ¼ 1651 THE ROSE AND CROWNE
(W.B. (E) ¼: See 19)
(W.B. (M) ¼ 1649: See 418)
6 GEORGE BANNISTER ½ 1667 Axe and bottle, DISTILLER
7 HENRY BARDGE ¼ BAKER
8 CALEB BIGG (E) ¼ Raven, THREAD MAK(A *or* E)R
9 ANTHONY BLAKE (½) TAPSTER YE GEORGE INN, 4 tankards, 3 pipes. **Plate 3**
10 RICHARD BLAKE (F) ½ 1669 Bust of Duke of Suffolk, TAPSTER £35
11 HVGH BLVNDELL ¼ Tobacco-roll, sugar-loaf, GROCER
12 SVSANNA BOND ¼ 1664
13 IOHN BRANDON ½ 1667
14 IAMES BRATHWAIT (D) ½ 1666 AT THE, frying-pan £32
(EDWARD BRENT ½ 1668: See 340)
14A AVGVSTIN BROMFEILD (M) ¼ AT THE MVM HOVSE
15 IOHN BVCKELY (M) ¼ 1657 Plough
16 RIC BVLL ¼ FRYING PAN, 3 birds flying, SALTER
17 —— ¼ FRYNPAN, Tallowchandlers' Arms, SALTER. In *pb*
17A PHILLIP BVTCHER ¼ Still; plough
17B WILL BVTCHER (A) ¼ 1664 AT THE, still, AND, tobacco-roll
17C IOHN BYBEE (I) ¼ '64 AT THE, chequers
17D E.C. ¼ 1650 THE 3 CRANES TAVERN
18 R.C. (M) ¼ 1649 AT THE STARE TAVERNE
19 W.B. (E) ¼ AT THE STAR TAVERN
(M.C. (A) ¼: See 430)
20 T.C. (C) ¼ AT THE COCKE, GROCER £20
(IEREMIAH CALLOWAYE ½: See 42)
21 IOHN CARTER (M) ¼ Tallowchandlers' Arms
22 *Humphrey Clarke* ½ 1668 *his Coffee house*
22A RICHARD CLEMENT ¼ Man making candles
23 THO COKAYNE (C) ½ AT THE COCK, DISTILLER
(IOHN COLE ½: See 33)
24 NATHANIEL COLLYER ¼ Grocers' Arms b.s. £25
25 *George Corfeild* (K) ½ 1666 *at ye Lyon & Lambe* £18
26 THOMAS DALLENDER ¼ 1659 Crown

27 IOHN DAVIS (E) ¼ 1664
28 WILLIAM DAVIS ¼ Sugar-loaf, SALTER
29 RICHARD DAVIS ¼ Man holding up hand; man with sword
30 WILLIAM DAVIS (I) ¼ Sun
31 IOHN DEWSBVRY (E) ¼ '58 3 apples
31A WILLIAM DORRELL ½ AT YE, savage with club
32 IOHN DYSON ¼ '57 WHEAT SHEAF, initials I.P.F. (?)
33 IOHN COLE ½ NEXT THE 3 CVPS AGAINST YE GEORG, monogram and merchant's mark
34 IOHN ELLIOTT (M) ½ '67 Unicorn, HABERDASH(E)R
35 EDWARD FARMER (F) ½ 1669 Arms, CONFECTIONER
36 RICHARD FARMER (E) ¼ 1656 Salters' Arms
36A CHRISTO FARRINGTON (L) ½ 1666 Falcon?
36B ED FLOYD (A) ¼ AT THE RED, cross
37 IOHN FOSTER ½ 1667 3 swans. *Octagonal* £55
38 IOHN FOX ¼ 1657 AT THE CRWN, crown; fox
39 WILL FRITH ¼ 1655 AT THE 3 HORS SHOOS
40 IOHN GREEN (F) ¼ AT THE TOBACO ROLE
41 A.G. ¼ 1651 AT THE GREENE MAN £28
42 IEREMIAH CALLOWAYE ½ 1667 Crossed keys £28
42A THOMAS GARDNER ½ 1666 Winged horse
43 EDWARD GORE (M) ½ Hand holding bird
43A MARTIN GRAY (I) ½ 1669 AT THE, ship. *Square*
44 IOSEPH GRIFFITH ¼ 1659 Chequers
45 IAMES GVNTER (A) ¼ St George & dragon, date 16 (only)
46 M.H. (E) ¼ AT THE 3 KINGS
46A N.H. (I) ¼ AT THE THREE CRANES TAVERN
47 HVGH HANDY ½ 1666 Merchant's mark, CHESSMONGER
47A ROBERT HAYNES ½ Cavalier's boot
48 (Same as 52)
49 RICHARD HETHER (I) ¼ 1664 Salters' Arms
50 T.H. (S) ¼ AT THE HARROW
51 THOMAS HALL (I) ¼ AT THE 3 CVPS
52 IOHN HOLLOWAY ¼ Wheatsheaf £25
53 I.I. (I) ¼ 1651 AT THE WATER SPANEL, spaniel dog
53A WIDDO AN IAMES ¼ Savage
54 EDWARD IOYE (E) ¼ King's Arms
55 RICHARD IVDERY ½ 1668 Dragons fighting
56 H.L. ¼ 1649 AT THE GOLDEN KEY, Grocers' Arms £18
56A THOMAS LAMSON ½ 1666 AT THE, 3 tuns
57 IAMES LANE (A) ¼ AT THE, King's Arms
58 HEN LANGLEY (M) ¼ Spur, SALTER
59 THOMAS LENTON (H) ¼ 1661 AT THE, fleur-de-lis
60 — — (H) ¼ 1651 — —
60A WILLIAM LITTLE (M) ¼ Plume
61 WILLIAM LONGE (I) ¼ WOOD MOVNGER
62 EDWARD LOLE ½ 1666 Man making candles £20
63 WILLIAM LVCAS (M) (½) Savage with club
64 FRANCIS MORTIM(E *or* O)R (E) ¼ Fox
65 ROGER MIDLETON ½ 1668 AT YE, Brewers' Arms
(IOHN NELSON: See 71)
66 THOMAS NEWSVM ¼ Thistle-flower and leaf
67 (See after 322)
(C.P. ¼: See 82)
68 W.P. ¼ 3 hats, IN SOVTHWARKE, *rev.* blank
178 W.P. ¼ — no legend —
68A SAMVEL PARMENTER (D) ¼ Cow tethered
69 IAMES PITMAN ½ 1669 Beacon
70 — — (I) ¼ 1655 — £20
71 IOHN NELSON ¼ 1664 AT YE, tobacco-roll
72 WILL PALMER (I) ¼ 1663 AT, mop
73 IOHN POORE (M) ¼ Weavers' Arms, VITLER
74 RICHARD POORE (E) ½ 1667 Ape on horseback
75 — — (E) ¼ n.d. —
76 RICHARD PERKINS (M) ¼ Mercers' Arms
77 FRANCIS PRESCOTT (S) ½ 1669 AT YE, key. *Octagonal* £45
78 W.P. ¼ AT THE KINGS HEAD, bust of Henry VIII £20
79 I.R. (I) ¼ 1651 AT THE CHECKER £18
(I.R. (S) ¼: See 463)
79A MILES REILLY ¼ AT YE SVN
80 *Richard Roberts* ½ 1667 *at ye Bull Head Taverne* £22
81 THOMAS ROE (R) ½ AT YE BLAK, bull, SILKMAN. *Square*
82 C.P. ¼ 1649 THE ROSE AND CROWN
83 WIL ROGERS (A) ¼ SWAN & STIL, DESTILLER
(E.S. (M) ¼ 1651: See 224)
84 M.S. ¼ AT THE 7 STARES (= stars)
85 IOHN SANDON (E) ¼ AT THE SONNE £28
86 IOHN SAVAGE (E) ¼ Unicorn, HABERDA
87 *William Shelley* ½ 1667 *Cheesemonger*
88 WILLIAM SHELLEY (M) ¼ 1662 CHESMONGER
89 IOHN SHEPHEARD ¼ GROSER
89A GREGORY SILVESTER, WILLIAM LEAVER (½) 1664
90 IOHN SMAL(L)BON (E) ½ AT YE GOLDEN HORSHOOE
90A WILL SMEE (E) ¼ 1658 GROCER
91 ADAM SMITH ½ 1668 Hat and feather £30
91A HENERY SOVTHWICKE ½ '68 AT YE KETTLE, cauldron
173 IOHN STANLY (M) ¼ 1656 Catherine wheel
92 RICHARD STANNARD (M) ¼ 1659 Cock in hoop
93 WILL STEERE ½ 1667 Tallowchandlers' Arms, SALTER £32
94 THOMAS STONSTEELE ¼ '57 7 stars; 3 birds
95 ROB THORNTON (E) ½ 1667 HABERDASHR NEXT THE THREE BRVSHES £22

96 WILLIAM TINDALL (D) ¼ Fleece
97/8 IAMES TODD (M) ¼ 3 TOBACO ROLES
99 IOHN VAINE (M) ¼ '58 Lion
99A R.W. (A) ¼ '58 YE HALFE MOONE INN
100 T.W. (V) ¼ AT THE . . . BREWERS
101 WILL WALKER 6d(?) Sun; VI (only: no legend)
101A —— 4d(?) Sun; IIII, no legend
101B EDWARD WALTON ½ Chequers
174 *John Warner ½ near the Katherin wheel*
102 ELIZABETH WEST ¼ 1667 YE 2 HORSHEWES
103 I.W. (H) ¼ '57 AT YE DEATHES HEAD
104 MARY WEEKES ¼ 1652 SALTER, initials M.S.
105 IOHN WEST (A) ¼ Cannon
106 CHARLES WESTON (M) ¼ 1666 7 stars, POTER
107 FRANCIS WHITE ½ 1667 Angels supporting crown £20
108 WILLIAM WIGFALL ½ Triskelis £50
109 THOMAS WITTS ½ 1667 AT THE, Friar Tuck carrying Little John
110 RICHARD WOODEN (D) ¼ Scales
(RICHARD WORRALL (M) ¼: See 473)
110A *John Young* ½ Man smoking pipe

Angel Alley and **Street**
111 IOHN ABETHELL (A) ¼ 7 stars
112 SARAH DOWINE ½ 1671 Watermen's Arms
112A John Fish ¼?*
113 AVGVSTINE GRIFFITH (E) ½ YE NEPTVNS PALLAS, Neptune in car
114 IOHN SMITH ¼ Angel

Axe Yard (Blackman Street)
114A E. MARSHALL (E) ¼ 1652 Corsets (?)

Bank End
115 ANTHONY CRAVEN (B) ½ Castle £25
116 THO RAYNER ½ Bakers' Arms £32

Bank Side
117 IAMES BAILLIE (E) ½ 1668 AT THE, St. George & dragon £28
118 HENRY BAYLY (S) ¼ 1657 Cannon
119 DANIEL BARO (M) ¼ Shuttle
120 WILLIAM BOORMAN (E) ¼ Haberdashers' Arms £17
121 WILLIAM CHAPMAN ½ Bushel measure £25
121A MARTIN CRAWLEY (I) ¼ Fleur-de-lis
122 MELCHISEDECK FRITTER ½ Cardinal's hat, BREWER
123 ALEX HILL ¼ AT THE, St. George & dragon, AT MASLIN STAIERS
124 IOHN LOVE (M) ¼ St. George & dragon
125 IOHN LVDGALL ½ 1668 Crooked billet; Watermen's Arms £35

* Perhaps not Southwark, but one of the several Angel Alleys in London

126 THOMAS MARTIN (E) ¼ Hedgehog £32
127 EDWARD MASTERES ½ Fish, BAKER
128 R.P. (E) ¼ AT THE EARLE OF ESEX ARMES, stag
129 *Elizabeth Port* ½ 1668 Crossed keys. *Octagonal* £35
130 THOMAS SEABRO (E) ¼ Unicorn £20
131/2 HANDREY *or* HENERY STROVD (E) ¼ 1658 Unicorn £20
133 EDWARD SHAPARD ½ 3 tuns £28
134 GILES STVCHBERY ½ 1658 Cooper's adze
135 —— ½ n.d. — £30
136 HENRY STILES (M) ¼ 1666 Watermen's Arms
137 WILL TOMMAS (A) ¼ Heart, star above £22
138 GEORGE VAVASOVR (F) ¼ Family Arms £28
244 R.W. (A) ¼ '59 AT YE PRINCES ARMES
139 WILLIAM WILLIAMS (B) ¼ Plough £20
139A ABRAHAM WILLIAMSON (M) ½ '68 AT MOVLSTRAN
243 EZE(R)KIELL WORSLEY (E) ¼ AT HORS SHOW. Sugar-loaf; horseshoe
140 R. YOVNG (E) ¼ Merchant Taylors' Arms

Battle Bridge
141 ARCVLVS CROSDELL ½ 1668 Weavers' Arms. *Heart-shape*
142 (See under Bridge House)
143 A.F. (M) ¼ Angel, CHESMOVNGER
144 IOHN HOLLAND (E) ¼ Castle £25
145 HENERY HAWARD ¼ 1652 £25
146 THOMAS NEALE (W) ½ Salters' Arms. *Octagonal* £50
147 L.S. (E) ¼ THE BROOD HEN £28
148 RICHARD SAPP (S) ¼ Peacock, tail displayed £25
149 EDWARD TVRNER (A) ½ 1668 4 dogs dancing
150 ELINER WHITE ¼ 7 stars; crescent £30

Bear Alley and **Quay** (Bridge Foot)
151 ROWLAND PENNIFATHER ½ Bell
152 PHILLIP STOWER (S) ¼ AT THE BEARE
152A —— ¼ AT THE BARE

Bell Yard
153 ANDRA RANOLS (M) ¼ Fox

Bermondsey Street
153A HENRY BLAND (M) ¼ 1658 STAR CORNER, star
154 GEORGE CAVE (A) ¼ STON BRIDG, king's head
155 P.T. (F) ¼ AT THE CHEQVER & BLOCK
156 SARAH EVERIT ½ 1667 AT THE, sun
157 RAF GLADMAN (M) ¼ BAKER
158 RICHARD GRAVES (A) ¼ Men carrying barrel £30
159 ELIZABETH HOPTON ¼ Man smoking
159A FOVLKE IENKES (T) ¼ Men greeting each other

160 PAVL IAMES (E) ½ 1668 MEALEMAN
161 RICHARD MELTON (A) ¼ Crossed keys £22
161A MICHAEL PARHAM (B) ¼ Carpenters' Arms
162 W.R. (D) ¼ AT THE RED BVLL
163 R.S. (M) ¼ AT THE SHVGER LOFFE £25
164 I.S. (L) ¼ THE COCK AND PIE
165 WILLIAM RICHARDSON (M) ¼ Wheatsheaf
166 NICHOLAS SHELLEY (M) ½ 1666 CHESEMONGER
167 IOHN SKINNER ½ Holy lamb. *Square*
168 IOHN STEVENS (A) ½ 1666 £22
169 IOHN SONE ½ 1668 AT YE QVARTE, jug
(P.T. (F) ¼: See 155)
170 W.T. (A) ¼ AT THE WHITE SWAN £30
171 RICHARD WADE (S) ¼ AT THE, Weavers' Arms
172 WILLIAM WALLIS ¼ MEALMAN
173 (See after 91)
174 (See after 101)

Blackman Street
175 IOHN THORPE (M) ½ King's head, 3 hats
176 (Same as 78)
177 (Same as 68)
178 (See after 68)
179 MICHAELL RAYNER (E) ½ 1667 Bakers' Arms
180 EDWARD SALTER (M) ½ 1667 AT YE WHITE, horse
181 WILLIAM ALLSVP ½ AT THE, hart's horns
182 H.B. (E) ¼ AT THE PRINS ARMES
183 ANN BROAD ¼ AT THE (THREE *or* 3) CONIES
184 HENRY BRIDE ¼ Man in moon; Grocers' Arms
185 WILL CLAPTON (M) ¼ Queen's head £32
185A W.C. (M) ¼ AT THE BLACK SWAN
186 WILLIAM COYTE (A) ¼ Dragon
187 WILLIAM COLLARD (A) ½ AT THE BALL
188 ROB DRINKELL (M) ½ Stag's head, bell
189 D.E. (B) ¼ AT YE 3 MARYNERS
190 C.H. (M) ¼ AT THE BLEW BELL £35
191 IOHN IVES (I) ½ 1667 Horseshoe £22
192 ROBERT MAYOW ½ 1667 Man smoking
192A IOHN MEGER ¼ 1664 Anchor, NAILER
193 HENRY POWELL (S) ½ 1667 Coopers' Arms
193A —— (S) ¼ n.d. —
194 IOHN PRINCE (E) ¼ Unicorn
194A C.W. (A) ¼ AT 3 PIDGONS
194B IOHN WABB ½ Rose and crown

Bridge Foot and **House**
142 RICH ALDER ½ 1669 GINGER BREAD BAKER
195 RANDALL ALDERSEY (M) ½ AT YE BRIDG HOVSE GATE
196 IOSEPH BROCKET (M) ¼ Talbot chained
197 ABRAHAM BROWNE ½ AT YE, bear chained £30
198 CORNELIVS COOKE (A) ¼ AT THE BEARE £25
198A T.G. (I) ¼ 1649 Merchant's mark
199 (Misreading of 440)
200 T.H. (M) ½ 1668 Grocers' Arms, SILKMAN. *Heart-shape*
200A E.P. (A) ¼ GROCER
201 HENRY PHILLIPS (S) ¼ Sugar-loaf £20

Castle Lane
(See *London* 478)

Castle Street and **Yard**
202 (See before 495)
202A ARTHVR CROPPER(?) ½ 1667 Catherine wheel
202B —— (S) ¼ 1657 —
203 RICHARD HODGKINE (B) ¼ Boot £25
204 SAMVELL HODGKINE ¼ Boot b.s. £25
205 EDMVND PERKINS (M) ¼ 1659
206 GEORGE PICKFAT (E) ½ 1666 Castle, TALLOW CHANDLER
207 IOHN WALKER (E) ½ Wild boar

Carter Lane or **Walnut-Tree Alley**
208 EPHRVM BVLL (L) (½) 1667 Walnut tree

Chain Gate
209 NICHOLAS MOORE (L) ¼ Butchers' Arms
210 G.T. (K) ¼ THE RED LION £28

Churchyard Alley (Tooley Street)
211 WILL BARNES ¼ 1665 Thistle and ?ball
212 IOHN COX ½ THE PVMP RVNS CLEER WITH ALE (AND *or* &) BEER £45
213 —— (½) Horners' Company Arms
213A IOHN DERMAR (A) ½ Salters' Arms

Clink Street
214 *John Rollings* ½ Savage with club. *Octagonal*

Counter Lane
215 SAMVEL SMITH (M) ¼ £32
216 MARK WYN (E) ¼ Dog leaving wood £35
217 RICH WHEELER ½ 1669 3 bell-pulls and bell. *Octagonal*

Crucifix Lane or **Alley** (Horsey Down)
218 THOMAS ADAMSON (A) ½ Bakers' Arms £28
219 THO ADAMSAND (A) ¼ BAKER

Deadman's Place (St Saviour's)
220 IOHN FREMAN ½ Griffin £20
221 T.M. ½ 1668 RED HART BREWHOVS, CONCORDIA PARVA RES CRESCVNT. *Heart-shape*
222 I.M. (E) ¼ THE RED HART BREWHOVS
222A E.R. (D) ¼ 1651 AT THE RED HART
223 A.T. (R) ¼ AT THE FRYING PAN
224 E.S. (M) ¼ 1651 AT THE DOGG AND DVCKE £35

225 WILLIAM MORIS ¼ Hart; anchor

Eglin's Gate
225A IOHN LEAK (M) ¼ Sheaf of arrows

Falcon Court
225B RALPH WARNER ½ Bull's head

Farthing Alley
226 THO PLANT ½ 1668 Chequers £30

Five Foot Lane
226A THO CHAPMAN (A) ¼ Man holding board or door
226B John Farmer ¼?

Fleur-de-lis Court (Tooley Street)
227 WILLIAM GVISE (A) ½ Fleur-de-lis
227A O.P. ½ 1667 Fleur-de-lis, COVRT. *Heart-shape*

Foul Lane
228 ANDREW WATERS (E) ¼ Man making candles
229 THOMAS POTTER (A) ½ 1667 Stag £38
229A IOHN VERE ½ '69 AT YE, man making candles

Freeman's Lane
230 IOHN STOCK ½ 1667 3 figures
231 —— ¼ — Feltmakers'(?) Arms

Glean Alley (Tooley Street)
232 WILLIAM ALLEN (M) ¼ Bust of Chas. II
232A THOMAS BRANCH (A) ½ 1664 AT YE, bust of Chas. II
233 IOSEPH CAVNT (R) ¼ Stick of candles
234 RICHARD CLARKE ½ AT THE, queen's head
235 HEN MVMFORD (E) ¼
236 ROBERT WEBB (I) ½ 1668

Goat Yard
237 RICH SMITH ½ 3 horseshoes; trumpet

(The) Grange (Bermondsey)
238 THO PRICE ½ THE RED COWE, cow and sugar-loaf

Gravel Lane (Bankside)
239 ROOB COLLINS (M) ¼ Hart
240 ROGER DANNIELL (K) ¼ AT YE, hart
241 HENRI ENGLISH ½ Pipes crossed £35
242 I.F. (H) ¼ AT THE ROVND HOWSE
243 (See after 139)
244 (See after 138)

Hickman's Folly
245 WILLIAM HOPPEN ½ Crescent, 7 stars

Horslydown (or **Horsey Down**)
246 ALLICE ACTOON ½ 1668 Sword thrust through boar's head £30
246A REBECKAH BAKER ½ 1668 Ship
247 RICHARD BAXTER ½ Woman churning £35
247A LEWIES BOVLDEN (M) ¼ 1662
247B IOHN BRIGHT ½ 1668 Apple tree
248 IAMES BVRLY (D) ¼
249 SAMVELL CHRISTOPHER (I) ½ 1667 Grocers' Arms £25
250 IOHN COLLINGTON (K) ¼ Blazing star £25
251 HENRY CRICH (A) ½ Wheatsheaf £20
252 EDWARD DELAMAINE ½ Globe on stand. *Heart-shape*
253 W.F. (K) ¼ THE SHVGER LOEF £22
253A IOHN GOLLOP ½ 1667 Crooked billet
254 R.S. (I) ¼ AT THE SHVGER LOEF
255 PETER HALL (M) ¼ MELMAN £18
256 MARY HARLOE ¼ Mill-rind (?)
257 IOHN HIND (I) ¼ 1668
258 IOHN HOBSON (A) ¼ Name in monogram £35
259 WILLIAM IONES (M) ¼ CHANDLER
260 CORDELIA IOYNER ¼ Hands joined
261 IOHN KEMP ½ 1666 Carpenters' Arms
262 T.L. (E) ¼ AT THE GVY OF WARRICK, Guy on horseback
263 IOHN LOCKSMITH (F) ½ 1668 IN NEW LANE £35
264 KATHERINE MINTER ½ Castle £25
265 RICHARD PACK ½ 1669 Butchers' Arms £25
265A RICHARD PARHAM ½ 1668 AT THE, bust of Chas. II
265B ROBERT PARSONS ½ 1668 AT YE DVN COW, girl milking cow
266 IOSEPH PETTY ½ 1667 Windmill £40
(R.S. (I) ¼: See 254)
266A RICHARD ROFFEY (E) ¼ 1664 3 stills
267 R.S. (S) ¼ 1657 AT YE 3 MARRINERS
268 THOMAS STOKES (A) ½ Hands joined £22
269 T.S. (A) ¼ 1653 KINGS HEAD TAVERN, bust of Jas. I £30
270 THOMAS SHIMMINES (S) ½ 1667
271 W.V. (T) ¼ THE GREEN MAN

Isle of Dogs (?Ducks)
272 IAMES WINSOR (B) ½ '67 Stag's horns

Jacob Street
272A ROBERT BROWNE ¼ AT SAVORY MILL, St. George & dragon
273 IOHN BVRTON (I) ¼ 3 hats
274 W.C. (A) ¼ THE BVNCH OF GRAPES
275 ISAAC CAMMOCK ½ '69 AT BLEW BOOT, Cordwainers' Arms, boot crest. *Square*
275A As last, but *round*
276 THOMAS GESKINGE (E) ¼ 1666 Carpenters' Arms
277 RICHARD LEE (E) ¼ 1657 Hands joined
278 EDWARD NEATE ½ 1668 MEALMAN
279 IOHN PRESTON (A) ½ '68 AT YE ESSEX ARMES, Arms and crest of Earl of Essex £35

King's Bench
279A THO CATMER (D) ¼ Poulters'(?) Arms
280 RICHARD HART ½ 1671
281 R.O. (A) ¼ 3 sugar-loaves
281A HENRY OVERSTREET (M) ½ 3 shoe soles
282 IO POORE (S) ¼ Weavers' Arms
282A IOHN POOR ½ —
283 ROBERT STONIER ½ 1669

Kent Street
283A RICHARD BRILL ½ 1668 Blacksmiths' Arms
284 WILLIAM CHRISTOPHER (A) ½ AT YE, anchor. *Square*
284A THO CLIFFORD (E) ¼ Naked man, BAKER
284B S.D. ¼?
285 RICH FORMAN ½ Unicorn
285A HVGH HAYLE ½ 1669 King's Arms
286 IOHN IOHNSON (A) ¼ 3 goats' heads
287 GEORGE IONES ½ Spread eagle
288 H.M. (E) ¼ AT THE WHITE BARE, A FARTHING CHANGER £25
289 A.B. (I) ¼ AT THE BEARE AND RAGED STAFE, 3 sugar-loaves £28
289A M.M. (I) ¼ AT THE MAEDEN HEAD
290 BENETT MARINOR (E) ¼ 1657 Bear and ragged staff
291 HENRY MILES (E) ¼ WOOLCOMBER
292 MICKELL RIDLEY (I) ¼ Mercers' Arms
293 THOM STIVER ¼ 1652 3 doves £20
294 WILL WILLIAMS ½ AT YE WHITE, horse and bucket. *Octagonal*

Long Lane
295 IOHN GILBERT ½ Hand holding bird
295A I.H. (S) ¼ AT THE COCKE
296 *John Holmes ½ Silk weaver*
297 *John (?)Shulrock ½ at the*, bear's(?) head
297A IOHN SHERBROCK ½ AT THE, boar's head

Lord Mayor's Barge House
297B HARBERT DOVER (S) ½ '68 Castle

Maid Lane
298 GEORGE BALL (H) ½ Basket, CHANDLER
299 IOHN HARRISSON (H) ¼ 1663 Sugar-loaf
300 WILL HVMPHREY (A) ¼ Bakers' Arms £32
301 ELIZABETH IOYNE ½ 1667 AT YE, anchor
302 IOHN ROBERTS ½ 1666 Fountain
303 MICHAEL STEELL ½ AT THE, wine cask, measure

(St) Margaret Hill
303A WILLIAM BORNEFATHAR ½ 1667 Men carrying barrel on pole
304 H.H. (P) ¼ THE BLAC BOY

(The) Marshalsea
305 IOHN LOWMAN (M) ½ Portcullis

(The) Maze and **Maze Pond**
306 MICH BLOWER (A) ¼ Cock
306A THO HAWES (E) ¼ BY YE DYERS ARMES
307 GEORGE HORSLEY ½ 1668 St. George & dragon
308 NICHOLAS MACKRETH (S) ¼ Sun

Mermaid Court
309 DANIELL WRIGHT ½ King's Arms

Mill Lane (Tooley Street)
310 IAMES TOVCHIN (A) ½ 1666 AT YE RED, lion £18

(The) Mint
311 IOHN BELL ½ 1669 3 bells
312 I.G. ¼ Harrow
312A WILLIAM HAMOND (E) ¼ 1659
313 RICHARD PERKINS (M) ¼ Mercers' Arms £28
314 IOHN PLATTEN ½ Coopers' Arms

Montague Close
315 D.C. (E) ¼ AT THE HORS SHOO
316 T.C. (I) ¼ AT THE CROOKED BILLET
317 W.H. (E) ¼ AT THE COCK
318 EDWARD DRAKE (R) ½ 1668 AT YE, bust of Chas. I
319 MARY LOVDELL ¼ £30
320 R.K. (I) ¼ AT THE HORSE SHOOE
321 A.N. (E) ¼ AT YE DYERS ARMES £28
322 STEPHEN OVERMAN (M) ¼ Unicorn
322A R.W. (M) ¼ YE HORNES

Morris's Causeway
322B MARCKE COCKE (M) ½ 1666 AT THE, cock

Nag's Head Alley
67 I.N. (I) ¼ 3 HATS

New Rents
323 IOHN BAILEY (S) ¼ Soldier
324 THOMAS FLETCHER (M) ¼ Rose crowned
325 G.L. (E) ¼ Bell
326 IOHN LOOMEAR ½ 1668 AT THE, harrow
327 HENRY LYBORN ½ '69 Harrow
328 HENRY THARPE (R) ½ Sugar-loaf
329 WILL THVRSTON (M) ¼ Rose crowned
330 IOEL VAVSE (M) ¼ AT THE, mermaid

New Street (Horsey Down)
330A IO IEESVIT (L) ¼ CHANDLER

(The) Park
331 RICHARD BAVGH ½ 1668 AT RED, cross £32
332 PETER BEALE ½ Star, MEALMAN
333 HVGH CHAFFIN ½ 1665 Crown
334 IAMES BRIGNELL ½ Horseshoe

Pepper Alley
335 ARTHVR ADAMS ¼ 1652 Boat oar; peacock displaying tail

336 THOMAS CROWDER (S) ¼ £20
337 IOHN HADING (L) ¼ 1664 Turners' Arms
338 ELIZABETH MILNER ½ 1666 Goat £30

Pickle Herring Stairs (Tooley Street)
339 IAMES AYCRIGG ½ Elephant and castle
340 EDWARD BRENT ½ 1668 Sailing boat £16
341 — — (C) ¼ n.d. —
342 MARGRET BROWNE ½ 1668 AT YE BLVE, anchor. *Octagonal* £30
343 R.G. (A) ¼ THE WOODMONGRS ARM £32
344 IAMES HOLLAND ½ 1668 Bakers' Arms £20
345 — — (M) ¼ n.d. —
346 THOMAS HVTHINSONN ½ 5 tobacco-pipes £25

Pied Bull Alley
346A ANTONY HOG ¼

Rochester Yard
347 RICHARD CRIPES ½ Crown

St George's Church (Blackman Street)
348 IOHN ALLAM (M) ¼ Shuttle
349 DANIEL ARNOLD ½ 1668 WINE COOPER. *Octagonal*
349A IOHN DICKINSON ¼ 1650 Raven; St. George & dragon, SEXTVN. *In pb.* **Plate 3**
350 IOHN EWING ½ Ape smoking pipe. *Octagonal* **Plate 3** £50
351 AN GRASON ¼ AT THE SWAN £22
352 ELYZABETH HOARE ¼ 1657
353 ELIZABET – ¼ 1665
354 HVGH LEY ½ AT THE WHITE, swan. *Heart-shape* £150
354A G.O. (M) ¼? 'Hand'
355 C.R. ½ 1668 AT YE, Mercers' Arms. *Octagonal* £35
356 IOHN SAMSON ¼

St George's Fields
357 WILL HAGLEY (M) ½ AT YE RESTORATION
358 THOMAS MICHELL ½ AT THE MVSIK HOVSE

St Mary Overy's Stairs and **Churchyard**
359 IEMES BRIGNELL (I) ¼ Skinners' Arms
359A SAMVELL FERRIS 1d 1668 AT YE, ? Turk's head
360 SAM GLADMAN (K) ¼ Man making candles £32
361 IOHN ROBINSON (M) ½ Mermaid with mirror and comb
362 GEORGE SHELTON ½ AT YE COALE WHARF
363 *John Standbrooke* (S) ½ *Lymeman. Octagonal* £38

St Saviour's, Dock Head and **Mill**
364 IOHN BATES (D) ¼ 1658
365 HENRY BEDFORD (I) ¼ Prince of Wales' feathers £25
366 THOMAS BENNET (D) ¼ Hour-glass
367 RICHARD BERRY ½ 1666 AT THE 3, men around globe with astronomical instruments
368 CHRISTOPHER BRIANT (A) ¼ Noah's Ark, dove
369 WILLIAM COVLTMAN (A) ¼ Shovel
370 IAMES COWAN ½ Man rowing boat, LITER MAN £28
371 WILLIAM EDWARDS ¼ 3 sugar-loaves
372 PHABEE GODWIN ¼ Drapers' Arms
373 I.H. (K) ¼ AT THE SHIP
374 GRACE HARWOOD ½ 1667 3 porters
375 CHARLES HARWOOD (I) ¼ 1658
376 THOMAS HILL (I) ¼ BAKER
377 GEORGE KERINGTON (M) ¼ BAKER £30
378 (Probably misreading of 377)
378A IOHN KEYSER ½ 1667 Bust of Chas. II
379 ROBERT KINGSLAND (E) ¼ Noah's Ark
379A — — (E) ¼ — dove above
380 SAMLL MANSELL (G) ½ 1660 AT YE 2 LASTS
381 THOMAS NORRIS (M) ¼ 1666 3 birds
382 BINIAMIN PARRAT (E) ¼ Lion
383 L.R. (E) ½ 1668 AT YE DOCKHEAD BREWHOVSE, pentagram
384 IOHN SHILEN (N) ¼ 1659 Windlass
385 ELIZABETH WAPSHOTT ½ 1666 AT YE, men carrying barrel £30
386 HENRY WATKINS ¼ Rose
387 SAMVEL WHITE (A) ½ AT YE VIRGINNY, Indian among trees £40

St Thomas
387A G.C. (M) ½ '68 Casting mould
388 I.F. (A) ¼ THE TALLOV CHANDLER
389 IANE HART ¼ Heart £32
390 THO HAWES (H) ¼ 1664
391 THOMAS HOOPGOOD ½ Ball suspended
392 FERMAN HOVLT (A) ¼ Blacksmiths' Arms £22
393 I.M. (I) ¼ THE TALLOV CHANDLER
393A THO MIDLETON SENIOR ½ 1669 Elephant, COMBMA
394 IOHN NELSON ½ 1667 Mercers' Arms. *Heart-shape*
395 WILLIAM PANTOLL (E) ¼ 1665 NEAR YE WHITE HART
396 IAMES PARRY ½ 1667 Lion £35
397 IOHN POND (M) ¼ 1659 £20
397A P.T. ¼ 1664 AT THE WEAVERS LVME, loom
398 IAMES TAVEY ¼ Lion
399 (Probably misreading of *London* 3131)
400 H.W. (K) ¼ YE GREEN MAN

Shad Thames
401 W.B. (I) ¼ 1649 AT THE PRINCIS ARMES
402 IOHN CANVTY ½ 1666 Tree £25
403 RICHARD RATHBORNE ¼ 1665 Prince of Wales' feathers; St. George & dragon
404 EDWARD WINCE (M) ¼ 1659 Anchor; boat-oar

405 EDW WINCEHVST ½ Anchor with cable; horse. *Octagonal*

Snow's Fields

406 BEN BATES ½ Guy of Warwick riding on cow

Star Corner

407 THO POWELL (I) ¼ Winged horse
408 WILL WEST (A) ¼ Paper of pins
409 ALEX RICHMOND ½ Star, winged horse, Mercers' Arms. *Octagonal*
409A RICHARD TOWERS (A) ¼ Winged horse

Stony Lane and **Street** (Tooley Street)

410 WILLIAM FLEMING ½ 1668 AT YE 3, porters
411 I.L. (H) ¼ THE SHIP
411A RICHARD NEWNHAM ½ 1668 AT YE, rose

Suffolk Street

412 ISAAC MARDOCK (I) ½ 1666 OYLEMAN £22
413 ½ 1668 *the black Boy*, boy smoking; Grocers' Arms

Three Crown Court

413A *Edward Jones* (M) ½ 1666 Still

Tooley Street

414 S.S. (E) ¼ AT THE 3 CHRANES
415 T.B. (E) ¼ AT THE 3 SVGER LOFES
416 NIC(H)OLAS BARNARD (S) ¼ 1654 £32
417 WILLIAM BEBOW (M) ¼ Boar's head
418 W.B. (M) ¼ 1649 AT THE BORES HEAD £22
419 I.B. (E) ¼ AT THE WIND MILL £40
420 W.B. (A) ¼ AT THE 3 DOVES
421 HANNAH BELL ¼ Bell
422 THO BELL (M) ¼ AT THE, swan
423 THO BLACKWELL (B) ¼ Ram's head
424 BRIAN BOWDLER (S) ½ Anchor
424A BRYON BOWLER ½ Anchor and buoy
425 PHILLIP BROWNE ½ Bunch of hops
426 AMBROSE BVTLER (M) ½ AT ST OLIVS WATER GATE, bushel measure £32
427 M.C. ¼ AT 3 TOBACCO PIPES, 3 tobacco pipes; clove £22
428 R.C. (M) ¼ THE BLEW ANKER TAVERN
429 T.C. (A) ¼ '57 YE WHITE LYON
430 M.C. (A) ¼ AT THE RAMS HEAD, COOKE
431 CHARLES COOKE ½ 1667 AT THE KINGS ARMS
432 ROBERT CORNELIVS (D) ½ 1665 2 heads facing, WE ARE 3
433 —— (D) ½ —— WEE THREE LOGER HEADS
434 SAMVELL DEWELL ¼ AT THE, dog with duck in mouth b.s.
435 MOSES DIX ¼ Stick of candles; plough
436 NEHEMIAH DROVGHT (M) ¼ Sun £25
437 EDETH EDLINSON ½ 1665 Hand holding scissors
438 WILL ELLIS (M) ¼ AT ST CLEMENTE, bishop holding crozier, leaning on anchor £22
439 IOHN FARRAH ½ 1667 Cat fiddling, 3 mice dancing, SHOOEMAKER
440 WILL GREENING (I) ¼ AT BRIDG FOOTE, drum
440A WILLIAM —— (I) ¼ Drum
441 IOHN HARRIS (E) ¼ Chequers
442 IOHN HICKS (E) ¼ Ram's head
443 ANDREW HVRD (E) ¼ Indian holding bow
444 IOHN IBBOTT (H) ½ AT YE, anchor
445 WILL(IAM) KELIN (A) ¼ 1658 AT (YE *or* THE), swan
446 FRAN KING (S) ¼ 1657 ST OLIVES CHVRCH DORE
447 DANIELL KING ½ 1668 AT THE, bust of Chas. II. *Heart-shape*
448 E.L. (E) ¼ AT THE GOLVDEN HART £32
449 EDW LEADER (E) ¼ SOPE BOYLER
450 THOMAS MACKLIE (M) ¼ 3 candles within horseshoe £30
451 IOHN MADELEY ½ 3 nuns
452 RICHARD MARSON (I) ¼ 7 stars £32
453 *Thomas Mills* ¼ 1666 Bust of Chas. II
453A THOMAS MORGAN (E) ¼ Grocers' Arms
454 WILLIAM NORRIS ½ 1670 Lion in hoop £30
455 ED ORPIN ½ 1666 AT COFFE HOVSE, angel
456 LEONARD OTTER (E) ¼ 1663 Man smoking pipe
457 I.P. (E) ¼ AT THE KINGS ARMES, GROCER £20
458 RICH PACKER (E) ¼ Crown
459 MATHEW PEARCE (K) ½ MEALE MAN £17
460 TIMOTHEY PHELPS ½ 1665 AT THE, eagle and child £35
461 STEVEN POPE ½ NEARE YE PVMP, Arms of London. **Plate 3** £25
461A ROBERTT PRATT ½ 1667 AT YE, sun
462 (Misreading of 420)
463 I.R. (S) ¼ AT THE RAMES HEAD TAVERNE
464 I.R. (H) ¼ AT THE KINGS HEAD, bust of Chas. I £28
464A IOHN RAWLINSON (G) ¼ Man on horseback
(S.S. (E) ¼: See 414)
465 R.(?) SPIER (H) ½ '66 Lion within garter
466 R.T. (M) ¼ AT THE ST CLEMENT
467 RICHARD THOROWGOOD (E) ¼ Sun £25
468 IOHN TVRNER (M) ¼ AT THE, king's head, AND, drum £25
469 I.V. (E) ¼ AT THE GOVLDEN BELL
470 I.W. (S) ¼ THE SHEEPHEARD AND DOGG £18
471 W.W. (S) ¼ AT THE SVGGER LOFE
472 WIL WATKIN (R) ¼ Lion, PIN MAKER
472A WILLIAM WATKING (R) ¼ Lion
473 RICHARD WORRALL (M) ¼ Ram's head

Upper Ground
474 G.B. (I) ¼ AT THE NEW SHIP
475 HENRY BACHELOR (E) ½ Butchers' Arms
475A SAMVELL CASTELL (E) ½ MEALMAN
476 IOSIAS CHECKET (E) ¼ Swan, BREWER
477 GILES COX (P) ¼ Cock, BAKER £30
478 ELIZABETH CLIFTON ½ AT BLEW, last £32
479 RICHARD DYER (M) ½ '67 AT THE, bear and ragged staff
480 E.G. (R) ¼ 1656 Anchor with cable, CHANDLER £28
481 GEORGE HOLLYWELL (A) ¼ Goat £25
482 PETER HENDY (I) ½ '68 Prince of Wales' feathers
483 DANIELL IARMAN ½ Initials in triangle, BREWER
484 ARNOLD KNIGHT ½ Boat-oars crossed
485 EDWARD LEWIS (E) ¼ Crescent
486 O.L. (M) ½ NEER THE KINGS OLD BARGE HOVSE
487 NIC YATES ½ 1669 AT YE KINGS OLD BARG HOVS, Bakers' Arms
488 PETER SALLWAY (M) ¼ 1666 3 nags' heads
489 THO LAMBE (M) ¼ SALTER AT YE KINGS BARGE HOVSE, Vintners' Arms £35
490 ELYZABETH SMITH ¼ '59 Man rowing boat £30
491 WILLIAM STEWART ½ AT YE BLAK BVLL £22
492 WILLIAM WARNER (R) ½ 1669 Angel £22
493 ANN WHITE ½ Mercers' Arms £22
494 IOHN WHITHOWSE (I) ¼

Winchester Yard and **Street** (Castle Street)
202 IOHN COOKE (M) ½ Tobacco-roll
495 I.C. (M) ¼ Brewers' Arms
495A THOMAS COMFORT ½ AT, Brewers' Arms
496 THOMAS IEFFS (I) ½ 1668 Merchant Taylors' Arms £32
497 WILLIAM RIVERS (M) ½ Lion, lamb
498 EDWARD ROBERTS ½ AT YE WHIT, swan
499 —— (E) ¼ Swan
500 WILLIAM THOMPSON ½ AT THE, vulture
501 IOSEPTH WIGHT (M) ¼ St. George & dragon

Worcester Street (The Park)
501A FRANCIS COCKE (B) ½ AT THE, sugar-loaf

Zoar Street
502 I.H. (N) ½ THE SWAN INN

Staffordshire

Major reference: E. A. Watkin, 'Staffordshire Tokens and their Place in the Coinage of England' and 'Staffordshire Trade Tokens of the Seventeenth Century' (*North Staffordshire Journal of Field Studies*, vol. 1, 1961 and vol. 13, 1973, respectively). 1 plate of 17th cent. tokens; has additions to 'Williamson', a re-listing of the others and a few extra notes.

A further new token recorded from *SCMB*, Sep. 1979.

Believed entirely unpublished: 6B, 43A, 72A, 102A.

Minimum price for unvalued tokens: £80

Abbots Bromley
1 GEORGE TRIGG ½ 1670 Grocers' Arms

Alstonefield
2 IAMES SHELDON ½ 1666 Grocers' Arms

Betley and Balterley
3 *Thomas Richardson* ½ 1667 Grocers' Arms

Bilston
4 HENRY PEARSON (E) ½ 1666 Packhorse £75
5 —— (E) ½ —— error initials H.E.B.

Burntwood
6 (See *Essex* 46A)

Burslem
6A SAMVELL LEIGH ½ 1668 Mercers' Arms
6B IOHN STEAD (M) ½ 1669 Blacksmiths' Arms

Burton-on-Trent
7 *John Blundell* (E) ½ 3 hats
8 DANIELL BOTT (I) ½ 1669 Mercers' Arms. *Heart-shape*
8A SOL CLARK ¼ CLOTHIER
9 IOH W. A. FEILD ¼ Mercers' Arms
9A IOHN W. A. FEILD ½ 1666 —
10 BENIAMIN HAFTEN ¼ Grocers' Arms; initials E.M.H.
11 WILLIAM MORETON (I) ½ 1666 Mercers' Arms
11A —— (I) ¼ Drapers' Arms
12 WILLIAM TAYLER (M) ½ 1668 CARIER
12A IOH WAKEFEILD ¼ Mercers' Arms

Cheadle
13 RICHARD ASTON ½ 1666 Bull's head
13A WILLIAM CHALONER ½ 1667 Family Arms
14 ROBERT SMITH (I) ½ 1667 3 greyhounds

Darlaston
14A WILLIAM KEELING (S) ¼ 1657
15 WILLIAM TVNKES ½ 1669 Scales

Eccleshall
16 RICHARD HARDMAN ½ 1666
16A IOHN SNELSON (K) ½ 1669 Mercers' Arms. *Heart-shape*
16B —— (K) 1d 1671 —. *Heart-shape*

Gnosall
17 (½) 1667 3 cloves, SEND MEE TO THE MERCER OF GNOSHALL. *Octagonal*

Great Haywood
18 RICHARD TETTLEY ½ Grocers' Arms

Hanch Pits
19 WILLIAM BENT ¼ 1657 AT YE, bunch of grapes

Horton
20 (See *Bucks.* 67B)

Kingswinford
21 IOSHVA HANCOX (D) ½ 1669 Scythe

Kinver
22 IOHN COOKE ½ 1663 MERCER £55

Leek
23 IOSEPH CLOWES ½ 1670
24 IOHN GENT ¼ Grocers' Arms
25 —— ½ 1666 —
25A WILLIAM HVLME ½ 1668 Apothecaries' Arms. *Heart-shape*
25B IOHN WARDLE (E) ½ 1669 Mercers' Arms. *Octagonal*
26 IOHN WOOD ½ 1667
26A —— ½ 1666

Lichfield
27 *Citty* (½) 1670 TO SVPPLY THE POORES NEED IS CHARITY INDEED. *Octagonal* £90
28 IOHN BVRNES ½ 1666 Mercers' Arms £48

29 — — ¼ — —
30 THO CATTERBANCKE ¼ Mercers' Arms
31 EDWARD MILWARD ½ Stationers' Arms, BOOK SELER £55
32 THOMAS MYNORS ¼ 1656 Mercers' Arms
33 — MINORS ¼ 1657 —
34 — — ¼ 1658 on *obv.*, 1657 on *rev.* —
35 — — (S) ¼ 1660
36 IOSIAH MOSSE ½ 1667 Ironmongers' Arms £65
37 — — (R) ¼ '66 IRONMONGER
38 IOHN QVINTON ¼ MERCER
39 — — ¼ 1659 —
40 HVMPHREY ROGERSON (E) ½ 1670 MERCER

Newcastle-under-Lyme

41 WILL BEARD ¼ 1656 Salters' Arms
42 RICHARD COOPER ½ '65 Mercers' Arms £75
43 RALPH LOVATT ½ 1667 Lion, unicorn
43A — — ½ 1666 Mercers' Arms

Penkridge

44 IOHN PHILLIPES ½ 1665 Mercers' Arms £35

Rowley Regis

45 RICHARD RVSSELL ½ Ironmongers' Arms
46 WILLIAM RVSSELL ½ 1667
46A IOHN SIDAWAY (E) ¼ '59 Man carrying pack on head
47 HENRY WAKEMAN ½ 1666 Horseshoe

Rugeley

48 NICHOLAS GOSLING ½ MERCER

Sedgley

48A IOHN MARSH ½ 1666 Roll of cloth?
49 *Thomas & Joseph Smiths* ½ 1668 Scales

Smethwick

50/1 THOMAS PAR(K *or* I)ES ½ Ironmongers' Arms £55

Stafford

52 THOMAS ABNETT (M) ¼ 1664
53 WILL BARKER (E) ¼ Crown
53A IOHN BATTMAN (D) (½) 1671 IRONMONGER. *Square*
54 THOMAS COLLINS (S) ¼ 1667 Stafford knot £85
55 SAMVELL COTTON ½ 1667 MERCER
56 THO DAVENPORTE ¼ 1661 Family Arms
57 WILLIAM ELVEIS (A) ½ Closed hand
58 — — (A) ¼ —
59 THO GYLES ½ Stafford knot, APOTHECARY
60 RICHARD HICHCOCK (A) ½ 1667 Bust of Chas. II
61 IOHN HVDSON ¼ 1659 IREMONGER
62 FRANC MOSSE ½ '66 Stafford knot
63 HVGH RODD ¼ (Mule of *Herefs.* 28 *obv.* and *Staffs.* 58 *rev.*)
64 IOHN SOVLE (E) ¼ Stick of candles
65 SAMVEL TANNER ½ 1668 Rose, IRONMONGR
66 RICHARD WALTER (M) ½ 1664
67 IOHN WELLS ½ 1665 Unicorn's head

Stone

68 ANDREW GERVILL (E) ½ 1669 Blacksmiths' Arms. *Octagonal*
69 IOHN WHITTACRES (M) ½ 1664
70 — WHITACRES (M) ½ 1667 MERCER
71 RICHARD WHITMORE (L) ½ 1667
72 THOMAS WHITMORE (I) ½ 1665
72A WILLIAM WRIGHT (H) ½ 1666

Tipton

72B IAMES COLLIER ½ 1669 Crown over arm holding hammer
72C IOHN NIGHTINGALE ½ 1666 Hart

Uttoxeter

73 IOHN BVRTON ½ 1664 Haberdashers' Arms
74 WILLIAM CARTWRIGHT ½ 1668 Mercers' Arms; scales. *Octagonal*
74A IOHN DAINE (A) ½ 1667
75 ROBERT GILBERT ½ 1664 Mercers' Arms
76 IOHN HALSEY ½ 1668 Mercers' Arms. *Octagonal* £50
77 WILLIAM LATHROPP ½ 1663 King's Arms
78 WILLIAM LEESE ½ 1668 Grocers' Arms. *Octagonal*
79 THOMAS LEESE ½ 1663 Grocers' Arms £50
79A IAMES LOYED ½ 1660
80 IEFFERY POWER ½ 1666 St. George & dragon
81 WILL WAKELIN ½ 1663 Crown, VIVE LE ROY

Walsall

82 CHRISTOPHER DICKEN (E) ¼ MERCER
83 I.F. ¼ 1656 WALSALL AND WEDGBVRY. In *pb*
83A As last but in *Æ*
84 HENRY HOGDKINSON (A) ½ 1664 Hart
85 IOHN LANDER (S) ¼ 1656 Heart
86 ROBERT STOTESBVRY (T) ½ 1663 Bear and ragged staff
87 ELIZABETH WEBB ¼ MERCER

Wednesbury

88 THOMAS ATENE ½ 1666 Merchant Taylors' Arms £70
89 HENRY FIDOE ½ 1666 Ironmongers' Arms
89A — — ½ 1667 —
90 THOMAS FLETCHER ½ 1666
91 THOMAS HINES (A) ½ 1666
92 WILLIAM KEELING ½ 1667 AT THE, angel £75
93 IOHN RATLY ½ 1668 Hand holding hammer

Willenhall

93A ESTHER BRINLEY ½ 1670 Anvil and hammer
93B THOMAS BRINLEY ½ 1668 Anvil and hammer, SMITH
93C WILLIAM TVRNER ½ 1666

Wolverhampton

94 WILLIAM ALBBORROW (I) ½ WEAVER
95 IOH COMBERLADG ½ 1664 Bell; tankard
96 ISAAC FLECTCHER ½ 1666 Mercers' Arms
96A MATHEW FOXALL ½ MERCER
96B THOMAS HINCHES (B) ½
97 FERDINANDO LEE ½ 1664 Cavalier's boot £65
98 KITT OTH COCK ¼ Barrel £50
99 FRANCES PARKER (I) ¼ IN THE, cock, STREET £75
100 WILL PARKSHOWSE (I) ¼ Crown
101 IOSEPH TVRTON ½ 1670 Ironmongers' Arms £70

Yoxall

102 THEOPHILVS FELKINGHAM ½ 1667 Tallowchandlers' Arms
102A — FOLKINGHAM (A) ¼ 1664 —
103 ZACHARIAH LIGHTWOOD (K) ½ 1671 Ironmongers' Arms. *Octagonal* £45

Suffolk

Major reference: The Earl of Cranbrook, 'Notes on Some New and Doubtful 17th Century Suffolk Tokens' (*Proceedings of the Suffolk Institute of Archaeology and Natural History*, vol. XXIV, 1946/7). A few illustrations.

A further new token recorded from *BNJ*, 1978.

See also *SCA* 43, 18 Apr. 1985: notes on the chronology of die varieties in the Harris collection.

Believed entirely unpublished: 84A.

Minimum price for unvalued tokens: £45

Aldeburgh

1 IOHN BRIGGS ½ 1671 Ship £42
2 IOHN MVRDOCKE (A) ¼ 3 doves
2A SAMVEL STANNARD ¼ Grocers' Arms, initials I.A.M.*
3 (See *Yorks.* 2)

Barningham

4 IOHN HOWARD (A) ¼ Stag

Beccles

5 Town ¼ 1670 House, sheep-pen £12
6 WILL CRANE ¼ Family Arms; Drapers' Arms £16
7 WILLIAM CVTLOVE (M) ¼ 1664 Fishmongers' Arms £24
8 —— (M) ¼ 1667 — £35
9 HENREY FARRER (F) ¼ Lion £28
10 DAVID GRICE (E) ¼ 3 boars' heads £18
11 IOHN KING (M) ¼ 1657 Grocers' Arms
12 TOBIAS MVRDOCK (M) ¼ Man making candles £20
13 IOHN NICHOLLS (R) ¼ Tobacco-roll £18
14 IOHN WARDE (E) ¼ 1659 Haberdashers' Arms £25

Bildestone

15 ABRAHAM ALSTONÊ ¼ Heart
16 EDWARD BROWNSMITH (A) ¼ '59 Grocers' Arms
17 WILLIAM BVRCH (E) ¼ 1667 Man making candles £35
18 IOHN CVLPICKE (E) ¼ Mercers' Arms
19 I.K. (A) ¼ AT YE CROWNE

Botesdale

20 IOHN SEAMAN (M) ¼ 1664 Drapers' Arms £45
21 IOHN WHITINGE ¼ Grocers' Arms £45

Boxford

22 DANIELL BOWTELL ¼ Heart, MERCER £22

* A mule of nos. 193 (*obv.*) and 2(*rev.*). Cf. no. 185.

23 SVSANA KING ¼ 1664 Swan
23A AMBROSE PONDER ¼ 1670 Mercers' Arms
24 IOHN RIDD(E *or* I)LSDALE ¼ 1667 Sun £22
24A — RIDDELSDALE ¼ 1670 —
24B MATTHEW TEPER ¼ 1664 Eagle, initials S.K.*
25/6 IAMES WA(R *or* C)WELL ¼ Fleur-de-lis, crown, DRAPER £20

Brampton

27 (See *Derbys.* 33)
28 (Probably *Northants.* 13A)

Brandon

29 WILL BREWSTER (P) ¼ £25
29A WILLIAM — (P) ¼ 1667
30 HENRY EVERARD (E) ¼ 1668 Grocers' Arms

Bungay

31 Town ¼ 1664 Shield; castle £32
32 HENRY BLOMFIELD (I) ¼ 1670 Grocers' Arms
33 THOMAS NOWELL ¼ 1660 Brewers' Arms £20
34 THOMAS WALCOTT ¼ 1660 £28
35 HENRY WEBSTER (I) ¼ '67 DRAPER

Bures

35A THOMAS DANIELL ¼ 1659 Grocers' Arms £50

Burgh

36 (See *Lincs.* 49)

Bury St Edmunds

37 GEORGE ADKISSON ¼ Bakers' Arms £17
38 AMBROSE ALEXANDER (M) ¼ Bakers' Arms
39 EDWARD BARNBE ½ 1669 Bunch of grapes, GARDINER £22
40–2 IOHN BAYTHORNE (B) ¼ 1657 Family Arms £10

* Probably a mule of nos. 134 (*obv.*) and 23 (*rev.*).

43 WILLIAM BRYDON ½ 1670 Shoe £40
44 THOMAS BVLL ¼ Waggon £20
45 THOMAS CHAPMAN ½ 1668 GROCER
46 IOHN CHESSON ¼ 1666 £16
47 —— ½ 1669 Haberdashers' Arms £20
48 WILLIAM COLBVRN ½ AT THE STILL £32
49 IOHN COPPIN ½ 1669 Hare £28
50 MARIE CRESSENER ¼ Mortar and pestle £17
51 DANIELL CROSLAND ½ 1668 AT THE, griffin £22
52 THOMAS ELLIS ½ 1668 AT THE, waggon £28
53 IOHN FARECLOTH ¼ 1667 Grocers' Arms £15
54 ROB FIDEMAN ¼ Grocers' Arms
55 MATHEW FRITH ½ Bricklayers' Arms £35
56 FRANCIS GODFREY (E) ¼ Mercers' Arms £28
57 IAMES GRANDY ¼ 1664 Haberdashers' Arms £17
58 THOMAS GRIFFIN ¼ 1666 Pike-fish £40
59, 60 NICHOLAS G(YR *or* IL)LING (R) ¼ Mercers' Arms
61 HEN HAMOND (E) ¼ CLOTHIER £25
62 HENRY HEADACH (M) ¼ Bacchus on barrel, VINTNR £20
63 —— (M) ¼ Man's head in field. —
64 EDMVND HEASEL ½ 1669 Bakers' Arms
65 —— ¼ 1664 — £25
66 IOHN LANSETER ¼ IN COOKE ROW £28
67 IOHN LVCAS ½ 1668 Roll of cloth £24
68 EDWARD PANE ¼ Grocers' Arms
69 THOMAS PAYNE ½ Baker's peel, BAKER £35
70 THO PRETYMAN SENIOR ½ 1667 Lion £20
71 RICHARD PRIME (M) ¼ 1660 Grocers' Arms £32
72 IOHN PVRCAS ¼ 1664 Grocers' Arms £13
73 MARTIN SEYDEN (G) ¼ 1666 Shoe on leg £28
74 —— ½ 1669 Boot with spur £35
75 IOHN SHARPE ¼ 1666 Woolpack £20
76 FRANCES SMITH ¼ 1666 £15
77/8 GEORGE STANARD ¼ Market-house £18
79 —— ¼ 1667 —
80 RO STANTON 1d 1669 AT THE COFFEE HOVSE, hand pouring coffee from pot to cup
81 EDWARD TAYLER ¼ GROCER £17
82 IOHN VSHER ½ 1670 Woolpack
83 WILLIAM WARRIN ¼ 1666 Tobacco-roll
84 SIMON WILKIN (K) ¼ Grocers' Arms £25
84A GEORGE WOOD ¼ 1655 Dog
85 EDWARD WORTON ½ Cog-wheel, OTMELMAKER £30
86 NATHANELL WORTON ½ Bushel measure, MAVLSTER

Cavendish
87 WILLIAM ALCOCKE ¼ 1657 Cock £32
88 DANIELL CHICKELL ¼ 1657
89 IAMES ELLIS ½ 1669 Scales £22
90 IAMES FITCH ½ 1669 Scales
91 THOMAS FVLLER ¼ Blazing star
92 IOHN MERRILLS ¼ 1664 Sun
93 IOHN WOODS (M) ¼ 1663 Oak £32
94 —— (M) ¼ — Royal oak

Clare
95 WILLIAM CADGE ¼ 1655 Crescent moon £20
96 WILLIAM COLTE (R) ¼ 1664 Colt £40
97 GEORGE CRISP ¼ 1656 Anchor, WEBSTER £18
98 RICHARD CRISP ¼ 1656 WEBSTER £20
99 —— ¼ 1664 — £42
100 FRANCES CROSSE (M) ¼ '64 Cross patée; fleur-de-lis
101 WILLIAM CROSSE (S) ¼ 1668 Woolpack
102 IAMES ELLISTON (A) ¼ 1659 Family Arms £45

Cotton
103 PETER HOLMES (K) ¼ 1654 Stocking £50

Cratfield
104 ROBERT PALLANT ½ 1668 Peacock, GROCER £25
105 IOHN WILLIAMS ½ DRAPER. **Plate 3** £22
106 —— ¼ Drapers' Arms £28

Dalham
107 IOSEPH PEAKE ½ 1670 Roll of cloth £30

Debenham
108 AVGVSTINE CVLLYER (M) ¼ 1666 £35
109 IONATHAN DAVIE (S) ¼ 1664 Drapers' Arms
110 WALTTER DENANT ½ 1667 HOSIER £48
111 ROBERT DRAPER (M) ¼ 1659 Grocers' Arms
112 (Probably misreading of 111)
113 AMOS FISHER ¼ 1661 Grocers' Arms
114 —— ½ 1668. *Heart-shape*

Dennington
115 EDWARD STVBBES 1d 1669 Rose crowned £40
116 —STVBBS ½ 1668— £25

Dunwich
117 IOHN WHITTMAN (F) ¼ £35

East Bergholt
118 LANCELOT FELTON (S) ½ BAKER. *Heart-shape*
119 HABBAKKVK LEYMAN ¼ £40

Eye
120 GEORGE BRAYHAM (M) ¼ GROSSER £32
121 NATHANIEL FLOWERDEVO ¼ GROCER £28
122 RICHARD GVILBERT ¼ 1659 GROCER £38

Framlingham
123 DANIEL BARNES ½ 1669 Wheatsheaf £18
124 NICHOLAS BROWNE ¼ AT YE, castle
125 IOHN CAPON (E) ¼ 1653 Castle, GROCER £15
126 —— ¼ 1656 — GROSER £18

127 IOHN DAWSON ¼ Apothecaries' Arms £40
128 FRANCIS IRELAND ¼ Castle £35

Glemham Parva
129 THO MARCKES (A) ½ 1669 Bird in shield
130 (Probably misreading of 129)

Glemsford
131 EDMOND BIGGES (M) ¼ Sun £45
132 GILES MIDLEDITCH ½ 1669 Lion

Groton
133 THOMAS GOODALE ½ 1670 AT THE FALCON, initials I.E.G.
134 MATHEW TEPER (E) ¼ 1664 Eagle £25
135 IAMES WARWELL ¼ Fleur-de-lis crowned, DRAPER
136 —— ½ 1668 —— £32

Hadleigh
136A RICHARD BARRELL ¼ 1667 Grocers' Arms
137 THOMAS BVMPSTED (A) ¼ 1656 Heart £45
138 RICHARD DIPLAK (M) ¼ 1665
139 ARTHVR GAILE (A) ¼ 1655 Grocers' Arms £45
140 — GALE (A) ¼ 1664 Apothecaries' Arms
141 NATHANIELL GOLDING (A) ¼ GROSER £32
142 THOMAS MARTIN (S) ¼ 1667 Apothecaries' Arms
143 SIMEON MOISE ¼ GROCER
144 RICHARD RAND ¼ 1664 Man making candles £22

Halesworth
145 MICHAELL BARFOOT (S) ½ 1668 £22
146 SAMVEL WATTS (M) ¼ Grocers' Arms £25

Haverhill
147/8 IOHN BOR(AM *or* HAN) ¼ 1658 £24
149 ROBERT DARKIN (E) ¼ 1656 £25
150 THOMAS EWIN ¼ 1669 Man with hatchet
151 GILBERT IAGGERD ¼ Grocers' Arms

Herringswell
152 MARY KENT OF SOHAM, IOHN KENT OF HORNSWELL ¼ 1666 £38

Hoxne
153 ROBERT MORPHEW ¼ Grocers' Arms
154 —— ¼ — DRAPER
155 BENIAMIN WHYT ¼ GROCER £40

Hundon
156 ROGER GARNONS ¼ Lions, DRAP
157 THO HEMPSTED (M) ¼ £45

Ipswich
158/9 Town ¼ 1670 Town Arms. **Plate 3** £8
160 IOHN ALLEN ¼ 1657 3 cloves £40
161 ANTHONY APPLEWHIT ¼ 1664 Haberdashers' Arms
162 RICHARD BEAVMOND ¼ APOTHECARY
163 IOHN BORRET (A) ¼ 1655 Grocers' Arms
164 IOHN BRENN (M) ¼ 1659 Prince of Wales' feathers, coronet £30
164A —— ¼ ———
165 IOHN BVRROVGH ¼ Grocers' Arms £18
166 THOMAS BVRROVGH (A) ¼ GROCER. **Plate 3** £18
167 —— ¼ Grocers' Arms, initials I.B.
168 R.C. (A) ¼ 1648 AT THE IPSWICH TAVREN, grapes within hoop
169 WILL CANNE (M) ¼ 1668 BVCHER
170 IOSEPH COLMAN (D) ¼ 1664 Grocers' Arms £25
171 NICHOLAS COOKE (I) ¼ 1656 Pump
171A —— ¼ ——
172 IOHN CVTTRIS ½ 1669 Grocers' Arms. *Octagonal*
173 LEBBEVS DIMBLEBY (A) ¼ 1666 Bust of Chas. II £28
174 WILLIAM DOGGETT ½ 1668 Grocers' Arms, GROCER. *Square* £150
175 —— ½ — Mercers' Arms —. *Square*
176 *Samuel Douer ½ Apothecary. Heart-shape*
177 CHARLS FAREWEATHER ¼ 1656 Ship £30
178 GEORGE GIRLINGE (M) ¼ 1666 Grocers' Arms
179 STEPHEN GREENE ¼ AT YE GRAYHOVND, merchant's mark
180 IAMES HARWELL (M) ¼ 1659 Grocers' Arms
181/2 IOSEPH HAYMER ½ 1666 Grocers' Arms £22
183 ABIGALL HVLLEN ¼ Pot of lilies
184 IOHN MORRIS (M) ¼ Cannon on wheels
185 IOHN MVRDOCKE ¼ 1651 3 doves, GROCER, initials S.A.S.*
186 (Probably misreading of 187)
187 EDWARD PAYNE ¼ 1657 Scales
188 ROBERT REDNALL ¼ 1663 Haberdashers' Arms. **Plate 3** £28
189 WILLIAM SAYER ¼ 1666 GROCER £40
190 WILLIAM SPALDINGE (T) ¼ 1656
191 IOHN SPARROW ¼ 1659 7 stars, DRAPER
192 ROBERT SPAROW ¼ 1654 3 birds
193 SAMVEL STANNARD (A) ¼ 1651 GROCER £18
194 IAMES STORY ¼ GROCER £28
195 W.T. ¼ 1656 AT THE ANGELL £28
196 ELIZABETH TOMPSON ¼ 1656 £30
197 ROBERT TVRNER ¼ 1655 Apothecaries' Arms £28
197A MYLES WAWLMESLEY AND IOSEPH BEALE ½ 1667 3 hammers crowned
198 WILLIAM WILKINSON (M) ¼ Ship
199 W. WYE ¼ 1663 APOTHECARY

* A mule of nos. 2 (*obv.*) and 193 (*rev.*). Cf. no. 2A.

Ixworth
200 REBEKAH BOVLDERO ½ 1669 AT YE, pike-fish £20
201 GARDENAR ISHAM ½ 1668 GROCER
202 WILLIAM SYER ½ 1670 Rose, WEAVER £35

Lakenheath
203 IAMES PARLETT (M) ¼ £50

Landguard Fort
204 POYNT FORTE ½ 1667 Lion, OB £38
205 —— ¼ —— £35

Lavenham
206 IOHN BROWNE ½ 1669 Eagle
207 RICHARD CAGE (M) ¼ 1662
208 SOLOMAN CLARK (M) ¼ Clothworkers' Arms
209 NICHOLAS DANSIE ¼ Man making candles £24
210 —— (S) ¼ 1667 — £28
211 IOHN GIRLING (B) ¼ 1667 Swan
212 BENIAMIN MILLS (A) ¼ 1657
212A WILLIAM PAINE (A) ¼ 1669 Cow (or packhorse?)
213 ROBERT SAVL ½ 1669 Lion £32
214 —— (G) ¼ n.d. — £30
215/6 IOHN WHITINGE (E) ¼ Grocers' Arms £18
217 —— (E) ¼ 1661 —
218 (Probably misreading of 217)
219 IOHN WILMOT (E) ¼ Grocers' Arms
220 — WILLMOT ¼ —

Laxfield
221 IOSEPH RAY ¼ 1665 Family Arms £35
221A —— ¼ 1668 —
222 IOHN STAGOLL ½ Royal oak, GROCER £22
223 ROBERT TOVILL (S) ¼ Drapers' Arms

Lowestoft
224 Town ¼ Arms £11
225 — ¼ 1669 — IOS SMITHSON, ROB BARKER CHVRCH WARD £15
226 ROBERT BETTS (G) ¼ 1655 Bakers' Arms. **Plate 3** £12
227 THOMAS BOTSON (A) ¼ Bakers' Arms £32
228 THOMAS HARVY ¼ GROCER £32
229 THOMAS PASEY (M) ¼ 1659 Brewers' Arms £38
230 IOHN SMITH ¼ 1656 7 stars £12
231 WILLIAM VNDERWOOD (E) ¼ 1651 Grocers' Arms £25

(Long) Melford
232 ANDREW BYAT ¼ 1652 £14
233 — BYATE ¼ n.d.
234 — BIATE ¼ 1667 £20
234A GEORGE CARV ¼ 1667 Grocers' Arms
235 (Probably same as 236)
236 WILLIAM CLARKE (A) ¼ 1667 Bakers' Arms
237 IAMES GILSON (R) ¼ AT THE, hart
238 TOBIAS GROOME ¼ Hand holding dog £28
239 THOMAS HVBBART (M) ¼ 1655 Grocers' Arms £14
240 IOHN KNOPP (M) ¼ 1657 £42
240A HENRY STEABBING ¼ Grocers' Arms

Mellis(?)
240B IOHN LANGLEY (I) ¼ 1666 Ark

Melton
241 IOHN HILL ½ 1668 Ship £30
242 —— (E) ¼ AT THE SACKE SHOPE, ship £25

Mendham
242A THOMAS GOODWIN ¼ 1664 Grocers' Arms £35

Mendlesham
243 THO SOLLEY (S) ¼ 1663 GROCER £32
244 IOH TANN ¼ GROCER

Metfield
244A WILLIAM COTTEN ¼ 1666 Unicorn

Mildenhall
244B IOHN ABBOTT (M) ¼ 1668 Man making candles
245 FRANCIS BVGG (E) ½ 1667 Packhorse £22
246 ROBERT COOKE ¼ 1668 Mercers' Arms £25
247 ROBERT CRANNIS (A) ¼ Woolpack £18
248 NATHANIEL HOWLETT ¼ 1667 Drapers' Arms £16
249 MYLES RODGIN ¼ 1666
250 ANDREW SARGENT (P) ¼ Packhorse
251 IAMES WEB ½ 1668 Tallowchandlers' Arms £14

Monks Eleigh
252 WILLIAM CHAPLIN (S) ¼ Grocers' Arms
253 THOMAS KING (S) ¼ 1666 Swan

Nayland
254 WILLIAM BLYTH ¼ 1656 Cock £30
255 MATHEW HALLIETT ¼ Crown £38
256 WILLIAM MEGGS ¼ 1657 Clothworkers' Arms £25
257 EDMAN TOWLLE (R *or* I) ¼ 1654 BAKER
257* — TOWLLER ¼ 1652 —
258 HONEST GEORG TVRNER ¼ 1657 Rose

Needham Market
259 ROBERT CHENERY (R) ¼ 1658 £38
260 IAMES HARLWIN (M) ¼ 1666
261 THOMAS LOVE (E) ¼ 1664 £45
262 IOHN ROZER (E) ¼ 1664 Rose £30
263 IOHN SHIPP (E) ¼ 1664 Ship £28
264 M.H.S., WE 3 SISTERS ½ 1667 £25

Newmarket
265 WILLIAM BRIANT (M) ½ 1669 £25

266 — BRYANT (M) ¼ 1659 £28
267 FRANCIS GREENE ¼ 1664 Apothecaries' Arms
268/9 (See *London* 2207)
270 I.H. ¼ AT THE 3 TVNS
271 (Probably *London* 646A)
272 (Probably *London* 650A)
273 (See *London* 651)
274 WALTER POVLTER ½ 1669 AT THE, queen's head £18
275 — PONLTER ½ n.d. — —
276 THAMAS PECKE (A) ¼ 1663 3 tuns
277 THOMAS PRATT (E) ¼ Ship
278 (See *London* 652)
279 WILL WAITE ¼ 1657 Stick of candles

Orford
280 MARY THVRSTON ¼ 1659 Scales

Rickinghall
281 SAMVELL FITCH ¼ 1665 Merchant's mark £20
282 ROBERT SPENCER ¼ 1667 Swords crossed £20

St Olave's Bridge
283 IOHN DEERING (E) ½ Swan, pitcher

Saxmundham
284 IOHN HVNT (E) ½ 1669 APOTHECARY £20
285 THOMAS KNIGHTS (E) ¼ Family Arms £8
286/7 NICHOLAS SHEPHERD ½ Drapers' Arms, DRAPR £12
288/90 — — (M) ¼ Drapers' Arms in shield, DRAPR *or* DRAPER £7
289 — — (M) ¼ Drapers' Arms not in shield, DRAPER £7

Sibton
291 PHILLIP THORNE ¼ Crossed keys, GROCER £38

Southtown (Yarmouth)
292 RICHARD BARTON ¼ 1668 Cordwainers' Arms
292A WILLIAM HARVEY (E) ¼ Merchant's mark £35
293 SAMVELL THOROLD ¼ 1668 Mercers' Arms

Southwold
294 Town ½ 1667 Town Arms, initials E.S., FOR THE POORES ADVANTAG £17
295 IVDETH LVSCOE ¼ 1666 Bakers' Arms; Brewers' Arms £42
296 DANIELL MORE (M) ½ 1668 GROCER £17
297 — — (M) ¼ 1663 — £18
298 THOMAS POSTLE ¼ 1652 Grocers' Arms; heart £10
299 — — ¼ 1659 Heart b.s. £17

Stanstead
300 (See *Herts.* 186B)

Stanton
301 THOMAS BVCKELL ½ 1669 AT YE COCK
302 — — ½ — — GEROCER
303 THOMAS GOFFE (M) ¼ COCK £35
304 STEPHEN HOVELL (H) ¼ GROCER £30
305 IOHN SEAMAN (A) ¼ Talbot £50

Stoke-by-Clare
306 IAMES SMITH (S) ½ 1670 £18
307 — — (S) ¼ 1655 £25

Stoke-by-Nayland
308 IOHN GROOME ¼ £32

Stowmarket
309 ISRAELL BARREL (M) ¼ Grocers' Arms £40
310 PETER BRASIER ¼ 1658 £38
311 GEORGE FLINTE (S) ¼ 1655
312 ROBERT GREENE ¼ 1657
313 IONATHAN PEKE ¼ Grocers' Arms
314 IOHN TARVAR ¼ 1664

Stradbrooke
315 THOMAS FOVLGER ½ 1670 Lion. *Heart-shape*

Stratford St Mary
316 (See *Essex* 306)
317 I.B. ¼ MERCER
318 IOHN CANDLER ¼ Swan £45
319 IOHN CLARKE ½ 1670 3 diamonds
320 (See *Warwicks.* 146B)
321 (See *Essex* 307C)
322 (See *Essex* 308)
323 (See *Warwicks.* 153A)
324 SVSANA ROBINSON ½ 1670 Lion
325 (See *Essex* 309A)

Sudbury
326 WILLIAM ABBOT ¼ 1667 Grocers' Arms £38
327 ROBERT CHAPLYN ¼ 1667 Family Arms £42
328 DANIELL COOKE ¼
329 FRANCIS DYER (I) ¼ 1667
330 IOHN EDWARDS (S) ¼ 1657
331 WILLIAM ELLERY (S) ¼ 1655 Mercers' Arms £40
332 WILLIAM FRENCH YE ELDER (I) ¼ 1657
333/3* IOHN *or* IONATHN HAYWARD ¼ 1657 £40
334 EDWARD INGRAM ¼ 1669 Rose crowned
335 IOHN IONES ¼ 1657
336 RICHARD PAINE ¼ 1667 AT YE, half-moon
337 IOHN PARISH ¼ 1667 Mullet b.s.
338 IOHN RAY ¼ 1654 Drapers' Arms £28
338A — — ¼ 1667 7 stars
339 MARKE SALLTER ¼ Woolpack
340 WILLIAM SHERMAN ¼ 1663 Haberdashers' Arms £42
341 RICH SKINNER ¼ Family Arms
342 RICHARD WAITT (H) ¼ 1664 £28

343 RICHARD WEST ¼ 1651 £20

Thelnetham

344 ABRAHAM WOTHERELL ½ Shuttle £35

Thurlow

345 THOMAS IAGGARD (D) ¼ Mercers' Arms

Ufford

346 ROBERT TERRY (M) ¼ Heart, GROCER £32

Walpole

347 SAMVELL FOLKARD ½ 1670 Scales, GROCER £35
348 SAMVEL — ¼ '68 — GROCER £38

Walsham-le-Willows

349 ROBERT GOVLSELL (E) ¼ 1665 £30
350 IOHN HYNSBY ¼ 1667 Grocers' Arms
351 STEPHEN VINCENT (E) ¼ Grocers' Arms £35

Walton

352 IOSEPH SCOTT (M) ½ 1667 GROCER IN COLDNES HVND, OB
353 — — (M) ¼ — — (no OB)

Wangford

354 IOHN ROPE ½ 1668 TALOW CHAND £32

Whitton

355 (See *Lincs.* 269A)

Wickhambrook

356 IOHN RAYMENT ½ 1669 Rose, crown, GLASYER

Woodbridge

357 Town ½ 1670 THE POORES ADVANTAGE £16
358 (Probably misreading of 359)
359 IOHN COCKSON (S) ¼ Merchant Taylors' Arms £32
360 THOMAS EDWARD ¼ Grocers' Arms
361 HENRY STEBBING ½ 1667 Bird, GROCER £13
362/3 HEN(E)RY STEBBINGE ¼ 1656 — GRCER £12
364 PETER TOWSON (M) ½ 1669 HOSIER £38
365 DANYELL WAKER ½ 1669 Grocers' Arms £40
366/7/9 DANYELL WAKER *or* DANIELL WALKER *or* DANELL WLKER (S) ¼ Grocers' Arms £12
368 (Probably misreading of 369)
369A DANELL WALKER ¼ Grocers' Arms
370 SVSAN WALKER ½ 1668 Grocers' Arms £38
371 FREDERICK WOODALL ½ 1669 Bird, GROCER

Woolpit

372 THOMAS HVDSON ¼ 1664 Crown £45

Worlingworth

373 IOHN BLVMFEILD ½ GROCER £32

Yoxford

374 WILL SMITH ½ 1667 WOLLEN DRAPER £18
375 WILLIAM — ¼ 1666 £30

Surrey

Major reference: J. L. and N. L. Wetton, 'The Surrey Seventeenth-Century Traders' Tokens' (*Surrey Archaeological Collections*, vol. LVI, 1959). 1 plate; updating and revision of 'Williamson'.

Further new tokens recorded from R. Sharman, 'Unpublished . . .' (see under London); *SCA* 35, 11 Apr. 1984, 43, 18 Apr. 1985, and 51, 16 Apr. 1986.

See also W. Hooper, 'Surrey Seventeenth Century Tokens' (*Surrey Archaeological Collections*, vol. XLVIII, 1943). Notes on some issuers and minor die varieties, not given by the Wettons.

Believed entirely unpublished: 226A, 269A.

Minimum price for unvalued tokens: £45

Abinger
1 FLORRANCE WEBB ¼ '63

Bagshot
2 WILLIAM MOORE ½ 1669 Tree £35

Barnes
2A IAMES EDWARDS (A) ¼ 1660 Malt shovel
3 THOMAS EMBERTON (M) ¼ 1667 Blacksmiths' Arms
4 —— (M) ¼ 1657 —
5 CHARLES GOODWIN ½ Bear, VINTNER £30
6 TIMOTHY HARLEY (M) ½ 1667 AT THE HORSE, man on horseback £30
7 (Misreading of 6)

Battersea
8 RICHARD GREENE ½ Oars crossed £25
9 IOHN KEMP ½ 1663 IN PUTNEY OR BATERSEY, Cordwainers' Arms £38
10 —— (B) ¼ ———
11 *John Sole* ½ 1668 Earl's coronet above bird within garter and motto £28
12 STEVEN THECKSTŎN (G) (½) LYON. In *pb*
12A —— (G) ¼ WHIT LYON. In *pb*

Beddington
13 ROBERT HILLER ½ Adze

Bletchingley
14 IOSEPH BVTTRE ¼ 1666
15 (Misreading of 14)
16 RICHARD MILES ¼ 1656 Grocers' Arms
17 —— ¼ 1665 —

Bramley
18 IOSEPH CHITTY (S) ¼ 1666 Blacksmiths' Arms

Camberwell
19 THOMAS PHILIPS (M) ¼ 1666 AT YE, bull's head

Capel
19A DAVID COOPER ¼ 1666

Chertsey
20 Town ¼ 1668 Church £30
21 WILLIAM BVRNETT (M) ¼ 1666 Woman churning
22 —— (M) ¼ n.d. —
23 THOMAS BVTTERFEILD ¼ 1652 3 doves £28
24 —— ¼ 1659 2 doves
25/6 RICHARD CHAPMAN (A) ¼ 1652 £32
27 WILLIAM LEE (I) ¼ 1656 Portcullis £42
28 FRANCIS POND (I) ½ 1670 Scissors

Chiddingfold
29 THOMAS LVSHER (E) ¼ '68 Pipes, tobacco-roll

Chobham
30 WILLIAM LVFFE (A) ¼ Hart £65

Clapham
31 WILLIAM GVRNEY (A) ¼ 1664 Watermen's Arms
31A WILLIAM SMALPEECE (A) ¼ AT THE WHITE HART

Cobham
32 THOMAS KING (E) ½ £28
33 FRANCIS TVRILL (A) ½ 1667 £38

Cranleigh
34 WILLIAM DIDLESFOLD ¼ Mercers' Arms*

* From same obv. die as *Hants.* 64

35 IOHN MOWER ¼ 1667 AT THE, Mercers' Arms £35

Croydon

36 EDMOND ATWATER (E) ½ St. George & dragon
37 — — (E) ¼ —
38 EDWARD BVSH (K) ¼ Thornbush
38A DORATHE EATEN ¼ 1666 Tankard
38B — — ½ 1671 —
39 MATHEW GLOVER (M) ½ 1668. *Heart-shape* £150
39A NICHOLAS HATCHER ¼ Family Arms
40 IOHN HEFFEILD (M) ¼ Man making candles £48
41 IOHN IOHNSON ½ 1668 Spade £32
42 ROBERT LITTLE ½ 1667 AT THE, 3 tuns £30
43 ROBERT LLOYDE ½ 1668 AT THE GRAYHOVND £45
43A HENRY MILLES (M) ¼ 1667
44 RICHARD RAGG (A) ½ 1668 AT YE, catherine wheel £50
45 CHARLES AND MARGERY SEALE ½ 1667 £18
46 ANTHONY STOCKES (E) ½ 1668 Man making candles £42

Dorking

47 ELZABETH BOTHEL ¼ £32
48 EDWARD GOODWIN (E) ¼ Man making candles £28
49 EDMOND LISSNE ¼ £38
50 IOHN PENFOLD ¼ £35
51 (Probably misreading of 52 or 53)
52 WILLIAM PENFOLD (M) ¼ 1665
53 — — (M) ¼ 1663 £38
54 THOMAS STEEDMAN (E) ¼ Sugar-loaf
55 (Misreading of 54)
56 IOHN WATKINS (A) ¼ 1667 £48

Egham

57 STEPH(E *or* O)N HALL ½ 1667 AT YE, bust of Chas. II £40
58 NICHOLAS ESTWICKE (M) ½ 1669
59 GEORGE FRY (A) ¼ 1666 AT WHIT, lion
60 EDWARD HIDE ½ 1667 Crown £38
61 ROGER LIVEING (I) ¼ Yoke for carrying barrel, BREWER £40
62 IOHN LVFFRVM (A) ½ 1668 Coach and horses
63 ROBERT NAISH ¼ Catherine wheel
64 ELLENOR RIGHT ¼
65 MATHEW TERRY (A) ½ 1668 Catherine wheel £40
66 IOHN WILLMER ½ Butchers' Arms

Epsom

67 ELIZABETH AMVS ½ 1667 AT THE, bust of Chas. II £25
68 — — ½ 1668 — — £40
69 ANTHONY ARNOLD (M) ¼ 1657 Stag
70 (See *Devon* 339B)

Ewell

71 *Fardinando Downeing* ½ 1665 Lion
71A FERDINANDO DOWNEING ½ 1663 —
72 *Samuell Hawkins ½ Chandler* £35

Farnham

73 I.D. (M) ¼ 1658 Blacksmiths' Arms £32
74 ROB FRIOR (I) ¼ Fleur-de-lis, OATMEALE MAKER
75 IOHN GENANG (I) ¼ 1669 Cordwainers' Arms
76 IOHN GODDARD (B) ¼ Sugar-loaf £30
77 IOHN HOLLOWAY (M) ¼ 1658 Stick of candles £25
78/9 IAM(E)S HVNT ¼ Castle; fleur-de-lis £20
80 RICHARD LVNN (M) ¼ AT THE, fleur-de-lis; griffin £35
81 FRANCIS MABBERLEY (A) ¼ FISHMONGER £35
82 HENRY MORRIS (E) ¼ Fishmongers' Arms £22
83 IAMES WRATH (M) ¼ 1658
84 — — (M) ¼ 1664 £45

Godalming

85 HENERY BRADFOVLDE ¼ 1657 Stick of candles
86 HENERIE CHITTIN *or* HENRIE CHITTY (E) ¼ Grocers' Arms
87 ROBERT CHINTON (X) ¼ Gown
88 — — ¼ —
88A — — ¼ — SALS MAN
89 LAWRANCE COLLINGS ¼ '69 Woolpack £50
90 (Misreading of 91)
91 HENRY MAY (I) ¼ 1666 Leathern bottle £60
92 HENR — ¼ 1661
93 IOHN RANDALL (D) ¼ Dove with olive branch
94 WILLIAM RAPLEY (R) ¼ Malt shovel
95 — — (R) ¼ 1666 — £42
96 (Misreading of 95)

Godstone

97 MARY OSBVRN ¼ Grocers' Arms

Guildford

98/9 Town ¼ 1668 Castle between woolpacks; town Arms, initials F.M., F.S. **Plate 4** £11
100 IOHN BROWNE ¼ 1656 Woolpack; castle
101 SIMON CRANE ¼ 1656 Woolpack; castle
102/3 CHARLES HAN(D)BY ¼ 1662 Woolpack; castle £32
104 IOHN KING ¼ '64 Woolpack; castle £32
105 — — ¼ 1658 — —
106 EDWARD LEE ¼ 1658 Castle; woolpack
107 — — ¼ 1664 Woolpack; castle
108 HENRY LEE ¼ 1658 Woolpack; castle
109 (Misreading of 108)
110 NICHOLAS LINTOTT ¼ 1656 Castle; woolpack £18
111 (Probably misreading of 110)

112 NICHOLAS LINTOTT ¼ 1658 Castle; woolpack
113 IOHN MAY (S) ½ 1668 SHOOMAKER £32
114 ABDIAH MARTIN ¼ 1664 Woolpack; castle £17
115 — — ¼ 1664 on *obv.*, 1652 on *rev.* — —*
116 (No. 114 double struck)
117 (No. 114 with edge knocked up)
118 IOHN MARTIN ¼ 1652 Woolpack; castle £16
119 — — ¼ 1657 — —
120 IOSEPH NETLES (E) ¼ Thistle?
121 IOHN REMNANT ¼ 1667 Castle; woolpack
122 DANIELL SARLLE ¼ 1667 Castle; woolpack £32
123 IOHN SMALLPEECE ¼ Castle, woolpack; 4 men rowing barge £28
124 IAMES SNELLING ¼ Woolpack; castle
125/6 THOMAS TOMPSON ¼ 1657 Castle; woolpack £14

Shalford
127–30 THOMAS WILMOT ¼ Postman(?) with staff and bag £17

Haslemere
131 IOHN EDE (M) ¼ 1665 AT THE SWAN
132 IOHN OSBORN ¼ 1666
133 (Probably misreading of 134)
134 HENRY SHOTTER (E) ¼ 1667 £48

East Horsley
135 IOHN MOODY ¼ CHANDLER

Kennington
136 EDMVND WARRIN ½ Man and dogs hunting rabbit
137 (Misreading of 136)

Kingston-on-Thames
138 ROBERT BALLARD (M) ½ Crane. *Square*
139 IOSEPH BRYAN (F) ½ 1666 £28
140 EDWARD BVLDWIN (M) ¼ 1654 3 salmon (= town Arms) in triangle
140A IOHN *or* IHON DELAMAIN (M) ¼ 1650 Grocers' Arms
140B THOMAS EDMONDES (M) ¼ 1650 Arms £22
141 IOHN FEILLDER (A) ¼ 3 shuttles £18
141A — — (A) (½) —
142 — FIELLDER ½ —
143 STEPHEN FEILDER ½ 1668 3 salmon. *Square.* **Plate 4**
144 — FELLDER (S) ½ 1666 £35
145 — FELDER (S) ¼ n.d. CHANDLER £50
145A RICHARD HAMMOND ½ Butchers' Arms
146 *John Hollis* ¼ 1666 Buytchers' Arms
147 *Stephen Hubbard* ¼ 1666 Cordwainers' Arms
148 IAMES LEVITT (M) ¼ 3 salmon
148A WILLIAM LIDGOWLD (M) ½ Rose crowned

* Apparently a mule of nos. 114 (*obv.*) and 118 (*rev.*)

148B HENRY MALE (A) ¼ 1658 Ironmongers' Arms
149 HENRY MARTINE (M) ½ AT YE GOVLDEN, griffin
150 ROBERT PEARSON ½ 1669 3 rabbits
151 CHARLES SALTER (M) ¼ 1665 Tallowchandlers' Arms £38
152 I.T. (T), I.L. (M) ¼ 3 salmon
153/4 IAMES WIGHT *or* WHITE (I) ½ 1669 Barber-Surgeons' Arms
153A — WIGHT (I) ½ n.d. —
155 GEORGE WOODMAN (B) ¼ Man making candles
156 ROBERT WOORNVM (F) ¼ Shovel

Lambeth
157 RICH ALLFORD ½ 1668 ON YE NAROW WALL, arm holding oar £50
158 IOHN BVRTON (E) ½ Negro's head £50
159 IOHN BORGEINE (A) ¼ 1663 Fish
160 ARON CARTAR (A) ¼ Sword £60
161 HERCVLIS COX (E) ½ '69 Wheatsheaf, 3 birds, STARCH MAKER £42
162 T.D. (I) ¼ 1651 AT THE BLVE BOOR
163 THOMAS EDMONDS ½ 1668 Porters holding barrow, on which another places sack
164 (Probably misreading of 163)
165 GABRIELL FISHLOCKE (C) ½ 1665 Bakers' Arms
166 ROWLAND HILL (F) ½ 1667 Crowns above lion and anchor
167 T.I. (E) ¼ THE BARE AND RAGED STAFE
168 CHRIST IONES ½ AT YE RED ONE, cow, YE NARROW WALL
169 WILLIAM KIMBEL (B) ½ Punch in chair, YO PVNCHNELLY
170 IOHN RAINE (A) ½ NEW PLANTACVN, NARROW WALL, sawyers. **Plate 4** £60
171/2 I(E *or* A)SPER ROASE (E) ¼ 1667 Noah's Ark, dove above £65
172A MICHAELL WARDNER (E) ½ AT YE, bust of Henry VIII
173 IAMES WAST (I) ½ 1669 St. George & dragon
174 WILLIAM WILLKESON ½ 1668 Men carrying barrel

Leatherhead
175 EDWARD SHALES ½ AT YE, swan £50

Limpsfield
175A IOHN GRATWICK (K) ¼ 1666 Swan

Lingfield
176 THOMAS HEATH (I) ¼ 1668 Merchant Taylors' Arms £65
177 IOHN KNIGHT (E) ¼ Mercers' Arms
178 (See *Sussex* 120)

Malden
179 (See *Beds.* 73C)

Merstham
179A THOMAS CLEMENT ½ GROCER
180 WILLIAM SHORTER ¼ 1658

Mitcham
181 HENRY LVKE (A) ¼ 1667
182 —— (A) ¼ 1664
183 DAVID MORGAN ½ AT YE, buck's head
184 W. THORPE (I) ¼ 1667 Dog, duck on back

Mortlake
184A EDWARD RAKENS (E) ¼ 1659
185 (Misreading of 186)
186 WILLIAM THORNETON ½ 1665 Merchant Taylors' Arms £30
187 PETER WHITE (D) (½) London Arms, HONI SOIT QVI MAL Y PENSE £30

Newington Butts
188 EDWARD BATT (A) ½ 1667 AT THE BELL £35
189 W.B. (I) ¼ AT THE 3 TVNNES
190 IOSEPH HALL (M) ½ 1667 AT OLD SMVGGS, smith at anvil
191 EDWARD NIX ½ 1669 Lion
192 *Jaspar Patridg* (½)
193 IESPAR PARTERIDG ½ 1666 AT YE, lion
194 M.R. ¼ AT THE BVLL HEAD
195 (See *Middx.* 156)
196 THOMAS WELLS (M) ¼ 1668 CHANDLER
197 WILLIAM WIMBLE (S) ¼ 3 IVNE 1652

Oxted
198 THOMAS STONE (I) ¼ 1653 £35

Peckham
199 WILL ERBERY (M) ¼ AT THE GRAYHOVND
200 WILLIAM MARSHA(L *or* LL) (M) ¼ 1658 Lion
201 WILLIAM WALL (E) ¼ Bust of Chas. II

Petersham
202 (Misreading of 203)
203 (See *Kent* 272)

Putney
204 RICHARD BROVGHTON (E) ½ 1668 Watermen's Arms £38
205 RICHARD FISHER (M) ¼ AT YE WHIT HART £55
206 —— (M) ½ AT THE WHIT, hart
207 RICHARD FOSTER (E) ¼ 1658 Oars crossed
208 ROBERT IACKSON ¼ 1657 Man making candles
209 —— (I) ¼ 1663 Salters' Arms
210 WILL KEMP (D) ¼ OR AT PARSONS GREENE £38
211 IOHN LEE ½ 1668 3 tuns; AT YE, anchor £55
212 THOMAS MARQVES (M) ¼ 1660 Wheatsheaf
213 IAMES RVSHELL ½ 1667 AT THE FALCON £30
214 ELIZABETH SMITH (A) ¼
215/6 ANDREW WELLER ½ AT YE RED LION

Puttenham
217 IOHN WOLLASTON (D) ¼
218 —— (D) ¼ 1667

Reigate
219 WILLIAM CASTLEMAN (K) ¼ 1652 £30
220 MARGARET CATT ¼ Tallowchandlers' Arms
221 THOMAS HEATHFIELD ¼ Sugar-loaf £35

Richmond
221A WILLIAM BAILY ¼ 165(1?). *Octagonal*, in *pb*
221B NICHOLAS BECKETT ½ 1667 Tree £28
222 RICHARD CAMPION ½ 1668 TALOW CHANLR £32
223 LVKE CHYNNALL (E) ¼ 1657 Windmill £45
224 —— (E) ¼ 1667 —
225 MICHAELL FLAYLE ½ 1669 Catherine wheel, TVRNER
226 WILL FARLEY (M) ½ AT YE READ LION £38
226A IOHN KING (E) ½ THE WATORMANS ARMES
227 ROBERT KING (M) ½ 1666 AT THE FERRY, bust of Chas. II £32
228 —— (M) ½ 1667 ——
229 —— (M) ¼ AT THE, bust of Chas. II
230 IAMES KNOWLES ½ 1664 Drapers' Arms
230A —— ½ 1671 —
231 —— ¼ n.d. — £40
232 WILLIAM MARSHAM (S) ¼ 1663 Bakers' Arms
232A RICHARD PRICE (I) ¼ 1659 Ship
233 IOHN RANDELL (S) ½ 1668 Watermen's Arms
234 IOHN SKINNER ¼ 1658 Man making candles £55
234A —— ¼ 1662 —

Ripley
235 THOMAS EELES ½ 1668 Haberdashers' Arms £32
236 THOMAS GARFORTH ½ 1669 Merchant Adventurers' Arms
237 — GARFORITH (A) ¼ Turners' Arms
238 — GARFORTH (E) ¼ Christ's Hospital Arms

Roehampton
239/40 WALTER NORWOOD (M) ¼ Rose crowned £25
241 R.W. (A) ¼ 1659 THE 3 STAGGS HEADS £55

Rotherhithe
242 WILLIAM ADAMS ½ Bull
243 MARY KNOT ½ 1668 Merchant's mark
243A WILL ATKINS (M) ¼ AT YE, cock and bull
244 WILLIAM BATES ½ 1669 3 dolphins
245 MARY BERRY ½ Carpenters' Arms
246 HENRY BODDY ½ 1668 AT THE, men greeting
247 EDWARD BVRD ½ Boar's head
248 IAMES BVRTON (M) ¼ '66 Grocers' Arms

249 — — (M) ½ 1668 Drapers' Arms
250 E.C. (B) ¼ 1659 AT OLEVANT STAIRES, spread eagle £48
251 THOMAS CLIFFORD ½ 1666 Roll of cloth £42
252 PHILLIP COOKE ½ 1669 Shipwrights' Arms
253 THOMAS COOPER (E) ½ 1668 Sugar-loaf, scales £35
254 EDMVND CROSS ½ Spread eagle
255 SVSANNA DANNILL ¼ 1655 Ship
255A IVDITH DAVIS ¼ 1666 IN LOVE LANE, sun
256 M.F. ¼ 1653 AT THE DARKE HOVSE £38
257 THOMAS FARENER (H) ½ 1668 BAKER
258 IOHN FARMER (I) 1d 1669 AT YE WATERMANS ARMES
259 IOHN GIBS (S) ¼ AT THE ORCHARD HOVS, tree
260 RALPH GOLDSMITH (C) ½ 1669 IRON MONGER
261 EDWARD GREENE (E) ¼ 1666 AT YE, royal oak
262 M.H. ¼ AT THE THREE NAGGS HEADES
263 T.H. (I) ¼ AT THE CASTLE
264 IOHN HARISON (K) ¼ MEALMAN
265 SARA HEYWOOD ½ 1669 AT YE WHEAT SHEAFE, bird on wheatsheaf
266 (Probably misreading of 267)
267 THOMAS HEYWOOD (S) ¼ 1664 Bird on wheatsheaf
268 THOMAS KAM ½ 1666 AT YE, Bakers' Arms £40
269 WILL MANARD (E) ¼ 1666 AT THE, cradle, sugar-loaf
269A SAMVEL MARTIN ½ IN LOVE LANE, cheese-knife
270 THOMAS MAY (E) ½ 1669 AT YE BVNCH OF GRAPES £40
271 EXILL MICAELL (E) ½ Barrel
272 EDWARD MOSELEY (E) ¼ 1666 Still
273 GEORGE NVTKIN (F) ¼ Ship
274 IOHN OTTER ½ Bird £40
275 GEORGE PRICE (S) ¼ 1666 3 men around globe
275A HENRY RISE (A) ¼ 1655 Cannon
276 WILLIAM RVSHLEY (R) ¼ Mill-stone, MILLER
277 ROGER SEAMER (M) (½) 1667 AT YE AXE
278 FRANCES SEELLE ¼ 3 sugar-loaves
278A IOHN SHAW (S) ¼ St. George & dragon
278B IOHN SHEWELL (M) ¼ Rose crowned
279 WILLIAM SIMONS (E) ¼ Bull £42
280 REBEKAH SMALMAN ½ 1669 AT YE POWDER MILL, mill-stone
280A WILLIAM SMART (M) ½ '69
280B GEORGE SMITH (E) ¼ BAKER
281 IOHN SNOADE ½ 1667 Angel
282 GEORGE SYMONS ½ 1668 Lion
283 — — ½ n.d. —
284 ELIZABETH SWAN ½ Swan
284A I.W. (T) ¼ AT YE SHIPP CARS ARMS, Shipwrights' Arms
285 MARY WARREN ¼ Crown
286 ROBERT WEBB (H) ½ AT YE, ship, TAVERN
287 IAMES WRIGHT (D) ¼ 1667 BAKER

Shalford

(See nos. 127–30)

Sutton

288 (Probably *Devon* 278)

Thames Ditton

289 SAMVELL HOY (E) ¼ 1662 £55

Tooting

290 EDWARD ELDERFIELD (E) ¼ 1665 Fleur-de-lis £60
291 IOHN WILLIAMS ½ 1670 King's Arms

Walton-on-Thames

292/3 CHARLES ERWIN (L) ½ AT (YE *or* THE) WHITE, lion £40
294 FRANCIS HOLDEN (M) ¼ Grocers' Arms
295 IOHN HOLES ½ Butchers' Arms
296 THOMAS KING ½ 1668 Grocers' Arms £38
297 THOMAS & WILLIAM SMITH ½ Grocers' Arms

Walworth

297A WILLIAM HOOTON ½ 1668 AT, standing figure

Wandsworth

298 CHRISTPHER BAYLEY (S) ¼ Man making candles £32
299 (Probably misreading of 298)
299A IOHN CLAMP (A) ½ THE GROSORS AREMES
300 ELIZABETH CROW ¼ £55
301 IOHN HAWKINES (M) ½ AT THE GEORGE £60
302 IOSEPH KELE ½ 1670 Drapers' Arms
303 IAMES STVBINGTON (E) ¼ Dragon £55
304 WILLIAM WOLCOCKS (C) ¼ BAKER

West Molesey

305 ROBART CORTES ½ 1669 THE RYALL OCKE

Wimbledon

306 THOMAS HEBVRNE (E) ¼ '59 Rose

Woking

307 IAMES COLLYER (K) ¼ 1657 Shuttles
308 RICHARD GARNER (E) ¼ Mercers' Arms

Sussex

Major reference: J. B. Caldecott, two works: 'Sussex Seventeenth-Century Tokens' (*BNJ*, 1941): corrections and additions to 'Williamson', with some notes on issuers, etc. Also 'The Penfold Bequest: Coins and Tokens' (*Sussex Archaeological Collections*, vol. 83, 1942/3): 2 plates.

See also L. A. Vidler, *A Numismatic History of Rye* (*BNJ*, 1937).

Believed entirely unpublished: 156A, 176A.

Minimum price for unvalued tokens: £55

Aldingbourne
1 WILLIAM DAMMER ½ 1669 Flowers. *Octagonal*

Alfriston
2 WILLIAM CHITENDIN ¼ Mercers' Arms

Angmering
3 IOHN STONE (E) ½ 1669 MERCER £65

Ardingly
4 WILL AND HENRY BINGHAM ½ 1669 3 fleurs-de-lis
4A GEORGE CHEESMAN ½ 1667 Hand holding scissors
4B —— ½ 1668 —. *Octagonal*

Arundel
5 IAMES CARTER (E) ¼ '58 AT YE BEARE
6 ALICE CHARMAYNE ¼ 1667 Pigeon
7 —— ¼ 1657 —
8 THOMAS DREWETT (E) ¼ 1657 Stick of candles
9 — DREWET (E) ¼ 1667 —
10 —— (E) ¼ 1666 —
11 IAMES MORRIS ¼ 1652 Swallow £60
12 IOHN PELLET ¼ 1659 MERSER £28
13 — PELLETT (M) ½ 1668 MERCER
14 (Probably misreading of 12)
15 GEORGE PENFOLD (S) ¼ 1657
16 IOSEPH RVSELL ½ St. George & dragon £32
17 THOMAS WITHERS ½ 1668 £38

Balcombe
18 GEORGE WHITE (A) ½ 1668 Butchers' Arms

Battle
19 IONAS LVLHAM ¼ Merchant Taylors' Arms
20 THOMAS MANHOOD (M) ½ Darts piercing heart, APOTHECARYE
21 IOHN MEDHVRST (I) ¼ Grocers' Arms £55
22 THOMAS PAGE ¼ AT THE SPRED EGEL
23 GILLES WATTS ¼ Mercers' Arms
23A EDWARD WELSH (M) ¼ 2-headed eagle

Bexhill
24 SAMVELL IVRY ¼ '65 Grocers' Arms

Billingshurst
25 MATHEW WESTON ¼ 1666

Bolney
26 THOMAS LINTOTT ¼ 1666 Hart

Boreham
26A IOHN COOPER ½ 1668 Weavers' Arms
27 IOSEPH EASTON ¼ 1666 Mercers' Arms

Bramber
28 (See *Salop* 21A)

Brighton
28A HENRY BEACH (I) ¼ 1669
29 IOHN BROOKER (A) ¼ 1660
30 HENRY FORSTER (E) ¼ Still £80
31 IOHN GVNTOR ¼ Family Arms
31A — GVNTER ¼ 3 gauntlets
32 IOHN PEERSY (G) ¼ Ship £70

Broadwater
33 WILLIAM ROBISON (M) ¼ Hand holding shears
34 ROBERT TVRNAGAINE (S) ½ 1669 £65

Burwash
35 EDWARD AVSTEN (C) ¼ 1658
36 —— (C) ½ 1669 Man making candles

Buxted
37 RICHARD TVCKER ½ 1668 Mercers' Arms

Chailey
38 IOHN COMPRIDGE (R) ¼ 1667

Chichester
39 RICHARD AYLWIN ½ 1669 3 horseshoes
40 MATHEW BALL ¼ 1657 £28

40A IOHN BARNARD ½ 1669 TALLOW CHANDLER
41 IAMES FARENDEN (I) (½) Blacksmiths' Arms £48
42 — — (I) ½ 1667 — £35
43 WILLIAM FLETCHER ¼ 1655 £40
44 — — ½ 1667
45/6 IOHN GITTINGS *or* GITT(I *or* O)NS ¼ Vintners' Arms £22
47 FRAN GOATER ¼ 1659 MERCANT £32
48 THOMAS GODLEMAN (C) ½ 1668 Oak tree £22
49 IOHN HATCH ¼ 1665 Man making candles £35
50 EDWARD HICHCOCKE ¼ Grocers' Arms £25
51 — — ½
52 ROBERT HICHCOCK ½ 1667 Needlemakers' Arms
53 FRANCIS HOBSON (M) ¼ 1652 £38
54 GEORGE IENINGS (A) ¼ 1667 Cordwainers' Arms
55 ANN MICHELL ½ 1669 BOOKSELER
56 RICHARD MILLS (C) ¼ Mallet
57 RICHARD PELLETT ¼ 1668 MERCER
58 STEPHEN PENFORD ¼ 1658
59 MARGREAT REYNOLDS ½ 1667 Bakers' Arms £22
59A WILLIAM ROYSE ½ 1669 Crossed keys
60 IOHN SMITH ½ WITHOVT THE EAST GATE, St Lawrence holding book and gridiron £40
61 — — ¼ GROCER £35
62 THOMAS SPATEHVRST ½ 1667 Stocking £22
63 WILLIAM SWAN (M) ½ 1668 Swan £50
64 MAREY TAYLOR ¼ 1666 Grocers' Arms
65 RICHARD TREVET ½ 1667
66/7 THOMAS VALER ¼ Man making candles £25
68 (Probably a mis-striking of 66)
69 IEFFREY WHITE (M) ¼ Butchers' Arms £25
70 ROBEART WIHITHER (I) ½ 1669 Butchers' Arms. *Heart-shape*
71 (Misreading of 70)
72 RICHARD YOVNGE ¼1658 £30

Cliff

73 MARY AKEHVRST ½ 1667 £25
74 RICH WHITE (S) ¼ Hammer
75 RICHARD — ½ 1668 — BRAZIER

Crawley

76 RALPH PATTRICKE (A) ¼ Harp £65

Cuckfield

77 EDWARD BRINCKHVRST (A) ¼ Lion £50
78 THOMAS HVRST ½
79 IOHN STONE (M) ¼ 1666 Griffin

Dallington

79A IOHN HICKS ¼ Lion

Eastbourne

80 WILLIAM & ELIZAB DONN ½ Glove
81 IOHN ELLPHICKE (E) ¼ Sugar-loaf
83 CHARLES LEEDS (K) ¼ Grocers' Arms, MERCER

Westbourne

82 WILLIAM HALE (A) ¼ 1667

East Grinstead

84 THOMAS BODLE (E) ¼ Mercers' Arms
85 WILL CLIFTON (S) ¼ Sugar-loaf
86 T.P. (E) ¼ AT THE CATT
87 RICH PAGE AND HEN PEASTED ½ Crown

Falmer

88 RICHARD ALDERTON (E) ¼ '67 Goose flapping wings

Fletching

88A EDWARD BRISTO (M) ¼ Mercers' Arms

Framfield

89 THOMAS PECKHAM ½ 1669 Grocers' Arms

Frant

90 NICOLES HOSMARE (I) ¼ Mercers' Arms

Hailsham

91 SAMVELL GILLES (E) ¼ 1657 MERCER £50
92 WILLIAM HARTNVP (E) ¼ Grocers' Arms £38

Harting

93 THO VALLOR (F) ¼ Fox, MERCER

Hastings

94 I.F. (K) ¼ 1651 AT THE MAYDEN HEAD

Hellingly

95 RICHARD PAGE ½ 1669 Bust of Chas. II

Henfield

96 THOMAS PILFORD (E) ½ '68 Mercers' Arms
97 ELIZABETH TRVNNELL (I) ¼ 1657

Horsham

98 RICHARD BARNARD (S) ¼ 1669 Stick of candles
98A RICHARD BRIANT ½ 1669 Cordwainers' Arms
99 WILLIAM HAMPER (S) ¼ 1653 Man making candles
100 (Probably misreading of 102)
101 IOHN HIGINGBOTTOM ¼ Mercers' Arms
102 IOHN HINDLY ¼ 1666 Hind
103 ROBERT HVRST (M) ¼ 1664 Stick of candles
104 THOMAS LVCAS ½ 1667 Fleur-de-lis £45
105 EDWARD PARKHVRST (E) ¼ 1657
106 ARTHER ROWLAND ½ 1669 Bust of Chas. II
107 WILLIAM SHORTT (F) ¼ 1667 King's Arms; horse

Horsted Keynes

108 EDWARD WATERS ½ 1668 Scissors. *Heart-shape*

Hurstpierpoint

109 THOMAS DONSTALL ¼ Woolcomb, MERSER

110 IAMES MATHEW (M) ¼ 1667 Lion £50

Itchingfield
(See 183)

Lewes
111 IOHN DRAPER (F) ¼ BY THE MARKET PLACE, lion £22
112 AMBROSE GALLOWAY (E) ¼ 1667 £38
113 IOHN HENTY ¼ Fleur-de-lis, PEWTERER £45
114 EDMVND MIDDLETON (E) ¼ 1666 Haberdashers' Arms £20
115 EDWARD MIDLETON (E) ¼ 1666 Haberdashers' Arms
116 IOHN PEMELL (A) ¼ '57 Arms, DRAPER
117 WILLIAM READ ½ 1669 AT YE KINGS HEAD, Chas. I with orb and sceptre

Lindfield
118 SAMVEL BLVNT (G) ¼ Grocers' Arms
119 GEORGE FLETCHER ¼ 1669
120 FRANCIS WEST (F) ¼ 1659 Grocers' Arms

Litlington
121 IOHN PEARCE ½ 1668 Bust of Henry VIII

Loxwood
122 GEORGE BILLINGHVRST ¼ Blazing star
123 HENERIE IERLAND (A) ¼ Grocers' Arms

Mayfield
124 CLEMENT READE (V) ½ 1668
125 CLEM — (V) ¼ 1652 Wheatsheaf
126 WILLIAM WESTON ¼ 1667 Grocers' Arms
126A WILL — (M) ¼ n.d. —

Midhurst
127 Town ¼ 1670 FOR YE VSE OF YE POOR, shuttle; pilgrims by palm tree £35
128 ROBAT ATKINSON (I) ¼ 1657 £45
129 THOMAS AYLWIN (R) ¼ 1657
130 HENERY CORTNEY (K) ¼ 2-headed eagle £38
131 — — ½ —
132 GEORGE CHANDLER ½ 1670 Hart
133 — — ¼ Blazing star
134 THOMAS CROVCHER ½ Tobacco-roll, pipes
135 IOHN PEPSON (E) ¼ 1669 Stick of candles
136 IOHN STENT (M) ¼ Castle
137 IOHN SHOTTER ¼ Grocers' Arms £35

Petworth
138 IOHN BARNARD (I) ¼ Stick of candles
139 IOHN EEDE ½ 1670 Ape smoking
139A Richard Eede ¼?
140 WILLIAM HVRST ¼ 1653 £38
141 IOHN IOHNSON ¼ 1656
142 IOHN LAVNDER ¼ 1663
143 RICHARD LEGATT (M) ¼ 1656 Swords crossed
144 WILLIAM MANSER (A) ¼ Stick of candles £28
145 IOHN PEACHEY ¼ 1656
146 IOHN SCVT ¼ 3 cloves
147 RICHARD STRINGER ¼ 1652 Drapers' Arms
147A IOHN WASHINGTON ½ Packhorse, CARIER

Pevensey
148 GEORGE FORD ¼ 1658 GROCER

Pulborough
149 *John Allen* ½ 1669
150 RICHARD HAINES ¼ '67 Pelican feeding young £65
150A PHILLIP WILSHARE ¼ '57 Pelican feeding young

Robertsbridge
151 ROBERT GROVE ½ 1667 Arms, DRAPER £30
152 IOHN PADIAM (E) ¼ Grocers' Arms

Rye
153 YE CORPORATION ¼ 1668 Ship; church £50
154 THOMAS BOYCE (E) ¼ Grocers' Arms £60
154A — — (F) ¼ —
155 MICHELL CADMAN (A) ¼ AT THE MEAREMADE
156 WILLIAM KEYE (I) ¼ 1652 AT THE SHEEPE, ship £50
156A ROBERT PARKER ½ 1669 Sugar-loaf
157 THOMAS TVTTY ½ 1668 Men carrying barrel

Seaford
158 IOHN HIDE ¼ 1656 Wheatsheaf £65

Shipley
159 BARNARD TVLLY ¼ 1668 Fleur-de-lis

Shoreham
160 (Same as 161)
161 RICHARD GLYD (A) ¼ Griffin

Slaugham
162 IOHN LISH ½ 1667 AT THE, chequers

Steyning
163/4 IOHN GROOMES (E) ¼ CAHNDLER £32
165 WILLIAM SMITH (I) ¼ 1667 MERCER £60
166 WILLIAM SQVIER ½ 1669 Apothecaries' Arms £65
167 PEETER SQVIER ½ 1670 Apothecaries' Arms

Storrington
168 CRISTOPH CAPPLIN ¼ 1657
169 IOHN PENFOLD ¼ MERCER £42
170 NATHANIELL STREATER ½ Fleur-de-lis

Tarring
171 GEORGE FLETCHER ¼ 1667 £60
172 — — ¼ 1659

Tenterden
173 (See *Kent* 553)

Thakeham
174 IOHN LEE ¼ 1667

Ticehurst
175 THOMAS NAYSH ½ 1667
176 RICHARD BIRCHET (L) ¼ 1667 Grocers' Arms
176A —— (L) ½ 1667
176B —— (L) ½ 1668
176C THO LAWRENCE ¼ Arms

Turnham Hill
177 NICHOLAS ARNOLL ½ 1669 Shears
178 (Probably misreading of 177)

Uckfield
179 IOHN DEVENISH (I) ¼ 1669 Mercers' Arms
180 IOHN HART (M) ¼ 1668 Heart

£45 **Waldron**
181 SAMVELL DVRRANT (M) ¼ 1666

Westham
181A EDWARD EDWARDS ½ 1667 CHANDLER £50

Wisborough Green
182 NICHOLAS HVNT ¼

£32 **Itchingfield**
183 RICHARD LINTOTT (½) Grocers' Arms

Warwickshire

New tokens recorded from W. J. Davis, *The Token Coinage of Warwickshire* (Birmingham, 1895): two new varieties and a few extra notes; *SNC*, Nov. 1896 and Aug. 1949; Davis collection (sold at Sotheby's, 12 Mar. 1901); *NC*, 1902; *BNJ*, 1926; W. Gilbert, 'Unpublished . . .' (see under Cambridgeshire); Carthew collection (*SCMB*, Mar. 1946); J. G. Milne, 'The Browne Willis Cabinet' (*BNJ*, 1951); Sotheby's sale, 26 May 1983.

See also A. P. Pridmore, *Catalogue of the Pridmore Collection of Coventry Tradesmen's Tokens* (Coventry, 1915): some notes on the issuers.

Believed entirely unpublished: 4A, 22A, 47A, 50A, 118A, 133A, 137A.

Minimum price for unvalued tokens: £65

Alcester

1 ROBERT BROOKE ½ 1668 £50
2 MATHIAS CRABB (A) ¼ Drapers' Arms £25
3 IOSEPH DEWES (B) ¼ 1654 Mortar and pestle £28
4 FVLKE EMES (A) ¼ 1657 Mercers' Arms £45
4A WILLIAM HOPKINS (M) ½ 1670 Lion
5 CHARLES IOHNSON ¼ Scales £20
6 THOMAS PICKARD ½ 1667 Grocers' Arms £55
7 THO PICKERD (E) ½ 1664 Grocers' Arms £40
8 IOHN REINOLES ½ 1670 MERCER £30
9 WILLIAM REYNOLDS (E) ¼ 1652 Fox £28
10 —— (E) ¼ 1662 — £32
11 STEPHEN ROVND ½ AT YE GRAY HOVNDS HEAD
12 THOMAS ROV(Y)ND ½ 1670 Crown
13 IOHN YARNOLD (E) ¼ 1668 Basket? £32
14 MARGARET YARNOLL ¼ 1651 Jar £25
15 ANN WADE ½ 1670 Man making candles

Atherstone

16 KATHERINE BERRY ¼ 1666 Angel
17 WILL CRISPE (A) ¼ 1667 Swan
18/9 WILLIAM — (A) ½ —— £45
20 RICH EVERETT (E) ¼ 1666 Man making candles
21 IOHN POWER (A) ¼ '57 BAKER
22 GEORGE SADLER (A) ¼ 1667 Grocers' Arms
22A —— (A) ½ ——

Barford

23 MARY BRINE ½ 1667 Ironmongers' Arms £40
24 WILL COCKBILL ½ 1668 £38

Birmingham

24A WILLIAM BRIERLY ½ Mercers' Arms
25 IOHN BRINGTON ½ Cutlers' Arms
26 —— ½ 1666 —
27 WILLIAM BVRBERRY ½ Catherine wheel
28 WILLIAM COLMORE ½ Bust
29 EDWARD ENSOR ¼ 1652 Grocers' Arms; fleur-de-lis
30 —— ¼ 1660 ——
31 —— ½ ——. Centre in *copper*, outer ring in *brass* £100
32 GEORGE FENTHAM ½ Haberdashers' Arms
33 EDWARD FREEMAN ½ Grocers' Arms £55
34 SIMON HEATH ½ Ironmongers' Arms
35 EDWARD HENSON ½ 1666 Grocers' Arms
35A HENRY HODGITS ½ Arms, crest
36 IOSEPH HOPKINS ½ 1666 Ironmongers' Arms £60
37 IOHN IESSON ½ 1670 MERCER
38 WILLIAM KING (A) ½ 1668 Blacksmiths' Arms £65
39 EDWARD LEATHER ½ 1662?
40 RICHARD LEATHER ½ 1669 Daggers crossed £45
41 WILLIAM NASEBIE (E) ½ 1669 Scales. *Octagonal*
42 THOMAS PEMBERTON ½ Ironmongers' Arms £70
43 THOMAS PEWTRILL AND IOHN POTTERILL ½ 1666 £75
44 THOMAS RVSSELL ½ 1667 Ironmongers' Arms £75
45 NICHOLAS SANFORD ½ Ironmongers' Arms
45A RICHARD SMALBROKE ¼ Arms
46 ROBERT SMALBROOKE ½ Mercers' Arms
47 IOHN TAYLOVR ½ 1662 Lion's head
47A —— ¼ ——

Brailes

48 THOMAS RIMILL (M) ½ 1666 £35
49 FRANCIS SHARLEY ½ 1666 St. George & dragon. *Square* £135
50 IANE SHERLEY ½ 1665 Grocers' Arms £28

Coleshill

50A THOMAS BOSEN (M) ¼ 1669 MERCER

51 THOMAS CROOKE (M) ¼ 1670
TALLOW CHANDLER £42
51A RICHARD IOHNSON ½ APOTHECARY
51B THOMAS STONE (M) ¼ Mercers' Arms
52 WILLIAM WALKER ½ 1669 Mercers' Arms
52A —— ½ 1665 —

Coughton

53 EDMVND HORNBLOWAR ½ 1667 Hammer £38

Coventry

54 CITTY ½ Elephant and castle; leopard £45
55 City ½ 1669 — £14
56 — ¼ —— ; leopard £25
57 SAMVEL ALLSOP ¼ 1666 Cordwainers' Arms
58 NATHANIELL ALSOPP ¼ 1656 Merchant's mark
58A NATH ALLSOP ¼ 1667
59,60 WILLIAM AVSTEN (A) ¼ 3 tuns
61 NATHANILL BARNARD ¼ Globe, MERCER
62 (Probably misreading of 63)
63 ROBERT BEDFORD ¼ 1666 Weavers' Arms
64 —— (A) ¼ Anchor
65 IOHN BROOKES ½ 1668 STATIONER £65
66 E.C. (A) ½ BIRMINGHAM HINKLY
COVENTRY WARWICK
67 F.C. ¼ AT THE SVGAR LOFE, MARCER £45
68 (Probably misreading of 69)
69 F.C. ¼ 1665 MERCER AND GROCER
70 IOHN CARPENTER (E) ½ Crescent, 7 stars
71 IOHN CRICHLOWE (½) 1668 DRAPR £25
72 EDWARD CRVSSE (M) ¼ 1663 Packhorse
73 (Probably misreading of 74)
74 MICHAELL EARLE (M) ¼ MERCER
75 EDWARD FAYERBROTHER (S) ¼ '66
Fleece, CLOTHIER
76 WILLIAM GILBERT ¼ Boot between spears,
MERCER £50
77 —— (M) ¼ Arms, MERCER
78 EDWARD LAPWORTH ¼ 1659 Dove
79 IOHN LAX (M) ¼ 1659 AT THE, star £45
80 ABRAHAM LVCAS (E) ¼ GROCER £42
80A GEORGE MONCK ¼ 1664 Men carrying
barrel; tree
81 IOHN MVRDOCK ½ 1668 BAKER £55
82 E.O. (½) 1667 Hat with feathers, FELTMAKER
83 MATHEW PARKER (S) ¼ King's Arms, MERCER
84/5 SAMVEL(L) PEISLEY ¼ AT
(YE *or* THE) SONN, barrel £40
86 SAMVEL PEASLYE (E) ¼ THE SVN
87 T.P. ¼ APOTHECARIE
88 WILLIAM ROWNEY SENIOR ½ '63 Elephant and
castle
89 WILLIAM ROWNEY ¼ Elephant and castle,
MERCER £55
90 WILL(IAM) ROWNEY SENIOR ½ 1665
Globe and castle
91 IOHN SMITH (L) ¼ 1651 Pewterers' Arms £60
92 WILLIAM SNELL (A) ¼ 1665 MERCER
93 (Probably misreading of 94)
94 SAMVELL TISSALL ½ 1668 AT, thistle
95 (Probably misreading of 96)
96 S.W. (½) 1666 Shuttle, WOOLLSTED WEAVER
97 IOHN WOOLRICH ¼ 1663 Rose; sunflower,
MERCER
98 H.W. (E) ¼ 1666 IN COVENTRY SOVTHAM
RVGBY LVTTERWORTH, DYER

Deritend (Birmingham)

99 *Malin Lilly* ½ 1667 £65

Griff (Chilver's Coton)

100 V.W. ¼ 1654 Miner holding pick £60

Hemlingford Hundred

101 EDWARD TAYLOR ½ 1668 Head, BAYLIFE £35
102 —— ½ 1669 Head in profile, BAYLIFFE £28

Henley-in-Arden

103 SAMVELL PERKINES, ROB HANDEY
½ 1666 MERCERS £65
104 (Probably misreading of 105)
105 IOHN HEMINS ½ YE PORCH HOVSE,
Bakers' Arms £40

Kenilworth

106 IOHN NORTON ½ 1664 Mercers' Arms £38
107 THO BOVCHER ½ 1668 AT THE SWAN £48

Keresley

108 ROBERT SEDDON (M) ½ 1669 Man with
pole on shoulder, dog at side £40

Kineton

109 SAMVEL BACON ½ IRONMONGER* £30
110 (Later striking in *AR*)
111 IO EBORNE ¼ Grocers' Arms £28
112 (See *Herefs.* 43B)

Knowle

113 (Probably misreading of 114)
114 WILLIAM EEDS (E) ½ 1666

Lapworth

115 THOMAS HALL ¼ 1667 Chopper; cock

Merevale

116 IOHN RAYNOR ¼ Hart; man mining coal

Meriden

117 THOMAS AVERY ½ 1667 SHOO MAKER

Nuneaton

118 GERVASE BOSWELL (M) ¼ MERCER
118A —— (M) ¼ '58 —
119 WILLIAM FAWCETT ½ 1666 £55
120 WILLIAM GLASCOCKE (M) ¼ 1652 Cock £60
121 EDWARD WARDEN (A) ¼ 1652
Heart pierced with arrow, MERCER

* Later strikings on large flans (? 18th cent.) are known

Pillerton
122 WILLIAM EARLE (A) ½ 1666
123 —— (A) ½ 1670 £60

Rugby
124 LVKE BARROW (E) ¼ '67 3 hats, FELT MAKER £65
125 —— (E) ¼ n.d. ——
126 —— ¼ ———
127 WILLIAM BOYS ½ 1669 Knot, MERCER
128 WILLIAM CHEBSEY ¼ Sugar-loaf, MERCER £38
129 ABRAHAM HARPER ¼ MERCER £30
130 MILLECENT TILGMAN ¼ Crown £38

Shirley Street (Solihull)
131 (Probably misreading of 132)
132 HVGH HYMAN (F) ½ 1667 Lion

Solihull
133 IOHN BRANDAN (M) ½ 1666 Scales
133A —— (M) ½ 1668 —
134 THOMAS PALMER (A) ½ 1669 BAKER

Southam
135 IOHN CHEBSEY (E) ¼ 1666 2-headed eagle. **Plate 4** £32
136 STEPHEN CHESTON ½ 1669 Drapers' Arms
137 —— (S) ¼ 3 lions
137A THO COALES (I) ¼ Grocers' Arms
138/9 THO EADY *or* EADS ½ APOTHECARY
140/1 MARGRAY HANSLAPP ¼ 1658 Mercers' Arms £28
142 MARGERY — ¼ 1667 — £45
143 BRIDGET LOE ½ 1665 Bunch of grapes £35
143A WILLIAM LYNDON ¼ 1665 Man making candles; man with bow
144 IOHN NEWCOMBE (A) ½ Packhorse

Stratford-on-Avon
145 Town ½ 1669 Borough Arms £50
146 IOHN BOVLTON (M) ½ Woolpack, CARIER £45
146A I. Brook ¼? "Mercer"
146B IOHN ESON (A) ¼ 1657 £55
147 RICH HICKES (E) ½ Angel £35
148 LAWRANCE HORWOOD (E) ¼ £55
149 RICHARD HVNTT ½ 1667 £32
149A — HVNT (A) ¼ 1651 £42
150 DANIELL MASON ¼ Grocers' Arms
151 —— ½ 1668 —
152 (Probably misreading of 153)
153 IOSEPH PHILLIPS (A) ½ 1668 AT YE, falcon
153A SAMVEL PHILLIPS (I) ¼ 1652 Ironmongers' Arms £42
153B —— (I) ½
154 EDWARD ROGERS (M) ½ 1668 Keys crossed, BOOKBINDER £60
155 EDWARD SMITH (M) ¼
156 —— (M) ½ £40
157 FRANCIS SMITH (A) ½ Keys crossed £60
158 THOMAS TAYLOVR (A) ¼

Tamworth
159 (Probably same as 160)
160 CHAMBERLAINS ½ Fleur-de-lis. *Octagonal* £70
160A THO BOSS . . . (H?) ¼ Grocers' Arms
161 WILLIAM AND ROBERT CAWNE ½ 1668 Man making candles £40
162 ROBERT GREENE ½ 1671 MERCER £45
163 WILLIAM MICHELL ½ 1667 Mercers' Arms £30
164 THO WAGSTAFF (F) ¼ Mercers' Arms
165 IOHN WELCH (E) ½ 1667 IRONMONGER £65
166 EDWARD WHITE ¼ 1663 Fleur-de-lis
167 —— ¼ 1658 —

Tanworth
168 IOHN CHAMBERS ½ Family Arms b.s. **Plate 4**
169 EDWARD MORGAN ½ 1668 Apothecaries' Arms

(Middle) Tysoe
170 EDWARD BOREMAN (A) ¼ 1656 Mercers' Arms
171 IOHN LAGOE (K) ½ '68 Crowned rose £50

Warwick
172 CRISTO AYLESBVRY ¼ 1665 Still £38
173 RICHARD BIRD (M) ¼ 1654 Bird
174 T.C. (M) ¼ 1657 AT YE CROWNE
175 (Probably misreading of 176)
176 IVDETH DVNN WIDDOWE ½ 1669 Butchers' Arms £45
177 ROGER EEDE ¼ £35
178 IOHN GARLIC (A) ¼ AT THE ANGELL
179 M.H. (E) ¼ AT THE SWAN IN THE CROWNE, swan on coronet £42
180 M.H. (E) ¼ AT(T) THE SWANN CROWNE, swan £50
181 RICHARD HAWKS (E) ¼ AT YE BLACK RAVEN £45
182 THOMAS HEATH (L) ½ 1666 Melting pot, PEWTERER £55
183 (Probably misreading of 184)
184 THOMAS HICKS (S) ¼ Dolphin
185 IOHN IACKSON (S) ¼ Horse £40
186 IOHN KERBY (I) ¼ Grocers' Arms £30
187 STEPHEN NICHOLS ¼ Castle; bear and ragged staff, CHANDLR
188 THOMAS STRATFORD (E) ¼ 1656 Bell £38
189 SAM WHEELER (E) ½ 1668 Man making candles £32
190 ROB WHINICKE ¼ 1666 Rose crowned, PIPE MAKER £35
191 EDMOND WILLSON *or* EDMVND WIL(L)SON (M) ¼ Apothecaries' Arms

Willington
192 (Probably misreading of 193)
193 IOHN WALLES (E) ½ 1667 Royal oak £42

Westmorland

New token recorded from *SCA* 35, 11 Apr. 1984.
Believed entirely unpublished: 7A.

Minimum price for unvalued tokens: £100

Appleby

1 CHRISTOPHER BIRKBECKE ½ 1666 Bust of Chas. II
2 EDWARD GVY (M) ¼ 1666 I SERVE FOR CHANGE
3 WILLIAM SMITH ¼ 1669 Pigeon pecking

Grayrigg

4 RIC ROWLANDSON ½ 1669 Scales, spade £65

Kendal

5 MERCERS COMPANY ¼ 1657 Corporation Arms, K.K. **Plate 4** £35
6 COMPANY OF SHEARMEN ¼ 1666 Croppers' shears; teasel-brush £50
7 — — — ¼ — — teasel-brush, star each side. In *pb*
7A As last, but in *Æ*
8 EDMOND ADLINGTON (I) ¼ 1659 Dyers' Arms
9 IAMES COCKE IVNIOR ½ 1667 Cock £45
10 IOHN HADWEN (E) ¼ Sugar-loaf
11 OLIVER PLAT ¼ 1659 3 Maltese crosses £40
12 THOM SANDES ¼ 1656 Teasel, wool-hook; woolcomb £75
12A THOMAS TVRNER (E) ¼ Teasel, wool-hook

Kirkby Stephen

13 IOHN FALLOWFEILD & R.P. ¼ MERCERS
14 H.R. ¼ 1659 Scales
15 W.H. (R) ½ Merchant-Adventurers' Arms. *Heart-shape*
16 G.S., I.P. ½ 1669
17 MARGRE SANDERSON, H.A., I.B. ¼ Crown £90
18 IEOFFERY THOMPSON ¼ Crown; arrows piercing heart, eye above

Kirkland

19 THOMAS WILSON, THOMAS WARDE ¼ 1666 Arms

Wiltshire

Major reference: E. G. H. Kempson, *Wiltshire XVII Century Tokens* (2nd edition, 1978). Updating and revision of 'Williamson', more notes on some issuers, some locations of specimens.

See also C. M. Rowe, *Salisbury's Local Coinage* (Salisbury, 1966): many enlarged illustrations and notes on the issuers; and E. G. H. Kempson, 'Indictments for the Coining of Tokens in 17th Century Wiltshire' (*BNJ*, 1973).

Mimimum price for unvalued tokens: £50

Aldbourne
1 IOHN ADEE ¼ 1656 3 rabbits feeding £22
2 —— ¼ Mercers' Arms
3 —— I. CLARK BISHOPSTON ¼*
4 RICHARD CLARK (E) ¼ 1658 £48
5 FRANCIS STRONG ½ 1669
6 EDWARD WITTS ¼ 1666 Shuttle

Amesbury
7 ROBERT HARRISON (M) ¼ 1653 Wheatsheaf £35
8 IOHN MOORES (D) ½ 1667

Ashton Keynes
9 RICHARD MARSH (A) ¼ Horse's head £42

Barford
10 (See *Warwicks*. 23)

Bishopstone
11 I. CLARK ¼ 1656 Mercers' Arms £40

Bradford-on-Avon
12 WILLIAM BAILY ¼ 1668 Horse's head, MERCER £42
13 —— ¼ 1667 — MERCR
14 WILLIAM CHANDLER ¼ 1663 *or* '63 Grocers' Arms £28
15 —— *or* WILLAM CHANLER ¼ 1650 — £20
16 SAMVELL DAVISSON ¼ 1669 Stag
17 DANIELL DEVERRELL ¼ 1663 Crown £22
18 IOHN GAGE ¼ 1649 Mercers' Arms £25
19 IACOB SELBEE ¼ 1665 Pipes crossed £30
20 PAVLE METHWIN ¼ Arms; Latin cross £22

(North) Bradley
20A IAMES ISHER ¼ 1669 Grocers' Arms

Bratton
21 IOHN ALLDREDG (E) ¼ 1664 Merchant Taylors' Arms

* A mule of the obvs. of nos. 1 and 11

Calne
22 IAMES BARTLETT ¼ 1669 Crown £38
23 (Probably descriptive error for 24)
24 STEPHEN BAYLIE (S) ¼ Mercers' Arms £25
25 IOHN DASH (P) ¼ 1669 Tallowchandlers' Arms
26 ROBERT DIER (I) ¼ Talbot
27 (Probably misreading of 28)
28 ARTHVR FORMAN (I) ¼ 1669, HILMARTEN, CHANDLER
29 IOHN FORMAN (A) ¼ Pipes crossed £38
30 IOHN IEFFREIS (M) ¼ 1668 Grocers' Arms £35
31 WIL IEFFREY ELDER ¼ Grocers' Arms £30
32 GRACE LAWRENCE (G) ¼ 1669 Anchor
33 WITHERSTONE MESSENGER (M) ¼ BAKER
34 IOHN NORMAN (M) ¼ Grocers' Arms
35 A.S. (I) ¼ 1669 AT THE GLASS HOVSE £60

Castle Combe
36 IEREMIAH BERRY (E) ¼ '68 Grocers' Arms
37 THOMAS BERY (I) ¼ '66 Castle, MERCER

Chippenham
38 WILL ADYE (E) ¼ 1665 MERCER £28
39, 40 IOHN EDWARDS ¼ 1665 LINEN DRAPER £45
41 (Probably misreading of 42)
42 SAMVELL ELLIOTE (A) ¼ 1666 Swords crossed, carbine
43 SAMVELL GAGE (E) ¼ 1653 Tallowchandlers' Arms £20
43A —— (E) ¼ 1668 —
44 (Probably misreading of 43)
45 IOHN HACKMAN (M) ¼ 1671 Woolcomb
46 HENRY LAMBERT (S) ¼ MERCER £28
47 I.S. (A) ¼ 1665 BRISTOW PLACE £42
48 IOHN SHORTE (A) ¼ Tallowchandlers' Arms
49 IOHN STEVENS (M) ¼ 1652 £25
50 IOHN WEBB (I) ¼ 1652 Tallowchandlers' Arms
51 IOHN WILLSHEARE, ANDREW WILCOX ¼ 1668 MERCER

Clack (Parish of Lyneham)
52 ROBERT GOODMAN ¼ Scales; crescent moon
53 FRANCES ROGERS (I) ¼ 1658 Mercers' Arms

Collingbourne Kingston
54 RICHARD BLACKMORE (E) ¼ 1665

Collingbourne Ducis
55 BARNABAS RVMSEY ¼ 1667 Grocers' Arms
56 — — ¼ 1664

Corsley
57 GEORGE CAREY (M) ¼ 1666 Clothworkers' Arms £50
58 (Misreading of 57)

Corsham
59 WILLIAM GIBBONS ¼ 1669 Lovers' knot
60 EDW SALWAY (K) ¼ Shears, CLOTHIER
61 EDITH AD DAD WOODMAN ¼ Still; MERSER, initials D.M.W. £48

Cricklade
62 THOMAS DEIGHTON (S) ¼ Cross on steps, MERCER £30
63 ANTHONY WORME (A) ¼ Horse, CARRIER

Devizes
64 STEPHEN BAYLY ¼ 1668 Mermaid, MERCER £45
65 IOHN FREY ¼ Grocers' Arms £25
66 — FRY ¼ 1664 Hand; pipes crossed £16
67 FRANCIS GOVLDING ¼ Castle, GROCER £25
68/9 EDWARD HOPE ¼ 1652 Ship; anchor £18
70 IOHN HAMMOND (S) ¼ 3 books £28
71 GRACE NAISH ¼ 1652 Castle; 3 cloves £16
72 FRANCIS PARADICE (M) ¼ 1669 CHANDLER £18
73 IOHN SLADE ¼ 1666 GROCER £18
74 RICHARD SLADE ¼ 1663 £18
75 (Descriptive error for 74)
76 WILLIAM SOMNER ¼ 1652 GROCER £16
77 WILLIAM STEVENS (A) ¼ 1663 Grocers' Arms £20
78 (Misreading of 77)
79 RICHARD WATTON ¼ 1666 GROCER £17
80 — WOTTEN ¼ n.d. — £38

Downton
81 PHILLIP ROOKE ½ 1670 Rook

Great Bedwyn
82 IOHN BVSHEL (E) ¼ 1669 Tallowchandlers' Arms, MERCER
82A THOMAS GREENE ¼ 1669 3 rabbits

(East) Harnham
83 IOHN VENABLES (A) ½ 1668 Shuttle £40

Heytesbury
84 (See *Bucks.* 7)

Highworth
85 RICH BATSON, EDWARD FORDER ¼ £35
86 LEONARD BOLT ¼ GROCER
87 IOHN ELTON (C) ¼ Paschal lamb; lamb
88 — — ½ 1669 AT YE LAMBE
89 (Listed under *Berks.* 6)
90 EDMVND HIDE, RICH LEADER ½ Bear with chain; greyhound. *Heart-shape*
91 EDMVND LEWIS (K) ½ 1669 Armourers' Arms, BRAZEAE
92 WILLIAM MATHEW ¼ 1659 Lion
92A RICHARD NEAST ¼ 1664
93 THOMAS OSBORNE ¼ 1653 Grocers' Arms £50
94 (See *Sussex* 145)
95 IOHN TOMES ¼ 1652 Grocers' Arms £25
96 RICHARD WILLIAMS, WILL FRANCKLIN ¼ Spectacles £50

Hilmarton
97 (Same as 28)

Hindon
97A RICHARD RANSOM ½ 1669 Crown
97B THOMAS SHERGOLD ½ 1669 Helmet

Keevil
97C CHARLES WILLCOKS ¼ Fleur-de-lis, MERCER

Kingswood
97D RICHARD CARTER (A) ¼ 1668
98 EDWARD TANNER (D) ¼ 1658 £18
99 THOMAS WALFORD (P) ¼ Clothworkers' Arms

Lacock
100 RICHARD GRIST (G) ¼ 1669 Scales £35
101 — GRYST ¼ — Lion £30

Lavington
102 IOHN HAYWARD ¼ 1663 Ship £28
103 ROBERT HAYWARD ¼ 1668 Ship £25

Ludgershall
104 W.I. ¼ 1665 Castle £60

Maiden Bradley
105 GEORGE AVDREY ¼ Crown

Malmesbury
106 IOHN BLONCE (M) ¼ 1661
107 EDWARD BROWNE (M) ¼ Man by still
108 SAMVELL CHAPP (M) 1665 Tallowchandlers' Arms
109 PHILIPP EDWARDS (M) ¼ 1658 Tallowchandlers' Arms £40
110 THOMAS EVAN(F *or* E)S (E) ¼ Grocers' Arms
111 ELIAS FERRIS (A) ½ 1669 APOTHECARY
112 IOHN GOLDNEY (M) ¼ CLOTHYR
113 EDMVND HANDY (E) ¼ AT YE, dragon £50
114 NICO IAFFRIS (M) ¼ ABYE, WOOL

114A NICO IAFFRIS ¼ — —
115 RICHARD PLAYER (N) ¼ 1657 3 cloves
116 IOHN SANSVM (I) ¼ 166 (*sic*). Still
117 THO TANNER (O) ¼ Woolpack, CARIER
118 — — ¼ — —
119 ROB THOMAS (H) ¼ '64 Bull £30
120 RICH THORNER ¼ '64 Grocers' Arms
121 WILLIAM WAYTE ¼ 1651 Grocers' Arms £22
122 WALTER WOODMAN (M) ¼ Grocers' Arms, CARIER £40
122A — — (M) ¼ — CVNDERS

Marlborough
123/4 Town ¼ 1668 Castle with 3 turrets; bull £13
125 — ¼ — Castle with 4 turrets; bull £12
126 IOHN BAYLY (N) ¼ Grocers' Arms
127 ROBERT BRIANT, D.S., E.S. ¼
128 ROBERT BVTCHER (M) ¼ 1663 Grocers' Arms
129 — — (M) ¼ '66 —
130 HENRY COLEMAN (E) ¼ Scales
131 WILLIAM CRABBE (M) (½) 1668 Man making candles £35
132 WILL CRABB (M) ¼ 1664 GROCER
133 (Misreading of 131/2)
134 EDWARD DELAMAINE ¼ 1665 Hand £40
135 IOHN HAMMOND (K) ¼ '66 Book
136 THOMAS KEENE ¼ 1652 Tallowchandlers' Arms £18
137 IOHN MORGAN ¼ 1656 Grocers' Arms £30
138 — — ¼ 1657 — £45
139 IANE PEARCE ¼ Ironmongers' Arms
140 SIMON PIKE (A) ¼ 1667 Grocers' Arms
141 WILLIAM PVREVR (D) ¼ Pinners' Arms, PINN MAKER £35
142 THOMAS SHIPPERE (A) ¼ Mercers' Arms
143 RICHARD SHIPRE ¼ Salters' Arms £20
144 OLIVER SHROPSHIRE ¼ 1665 Angel £35
145 IEREMIAH SLOPER (E) ¼ Sugar-loaf £30
145A — — (E) ½ 1665 —
146 IOHN SMITH (K) ¼ 1665 Pipes crossed £30

Marshfield
147 (See *Glos.* 116)

Marston
148 (See *Kent* 389)

Melksham
149 (Probably imaginary reading of 151)
150 A.A. OF MELKESHAM, I.A. OF STEEPLE ASHTON ¼ 1665 Mercers' Arms £55
151 Similar, but 1668

Mere
152 THOMAS GAMBLYN ¼ 1665
153 RICHARD PITMAN (I) ¼ 1669 Man making candles
154 ROBERT PITTMAN ½ 1668 DRAPER
155 WILLIAM ROGGERS ¼ 1666 Horse £35

Purton
156/7 (See *Herts.* 147/8)
157A EDWARD SAVNDERS ¼ Grocers' Arms £55

Ramsbury
158 IOHN STON (M) ¼ 1655 Man making candles £25
158A — — (M) ¼ 1653 —
159 (Misreading of 158)
160 WILLIAM WHITE (R) ¼ Haberdashers' Arms

Rode
161/2 (See *Som.* 204/6)

Rollstone
163 (See *Herts.* 169)

Salisbury
164 THE MAIOR ¼ 1659 2-headed eagle; City Arms. **Plate 4** £16
165 ROGER BEDBVRY (A) ¼ 1664 St. George & dragon
165A SAM BRIXEY (E) ¼ HABERDASHER
166 T.R. ¼ 1657 AT THE BVSH £45
167 GEORGE CLEMENS (A) ¼ 1664 Dragon £22
167A WILLIAM CLEMENS (E) ¼ 1664 Family Arms, MERCER
168 HENRY COLE ¼ 1653 Saracen's head £32
169 WILLIAM COVRTNEY ½ 1670 Angels supporting open book, BOOK BINDER £60
170 IOHN CRAGGE (P) ¼ Dog, GROCER
171 THOMAS CVTLER IVNIOR (I) ½ 1666 £20
171A — — — (I) ½ 1668
172 THOMAS CVTLER SENIOR ½ 1666 Snakes entwined £24
173 (Misreading of 200)
174 GODDERD ELLIOTT ¼ 1666 Family Arms; Grocers' Arms
175 G.F. (E) ½ 1667 Snakes entwined £28
176/9 EDWARD FAVLCONER (M) ¼ 1659 Skinners' Arms £32
177/8 (Misreadings of 176/9)
180 EDWARD FRIPP ½ 1668 Skinners' Arms £25
181 — — ½ 1669 —
182 IOHN GILBERT (H) ¼ AT THE BELL, NEW SARVM £45
183 Similar but NEW SARID
184 GEORGE GODFERY ¼ 1659 Rat £38
185/6 WILLIAM GAPEN ¼ 1652 Grocers' Arms £30
187 (Misreading of 185)
188 (Misreading of 170)
189 GEORGE GODFERY ¼ RAT KILR
190 ROGER GODFREY (E) ¼ 1666 Knife, whetstone
191 — — (E) ¼ 1664 — —
192 IOHN HELE ¼ Lion, GROCER £28
193 (Misreading of 192)

194 IOHN HANCOCK ¼ Bust of Turk, APOTHECARY £50
195 NICHOLAS HASKOLL ¼ 1658 IRONMVNGER £30
196 THOMAS HAYTOR ½ 1666 Cordwainers' Arms £24
197 IONATHAN HILL (E) ½ 1668 £24
198 GEORGE HVGHES ¼ 1658 Fox and goose
199 WILLIAM IOYCE ¼ 1652 Camel £22
200 CHRISTOPHER LEGG ¼ Ironmongers' Arms
201 EDWARD LISTER ½ AT WINCHESTER GATE, sun
202 (Sacrament token of St. Edmund's Church)
203 EDMOND MACKS ¼ Mitre £32
204 FRANCIS MANNINGE (I) ¼ 1664 Antelope £30
205 — MANINGS (I) ¼ IN KATHREN STREET, antelope
206 EDWARD MASON (E) ¼ 1658 Naked man
207 HENRY MATTERSHAW (P) ¼ '58 Knife, COOKE £42
208 RICHARD MINIFIE ¼ Skinners' Arms
209 (See *Bucks.* 116A)
210 I.P. (D) ¼ CHEESE CROSE IN THOMAS PARISH, Grocers' Arms £17
211 GEORGE PAGE (K) ¼ 1656 Dove with olive branch, GROCER £18
212 —— (K) ¼ 1657 —— £25
213 —— (K) ¼ 1658 ——
214 (Misreading of 212)
215 EDWARD PENNY ½ 1671 Butchers' Arms
216 —— ½ 1667 —
217 CHARLES PHELPS (S) ¼ Skinners' Arms, CONFECTIONER £42
218 I. POORE (S) ¼ AT BARNETS CROSS
218A THO RAY (M) ¼ Grocers' Arms, LINEN DRAPER
219 VAVGHAN RICHARDSON (E) ¼ 1666 KATHERINE STR, dolphin
220 WILL SACKLER (M) ¼ 1666 VPHOLSTER
221 (Misreading of 165)
222 SIMON ROLFE ½ 1666 Family Arms. **Plate 4** £8
222A —— ½ 1669 —
223 ARTHER SANDERS ¼ 1656 Squirrel £28
224 (See *Bucks.* 16A)
225 HENRY SEWARD (M) ¼ Arms, GROCER
226 THOMAS SHERGOLD ½ 1666 Crown £25
226A THOMAS TINHAM ½ 1667 PEWTERER
227 WILLIAM VINER (E) ¼ 1657 Bunch of grapes
228 CHRIS WILLMOTT ¼ 1666 Lamb £45
229 (? Misreading, or not a 17th cent. token?)

Shalbourn
230 (See *Yorks.* 342A)

Sherston Magna
231 THOMAS DAVIS ¼ 1651 Mercers' Arms £32

Steeple Ashton
232 ROB IEFFREYES (M) ¼ Building

Stratton
233/4 (See *Cornwall* 94, 93A)

Swindon
235 THOMAS FARMER (A) ½ 1669 Scales, BAKER
236 WILLIAM HEATH (E) ¼ £42
237 HENRY MVNDAY ½ 1669 Tallowchandlers' Arms, 3 cloves £35
238 HENERY RESTALL ¼ 1656 Pipes crossed; 3 sugar-loaves £28
239 —— ¼ 1668 ——
240 —— ¼ 1664 —— £48
241 (Probably misreading of 240)
242 IOHN SMITH (C) ¼ 1664 Bakers' Arms £24
243 WILLIAM WEBB ½ 1669 Pipes crossed
244 AMOS WILKINS ¼ Grocers' Arms
245 —— (M) ¼ Mercers' Arms

Tinhead (Parish of Edington)
246 IOHN BERRY (A) ¼ 1668 Mercers' Arms £40
247 —— (A) ¼ 1651 — £25

Trowbridge
248 IOHN CLARKE ¼ 1667 Drapers' Arms; merchant's mark
249 E.D., H.D. ¼ £24
250 ROBERT DARCKE ¼ 1669 Merchant's mark £35
251–4 WILLIAM SMITH ¼ Pipes crossed £16
255 ROBERT WITCHELL ¼ Fleur-de-lis

Warminster
256 IOHN BVCCHER ¼ 1651 Crowned heart £40
256A NICHOLAS BVTCHER ¼ 1651 Fleur-de-lis
256B WILLIAM BVTCHER ¼ '69 Fleur-de-lis
257 IAMES ELI(O *or* A)TT ¼ Hand; cock £28
258 IOHN SLADE ¼ 1667 Heart
259 THOMAS TOOMER ¼ 1651 Dove with olive-branch £25

Westbury
260 WILL COCKELL (S) ¼ '58 Merchant Taylors' Arms £25
261 THOMAS HANCOCKE ¼ 1656 Cock; hand £20
262 WALTER HAYNES ¼ Grocers' Arms
263 IOHN MATRAVERS (E) ¼ 1669 Fleur-de-lis
264 FRANCIS PASHENT (K) ¼ 1668 Tallowchandlers' Arms
265 IOHN WATTS ¼ Grocers' Arms
265A WILLIAM WILLINS (M) ¼

Westport (Parish of Malmesbury)
266 WILLIAM FRY (A) ¼ 1666 Weavers' Arms
267 GILES HOONE (I) ¼ AT THE, 3 cups £50

Wilton
268 STEPHEN BRASSIER (H) ½ 1667 £16

268A G.H. ½ 1666 Crossed swords, 4 fleurs-de-lis £38

268B WILLIAM NEWMAN ½ 1667 Croppers' shears £28

Wootton Bassett

269/70 GABR(IE *or* EL)L ARMAN (E) ¼ Mercers' Arms £35

271 IOHN KNIGHTON (I) ¼ Crown

272 —— (I) ¼ Keys crossed £42

(South) Wraxall

273 VALENTINE STEVENS (M) ¼ Butchers' Arms £50

274 IOSEPH STONE (M) ¼ 1667 Fleur-de-lis £50

Worcestershire

New tokens recorded from Glendining's sale, 15 Mar. 1917; W. Gilbert, 'Unpublished . . .' (see under Cambridgeshire); Faulkner collection (sold at Glendining's, 21 May 1940); Carthew collection (*SCMB*, Mar. 1946); *SNC*, Aug. 1949; and *SCA* 19, 3 Mar. 1982.

See also M. Perkins, *Dudley Tradesmen's Tokens* (Dudley, 1905).

Believed entirely unpublished: 31A.

Minimum price for unvalued tokens: £60

Alvechurch

1 ELIZABETH BALDWIN ½ 1669 DEALL WITH MEE AS I WITH THEE

Bengeworth

2 EDWARD PITTWAY (F) ¼ AT THE RED LYON £17

3 (Probably misreading of 2)

Bewdley

4 *The Wardens* ½ 1668 Anchor between rose and sword. *Octagonal* £70

5 SAMVELL CART (M) ¼ 1653 Lion £45

6 (Probably an imaginary reading of 5)

6A IOHN CLOWNAM (A) ½ Arms of Worcester

7 THOMAS DEDICOT ½ GROCER; SQ(V *or* Ɐ)ARE DEALING. *Square* £100

8 (Probably misreading of 9)

9 *Tho Farloe* ½ 1670 Hat, *Capper. Heart-shape*

10 THO FARLOE (½) — — CAPPER. *Heart-shape*

11 WALTER PALMER (A) ¼ 1656 Hat, CAPPER

12 (Probably misreading of 13)

13 PETER WALTER ½ Arms, MERCER £55

Blockley

14 (See *Glos.* 6)

Broadway

15 MICHAELL RVSSELL (A) ½ 1670 Dog

16 PHILIP HODGES ½ 1669 Hart

Bromsgrove

17 IOSIAH DINGLEY ½ 1668

18 — — ¼ 1669

19 HENRY IEFFREYS ¼ Grocers' Arms £60

20 — — ½ — Centre in *copper*, outer ring in *brass*

21 IOHN IEFFREYS ½ 1668

22/3 TIMOTHY IEF(F)ERYES ½ 1668 £60

24 IOHN MASON ½ 1667 Mercers' Arms

25 THOMAS PORTER ½ 1668

26 WILLIAM PORTER ½ 1668 £48

27 SAMVELL ROGERS ½ 1668

Chaddesley Corbett

28 (Probably misreading of 29)

29 HVMFREY POTTER ½ 1667 Arms of Worcester

Clifton-on-Teme

30 IOHN IENCKINS (A) ½ 1666 £35

Droitwich

30A ROGER ALLEN (E) ¼ '57 Part of Town Arms, MERCER £65

31 STEPHEN ALLEN ½ Town Arms on spade-shaped shield, APOTH

31A Similar, but round shield

32 THOMAS CALCOTT ½ Parts of Town Arms both sides

33/4/6 (Probably all same as 35)

35 GEORGE LENCH & WILL TOMSON ½ 1667 Town Arms

Dudley

37 (Probably misreading of 38)

38 WILL BRIGGS (M) ¼ Mercers' Arms

39 IOHN FINCH ½ Ironmongers' Arms £40

40 EDWARD NIGHTINGALE ½ Grocers' Arms, MERCER

40A — — ¼ 1659 Mercers' Arms. —

41 THOMAS OXFORD (E) ¼ Hand holding pen

Evesham

42/3 BVRROW ½ Borough Arms, FOR NECESSARY EXCHANG(E) £13

44 Town (½) — FOR NECESSARY EXCHANG (no obv. legend). **Plate 4** £22

45 — ¼ — — — £20

46/7 PHILLIPP BALL(O *or* A)RD ½ 1664 £22

48 RICHARD BENETT ½ 1666 Wheatsheaf £30

49 PAVLE BENNING ½ 1664 Sugar-loaf £35

50 WILLIAM BROOKE (A) ¼ 1656 £22
51 (Probably misreading of 52)
52 PETER CROSS (M) ¼ 1649 £15
53 PHILLIP CROSS (M) ¼ 1649
54 IOSHVA FRANSHAM (S) ½ 1666 £28
55/6 RIC GODDARD (M) ¼ IN BRIDG STREET(E) £20
57 IOHN LACEY (M) ¼ 1654 Flower £22
58 TIMOTH(I *or* Y) MATHEWS (I) ¼ Grocers' Arms £38
59 MATHEW MICHELL (M) ¼ 1653 Grocers' Arms £38
60 WILLIAM RVDGE (A) ¼ 1649 £20

Halesowen

61 (Probably misreading of 62)
62 WILLIAM BODELY (A) ½ 1667 Frying pan
63 WILLIAM ROBERTSON ½ 3 scallop-shells

Kidderminster

63A IOHN ALLEN ½ '66 APOTHECARY
64 R.B. (M) ¼ 1652 AT THE RAVEN £32
65 THOMAS BALAMEY (M) ½ 1667 Weavers' Arms £35
66 FRANCES CARTER (M) ¼ Shears
67 EDWARD CHAMBERLIN (A) ½ £28
68 (Probably misreading of 69)
69 EDWARD CHAMBERLIN (P) ¼ Man making candles £45
70 WILLIAM MOVNTFORD ½ 1666 Tankard
71 LAWRENCE PEARSALL ½ Arms £40
72 SIMON PITT (E) ¼ 1670
73 WILL PRITTY ¼ '57 Scales, MERCER
74 (Probably misreading of 75)
75 RICH RADFORD ½ '66 Weavers' Arms; Merchant Taylors' Arms
76 EDMVND & WILLIAM READE ½ 1666 Weavers' Arms £48
77 IOHN ROWDEN (A) ¼ 1656 Nag's head
78 NEVIL SIMMONS BOOKSELR, EDWARD BVTLER MERCER ½ 1663 £60
79 THO SADLER (A) ½ 1664 Tallowchandlers' Arms £30
80 WALTER THATCHER ½ 1670 Shuttle £38
80A WALTER WILKES (E) ½ 1666

Lye

81 WILLIAM BVFFERY ½ Catherine wheel

Old Swinford

82 IOHN RICHARDSON ½ 1669 3 pears £28
83 —— ½ Catherine wheel

Pershore

84 (Probably misreading of 85)
85 HENRY GIBBS ½ 1666 £18
86 GIDEON PALMER (S) ½ 1667 Mercers' Arms £30
87/8 SAMVELL PALMER ½ 1667 £35
89 EDWARD PERKINS ½ 1664 APOTHECARY £42

Shipston-on-Stour

90 (Probably misreading of 91)
91 RICHARD COOPER ½ 1669 Pannier-basket
92 —— (B) ¼ —— £55
93 HENRY COTTERELL ½ 1666 Mercers' Arms £38
94 ROBERT FITZHVGH ½ 1664 Apothecaries' Arms £40
95 EDWARD PITTWAY ¼ Ironmongers' Arms £25
96 (Probably misreading of 97)
97 SIMON SIMONS (I) ½ 1669 Mercers' Arms. *Octagonal* £75

Stourbridge

98 Town ½ Ironmongers' Arms; Clothworkers' Arms £28
99 (Probably misreading of 100)
100 IONATHAN BVTLER ½ 1665 Arms of Worcester, MERCER
101 *John Clare* ½ 1666 Ironmongers' Arms £40
102 ANDREW MVCHALL ½ 1669 IRONMONGER
103 THOMAS NOTT ¼ 1657 Grocers' Arms
104–7 EZEKEL(L) PARTRIDG *or* EZEKELL PARTRIG (M) ½ 1665 £22
108 EDWARD SPARRYE (I) ¼ 1656
109 HVMPHREY SVTTON (S) ¼ 1657
110 —— (S) ¼ 1656

Tenbury Wells

111 IOHN COVNLEY ¼ Grocers' Arms
112 EDMOND LANE ½ Family Arms, crest
113 —— ¼ ——
114 —— ¼ — (no crest)
115 (Probably misreading of 116)
116 ANTHONY SEARCH ½ 1670 *Plaine dealing is best*, Mercers' Arms £45

Upton-on-Severn

117 IOHN BAYLY ¼ Man making candles; Arms of Worcester
118 PHILLIP BOVND (K) ¼ 1654 Grocers' Arms £45
119 IOHN BAYLIS (E), RICHARD HVDSON (M) ½
120 WILLIAM COWELL (E) ¼ 1664 Cheese-knife
121 CHRISTOP WINBERY (E) ¼ MERCER

Worcester

122 City ¼ 1667 Castle, falcon above £20
123 (Probably misreading of 124)
124 RICHARD ADNEY ½ City Arms (3 pears)
125 EDWARD BARON ½ City Arms £35
126 RICHARD BEDOES ½ n.d. City Arms; Mercers' Arms £15
127 —— ½ 1664 —— £20
128 —— ¼ '59 —— £20

129 —— ¼ n.d. —— £32
130 (Probably same as 129)
131 IOHN CHERRY (S) ½ 1664 City Arms £22
132 (Probably same as 131)
133 WILL CHETLE (S) ½ IN BROD STRT, merchant's mark; City Arms, CLO £28
134 (Probably same as 135)
135 WILLIAM CHETLE ¼ 1666 Merchant's mark; City Arms CLOTHIER £30
136 WILL COLBATCH ½ 1667 City Arms £32
137 WILLIAM — ¼ City Arms on *rev.* £35
138 —— ¼ City Arms on *obv.* £35
139 WILLIAM FINCH (K) ½ 1665 City Arms £30
140 WILL — (K) ¼ ——
141 —— (K) ¼ 1666 —
142 THOMAS FOWNE (E) ¼ AT THE NAGS HEAD
143 THOMAS HACKETT (M) ½ 1666 City Arms £55
144 IARVAS HALL ½ 1667 City Arms
145 IOHN HILL ½ '64 City Arms, DISTILLER
146 IOHN HVRDMAN ½ 1667 City Arms £35
147 HENRY ISONLOW ½
148 IOHN IONES ½ 1666 City Arms; open book
149 THOMAS IONES ½ 1669 Feltmakers' Arms £35
150 IOHN LILLIE ½ 1667 Weavers' Arms; City Arms £38
151 ARTHVR LLOYD ½ 1663 City Arms
152 —— ½ — Woolpack
153 WILL MOORE ½ 1664 City Arms; Mercers' Arms £22
154 —— ½ 1665 ——
155 —— ½ 1664 —— and goblet £30
156 EDWARD PRITCHETT (A) ½ '67 City Arms, CHANDLER £30
157 FRAN RICHARDSON (A) ½ City Arms £45
158 IOHN SEABORNE ½ 1664 City Arms £28
159 IAMES SMITH ½ 1667 City Arms £25
160 WILL SWIFT ½ 1662 City Arms £24
161/2 —— ½ 1663 — £25
163 —— ½ n.d. —. Centre in *brass*, outer ring in *copper* £30
164 Similar, in one metal only £40
165–7 WILLIAM SWIFT, ¼ n.d. City Arms £20
168 (Probably same as 169)
169 WILLIAM SWIFT ¼ n.d. City Arms. *In Æ, tin(?) – plated* £30
170 IOHN TVRBERVILE ½ City Arms; Mercers' Arms £28
171 WILLIAM WEST ¼ City Arms

Uncertain Locality

171A John Robson ½

Yorkshire

New tokens recorded from W. Sykes, 'Unpublished Seventeenth Century Tokens of Yorkshire' (*Yorkshire Numismatic Fellowship*, First Annual Report, 1910); various articles, chiefly by T. Sheppard, in *Transactions of the Yorkshire Numismatic Society*, between vol. I pt. III (1913) and vol. II pt V (1925); the Hamer collection (sold at Glendining's, 26–28 Nov. 1930); T. Sheppard, notes in *Hull Museum publication* no. 172 (1931); *SNC*, Aug. 1949; H. Hird, 'Notes on some Yorkshire Seventeenth Century Tokens' (*Trans. Y.N.S.*, 2nd series, vol. I pt. I, 1951); and Philip Whitting, *Coins, Tokens and Medals of the East Riding of Yorkshire* (East Yorkshire Local History Society, 1969): 9 plates of photographs and other line drawings, some additions to 'Williamson' and extra notes.

See also W. Boyne, *Tokens issued in the Seventeenth, Eighteenth, and Nineteenth Centuries, in Yorkshire* (1858); W. E. Preston, 'Bradford Tradesmen's Tokens of the Seventeenth Century' (*The Bradford Antiquary*, New Series, pt. XXX, Mar. 1939); C. H. Theobald, *Doncaster Tradesmen's Tokens of the Seventeenth Century* (Doncaster Museum Publications, no. VI, 1944); and 'The Collection of Tokens formed by the late William Sykes (*SCA* 51, 16 Apr. 1986): notes on this and other collections of Hull tokens.

Believed entirely unpublished: 94A, 167A, 167B, 263A, 294A, 343C, 343D, 373A, 425A.

Minimum price for unvalued tokens: £75

Aldbrough
1 (See *Suffolk* 1)
2 IOHN YATES ½ 1669 Family Arms; globe

Almondbury
3 IOHN DIXON (M) ¼ 1667 Scales
4 NICHOLAS GREAVES ½ 1668
4A — — ½ — Mermaid combing hair, with mirror. *Heart-shape*
5 FRANCIS HORNE 1d 1669 Drapers' Arms
5A IOHN KAYE (M) ½ 1666 Mercers' Arms

Anlaby
6 IOHN NEWTON ½ 1669 Shin-bones crossed

Askrigg
6A WILLIAM AVKLAND ½ 1666 Bust of Chas. II
7 WILLIAM LAIDKEEN ½ 1666 Bust of Chas. II
8 IOHN LAMBERT ½ 1666 Crown

Attercliffe
9 STEPHEN CARRE (M) ½ 1664 Cutlers' Arms*

* Copies are known (late 19th cent.) of crude style.

Barnsley
10 THOMAS BROWNLEY (E) ½ Ironmongers' Arms
11 HENRY GREENE (M) ½ Grocers' Arms
12 IOHN SMITH (R) ½ 1666 Ostrich, with horseshoe
12A FRANCIS LANGLEY (E) ¼ Mercers' Arms
13 FRANCIS VSHER (H) ½ Talbot, MERCER £70

Batley
14 RICHARD CHESTER ½ 1668 Woolpack

Bawtry
15 FRANCIS FRENCH (A) ½ APOTHYCARY. *Octagonal*
15A ROBERT MALBIE ½ 1664 Mercers' Arms
16 *William Maltby* (R) ½ 1668 *Mercer. Heart-shape*
17 SAMVELL TRVBSHAW ½ 1664 Unicorn

Bedale
18 *William Lodge* ½ 1668 Rosebush. **Plate 4** £38
19 WILLIAM LODGE ¼ 1664 Mercers' Arms £60
20 WILLIAM PLVMER ½ 1666 Rose and crown £65

Bentham
20A IOHN OVEREND ¼ 1666 Mercers' Arms

21 WILL OVEREND (D) ½ 1666 Shuttle £65
22 WILLIAM — (D) ½ 1668 —. *Heart-shape*

Beverley
23 IONATHAN BROWNE (E) ½ 1670 Cheese-knife
24 TIMOTHEY BROWNE ½ 1668 Goat's head £65
25 STEPHEN GOACKMAN (M) ¼ Fleece, MERCER £60
26 WILLIAM IOHNSON (I) 1d 1671 AT THE COFFE HOVSE
27 GEORGE LAMPLVGH (A) (½) 1664 King's Arms £70
28 —— (A) (½) 1666— £50
29 MARMADVKE REDMAN ½ 1669 Armourers' Arms
30 W.S. (I) ¼ AT THE FOX £55
31 WILLIAM SHEEREWOOD (A) ½ 1667 Beaver
32 WILLIAM WILBERFOSS (M) ½ £40
33 WILL — (M) ¼ £60

Bingley
34 THOMAS SMITH ½ 1667 Bunch of grapes
35 IOHN TOMSON (M) ½ 1669 SHOO MAKER

Boroughbridge
36 FRANCIS CALVERT ¼ 1656 £55

Bradford
37 WILL BAN(C)KS ½ Arms of Kendal, CARRIER FOR KENDALL
38 IOHN COOKE (M) ½ 1666
39 —— AND IOSVAH FARRAND ½ Lion; 3 bugle-horns
40 *James Durham* ½ 1667
41 WILLIAM HOPKINSON (B) 1d Arms
42 THOMAS IBBOTSON ½ MERCER
43 DAVID PARKINSON ½ 1666 Mercers' Arms
44 IOHN PRESTON ½ 1666 Family Arms £90
44A THOMAS SHARPE ½ 1666
44B THOMAS WALKER (B) ½ MERCER

Bridlington
45 Town ½ 1670 FOR THE VSE OF THE POOR. 3 letter B's: two and one £40
46 Similar, but the B's arranged one and two £75
47 BARTHOL ANDERSON ½ Arms
48 THOMAS BISHOPP ½ 1665 Grocers' Arms
49 THOMAS CORBETT ½ 1668 Raven £85
50 — CORBIT ¼ Arms; 3 tuns
51 WILLIAM DICKESON ½ 3 tuns £80
52 THOMAS FENTON ½ Family Arms
53 —— (A) ¼ —
54 RALPH PORTER (M) 1d 1670 £75
55 NICHOLAS WOOLFE ¼ 1665 Arms
56 IOHN YATTES ½ 1666 Bust of Chas. II

Calverley
57 IOHN BESLY (E) ½ 1667 Fleece

Carleton
58 LEONARD BVMBY 1d 1669 Nag's head, INKEEPER £90
59 IOHN HANCOCKE ¼ 1668 Cock £70
60 —— WILLIAM BALME ½ 1666 Cock

Cawood
61 RICHARD SMITH ½ 1666 King's Arms

Cranswick
62 GEORGE WILBERFORCE (M) ½ 1670 Grocers' Arms

Dent
63 A.F., I.M., R.H. ¼ 1665 Rose and crown, FOR OVR GOOD NEIGHBORS
64 ANTHONY FAWCETT (H) 1d 1670 Tobacco-roll, pipes. **Plate 4**

Doncaster
65 THOMAS BVRTON ½ 1667 Mercers' Arms £55
66 (See *Northants.* 160)
67 THOMAS COOKE ½ 1667 Butchers' Arms
68 PETER DIXSON ½ Ship
69 NICHOLAS DOVGHTIE (S) ½ 1666 Saddlers' Arms
70 ANN FAYRAM ½ Grocers' Arms
70A AN FORTH ½
71 THOMAS GORST ½ Cooks' Arms, COOK
72 DANIELL HALL ½ 1667 Mercers' Arms
73 WILL HALL ½ 1669 Man with staff, TOLEMAN
74 *Gervas Holmes* ½ 1668 Mercers' Arms
75 *George Holmes* ½ 1668 Mercers' Arms
76 THOMAS HVNTT (S) ½ 1666 AT THE 3 CRANES
76A *Godfrey Ingman* (A) ½ 1666 Man with tobacco-roll and pipe on shield, 3 cloves
76B —— (A) ½ 1668 ——
77 BENIAMIN MARSHALL (E) ½ Angel £50
78 WILLIAM MOODY (A) ½ 1666 BAKER £65
79 ABRAHAM PILLIN (E) ½ 1665 CARRIER
80/1 GEORGE RASINE ½ 1665 Apothecaries' Arms £60
82 *George Rasine Junior* (M) ½ 1668 Apothecaries' Arms
83 OTTEWEELL ROBOTHAM ½ 1669 CHANDLER £85
84 RICHARD SPEIGHT ½ 1668 DIER
85 ROBERT THWAITS ½ 1666 Mercers' Arms
86 THOMAS WORTLEY (H) ½ 1666 Grocers' Arms

Easingwold
87 THOMAS WILSON ½ 1668 Skull; Arms
88 MICHAELL WOODWARD ½ 1668 Red Indian smoking pipe £75

Eastburn
89 HENRY REPLEY 1d AT THE RED LION

Elland
90 ABRAHAM SLATER ½ 1668 Fleur-de-lis

Ellerton
91 ROBERT IARVIS ½ 1667 Bust of Chas. II

Gargrave
92 EDWARD BRYAN (I) 1d 1671 Grocers' Arms
92A REBECCA SWAN ½ 1657 Fish

Gildersome
93 IOHN DICKINSON ½ 1668 Arms
94 HENRY SCOTT 1d 1670 Scales; woolpack, STRIKE LIGHT WEIGH RIGHT
94A —— 1d ——— SET STRIGHT HAVE RIGHT

Gisburne
95 WILLIAM HOLGATE (½) 1666 Mercers' Arms

Goole
96 CHRISTOPHER BVL(C *or* L)OCK ½ 1669 Man on horseback, CARRIER

Great Preston
97 WALTER WIDDOPE ½ Hammer between flowers £75

Guisborough
98 WILLIAM DENT ½ 1665 Bust of Chas. II £70
99 —— ¼ 1664 —
100 THOMAS HARRISON ½ 1666 Bust of Chas. II £85
101 IOHN LAMBE ½ 1666 Bust of Chas. II
102 —— ½ 1668 —

Halifax
103 MILES BATEMAN ½ 1667
103A IOHN BENSON ½ 1670 Pewterers' Arms
103B —— THOMAS DAWSON (? of Leeds) ½ 1666 Grocers' Arms
104 *John Brearcliffe* ½ Skull, cross-bones, RESPICE FINEM
105 IOHN DEANE, GABRIELL LEAROYD ½ 1667
106 RICHARD DOLLIFFE ½ 1666 Swan
107 IOHN EXLEY ½ 1667 Cross, crown
108 IOHN FARRAR ½ 1667
109 IONATHAN KIGHLEY (M) ½ 1666 Salters' Arms
110 GABRIELL LEAROYD ½ '68 Rose £70
111 IOHN LEAROYD ½ 1666 Grocers' Arms
111A *Samuell Newton* ½ 1667 Arms
112 EDWARD NOVBLE ½ 1668 AT YE, cock
113 TIMOTHY OLEAROID 1d 1670 Dolphin
114 IOHN PARKER ½ 1667 Drapers' Arms
115 IOHN RHODES (S) ¼ Lion
116 ROBERT WATMOVGH ½ 1667 Packhorse
117 IEREMIAH WORALL ½ 1666

Hatfield
118 MARY FARRER ½ 1666 Grocers' Arms £70

Haworth
119 SAMVELL OGDEN 1d 1670 Tankard

Hedon
120 SAMVELL BAINES ½ 1667 Sun

Helmsley
120A ROBERT GARBVT ½ 1667 Dove with olive branch; Grocers' Arms
121 IOHN WILLIAMSON ½ 1667 Royal oak, bust of Chas. II on trunk, lovers' knot below; hounds chasing stag by trees

Heptonstall
122 IOHN NOWELL (M) ½ 1666 Grocers' Arms

Holbeck (Leeds)
123 IOHN DIXSON (B) ½ 1668 Shears £75
123A —— (B) ½ 1667 —
124 IOHN SMITH ½ 1666 Clothworkers' Arms £100

Honley and Holmfirth
125 GEOR DIXON (S) ½ 1666 Barrel

Hornsea
126 BENIAMIN RHODES ½ 1670 Ship

Horton
127 (See *Bucks.* 67B)

Howden
128 THO OKES ½ 1667 Royal oak
129 *John Wighton* ½ 1668 Family Arms, crest £38

Huddersfield
130 EDMVND WALKER ½ 1666 £65

(Kingston-upon-)Hull
131 MARGRET ABBOTT ½ 3 crowns
132 IOHN BAKER ¼ 1663 Arm holding hammer
132A —— (½) 1665 — PEWTERER*
133 RICHARD BARNES ½ 1669 Grocers' Arms. *Heart-shape*
134 —— ¼ 1672 —
135 SAMVELL BIRKBY (H) ¼ 1666 Wheatsheaf
136 WILLIAM BIRKBY (K) ½ 1668 Family Arms £80
137 IOHN BLANCHERD ½ 3 crowns
138 —— (A) ¼ —
138A EDW BRANSLY (M) (½) '72 3 geese, DRAPER
139 WALTER BROKETT ½ 1666 Family Arms
140 LYONELL BVCKLE (A) ½ 1665 Buckle
141 —— (A) ¼ ——
141A MICHELL COPPY ¼ Town Arms
142 WILLIAM FEILD ½ 1669 AT YE BLAK, Indian with bow and arrow
143 ROBERT FELLOVES ½ 1668 Stocking £80
144 IOHN GOODWIN (R) ½ 1666 Rose crowned
145 —— ¼ n.d. —
146 HENRY HILLARD (E) ¼ 1669 Grocers' Arms
147 EDWARD HODGSON (M) ½ 3 hats, MARCHT

* The word PENNY on the token is erased

148 GEORGE HODGSON ½ 1668 Man smoking pipe, tobacco-roll under arm
149 PHINEAS HODSON (E) ¼ 1666 Tarbrush
150 THOMAS LAMBERT ¼ 1664 Drapers' Arms
150A —— ½ ——
151 RICHARD PERRY (M) ¼ AT YE WHIT, swan
152 WILLIAM ROBERTSON ¼ HIGHSTREET, hat, rabbit £85
153 WILLIAM ROBINSON (I) (½) Hatter's iron, rabbit
154 S. ¼ THE GOVLDEN LYON AT THE SOVTHEND, merchant's mark, heart
155 IOSHVA SCOTTE ¼ Rod; merchant's mark £65
156 RICHARD STOCKDAILL (M) ½ 1665 Anchor
157 RICH STOCKDAILE (M) ¼ ——
158 RICHARD SVGDEN ¼ 1664 Merchant's mark, MERCER
159 ELIZABETH THOMPSON ½ 1669 Ship. *Octagonal*
160 THOMAS WATSON ½ 1668 Tallowchandlers' Arms £85
161 *Mary Witham* ½ 1669 Tower. *Heart-shape* £175
162 IONAS YOVLE (A) ¼ 1666 Keys crossed £80

Hunsley
163 THOMAS DRAPER ½ 1670 Cordwainers' Arms

Idle
164 EDWARD MACKERETH ½ 1668 £60

Keighley
165 RICHARD DIXON (R) ½ 1668
166 IOHN HVDSON ½ 1669 Grocers' Arms

Kilham
167 ROBERT GIBSON ½ 1667 Grocers' Arms

Kippax
167A OBADIAH MOORE ½ 1667 Skull, MEMENTO FINIS

Kirkby Malzeard
167B THOMAS SHARPLES ½ 1668 GROCER

Kirkby Moorside
168 IOHN THORNVM ½ 1667 Thorn bush. **Plate 4**

Kirkstall
169 GEORGE WILLSON 1d 1671 Bridge; the Abbey

Knaresborough
170 ROBERT HILL ¼ Grocers' Arms
171 HVGH LEWIS (A) ¼ 1666 St. George & dragon
172 ARON LOWCOCKE ¼ Crown £75
173 THOMAS TVRNER ½ 1666 Grocers' Arms

Langton
174 (See *Lincs.* 137)

Leeds
175 ½ 1668 Sugar-loaf, I PASS TO & FRO
176 THOMAS ALLVM (S) ½ 1668 AT YE WHITE, lion. *Heart-shape*
177 AMBROSE AMBLER 1d 1669 Tobacco-roll, pipes £85
178 RICH ATKINSON 1d 1669 AT YE SCARBROVGH CASTLE £120
179 THOMAS ATKINSON ½ '69 Shears
180 WILLIAM BALLEY, IOHN COCKE ½ 1666 Cock
181 IEREMIAH BARSTOWE (A) ½ Grocers' Arms; unicorn
181A —— (A) ½ 1667 ——
181B —— (A) ¼ 1663 —
181C GRACE BRISCHO ¼ 1650 Fleece
182 HENRY COATES ½ 1666 Tobacco-roll £100
183 IOHN COCKE ½ 1668 Cock b.s.
184 THOMAS DAWSON 1d 1670 BEWARE OF YE BEARE*
185 GEORGE DIXON (M) ½ 1668 King's Arms
186 WILLIAM DOCKER 1d 1670 Man with hare on shoulder; cocks fighting
186A —— 1d 1669 Man as no. 186, dog; —
187 HENRY ELLIS, ARTHVR ROOME ½ 1667 Tobacco-pipe, cheese-knife
188 THOMAS ELSTON (S) ½ Arms
189 ROBERT FREEMAN AND THOMAS MESSINGER 1d Jug; 2-headed eagle £120
190 BENIAMIN GABBOTT 1d 1669 3 fishes
190A As last, cmkd. M K on obverse
191 IOHN GILMAN (O) ½ 1668
192 WILLIAM GLENSOVER ¼ 1650 Fleece
193 WILLIAM GOODYER 1d 1669 Tankard; jug, THE PORTTER
194 SAMVELL GREATHEAD ½ 4 fleurs-de-lis
194A *Sam Green(emood* or *wood)* ½ 1668 Arms
195 MATHEW HARDWICKE ½ 1668 Mortar and pestle
196 —— WILLIAM WAVGH ½ ——
197 TIMOTHY HARWOOD (D) ½ 1668 Horse bridled
197A RICH HATTON 1d COFFEE MAN
198 WILLIAM HODGSON ½ 1669 Man smoking pipe, tobacco-roll under arm
199 ROBERT HVRST (M) ¼ Town Arms
200 BARTH IBITSON ½ 1667 Butchers' Arms
201 *Lanc(e)lot Iveson* ½ '68 Arms
202 ANDR LISTER AND WILL CROFT ½ 1668 Arms (fleur-de-lis); arms (heart)
202A MARMADVK LOVELL ¼ 1650 Fleece
203 EDWARD MASSEY 1d 1669 GROCER
204 *Joseph Oddie* ½ 1668 Skull, O MEMENTO FINIS
205 C(H)RISTOPHER RIDER (A) ½ 1669
206 ARTHVR ROOME ½ 1672 Man walking with stick

* See also no. 103B

206A ZACHARIAS ROPER ½ '68 3 picks b.s.
207 (See *Kent* 369A)
208 *Thomas Saul* (B) ½ 1667 *Shooe maker*
209 TIMOTHY SMITH (M) ½ Glove
210 MATHEW STABLE ¼ 1650 Fleece
211 IOHN WALKER (L) ½ 1666 3 crowns
212 HENRY WILKINSON 1d 1668 Merchant's mark
213 WILL WOODHEAD ½ 1668 GROCER

Leyburn
214 IAMES ALLEN ½ 1666 Bust of Chas. II

Lightcliffe
215 SVSANNA WILSON ½ 1667 Tongs

Long Preston
216 THOMAS LAMBERT (I) 1d 1671 Chevron between 3 lambs

Lund
216A MARTHA PICKERING ½ 1666 Grocers' Arms

Maltby
217 GABRIELL NORMAVILE ½ 1669 Family Arms

Malton
218 LAWRENCE DICKINSON ½ 1670 Skinners' Arms
219 EDMVND DRING ½ 1666 Bust of Chas. II £60
220 THO GALLOWAY ½ Ship, GROCER £60
221 IOHN HARRINGTON ½ 1667 Grocers' Arms £50
222 IOHN HENDERSON ½ Hat and feather; Haberdashers' Arms £70
223 *Jer. Madox* ½ Hen and chicks. *Heart-shape*
224 WILLIAM PENNOCK ½ 1666 Fish rising out of water by buoy £55
225 MICHAELL PENNOCKE ½ 1666 Vintners' Arms £65
226 IOSEPH PRESTON ½ 1668 3 bells; Mercers' Arms £65
227 ROBERT RYMER ½ 1667 Mercers' Arms
228 *Will Snary* ½ Horse trotting £65

Market Weighton
229 NICHOLAS CHAPPILOW ¼ 1664 Mercers' Arms
230 RICHARD MARSHALL (M) ½ 1668 Bunch of grapes

Marsden
231 RICH KIPPAX ½ 1669 COALE PITT, bankman's hook, BANKES MAN

Masham
232 MICHAELL HAVKINS ¼ 1666 Man making candles

Middleham
233 LAWRENCE CARR ½ 1666 Grocers' Arms
234 CHARLES TODD ½ 1668 Grocers' Arms
234A — — ¼ n.d.—

Middleton (Parish of Rothwell)
235 FRANCES CONYERS ½ 1669 Falcon, FOR THE VSE OF YE COLEPITS

Northallerton
236/7 EDMVND B(A *or* V)RSTOW (I) ½ 1667 Arms £85
238 THOMAS BARSTOW (M) ¼ Mercers' Arms
239 WM. HVTTON ½ 1669 HATTER
240 THO REDMAYNE (M) ¼ KINGS ARMS, post-boy on horseback blowing horn
241 IOHN ROBINSON ½ Ship
242 FRANCIS RYMER ½ 1670 MERCER

Otley
243 THOMAS ENGLAND 1d 1670 Heart
244 STEPHEN TOPHAM 1d Crown
245 ANTHONEY WARD 1d 1671 Royal oak; Grocers' Arms
246 CRISTOPHER WARD ¼ 1664 Bust of Chas. II
247 CHRISTOPHER — AND IOHN PVLLEN ½ Bust of Chas. II; Grocers' Arms

Ovenden
248 MICHAELL HASLEDEN ½ 3 birds
249 — — ½ —. *Octagonal*

Pateley Bridge
250 ROBERT DOWNS ½ 1669 Sugar-loaf
250A As last, in *pb*

Penistone
250B STEVENS BLIZARD (E) ¼ TALLOW CHANLER £75

Pickering
251 *William Pennock* ½ 1671 Hare chased by group of hounds

Pocklington
252 BARNEY BVTTREY ½ 1666
252A IOHN COOK ¼ 1666 Grocers' Arms
253 IOHN HILL ½ 1667
254 — — ½ — Grocers' Arms

Pontefract
255 BONIFACE COWPER (A) ¼ Grocers' Arms
256 — — (A) (½) —
257 GEORGE DANIELL AND LEE HARTLEY ¼ Castle
258 GEORGE DANIELL (E) ¼ '67 Castle
259 THOMAS ENGLISH ¼
260 TIMOTHY FEILD ¼ Grocers' Arms
261/2 *Lee Hartley* ¼ 1666 Castle
263 — — ¼ 1668 —
263A — — ¼ 1669 —
264 THO HATHORNEWHITE ¼ 1669 Hawthorn-bush £85
265 RICHARD LYLE (M) ¼ Castle £85

266 ROBERT MORE ¼ Grocers' Arms £80
267 ISABELL OATS ¼ 1649 Castle
268 IOSEPH WILSON (E) ¼ 1666 Tallowchandlers' Arms
269 IO WITHER ¼ 1666 AT YE STAR, King's Arms

Popeley Gate
269A IOHN CLIFTON (probably *Middx.* 164A)
270 (Probably *Middx.* 166)

Richmond
271 FRANCIS ALLEN ¼ Bust of Chas. II, full-face £65
272 (Probably *Surrey* 221B)
273 IANE CHAYTOR ¼ Bust of Chas. II
274 IOHN CHAYTOR ¼ Bust of Chas. II
275 RICHARD DAVSON ¼ Bust of Chas. II
275A ENOCH HODGSON (M) ½ 1666 Bust of Chas. II
276 IOHN HOPPES ¼ 1665 Bust of Chas. II £75
277 CHRISTOPHER KIRTON (E) ½ 1665
278 ROBERT LOADMAN ¼ Crown, CARRIER
279 PEETER MARSHALL ¼ Bust of Chas. II
280 THOMAS MORLOE (M) ¼ 1664 Bust of Chas. II
281 —— (M) ¼ — AT YE, St. George & dragon
282 THO SOBER (E) ¼ Bust of Chas. II

Ripon
283 WILLIAM HOLMES (F) ¼ 1658
284 BARTHO KETTLEWELL (A) ¼ MERCER
285 WILLIAM KITCHIN ½ 1667
286/7 STEPHEN PAR(R *or* V)ING ½ 1667
288 LANCELOT WILLIAMSON ¼ 1666 GROCER £60

Ripponden
289 IOHN CLAYTON ½ 1668 Swan £75

Robin Hood's Bay
290 ROGER DICKINSON ½ 1669 Robin Hood, Little John, with bows and arrows. *Heart-shape*

Rotherham
291 TIMOTHY LINLEY (E) ½ 1669 Mercers' Arms
292 T.L. ¼
292A W.L. (S) ¼
293 WILLIAM MANDEVILE (½) 1664 Merchant Taylors' Arms
294 W.S., T.L. ¼
294A WILLIAM SMITH ¼ 1664
295 IOSEPH SORESBIE ½ 1669 Mercers' Arms

Scarborough
295A PETER DALE (L) ½ 1669 Cannon. *Heart-shape*
296 IOHN FOWLER ½ 1667 Man standing, gun on shoulder £90
297 PETER HODGSON ½ 1667 Salters' Arms £60
298 IOHN MARSHALL (E) ¼ Castle
299 EDWARD PORTER ½ 1671 GROCER £75
300 IOHN ROBINSON ½ 1667 Fishing boat
301 WILLIAM SAVNDERS ½ 1667 Nag's head
301A WILLIAM WALKER ½ 1667 Man walking, with stick

Sedbergh
302 NICHOLAS CORNEY (W) 1d 1672 Turk's head
303 IAMES HARRISON ¼ 1666 Grocers' Arms
303A IOHN MARSH ½ 1666 Metal spring
304 *Tho Shaw & Nicho Corney* ½ 1671. *Octagonal* £125
305 THO SHAW & NICH CORNEY ¼ 1666 Grocers' Arms; scales £70

Selby
306 CHRISTOPHER BACON AND IOHN PARROTT ½ 1669 £70
307 MARY CARTER, GEORGE CANBYE ¼ Swan
308 ELIZABETH CHEETHAM, KETTELWELL WAVDE ¼ 3 swans £80
309 ANTHONY COLYER (F) ¼ 1666 Dove with olive-branch £90
310 IOHN PVRRATT, CHRISTO BACON ¼ Grocers' Arms
311 BENIAMIN WAVD ¼ Mercers' Arms; 3 crowns
312 —— ¼ — initials

Settle
313 ROBERT CHAMBERLAINE ½ 1666 Ironmongers' Arms
314 THE COMPANY OF GROCERS IN SETTLE ½ Hands joined
315 IOHN & STEVEN SIDGSWICK 1d 1672 Arm grasping. . . ?
316 WILLIAM TAYLOR 1d 1668 Drapers' Arms

Sheffield
317 MICHAELL BAKER ½ 1667 Initials S.B.
318 SAMVELL BARLOW ¼ 1664 Grocers' Arms
319 ROBERT BOVGHTON (M) 1d 1668 Bust of Chas. II
320 —— (M) ¼ 1663 —
320A —— (M) (½) 1663 —. In *iron*
321 ROBERT BREIGHT, IOSEPH NAYLOR ½ 1666 Mercers' Arms
322 STEPHEN BRIGHT ½ 1667
323 GEORGE BROADBENT ½ 1670 Greyhound
324 *Josepe Butler* ½ 1668 *Draper. Heart-shape*
325 WILLIAM COOKE ¼ BRITLAND, Drapers' Arms; Grocers' Arms
326 ROBERT DOWNES ½ 1670 Bunch of grapes*
327 HENRY HANDCOCK ½ Ironmongers' Arms; cock
328 GILBERT HOLDSWORTH ½ 1670 Apothecaries' Arms

* Copies are known (late 19th cent.) of crude style. See plate 4.

329 RICH IBOTSON AND ABELL ROLLINSON ½ Ironmongers' Arms
330 ROBERT MADEN ½ 1670 Ironmongers' Arms
331 IOHN RAMSKER ¼ 1655 Swords crossed
331A LYONELL REVELL (A) ¼ Lion
332 ABELL ROLLINSON ½ 1667 Ironmongers' Arms
333 IAMES TAYLOR (S) ½ 1668 Elephant on *rev.*
334 —— (S) ½ — Elephant on *obv.*
335 BOAZ WARREN ½ Grocers' Arms
336 ZACH WILLSON, LIONELL REVELLS ½ Fishmongers' Arms; lion with branch
337 ABEILL YEATS ½ 1668 Merchant's mark

Skipton
338 RICHARD DIXON (R) ½ 1668 £80
338A —— (R) ¼ 1656
339 MARY FENWICKE 1d 1671 Tun
340 ANN GREENE 1d 1670 Grocers' Arms; fleur-de-lis
341 SAMVELL GREENE 1d '70 Drapers' Arms; Mercers' Arms
342 ROBERT LVND ½ 1666 GROCER

Slaidburn
342A IOHN BRADEL, LENARD LEE ½ '71 Bear

Slaithwaite
343 IOHN DYSON 1d 1670 Man with gun and dog £100
343A —— 1d n.d. —
343B — DISON ½ 1667 Dog
343C —— ½ 1668 AT YE GREYHOVND

Snape
343D IOHN HORNBY ¼ 1659 Grocers' Arms

South Cave
344 IOHN CHAPILOW ½ 1668 3 hats

Stainland
345 IOHN GERSED ½ Horse
346 HVGH RAMSDEN 1d 1670 Rose

Stokesley
347 ¼ 1665 Bust of Chas. II, GOD SAVE THE KING £50
348 RICH IACKSON ¼ 1663

Thirsk
349 ROBERT BELL (E) ¼ 1664 Family Arms £18
350 GEORGE IACKSON ¼ 1664 Crown, DYER
351 IOHN PAIGE (C) ¼ 1668 Grocers' Arms £55
352 WILLIAM WILSON ¼ MERCER £70

Thorne
352A WILLIAM BRIGS (T) ½ 166(6?) Grocers' Arms
352B THOMAS CVTTS ¼ 1664 Castle

Threshfield
353 IOHN HEWITT (T) ½ 1668 Merchant Adventurers' Arms; Merchant's mark, MERCHANT

Tickhill
354 THOMAS TVRNELL (½) 1664 MERCER

Wakefield
355 WILLIAM BAYNES (G) ¼ 1664 Grocers' Arms
356 THO CHERRIEHOLME (S) ¼ Apothecaries' Arms
357 SAMVELL CLARKE (E) ¼ Ship
358 IONAS DEANE ½ 1669 Grocers' Arms £90
359 IOHN DIXSON ½ 1666
360 —— ¼ — Bunch of (?) hops £75
361 IOHN NAYLOR (M) ¼ '64 Soldier on horseback with sword, GROCER

West Witton
362 HENRY KING ½ 1667 Dyers' Arms

Wetherby
363 *The Custome of Wetherby Markett* ½
364 FRANCIS SAYER ½ 1668 Scales £85
365 LAWRENCE WILSON ½ 1667 Blacksmiths' Arms £70

Whitby
366 WILLIAM HARRISSON ½ 1669 MERCER £50
367 IOHN HIRD (E) ¼ Vintners' Arms £50
368 WILLIAM LOTHERINGTON (E) ½ 1669 £70
369 IOHN RYMER ½ 1671 Mercers' Arms. *Heart-shape* £175
370 Similar but *round*
371 HENRY SNEATON ½ 1667 IN FLOWER GATE, 3 ammonites £30

Woodhouse
372 (See *Hunts.* 73)

Yarm
373 IAMES GRVNDEY ¼ Bust of Chas. II
373A — GRVNDY ¼ 1664 —
374 WILLIAM HVSBANDS ¼ Plough
375 THOMAS PARKINSON ¼ Bust of Chas. II £85
376 ALLEN SARTAN ¼ 1661 Bust of Chas. II
377 IAMES SMITH ¼ 1664 —
378 THO WHITE ¼ Bust of Chas. II, SALT SELER

York
379 THO ALLOTT ½ 1668 IN THVRSDAY MARKETT, griffin £55
380 HENERY ARMISTEAD ½ 1666 SKINNER £70
381 WILLIAM BARRON ½ 1671 Grocers' Arms
382 WILLIAM BELL ½ 1665 GROCER £65
382A —— ½ 1666 —
383 ROBERT BENSON (I) ½ 1667 Mercers' Arms £80
384 CHARLES BLANCHARD ½ 1666 AT THE, boy on barrel
385 RICH BOOTH (M) ½ AT THE GOLDEN FLEECE £48
386 —— (M) ¼ YE GOLDEN, fleece
387 ALLICE BOVLTON ½ 1671 Castle

388 ABRAHAM BOYES ½ 1670 3 tobacco-pipes in triangle £85
389 FRAN BRAY ½ 1666 YE GLOBE £80
390 THOMAS BROWNE ½ City Arms, GROCER
391 IAMES CAVTON (M) ½ 1667 Anchor, MARRINER
392 IOHN CAVTON (E) ½ 1667 FISHMONGER
393 THO CORNWEL (E) ¼ GROCER IN MIDLE GATE
394 WILLIAM COWPLAND ½ 1667 Lion £75
395 *Thomas Cundell* ½ Swan
396 *Charles Farnehill* ½ 1669 Pipe, tobacco-roll, hand holding cup £75
396A —— ½ — Hand holding cup
397 ROBERT GARDNER ½ 1667 Swan £65
398 WILL GARNETT ½ 1670 Bull's head; Girdlers' Arms, GIRDLER £90
399 FRANCIS HALL ½ 1666 SILKE WEAVER
400 WILLIAM HEATHER ½ 1666 Mercers' Arms
401 *John Hoopes* ½ 1668 Royal oak
401A As last, but *octagonal*
402 MATHEW HOTHAM (½) DRAPER
403 ROBERT HVNTER ½ 1670 Family Arms
404 THOMAS HVRST ½ '66 Pinners' Arms, PINER
405 —— ¼ 1666 ——
406 GEORGE HVTCHINSON ½ 1669 Bunch of grapes £75
407 IOHN HVTCHENSON (A) ½ 1666 Mercers' Arms
408 WILL INMAN ½ 1666 GROCER
409 GEORGE IACKSON ¼ St. George & dragon, GROCER
410 CHARLES IENKINSON (A) ¼ City Arms
411 IOHN KETTLEWELL ½ 1666 Pot of lilies; roses, GLASSMAN £65
412 *George Kighley* ½ 1668 Winged horse £60
413 *Richard Lambert* ½ 1668 Crown £75
414 IAMES LEECH ½ 1666 Skinners' Arms £55
415 EDWARD LEGG ½ 1669 Leg with boot and spur
416 IOHN LEGG ½ 1667 WITHOVT BOVTHAM BARR, Bakers' Arms £85
417 THOMAS LEGG (A) ½ 1665 PINNER
418 WILLIAM MANCKLINS ½ '66 ARTIZAN SKINER
419 IONAS MASCALL ¼ IN STONEGAT GROCER, man on bale, smoking
420 IOHN MOOER ½ 1666 Ship
421 — MOORE ½ 1667 —
422 WILL MOORE ½ IN STONEGATE TRVNKMAKER, 4 tobacco-pipes
423 CHRISTOPHER MORLEY (A) ¼ 1666 of OVS BRIDG BARBER, rose crowned
424 IOHN ORTON ½ 1666 Girdlers' Arms, GIRDLER
425 IOHN RAYSIN (P) ½ 1668 Family Arms, IOYNER
426 PEETER RICHARDSON ½ MILLENER
427 *William Richardson* ½ Talbot
428 ROWLAND RICHESON ½ 1668 Hen and chicks, PINNER
429 WILLIAM RIPLEY ½ 1666 Bust of Chas. II
430 IOHN ROOME ½ '68 CHANDLER £55
431 PHILLIPP ROSENDALL ½ IN WATER LANE, 3 figures around globe £65
432 *Samuell Saire* ½ 1669 Arms
433 IOHN SHARP ½ 1669 Lion; swan
434 CHRISTOP SIMSON (E) ½ BEARE, BRWER
435 ELIZ SMITH ½ PINER OOSE BRIDG
436 GEORGE STOCKTON (M) ½ 1666 SILKWEAVER
437 WILLIAM TVRNBVLL ½ Mitre, VINTNER
438 *Thomas Walliker* ½ 1669 *Dier* £85
439 *John Waller* ½ 1669 Carnation, *Girdler*
440 ROBERT WASSE ½?
441 DENNIS WATERHOVSE (E) ½ 1667 3 men inspecting globe, MARRINER
442 ROGER WILBERFOSS ½ 1666 IN LOEOVSGATE, hat
443 MARY WIND ½ 1668 AT YE BELL IN SPVRIER GATE £80
444 WILL WOOD ½ Punch, MVTISION PVNCHANELLA
445 ROB WRIGHT (M) ½ 1668 Arms

WALES

Major reference (including Monmouthshire): George C. Boon, *Welsh Tokens of the Seventeenth Century* (Cardiff, 1973) and a short *Supplement* (1976). Nearly all varieties photographed; updating and revision of 'Williamson', notes on many issuers, much background information, detailed classification of the tokens and locations and quantities of specimens. The most attractively produced work on the entire series.

See also D. W. Dykes, 'Seventeenth-Century Glamorgan Trade Tokens' (*Morgannwg: Transactions of the Glamorgan History Society*, vol. X, 1966).

The (original) county of each token-issuing locality is given in brackets.

Minimum price for unvalued tokens: £90

Conwy (Caernarvonshire)
1 HENRY HVGHES 1d 1663 Grocers' Arms
2 — — 1d n.d. —
3 ELIZABETH IONES 1d 1668 Head of Edward I

Abergele (Denbighshire)
4 IOHN HVMPHREYS 1d 1668 Mercers' Arms

Anglesey
4A ROWLAND HVHGES AND THO MORICE 1d 1667 Mortar and pestle
4B — — — — — — 1d 1671 —

Bala (Merioneth)
4C ROBERT EVANS 1d 1667 MERCER
5 ROBERT THOMAS 1d 1667

Bangor (Caernarvonshire)
6 RICHARD BOVLTON 1d 1667 Scales; Cathedral

Beaumaris (Anglesey)
7 RICE BOLD 1d 1669
8 IOHN DAVIS 1d 1669 Castle £120
9 BEN IONES, IOHN WORSLEY (½) Royal Arms in ship, sceptre on prow; part of borough arms
10 — — — — — ¼ Royal arms in ship, sceptres at prow and stern; part of borough arms

Brecon
11 Borough ¼ 1670 Robe £55
11A ROWLAND GWYN ¼ IN BRECKNOCK & HAY, family crest
12 THOMAS IVXSON ½ 1669 Shears, glove. GLOVER. *Octagonal* £120
12A IOHN WATTERS ¼ 1668 GROCER

Builth (Radnorshire)
12B DAVID PRYCE (E?) ½ 1669 Heart

Caerwys (Flintshire)
13 IAMES HVGHES (I) 1d 1669 Fox
14 THOMAS WYNNE (M) 1d '68 Towel, forceps, teeth. CHYRVRGEON
15 — — (M) 1d '69 — — — —

Carmarthen
16 DAWKINE GOVE ¼
16A —— ¼ '64 Crowned rose
17 ABRAHAM HEELY ½ 2-headed eagle, MERCER
18 IOHN HVGHES IVNIOR (S) ¼ Mercers' Arms
18A DAVID IONES (D) ½ MERCER
19 THOMAS NEWSHAM (K) ½ 1668
20 —— (K) ¼ 1666
21 IOHN WEBB ½ 1669 3 doves, SOPE BOYLER
22 ELIZABETH WILLIAMS ¼ 1663 Castle
23 IOHN WILLSON ½ 1669 Tallowchandlers' Arms, GROCER

Caernarvon
24/5 ELLIS IONES 1d 1664 Pheasant £60
26 THOMAS KNIGHT 1d 1667 Tobacco-roll, denomination on *rev.*
27 —— 1d —— denomination on *obv.*
28 GRIFFITH WYNN 1d '69 Castle

Conwy
(See nos. 1–3)

Corwen (Merioneth)
29 ROBERT WYNNE 1d 1669 Harp, MERCER

Cowbridge (Glamorgan)
30 WILL BASSETT (K) ½ 1669 MERCER £65

Denbigh
31 EDWARD DAVICE 1d 1664 Arms
31A THOMAS IONES 1d 1666 Grocers' Arms
32 OWEN LLOYD 1d 1666? MERCER
32A ROBERT ROBERTS 1d 1666 Mercers' Arms
33 THOMAS SHAW 1d 1666 Goat, GLOVER
33A —— 1d 1669 ——

Dolgellau (Merioneth)
33B ROBERT WYNNE (1d) 1671 Harp, MERCER

Haverfordwest (Pembrokeshire)
34 WILL BATMAN (S) ¼ MERCER, ø (= ½ obolus)
34A THOMAS BOWEN (I) ¼ Drapers' Arms, MERCER
34B —— (I) ¼ Drapers' Arms
35 HENRY BOWER (K) ¼ 1666 Mercers' Arms
36 THO BOVLTON ¼ Family Arms
36A *John Fowler* ¼ 1669
37 RICE IONES (A) ½ 1667
37A EDWARD LORD ¼ Mercers' Arms
38 IANE SPARKE ¼ 1667 Mercers' Arms
38A THOMAS TASKER ½ 1668 Ship issuing from castle
39 THOMAS WILKIN (D) ½ 1669 Ship issuing from castle
39A IACOB WOLFORD (E) ¼ '68 Hare

Hay-on-Wye (Brecknockshire)
39B WILLIAM IONES ½ 1669 Ironmongers' Arms
40 MATTHEW PARRY ½ 1663 *Ob*, MERCER

Holyhead (Anglesey)
41 HVGH DAVIS 1d 1666 3 books
42 IOHN HALL 1d Tulip
42A I. WHELDON & WM OWEN 1d Tobacco-roll, crossed pipes; pint and quart pots. INHOLDRS

Kidwelly (Carmarthenshire)
43 MORRIS HOWELL ¼ Church; castle
44 EDWARD LLOYD ½ Family Arms £60
45 —— ½ Family Arms, crest and motto £70

Knighton (Radnorshire)
46 IAMES MASON ½ 1668 MERCER £80
47 IOHN MASON (S) ½ 1668 PLAINE DEALING
48 IAMES WOOLLEY ¼ Grocers' Arms

Llantwit Major (Glamorgan)
49 EDWARD MADOCKES (M) ¼ Scales, MERCER
50 LEWIS MADOCKS ¼ Grocers' Arms

Llandeilo (Carmarthenshire)
50A IOHN EDWIN ½ 1668 Arms, MERCER

Llangollen (Denbighshire)
51 OWEN MORGAN 1d 1667

Llanidloes (Montgomeryshire)
52 IENKIN THOMAS ½ 1669 Mercers' Arms

Llanrwst (Denbighshire)
53 IOHN DAVIES 1d 1667 Mercers' Arms
53A —— 1d 1663 —
53B — DAVIS (M) ¼ 1656 —

Llanfyllin (Montgomeryshire)
54 WALTER GRIFFITHES (M) ½ Goat £55

Machynlleth (Montgomeryshire)
54A WILLIAM OWEN 1d 1672 Cock, MERCER
55 ISACK PVGH ¼ 1660 Rose

Mold (Flintshire)
56 (Probably misreading of *Worcs.* 82)
57 EDWARD WILLIAMS 1d 1666 GROCER £50

Narberth (Pembrokeshire)
58 MALLETT BATEMAN ¼ 1667 Drapers' Arms; bird

Neath (Glamorgan)
59 THOMAS LOVE (B) ¼ MERCER

Newtown (Montgomeryshire)
59A CHARLES LLOYD ¼ 1657?

Northop (Flintshire)
60 RICHARD WILLIAMS 1d 1668 Talbot

Overton (Flintshire)
61 IAMES OWENS (A) ½ 1667 Tobacco-roll

Pembroke
62 IOHN HINTON ½ 1669 Hart

Presteigne (Radnorshire)
63 IOHN CONWAY ½ 1665 Angel
64 IOSEPH GRONNOVS ½ Grocers' Arms
64A HVGH HOWELLS (E) ½ Lion, MERCER

Pwllheli (Caernarvonshire)
65 RICHARD PREECE 1d 1666 2-headed eagle
65A — — 1d 1667 —
66 WILLIAM REYNOLDS 1d 1667 Mercers' Arms
66A HVGH LLOYD ROSINDALE 1d 1666 Mercers' Arms

Ruthin (Denbighshire)
66B IOHN BAYNHAM ½ 1664 Family crest*
66C PETER EDWARDS 1d '66 MERCER
67 RICHARD GOODEN ½ 1664 Apothecaries' Arms
67A IOHN HVGHES 1d 1667 Haberdashers' Arms
68 DAVID VAVGHAN 1d 1668 MERCER
69 BASIL WOOD 1d '65 APOTHECARY
69A RICHARD WYNN 1d 1666 Grocers' Arms

Swansea (Glamorgan)
70 ISAAC AFTER ¼
71 MATHEW DAVIES ½ 1666 MERCER £65

Talley (Carmarthenshire)
71A WILLIAM IOHN ½ 1669 MERCER

Tenby (Pembrokeshire)
71B WALTER HENBROVGH ¼ 1669 MERCER
72 IOHN SAYES (O) ¼ 1667 MERCER
73 — — (O) ¼ 1668 —

* A mule of *Herefs.* 3A and *Wales* 67

Welshpool (Montgomeryshire)
74 RICH DAVIES ½ 1667 Lion, FELTMAKER
75 HVMPHRY DRAPER ½ Family Arms
76 THOMAS FARMER ½ 1670 Griffin, 3 lions' heads, MERCER. *Octagonal.* **Plate 4**
77 CHARLES HVMFFREIS ¼ 1658 Hand holding glove
77A CHARLES IONES ½ 1667 Bust of Chas. II
77B RICHARD MERCER ½ 1667 Merchant Taylors' Arms
78 SAMVELL WOLLASTON ½ 1667

Wrexham (Denbighshire)
79 THOMAS BAKER (I) ½ MERCER
80 (Misreading of 81)
81 GEORG BVTTALL (G) ½ 1668 IRONMONGER
82 LAWRENCE COOKE (E) 1d 1666 Tobacco-roll
82A — — (E) ½ 1667 —
83 EDWARD DAVIES ½ 1666 £70
84 IOHN DAVIES (I) 1d 1668. In *brass* with central plug of *copper*
85 IOHN HVGHES (K) ½ 1666 Spectacles
86 — — (K) ¼ — —
87 ROBERT IACKSON ¼ Family Arms
88 EVAN IONES ½ 1666 Scales
89 WILLIAM LEWIS (A) ½ 1666 Cordwainers' Arms
90 IOHN PERRY (K) ½ 1667
91 THOMAS PLATT (M) ½ 1666
91A The Lyon and Maidenhead ¼?

Unknown Locality
91B SARAH THOMAS ½ Oak tree; bust of Chas. II
92 OWEN WILLIAMS (I) ½ 1666 Lion

Monmouthshire

Abergavenny

1 WALTER DAVIDS (I) ½ 1661 *Ob* in lozenge.
Plate 4

2 *Edward L(e)wis* ¼ 1667 Fleur-de-lis in shield £65

3 *Phillip Morgan* ½ 1667 Mercers' Arms

4 PHILLIP MORGAN ¼ — —

5 — — ½ 1671 —

5A IOHN STEPHENS ¼ Fleur-de-lis in shield

Caerleon

6 WILLIAM MEREDITH ¼ 1668 MERCER

7 — — ¼ 1669 Plumes through coronet; pikeman £85

Chepstow

8 THOMAS DAVIS ½ 1671 Initials I.D.

9 WILL DAVIS ¼ 1670 MERCER £75

9A *Francis Herbert* ½ 1671 *Mercer*

9B IOHN MORGAN ¼ 1670 Grocers' Arms

10 RICHARD MORGAN ½ 1670. *Octagonal*

10A As last but *round* flan

11 SAMVEL MORGAN ¼ 1670 Portcullis

12 WALTER MORGAN ¼ 1670 Portcullis £40

13 — — ½ 1672 — £70

Monmouth

14 R.B. (A) ¼ 1661 Bust of Chas. II £65

15 RICHARD BALLARD ½ 1668 Bust of Chas. II, GOD PRESERVE OVR GRACIOVS KING £25

16 EDWARD BEVAN (E) ½ Man making candles £60

17 MICHAELL BOHEWNE ¼ MERCER

18 — — (E) ¼ — £70

19 THOMAS EDWARDS ½ 1671 Portcullis, MERCER

20 THOMAS MORGAN (G) ¼ '60 MERCER

SCOTLAND

See P. Frank Purvey, *Coins and Tokens of Scotland* (Seaby's Standard Catalogue, part 4; London, 1972).

Minimum price: £175

Braid (Lothian)
1A WILLIAME DICK. Forge; caduceus and cornucopia, VIRTVTI FORTVNA COMES (really an estate ticket)

Dunbar (Lothian)
1 GEO COOMBES ¼ 1668. In *pb*

IRELAND

Major references: Peter Seaby, *Coins and Tokens of Ireland* (Seaby's Standard Catalogue, part 3; London, 1970). Includes a check list of issuers and many illustrations.

R. A. S. Macalister, 'A Catalogue of the Irish Traders' Tokens in the Collection of the Royal Irish Academy' (*Proceedings of the Royal Irish Academy*, vol. XL, section C, no. 2, 1931). Additions and many corrections to 'Williamson'.

New tokens also recorded from: *SNC*, Jan. and Oct. 1902, Oct.–Nov. 1949, Feb. 1958; L. L. Fletcher, 'Some Notes on Irish Seventeenth Century Tokens' (*SNC*, Jan.–Feb. 1905); Glendining's sale, 25 Sep. 1907; T. B. Costello and M. J. Blake, *Trade Tokens of the County of Galway in the Seventeenth Century, with Notes on the Issuers* (Galway, 1911); *Catalogue of Irish Tokens* (Belfast Public Art Gallery and Museum publication 36, Feb. 1913): list of specimens there, with sources; *BNJ*, 1920, 1926, 1930, 1978; *Journal of the Louth Historical and Archaeological Society*, vol. X no. 2, 1942; J. G. Milne, 'The Browne Willis Cabinet' (*BNJ*, 1951); *SCMB*, Oct. 1958, July 1966, Mar. 1970, Mar. 1985; G. R. Chapman and W. A. Seaby, 'Unpublished Seventeenth Century Tokens of Lisburn, Co. Antrim' (*SCMB*, Nov. 1973); Robert Sharman, 'St Patrick for Ierland Token' (*Irish Numismatics*, May–June 1980); *SCA* 28, 28 Apr. 1983.

As the present work goes to press, an important new paper by Gerard Brady and Colm Gallagher has appeared: 'Munster "Siege Pieces" or Early Tokens?: Evidence from a Cork Scattering' (*SNC*, Apr. 1986). In this the authors discuss the emergency issues struck on rectangular copper flans for Youghal, Cork, Kinsale and Bandon between 1646 and the early 1650s. The conclusion drawn is that these pieces are not coins, but should belong to the seventeenth century token series.

See also L. L. Fletcher, 'The Seventeenth Century Tokens of Co. Antrim' (*BNJ*, 1928); J.A.S.S., *Unpublished Varieties of 17th Century Copper Tokens in the Robb Collection* (City of Belfast Museum and Art Gallery, Quarterly Notes LIV, publication 118, Sep. 1937); Colm Gallagher, 'Mr Tennant's Halfpennies?' (*Irish Numismatics*, Nov.–Dec. 1981), 'The Limerick Farthing of 1658,' (*Irish Numismatics*, Jul.–Aug. 1982), and especially his 'Post Restoration Irish Tokens: a Documentary Perspective' (*British & Irish Tokens Journal*, vol. 1 no. 1, Aug. 1980); Gerard Rice, 'The Seventeenth-Century Tokens of County Louth (*County Louth Archaeological and Historical Journal*, 1985).

Believed entirely unpublished: 23A, 159A, 253A, 349A, 410A, 412A, 428B, 493A, 529A, 618A, 623A, 640A, 694A, 721A, 731A, 753A.

Minimum price for unvalued tokens: £60

The county of each token-issuing locality is given in brackets.

Abbeyshrule (Longford)
1A PATERICK LYNCH 1d Arms, crest

Annamoe (Wicklow)
1 ROBART MELDRVM 1d Lion crowned

Antrim
2 MATTHEW BETHELL 1d 1671 Knot, POST MSTR £65
3 BRYCE CRAFORD 1d 1657 Merchant's mark
3A BRVCE — 1d 1659 —; heart
4 WILLIAM CRAFORD 1d 1656 Merchant's mark; heart
5 — — 1d 1657 — —
6 THOMAS PALMER 1d Heart
7 GILBERT ROSS (I) 1d Haberdashers' Arms
8 SAMVEL SHENNAN 1d '68 Haberdashers' Arms
9 IOHN STEWARD 1d Merchant's mark
10 WILL STEWART 1d 1656
11 IOH VAVCH 1d Arms
12 IOHN WHITE 1d Grocers' Arms
13 ROBART YOVNG 1d Shears between teazles, DYER

Oola (Limerick)
14 WILL PINCHLON 1d Hammer head, nails (?)

Ardagh (Longford)
14A THOMAS DRAKE 1d Drake

Ardee (Louth)
15 IOHN ALLEN 1d 1670 Arms; goat
16 IAMES ATKINSON 1d St. George & dragon £50
17 THO ROBEREY 1d 1670 Merchant's mark
18 TOBY SKERNE 1d 1665 Arms

Arklow (Wicklow)
19 IOSEPH BAYLY 1d 3 castles, 2 grasshoppers below
19A RICHARD BRODHVRST (1d) 16?? Sugar-loaf
19B ROBART PHELPS (C) (1d) Ship
20 SYMON SHEEHAN 1d Man on horseback

Armagh
21 IOHN DAVISON 1d 1671 Stag
22 IOHN HOLMES (1d) Acorn, oak-leaves; merchant's mark
23 ROBERT MCCONCHY 1d Merchant's mark; arrow piercing heart
23A — — (K) 1d — —
24 THOMAS SANDERS 1d 3 C's
25 IOHN SINKLER 1d Ship; heart
26 IAMES TAYLOR (ML conjoined) 1d 1664 Armagh Cathedral

Articlave (Londonderry)
27 IOHN HILLHOVSE (1d) Arrows piercing heart; merchant's mark

Athboy (Meath)
28 MATHEW NARLAN 1d Lion
29 IOHN RIGGS (1d) Fleur-de-lis

Athenry (Galway)
30 THOMAS CLOAN 1d Arms

Athlone (Westmeath and Roscommon)
31 WILL ANTREBVS 1d Swan, initial A
31A — ANTR(E *or* I)BVS 1d Swan, no initial
32 HVGH COFFY 1d Castle on river, swan
33 WALTER DOWDALL (B) (1d) Arms
34 RICHARD EATON (1d) Family Arms, CHANDLER
35 WILLIAM FALLON 1d Hand holding pen
36 WILLIAM HILL (1d) 1656 Stag, eagle
37 — — (1d) 1663 — —
38 (Same as 43)
39, 40 RICHARD KELLY 1d 3 fishes
41 WALTER KELLY 1d Lion
42 IAMES LENON 1d Stag crowned
43 WILLIAM LORTE (E) (1d) Dove with olive branch
44 NICHOLAS MALONE (1d) Family Arms
45 IOHN MILLES 1d 1656 Sugar-loaf
46 GEORGE MILLS 1d Ear of corn
47 WILLIAM MORHEAD 1d Bird on tree
48 MARTYNE MVRPHY (B) (1d) Tree
49 ALDRIGE SADLER (E) (1d) Wheatsheaf on *rev.*, BAKER
49A ALDRIDGE — (E) 1d Wheatsheaf on *obv.* —
50 IOHN SLATTER (1d) 1665 Chequers

51 STEPHEN SMITH 1d Leather-cutter's knife, SHOOMAKER
52 RICHARD W(AR?)REN 1d 3 castles

Athy (Kildare)
53 WILLAM ADDIS 1d 1659 Swan
54 IAMES SWANTON 1d EXCISE OFICES, lion
55 IAMES WALSH 1d 1666 2-headed eagle

Augher (Tyrone)
56 IAMES MORIE 1d Tree

Ballinakill (Laois)
57 NIC DANELL (1d) Arrows piercing heart

Ballinasloe (Galway)
58 ROBERT WARNER 1d POST MASTER

Ballyboy (Offaly)
59 ROB HVTCHINSON 1d 1668 Crossed keys; crossed swords
60 THO MAIRE (M) (1d) Anchor, TANNER

Ballyjamesduff (Cavan)
61 IOHN DALIN (E) 1d 1668 Demi-virgin

Ballymoney (Antrim)
61A IOHN HAMILL (1d) 1672 Merchant's mark; Arms
62 IOHN HARPER (1d) Lion playing harp; arrows piercing heart
63 DVNCAN LINNE (1d) 1670 Merchant's mark; crane, fish in talons
63A IAMES ROBINSON 1d Arms?
64 IOHN SINKLER 1d 1656 Haberdashers' Arms
64A —— 1d — MARCH
64B —— ½ — Haberdashers' Arms
64C ALEXANDER WYLY (1d) Merchant's mark, MARCR; unicorn

Ballymore (Westmeath)
65 THOMAS CONNELL 1d Pelican feeding young
67 EDMOND PETTIT 1d Winged horse £60
68 LVKE TVRRELL 1d Swords crossed

Ballymoe (Galway)
66 MARTINE LYNCH (1d) 1671 Arms

Ballymore Eustace (Kildare)
68A LAW BATHE 1d Paschal lamb

Ballymote (Sligo)
68B ROGER HORROGHIE 1d Woolpack
69 DANNIELL (KEL?)LY 1d 1657 Harp

Baltimore (Cork)
70 WILLIAM PRIGG (1d) Ship, castle

Bandon (Cork)
71 Town 1d 1668 3 castles; BOVND TO CHANG, initials M.P.
71A — ¼ —— initials P.B., P.
71B — ¼ OF FINE PEWTER. 3 castles; bird (?). In *pb*
72 CORPERASION 1d 1670 3 castles; bridge over river. Counterstruck BB
72A ROBERT CASE 1d 1668 Woolcomb
73 IOHN WREN (1d) 1659 BRIDEWELL, Arms; building £55

Bangor (Down)
74 IAMES CLEALAND 1d Church; anchor, rope
75 — CLEALARD 1d 1657 Anchor, rope; church
76 IAMES MOOR 1d 1657 Anchor; church

Belfast (Antrim)
77 Town 1d 1671 Ship; writing flourish £100
77A THOMAS AITKIN (1d) 3 crowns; Prince of Wales' feathers. *Heart-shape*
78 IAMES BIGGER 1d 1666 Merchant's mark; heart
78A —— 1d —— heart with fleur-de-lis
79 IOHN BIGGER 1d 1657 Bell
80 MICHAELL BIGGER (1d) 1657 Bell
81/2 IOHN BVSH 1d*
83 IAMES CHALMERS 1d 1670 Family Arms
84 IOHN CLVGSTON 1d 1656
85 —— 1d n.d. MARCHT
86 IOHN CORRY 1d 1656
87 HVMPHRY DOBBIN 1d 1670 Family Arms; crest. **Plate 4** £80
88 HVGH DVOK (1d) 1656 Bell
89 HVGH ECCLES 1d Arms; heart
90 IOHN GIVAN (1d) Still; Arms
91 IOHN KILPATRICK (1d) Ship; bell
92 WILL LOKART, THOS AITKIN (1d) Prince of Wales' feathers; 3 crowns. *Heart-shape*
93 GEORGE MARTIN 1d 1666 Merchant's mark; bell
94 —— 1d 1657 ——
95 IOSIAH MARTIN 1d 1657 Bell
96 GEO MICCARTNAY (1d) 1656
97 GEORGE MICARTNEY 1d 1657
98 WILLIAM MOORE 1d Ship; bell
99 ALEXANDER SINKLAR 1d 1657 Ship
100 HENRY SMITH 1d Family Arms
101 WILLIAM SMITH 1d
102 —— (1d) 1657 £70
103 HVGH SPEIRE 1d Merchant's mark b.s.
104 IOHN STEWARD 1d 1656 Ship; bell
105 IOHN STEWART 1d 1657 Bell; ship
105A —— 1d —— ship on shield
105B WILLIAM THOMBE 1d
106 ROBERT WHITSIDE 1d 1667 Ship

Ballymena (Antrim)
107 WILLIAM ADA(I)RE 1d Rose
108 ROBART BOYD 1d Squirrel on mound
108A GEORGE CVDBERT 1d Merchant's mark

* Struck on French *doubles tournois*

109 IOHN HARPER 1d Harp
110 IOHN WALLAS 1d 1671

Ballinalee (Longford)
111 P.C. (1d) AT THE DOLPHIN

Belturbet (Cavan)
112 ROBART HARES 1d 1659? Shears, curry-comb
113 RICHARD HARRISON 1d Man and horse, POSTMR

Birr (Offaly)
114 MARCVS ARCHER (N) (1d) Arms
115 As last, counterstruck HAPNEY
116 RICHARD ARCHER (1d) 1667 Arms
117 MICHAELL CANTWELL 1d Family Arms £65
118 ROBERT IEFFES 1d IN NECESRARY CHAINGE WITH LABOVRERS AN ORHERS
119 THOMAS LANGTONN 1d Initials T.M.; thistle-head
119A —— 1d Initials I.N.; —

Blackwroth (Kildare)
120 THO CVS(ACK *or* EK) (A) (1d) Sword

Borrisokane (Tipperary)
121 THOMAS WOOLLFORD (C) 1d 1668 Bell £65

Borrisoleigh (Tipperary)
122 STEPHEN RADFORD 1d Lion

Boyle (Roscommon)
123 CORMOCK DERMOTT 1d 1658 Boar
124 STEPHEN DOWDALL 1d Duck
124A EDMOND FRENCH (A) (1d) Grocers' Arms
125 EDWARD MVNNS 1d 1678 Knot; Arms

Broughshane (Antrim)
126 SAMVEL ANDREW 1d Knot; merchant's mark

Caledon (formerly **Kinaird**) (Tyrone)
126A ALLEN BAVGH (R) 1d
127 IOHN SPEARE 1d Dog, TANER

Carlow
128 IOHN MASTERS 1d 1657 Bull
129 THOMAS MOORE 1d Stag, POSTMASTER
130 GARRETT QVIGLEY 1d Harp £42
131 EDWARD R(E *or* Y)NOLDS 1d Family Arms
132 THO REYNALDS 1d Family Arms, TANER £70

Carrick-on-Suir (Tipperary)
133 PEETER AYLWARD 1d Arms
134 WALTER DEVEREVX (1d) '69 Initials H.A.
143 PHILIP DAYE 1d Arms

Carrickfergus (Antrim)
135 HENERY BVRNES 1d Castle; rose-branches
135A IOHN DAVADYS 1d?
136 ANTHONY HALL 1d 1656 Castle
137 —— 1d n.d. — £70
138 A.H. 1d Castle, initials C.F.B.
139 WILLIAM MAGEE 1d Castle
139A WILLIAM STVBBS 1d?
140 IOHN WADMAN 1d Castle
141 ANDREW WILLOVGHBY 1d Castle

Carrickmacross (Monaghan)
142 W.B. 1d n.d. Family Arms, crest; WHEN YOV PLEAS(E) ILE CHA(I)NG(E) THES £60
142A —— 1d 1659 —— WHEN YOV PLEASE ILE CHANGE THES
143 (See under Carrick-on-Suir)

Cashel (Tipperary)
144 PEETER BOYTON 1d Harp £60
145/9 EDMOND KEARNEY 1d Cross, pellets in quarters £55
146 —— 1d 1666 Cross, roses in quarters
147 —— ½ Cross pattée
148 (Probably misreading of 145)
150 EDWARD MIHILL 1d Cathedral £65
151 IOHN NEVE 1d Family Arms
152 IOHN PEENE 1d Arms
153 ROBART PRINCE 1d 1664 Castle £50

Castlechichester (Whitehead) (Antrim)
154 ROB BRICE 1d 1671 Arms, AVTH (?= authority) £65

Castle Dawson (Londonderry)
154A WILL HAMERSLEY 1d 1672 CLARKE, IRON WORKE

Castledermot (Kildare)
155 THOMAS ADERLY 1d Hammer and pincers crossed, SMITH
156 THOMAS CLINTON 1d Lion
157 HENERY MARRENER 1d Glove £60

Castlefinn (Donegal)
158 IOHN CALHOVNE 1d Cask; merchant's mark

Cavan
159 IOHN BALLARD (M) (1d) 1667 Swan
159A — BOLLARD (1d) — Arms; swan
159B —— (M) (1d) 1673 Swan b.s.

Charlemont (Armagh)
160 THOMAS CHADS (1d) Guns crossed; castle
161 EDWARD PARREY 1d St. George & dragon

Charleville (Cork)
162 IOHN BVTTELER, IOHN EXHAM (1d) 1668 Star; Catherine wheel £65
163 ROBERT COWEN (1d) '79 Thistle crowned; castle
164 A.C. (W) 1d 1667 Chained bear; St. George & dragon
165 As no. 212, cmkd. CHARLEVILLE

Clare County
166 (same as 559–62)

Clonakilty (Cork)
167 Town 1d 1678 Arms. Cmkd. I.B. FARTHING
168 — 1d — — (not countermarked)

Clones (Monaghan)
207 IAMES BRATTON 1d Harp
169 WILLIAM PARK(E) *or* PAKE 1d 1664 £60
170 IOSEPH SCOFEILD 1d 1670 3 crowns

Clonfert (Galway)
171 THO BVTLER 1d 1676 Croziers crossed; mitre
172 — — ½ Arms; mitre
173 IAMES COLMAN 1d Swan

Clonmeen (Cork)
174 T.C. 1d '72 Horse under tree, harp at side

Clonmel (Tipperary)
175 I.B. 1d 1658 Dog pursuing stag on bridge, fish below. (Town piece?)
176 RICHARD CARLETON 1d Dog pursuing stag on bridge £50
177 GEORGE CARR 1d 1656 Family Arms
177A MARTIN DIX 1d. In *pb*
178 IOHN FRYERS (1d 1668) Ship; dog pursuing stag on bridge, PEVTERER
179 RICHARD HAMERTON (1d) 1657 Initials on *rev.*
180 — — (1d) 1664 Dog pursuing stag on bridge; dolphin
181 — — 1d n.d. Dolphin; dog pursuing stag on bridge
182 — — (1d) 1657 Initials on *obv.* £55
182A — — (1d) 1656
183 IOHN HARWOOD 1d 3 fleurs-de-lis
184 ANN HENBVRY (1d) 1663 Harp
185 WILLIAM HENBVRY (1d) 1656 Harp
186 ANDREW ROBESON 1d Family Arms; woolpack £55
187 As last, cmkd ½^{D} in shield

Coleraine (Londonderry)
188 THOMAS ADAMS (1d) Mortar and pestle; town Arms, APOTHECARY
188A IOSHVA BROOKES 1d Arms
189 IOHN BROWNE 1d?
190 ROB(ER)T BROWNE 1d 1671 Arms
191 WILL GODFREY 1d 1656 Arms
192 ALEXANDER MILLER 1d 1665 Cross with sword, fish, rose in quarters; Arms
192A — — ½ 1656
192B HVGH MILLER 1d 1656 Town Arms
193 WIL ROSE (1d) Bear; rose on stalk, EXCHANGE FOR A CAN
193A WILM — (1d) Rose crowned; bear, HIS EXCHANGE FOR A CAN
194 IOHN TWADDELL 1d 1657 Town Arms
194A — — 1d 1656 —
195 GILBERT WILLSON (1d) '76 Town Arms; merchant's mark

Collooney (Sligo)
196 HENNERY DOWDALL 1d 1671

Connacht
197 IA BROWNE 1d Flowers; family Arms

Cork
198–200 (Probably all Great Rebellion emergency issues)
201 City 1d 1659 Ship between castles £14
202 — ½ 1656 Ship, castle £40
203 — ¼ Arms of England, arrow above; harp £40
204 — (1d) 1658 P.M. MAYOR, ship between castles £28
205 WILLIAM BALLARD 1d 1677 King's bust in royal oak, horseman and soldier below. Edge, TO PASS IN THIS CITY AND COVNTIE £60
206 As last, cmkd. with leopard's head, CORKE and palms
207 (see under Clones)
208 EDWARD GOBLE (1d) 1672 Castle, BRAZIER
209 (Probably misreading of 215)
210 IONAS MORRIS (1d) 1657 Ship between castles £40
210A As last, cmkd *ALB* (= ½?)
211 IONAS MORRIS (1d) n.d. Ship between castles £45
212 EDMOND YEOMANS 1d '78 Busts facing each other; Fruiterers' Arms
213 — — 1d '79 — —
214 GEORGE YOVNG (1d) 1657 Castle

Gorey (Wexford)
215 EDWARD CAVENAGH 1d Boat

Dingle (Kerry)
216 Town(?) 1d 1679 Head of Janus; Cupid shooting arrow at man and woman embracing under tree, house in distance
217 TOBY CREANE (1d) 3 fishes, crowns above heads; coronet, hammer, nails. COVCH IRON WORKE

Donaghadee (Down)
218 ROB BREARLEY 1d Cross between wings
219 M., W. 1d 1669 MARCHANTS

Donegal
219A ROBART RON(NAL?)DS 1d Dog, tree

Raphoe (Donegal)
220 WILL WIGSTON 1d Harp

Down County
221 ARTHVR SQVIRE 1d Crest

Downpatrick (Down)
222 ROBERT KING (1d) Crowned bust

223 IOHN LAWE 1d Merchant's mark
224 SENESCHALL 1d 1664 Arms
225 IAMES STEWART 1d DEC 1658 Merchant's mark; heart
226 IAMES THOMSON 1d 1670 Ship; merchant's mark
227 WILLIAM THOMSON (1d) Arms

Drogheda (Louth)
228 IOHN BELLEW (M) (1d) Family Arms
229 OLIVER BIRD (M) 1d Family Arms £60
230 IOHN BRAYE 1d 1663
231 EDWARD BYTHELL (1d) Family Arms £55
232 THO COKAYNE 1d 1656 Cock's head
233 HEN COKER 1d 1656 Harp, ES (= esquire). In *brass* with cross-shaped *copper* inset*
234 LVKE CONLY 1d 1670 Family Arms
234A SAMVEL FENTON 1d?
235 HVGH FOWKES (C) 1d Arms, GLASYR
236 EDMOND GRAVES (H) 1d 1664 Rose crowned
237 —— 1d ——; lion, MARC
238 ANDREW HAMLIN (A) 1d Family Arms £55
238A B.H. (A) 1d Hamlin family Arms
239 RICHARD IACKSON 1d Angel
240 IOHN KILLOGH (E) 1d
241 IOHN LEA (1d) Lion b.s.
242 — LEY 1d 1657 Lion
243 (Probably misreading of 244)
244 IOHN LEY (A) 1d 1664 Lion £55
245 LEBBEVS LOWND ½ 1667 Cheese-knife, GROSER
246 EDWARD MARTINE ½
247–9 — MART(T)IN (I) (1d) Grocers' Arms
250 THOMAS PIPPARD (A) (1d) Family Arms £60
251 FRANCES POOLE 1d 1656 Tallowchandlers' Arms
252 IOHN ROOKES (M) (1d) 1671 MART TAYLR
253 SAML STANBRIDG (M) (1d) 1653 Merchant Taylors' Arms
253A SA . . STANBRIDG 1d 1657 Grocers' Arms
254 RICHARD TIRELL (V) 1d Family Arms

Dromore (Down)
255 IOHN GVTHRY (M) 1d 1663 Haberdashers' Arms
256 EDWARD HALL 1d EVAGH, still
257 WILLIAM HALTRIGE 1d 1668 Heart
258 PHELEIM MAGENIS 1d 1656 Harp
259 — MEGENIS 1d n.d. —
260 WILLIAM MEATLAND (1d) Merchant's mark
261 WILL WILNE 1d 1667 DISTILLER

Dublin
262 City ½ 1679 City Arms; harp crowned (a pattern piece)

* See also no. 343

263 ALEXANDER AICKIN (M) 1d '65 IN SKINE(R)ROW, bear with mortar and pestle £60
264 —— (M) 1d '68 IN SKINEROW, —
265 ALEX — (1d) IN n.d. —
266 WILLIAM ALLEN (E) 1d 1663 Retort with spouts
267 (Misreading of 388)
268 (See below 289)
269 HENRY ASTON (1d) 1667 3 cocks; 3 gloves
270 WILLIAM BARRET (1d) CHRIST CHVRCH YARD, Arms £65
271 FRANCIS BEALING (1d) Bell
272 ROBERT BATRIP 1d 1657 CASTELL STREET, ship
273 IOHN BELLINGHAM (M) 1d Heart, CHANDLER
274 CHRISTOPHER BENNET (1d) THO STREET, 3 tuns b.s.
275 —— (1d) IN ST THOMAS, 3 tuns, b.s.
276 IOHN BETSON (E) 1d AT Y WHITE LION IN HIGH STREETE
277 ROGER BOLD 1d IN SKINNER ROW, griffin
278 HENRY BOLLARDT (E) 1d 1654 Pot of lilies, APOTICARY £40
279 —— (E) 1d 1663 —— £60
280 IOHN BRERETON 1d 1667 Family Arms
281 WALT BR(I)CE (1d) IN CORN MARKET, Family Arms
282 ELNATHAN BROCKE (1d) 1654 Fleur-de-lis b.s.
283 — BROCK (M) (1d) 1656 Fleur-de-lis on *obv.*
283A ELVATHAN BROCKE (1d) — Fleur-de-lis, b.s.
284 —— (1d) 1657 — £35
285 ELNATHAN — 1d —— SEEDMAN IN HYGHE STREETE
286 WILL BROOKING 1d Talbot, HABERDASHER £55
287 IGNATIVS BROWNE (I) 1d 1671 IN HIGH STRET PEVTR, tankard £70
288 RICHARD BVRNE 1d 1665 Swords crossed
289 IOHN BVSH 1d 1656 IN CASTLE STREETE £50
268 —— 1d 1663 —
290 IONATHAN BVTTERTON 1d '63 Dog with bird in mouth, PEWTRER HIGH STREETE
290A —— 1d '57 ——
291 SYMON CARCK (1d) IN BRIDG STRET, wheatsheaf
292 RICHARD CHESSES 1d IN ST WARBERS STRT, sugar-loaf
293 CHRISTOPHER CLEEAR 1d 2-headed eagle
294 STEPHEN CLARK 1d CHRIST CHVRCH YARD, Merchant Taylors' Arms
295 IAMES CLEERE (1d) IN BRIDG STREETE, Family Arms
296/7 GER(R)ARD COLLEY 1d AT RED, cross, IN HIGH STREET, APOTHECARY

298 WILLIAM COLLYS 1d 1666 IN SKINNER ROW, Family Arms £65
299 IO COOK, FRA BEALING (1d) Harp
300 IOHN COOKE (1d) GROCER IN DAMAS STREET, Family Arms
301 RICHARD COOKE 1d Unicorn £50
302 WI CRAVEN 1d IN CRIST CHVRCH YARD. Guns crossed; leopard
303 —— (1d) IN CHRIST CHVRCH YARD. ——
304 IOHN CREWES 1d 1657 VINTNER IN ST PATERICK STREET, mitres
305 —— 1d 1667 ——
306 NICH DELAMAIN (1d) IN STONIBATAR, crescent b.s.
307 MATHEW DAVIS 1d 1657 IN DAMASKE STREET, lion
308 IO DEMYNIERE (I) (1d) SVGER LOFE BRIG STRE(T) £55
308A —— (I) (1d) 3 SVGAR LOFE BRIG STRE £60
309 LEWIS DESMENIERES (1d) Acorn on branch £32
310/1 LEWIS DES (MYNIERES or MEYNIERS) 1d Arms £55
312 ANTHONY DERREY 1d 1657 IN CASTLE STREET, Arms £55
313 GEO DICKENSON 1d 1657 IN CHEKER LANE, chequers
314 MARTIN DIX 1d IN CORNE MARKET, St. George & dragon
315 MARY DRINKWATER 1d 1657 IN SKYNNER ROW £55
316 IOHN DVTTON 1d 1655 IN THOMAS STREET, Prince of Wales' feathers £42
317 LEONARD ELLIOTT (1d) 1657 CASTLE HILL, 8 diamonds
318 WILLIAM ETGER (1d) 1663 Key
319 WILL EVES 1d IN NICHOLAS STRET, 3 covered cups
320 IOHN FLEETWOOD (E) 1d CASTLE STREET
321 WILL FLEORY 1d POST MR
322 (Misreading of 323)
323 THO FLOOD 1d HIGH STRE(E)T, angel £50
324 (Misreading of 733)
325 IOHN FORRIST (A) (1d) AT THE BRIDG FOOTE, 3 castles
326/7 IOHN FOXALL (1d) AT (YE *or* THE) SIGNE OF THE FOX £40
328 ROBERT FREEMAN 1d IN CASTLE STREET, dove with olive branch
329 MATHEW FRENCH (1d) 1655 IN HIGH STREET. Dolphin; sugar-loaf
330 GEORGE GILBERT 1d IN BRIDG STREET, Family Arms
331 THO GOOLD 1d IN HIGH STRE(E)T, Family Arms £38
332 THO GOSSLIN 1d 1668 OF OXMANTOWNE, gateway
333 RICHARD GRENWOOD 1d HIGH STRET, St Patrick cursing vipers, church behind
334 IAMES G . . . NS ½ 1669 3 castles. In *brass*, circular centre of *copper*
335 ROGER HALLEY (1d) ARTIZEN AND SKINNER IN SKINNER ROWE £70
336 EDWARD HARRIS 1d IN COPPER ALLY. Mortar and pestle; wreaths
337 NICHOLAS HARRIS (L) 1d TAL(L)OW CHANDLER
338 WALTER HARRIS (1d) Merchant's mark; hen and chicks
339 ARTHVR HARVIE 1d Crown
340 — HARVEY (1d) 1656 IN HIGH STREETE, 3 rabbits feeding
341 ARTHER HARWIE (1d) 1653 3 rabbits feeding
342 RIDGLEY HATFEILD 1d 1654 Castle £50
343 IO HAYENS ON YE KEY, HEN COKER OF DROHEDA ES 1d 1656 Blazing star; harp. *Cross-shaped inset of different metal*
343A IOHN HAYNES (1d) ON THE KEY, VINT, blazing star. In *brass* with cross-shaped *copper* inset. **Plate 4**
344 WILL HILL 1d 1656 SKENER ROW, monkey with paws on mortar and pestle, PESTELL AN MORTAR £65
345 IOHN HOOGGON 1d AT THE TIMBER YARD, DAMAS STREET
346 RICHARD HOVGHTON 1d Swan £65
347 ROBERT HVCHINS 1d SWAN, BLIND KEY
347A IACOB HVDSON 1d Square (?), COME
348 WILLIAM HVLME (E) (1d) IN HIGH STREET, 3 mallets £35
349 GILBERT IOHNSON (1d) IN ST THOMAS STREET, Cordwainers' Arms
349A ALLIN IONES 1d 1657 Arms
350 IAMES KELLEY 1d IN NICOLAS STRET, 3 covered cups
351 (Worn example of 717)
352 IOHN KELLY 1d Castle, unicorns
353 OWEN KELLY (1d) 1666 IN SKINERS ROW, ? tun
354 RANDAL LESTER (R) (1d) 1655 IN THOMAS STREET, Red Indian smoking pipe† £65
354A —— (R) (1d) 1656 ——
355 ANDREW LLOYD (E) (1d) '58 Weavers' Arms £38
355A —— (E) 1d 16??*
356/7 IOHN LOVETT 1d 1657 IN THOMAS STRET(E), Saddlers' Arms
358 THO LOWEN (1d) IN PATRICK STREET, scales
359 RALPH MALBORN 1d Hat, HABERDASHER
360 HENRY MARTYN (E) 1d 1668 SKINNER ROW, martin

* known only with cmk. – see no. 704
† Also known cmkd. A K

361 RICHARD MARTIN 1d 1657 CASTEL STREET, Blacksmiths' Arms
362 IAMES MEADER 1d IN NICHOLAS STREET, still, cask, 3 small vessels £60
363 ROBERT MELLER 1d CASTLE STREET, APOTHECARY
364 EDWARD MICHELL 1d IN FISH SHAMBLE STREET, fleece
365 —— 1d OF OXMAN TOWNE. —
366 WILLIAM MILLES 1d 1671 Woolpack, CLOTHIR, HIGH STREET
367 — MYLLES (A) 1d HI STREET
368 WALTER MOTTLEY (D) 1d IN BRIDG STREET, oak tree £65
369 WILL MOVNT 1d IN CHRIST CHVRCH YARD, Arms £55
370 IOHN MOXON 1d 1667 IN SKINER ROWE, wheatsheaf £60
371 LIONELL NEWMAN (1d) 1664 THE COFFEE HOVSE, Turk's head, *Morat*
372 IOHN NICHOLAS 1d
372A MATHEW NVLTY (B) 1d FISHAMBLESTREET
373 THOMAS ORR .... 1d BRIDGFOOT, Arms
374 THO PAGETT 1d TALLOW CHANDLER HIGH STREET
375 STEPHEN PALMER 1d 1656 IN DAMASCK STREET, 3 storks
376 IO PARTINGTON 1d GOVLDSME KINGES HEAD SKINOR ROW, Arms £60
377 ROBERT PARTINGTON 1d 2-headed eagle
378 HVGH PRESTON 1d 1666 AT YE BLACK BOY IN ST GEORGES LANE, star £60
379 IOHN PVLLER 1d IN FISHAMBLE STREET, bird £30
380 DENNIS QVINNE (A) 1d 1654 Flying horse £65
381 MARKE QVINE (M) 1d 1654 APOTHYCARY, winged horse
381A WILL RABIS (A) 1d F(?ISHA)MBLE STREET, sheep
382 (Misreading of 354)
383 HENRY REYNOLDS 1d IN HIGH STREET, plough £60
384 IESPAR ROADS 1d 1657 BARBARDAS CASTELL STREET, plantation, men working
385 HENRY RVGGE 1d APOTHECARY IN CASTLE STREET, Family Arms
385A —— 1d APOTHECARY IN CASTLE STREET, —; swan crest
386 SAMVELL SALTONSTONE (1d) Angel
387 IOHN SEAWELL 1d BRASER IN SKINER ROW, stag
388 IOHN SENDELL (A) 1d IN ST FRANCIS STRET, horse £55
388A IO SIBBALD 1d IN CASTLE STREET APOTHCARY, bird
389 RICH SIMKIN 1d Eagle and child
390 IEREMY SMITH, IEREMY BERSTOW (1d) 1654 Squirrel b.s.
391 IOH SMITH 1d IN HIGH STRE, 3 birds
392 THOMAS SPEGHT 1d '65 EXCHANG CHRIST CHVRCH YARD, The Tholsel (City Hall) £75
393 EDMVND SPRING 1d Flying horse
394 THO SPRINGHAM (1d) HARRY STRETE, 3 lions
395 WILLAM STOKS (K) 1d 1671 IN HIGH STR £40
396 GEORGE STOVGHTON 1d Cross, crescent
397 HENERY ST ..... 1d 1657 MALSTER (?OXMAN)TOWNE
398 IOHN SWEETMAN (1d) CORNE MARKET, dolphin
399 ISAAC TAYLER 1d 1657 IN SKINER ROW, ?cockscomb
400 WILL TAYLOR 1d IN SKINNER ROW, ostrich
401 EDMOND THOMPSON 1d 1665 Grocers' Arms
402 IOHN TOTTIE 1d 1657 AT THE BRIDGFOOTE, bridge
403 —— (R) 1d 1663 Boar's head £42
403A (?ISA)CK TVRNELL 1d 1657 HI STREET PLAYT WORKER, 3 fishes
404 RICH TYLE (1d) OF ST PATRICKS CLOSE, Arms
405/6 ARLENTER VSHER (1d) (IN) FISH SHAMBLES STREET £60
407 DAN WALLSBY 1d 1657 INNKEPER DAMASKE STREETE, hart
407A RICHARD WARDE 1d DISTILLER
408 HENRY WARREN (I) (1d) IN HIGH STRET, wreath around plumed coronet
409 IOHN WARREN (C) (1d) HIGH STRET TALLOW CHANDLR Monogram as merchant's mark
410 RICHARD WARREN (E) 1d 1667 IN ST THOMAS STREET, chequers
410A As last, in *pb*
411 EDWARD WAYNMAN 1d IN CORKE HILL, dragon
412 WARNAR WESTENRA (1d) 1655 Ship £38
412A —— (1d) n.d. OF BRIDG STR, merchant's mark(?)
413 SAMVELL WESTON (1d) 1654 Chained swan; dolphin £32
414 EDWARD WHITAKER 1d CASELL STREET, 3 fleurs-de-lis
415 NICHOLAS WHITE 1d IN HIGH STREET, Grocers' Arms

416 MIC WI(LS *or* ST)ON ½ 1672 Butchers' Arms and crest; St. George & dragon*. **Plate 4** £14
417 (Probably misreading of 416)
418 HENRY YEATES (1d) IN COPPER ALLY, Family Arms

Dundalk (Louth)
419 CORPORATION 1d 1663 3 birds
420/1 BRANW(AYTE *or* YSE) CEASAR 1d 2-headed eagle
422 OATES CROWDER 1d 1656 Harp
422A PLEDGE FVGILL 1d 3 woolpacks(?)
423 GEORGE LAMBERT 1d Paschal lamb
424 IOHN WILSHIERT 1d

Dundrum (Down)
425 WILLIAM MEATLAND (1d) Merchant's mark; scales

Dungannon (Tyrone)
426 IAMES HANNA 1d Ship
427/8 RO(BT) NELLSON (1d) POTHERY *or* APOTHECRY. Pestle and mortar; still

Dungarvan (Waterford)
428A ROBRT COCK (1d) 1666 Cock
428B As last, cmkd. HP (? for ½d.)
429 DANIELL DAYNES (M) 1d Lion, merchant's mark, INN KEEPER
430 THOMAS NICOLL 1d 1677 Arms £50
431 (Probably misreading of 430)
432 IOHN PORTER ½ '68 Family Arms
433 —— 1d 1668 —

Dungarvan and Youghal (Waterford)
434 ROBART ROBENS 1d 1656 Merchant's mark

Dunlavin (Wicklow)
435 IONAH WOODMAN (M) 1d Scales
435A THAD . . . AM 1d Castle

Edgeworthstown (Longford)
436 FRANSIS WELSH (1d) '74 Fleur-de-lis; sugar-loaf

Elphin (Roscommon)
437 ANDREW MARTIN 1d Family Arms
437A PATRICK WHITE (1d) Arms

Ennis (Clare)
438 DAVID WHITE ½ Crowned harp; cross, annulet quarterly
439 (Probably misreading of 441)
440 (Probably misreading of 438)
441 DA WHITE ½ '79 Cross, 3 roses and mullet in quarters; crowned harp

Enniscorthy (Wexford)
441A P.G. 1d St Patrick in cope and mitre with patriarchal cross, ST PATRICK FOR IERLAND

* This token is thought to have been counterfeited at the time.

442 RICHARD WHITEARE 1d Plough

Enniskeen (Cork)
443 HENRY WHEDDON 1d 1678 Ship; men working in blacksmith's shop. Edge: pellets

Enniskillen (Fermanagh)
444 ABRAHAM CLEMENTS (1d) '57 Fleur-de-lis
445 WILLIAM COOPER 1d Arms
446 IAMES REID 1d 1663 Bell
447 DAVID RYND 1d Swan
448 IOHN RYND 1d
448A IAMES WORNOCK 1d Eagle

Ferry Carrig (Wexford)
449 IOHN NEAON ½ Man rowing boat

Fore (Westmeath)
450 GAROTT TYRELL 1d Cross pattée

Freshford (Kilkenny)
451 (Probably *Somerset* 126)

Galway
452 THOMAS ANDREWES 1d Arms; hat
452A RICHARD BALLARD 1d Bell
453 FRANCIS BANCKES 1d Pot of lilies, PEWTERER
454 IOHN BODLE 1d Arms
455 THO BROVGHTON (M) 1d 1669 Lion
456 PATR BROWNE 1d 1669 Sheep
457 PATRICK BROWNE 1d Merchant's mark
458 THOMAS BROWNE 1d Sun
459 ABRM CHRISTIAN 1d 1670 Fish, crown; bull. **Plate 4** £45
460 EDMOND COYNE 1d 1669 Winged horse
460A —— 1d n.d. Griffin
461 GEORG DAVISON 1d IN HIGH STREET, lion
461A PAVL DODD 1d 1658 Ship
461B GARRALD FITZGERALD 1d Shield with initials
462 BAR FRENCH (1d) 1659 THE SHIP INSHVRED
463 DOMINICK FRENCH 1d 1664 Dolphin
463A —— 1d 1665 —
463B DO(MINICK FRENCH?) 1d 16(7?)7 Ship
464 (Probably same as 463)
465 IOHN GROOME 1d 1664 Heart, VIVE LE ROY £70
465A ROB HADLOCKE 1d Fox
466 WALTER HICKES 1d 1669 Lion
467 IARVIS HINDE 1d Hind
468 WILL IACKSON (S) 1d Mercers' Arms, VINTNER
469 WILLIAM — (S) 1d 1668 —
470 NICHOLAS KIRWAN 1d Family Arms
471 AMBROSE LINCH 1d 1668
472 AMBROS LYNCH 1d Lion and harp
473 DOMINICKE LYNCH 1d 1665 2-headed eagle £50
474 MARCVS LYNCH 1d Mermaid with mirror, comb

475 IOHN MORREY 1d Arms
476 SAMVELL NEWTON 1d Family Arms
477 EDWARD ORMSBY 1d Angel
478 RICHARD ORMSBY (1d) Rose on heart pierced by arrows
479/80 PE(E)TER PARR (I) 1d 1669 Halberdier
481 ALDRIGE SADLER (E) 1d BAKER
482 WILL STANLY 1d 1659 Covered cups; Arms
483 GEORGE STANTON 1d St. George & dragon
483A ROBERT STORY 1d 1660
484 STE VINES 1d 1664 Bunch of grapes; anchor
485 ROB WARNER (K) 1d 1664 Rose

Glanerough (Kerry)
486 I.R. 1d 1667 Kiln with flames, IRON WORKES; 2 kiln entrances
487 I.R. 1d 1669 — — —

Glasslough (Monaghan)
488 IOHN PATERSON 1d 1671 Arms
489 WILLIAM IOHNSTON 1d 1659 Arms

Glenarm (Antrim)
490 ARCHIBALD ADDAIRE (1d) Gloves crossed; merchant's mark
491 WILM CRAGG 1d 1670 Dog with bird in mouth; man with scythe
492 — — 1d 1677 Dog?; —
492A IOHN STEWART 1d Arms

Gorey
(See 215)

Gowran (Kilkenny)
493 FRANCIS BARKER 1d 1656 Angel
493A — — (B) (1d) — —
494 THOMAS HVSSEY 1d 1658 2-headed eagle
495 WILL SANNIACH 1d Tower with flag

Hacketstown (Carlow)
495A ANTHONY RYAN 1d Barrel
496 IONAH WOODMAN 1d Scales

Hillsborough (Down)
496A THO LEATHES 1d Fleur-de-lis

Hollywood (Down)
497 IAMES SIM 1d Heart

Inniscrone (Sligo)
498 THO GOODIN 1d 1663 Castle
499 (Probably misreading of 498)

Jamestown (Leitrim)
500 BRYAN BIERNE 1d 1658 Acorn on branch
500A DANIELL MORAN 1d Lion, harp

Katherinestown (?)
500B WILL HVNTER (1d) Spade, GARDNR

Kells (Meath)
501 EDWARD DYES (1d) 1669 Loom; merchant's mark
502 IGNATIVS FLEMEING 1d Plume of feathers, crown £60

Kerry County
503 T.S. (1d) Arms of Commonwealth. *Rectangular*
504 (1d) IN THE COVNTY Swan; crane

Kilbeggan (Westmeath)
505 HENR(Y) DAY (1d) Blazing star
506 RICHARD HARISON 1d 1658

Kilcullen Bridge (Kildare)
507 THOMAS COWRAN 1d Lion

Kildare
508 CRISTOPH CV(S *or* Z)ACK 1d Bull
509 IAMES MONEY (B) (1d) Cross pattée

Kilfinan (Limerick)
510 IOHN GODSELL 1d
511 — — 1d 1667 Fleur-de-lis £32

Kilkenny
512 City 1d 1659 Castle, lion below. FOR THE POORE
513 THOMAS ADAMS 1d 1658 Castle, lion £50
514 — — ½ — — —*
515 IOHN BEAVOR 1d Beaver biting at plant £65
516 THOMAS DAVIS 1d EXCIS(E) OFFIS, lion's head
517 PETER GOODIN 1d Fleur-de-lis
518 RICHARD INWOOD 1d Windmill
519 WILLIAM KEOVGH 1d Mermaid, GOLDSMITH £70
520 IOHN LANGTON 1d Family Arms
521 THOMAS NEVELL 1d 1658 Harp £55
522 THOMAS POOLE 1d Lion
523 IAMES PVRCELL 1d IRISHTOWNE, Family Arms £40
524 EDWARD ROTH 1d 1663 Family Crest £35
525 EDWARD SEWELL 1d TALLOW CHAN
526 RALPH SKANLAN 1d 1656 Swan £65
527 THOMAS TALBOT 1d Sun, VINTNER
528 LVCAS WALE (I) 1d Family Arms
529 IOHN WHITTLE 1d 1656 Commonwealth Arms £50
529A — — 1d 1658 —
530 (Same as 532)
531 1d 1677 Castle, FOR YE VSE & CONVENIENCIE OF THE INHABITANTS
532 As last, cmkd HAPENNY

*Nos. 513/4 were issued by the Corporation during the Mayoralty of Adams. Specimens of 513 were recalled in 1672 and reissued as farthings.

Killarney (Kerry)
533 TIMOTHY FALVEY 1d Harp

Killashandra (Cavan)
534 IAMES FORREST (1d) 1667 Castle; anchor, merchant's mark

Killyleagh (Down)
535 DAVID POLLOK (1d) 1664 Merchant's mark; castle
535A ALEX (RE?)AD 1d
535B GEORGE S(EY?)ERS 1d 1659 DISTILAR
536 IAMES WILLIAMSON 1d 1668 Castle

Killucan (Westmeath)
537 IGNATIVS FERAYNE ½ 16?? Lion; unicorn

Kilmallock (Limerick)
538 IAMES CARPENTER 1d Church; arrows piercing heart
539 MATHEW MEADE 1d 1673 Family Arms

Kilrea (Londonderry)
540 NICHOLAS EDWARDS (1d) 1678 Female bust (crest); merchant's mark

Kilworth (Cork)
541 CHRISTO CROKER (1d) 1667 Family Arms. Cmkd. with interlinked C's
542 (Misreading of 541)

Kinsale (Cork)
543 Town ¼ 1655 Town Arms, crest
543A — ¼ 1659 — —
544 — ¼ 1668 — —
545 — 1d 1659 — — £48
546 — 1d 1668 — —
546A As last, cmkd. ½ (issued 1675)
547 Town 1d 1677 Portcullis; town Arms, crest. Edge, DEPRESSA RESVRGO. **Plate 4** £30
548 (Misreading of 547)
548A WILLIAM BILLINGE 1d 16(73?)
549 THOMAS BVRROWES 1d 1667 Griffin
549A AVGVSTINE CHARLE 1d 1668 Arms
550 IOHN SVXBERY (1d) 1660
550A — — (1d) 1658
551 IOHN WATTS 1d 1668 Family Arms

Knockmoan (Waterford)
551A HVGH W . . D 1d 1673 Castle on mound

Knocktopher (Kilkenny)
552 GEORGE ROBBINS (S) 1d

Lambeg (Antrim)
553 THO RICKABIE 1d Arms

Lazey Hill (Dublin)
554 WILLIAM CROSE (1d) Cross, woolpack
555 NIC DELONE 1d Fruiterers' Arms. **Plate 4** £45
556 NICHOLAS ROCHFORD 1d Crowned bust £50

Letterkenny (Donegal)
557 WILLIAM ANDERSON 1d Harp; merchant's mark
558 IAMES CONINGHAM 1d Merchant's mark; harp

Limerick
559–61 LIMERICK, CLARE (1d) Castle; castle of 3 towers £65
562 (Same as 559)
563/4 CIT(T)Y (¼) 1658 Castle, CHANG(E) & CHARITY £24
565 BVTCHERS ½ 1679 Paschal lamb; Butchers' Arms £40
566 ANTHONY BARTLETT 1d 1671 Arms; 3 castles £55
567 — — (1d) — — — £55
568 IOHN BELL (1d) Horse; tree
569 IOHN BENNET (M) (1d) 1668 Castle £60
569A — — (M) 1d 1663 — £60
569B — — (M) ½ 1668 —
570 EDWARD CLARKE 1d 1670 Cock
571 — — ½ — —
572 ROWLAND CREAGH (1d) 3 lilies; dove with olive branch
573 B.G. (1d) 1668 NEAR KEY LANE, merchant's mark
574 THO LINCH ½ 1679 Winged bull; harp £35
575 (Probably misreading of 576)
576 THOMAS MARTEN (1d) 1669 3 castles £55
577 RICHARD PEARCE (M) (1d) 1668 APOTHECA(RY) £50
578 WILLIAM RIMPLAND ½ 1679 Man making candles
579 — — ½ 1669 — £60
580/1 ED WIGHT ½ 1677 3 castles; ship £30

Lisburn (or **Lisnegarvy**) (Antrim)
582 WILLIAM ANDREWS 1d 1671 Merchant's mark; tree
583 — — 1d n.d. — —
583A WILLIAM BROWN 1d 1671 Merchant's mark; tree
583B WILLIAM DOVLAR 1d 1666 A(T?) (T?)ANARD
583C ED ELLIS 1d 1667 APOTHECARY
584 (Same as 595)
584A GEORGE GREGSON 1d 1659 Covered cup; scales
585 ADDAM LEATHES 1d Family Arms; heart, GENT
586 GEORGE LOCKHART 1d Heart; Family Arms
587 BRIAN MAGEE (1d)
588 DENIS MAGEE 1d Heart on shield
589 EDWARD MOORE (1d) 1666
590 IO PEERS 1d Parish Church
591 OLIVER TAYLOR 1d 1658 Heart on shield, MARCHANT

592 OLIVER TAYLOR 1d n.d. Heart, MERCER
593 —— 1d 1658 — MR
594 W.R., D.M. 1d 1656 Heart
594A W.R., 1d

Lisburn, and **Coleraine** (Londonderry)
595 ANTH WRIGHTSON LISB, ST IOHN GREEN COLRANE 1d

Lismalin (Tipperary)
596 GARRET QVIGLEY 1d 1659 2-headed eagle £65

Londonderry
597 (1d) EXCH FOR FISHING AND CLOATHINGE
598 IAMES BARTON 1d 1666 Family Arms
598A IOHN BIRNIE (1d) Arms; unicorn
599 IOHN BVCHANAN (1d) Dove with olive branch; merchant's mark
600 IOHN CAMPSIE 1d Merchant Adventurers' Arms; merchant's mark
601 ANDREW CVNINGHAME 1d Arms
602 IAMES CONINGHAM 1d '68 Merchant's mark; harp
603 SAMVELL DAWSON (1d)
603A IOHN DOVGALL 1d Arrows piercing heart
604 IOHN ELVIN (1d) 1657 AT YE FERRY
604A IAMES FISHER 1d Harp; merchant's mark
604B —— 1d 1657 Merchant's mark; harp
605 IAMES HOBSON 1d Tree
606 WILLIAM KYLLE 1d 2-headed eagle
607 PEETER LAWSON (1d) Arms; merchant's mark
608 WILLIAM LENNOX 1d Branches crossed; initials W.L.
608A —— 1d —, with C's in angles; no initials
609 IAMES MORRISON 1d Mortar and pestle
610 SAMVELL RATCLIFFE 1d Heart; merchant's mark
611 WILLIAM RODGER (1d) Ship; merchant's mark £70
611A IAMES SVTTON 1d 1665

Longford
612 ROGER FARELL 1d Unicorn

Loughgall (Armagh)
613 ROBERT BENNETT 1d Arms

Loughrea (Galway)
614 HENREY BARGERY 1d
615 FRANCES BLAKE 1d Stag
616 CHRISTOPHER FRENCH 1d 1656 Dolphin
617 RICHARD HARRIS 1d '77 Family Arms, SKNER
618 DANIELL KELLY 1d Sugar-loaf
618A —— 1d Tree
619 EDMOND KELLY 1d Tree
620 LAVRENCE MOORE 1d Swan
621 CHRISTOFER POORE 1d Lion on *rev.*
621A CHRIST(OPHER) POWER 1d Lion on *obv.*
622/3 IOHN PO(ORE *or* WER) 1d Lion
623A LARENCE WALDRON 1d Angel

Lurgan (Armagh)
624 THOMAS WHITE 1d 1666 Ship; anchor

Magherafelt (Londonderry)
625 HVGH RAINEY 1d 1671 Sun
626 WILLIAM RAINEY (1d) 1668 Mercers' Arms

Magheralin (Down)
627 GILBERT FERGESON (1d) Tobacco-roll

Magheramorne (Antrim)
628 IOHN BVRNES 1d 1672 Plough

Mallow (Cork)
629 IOHN HOLLANDS 1d 1668 Scales b.s., YE DE(M *or* RN)EENE & MOYALLO CHANGE

Manor Cunningham (Donegal)
629A IOH MACKMANVS 1d 1657 Groups of arrow-heads
629B —— 1d 1669 8 arrow-heads

Manorhamilton (Leitrim)
630 GEORGE ROBB 1d Merchant's mark; arrows piercing heart

Maryborough (Laois)
631 WALTER GORMAN 1d Man making candles, CHAN
632 EDWARD NICHOLLS (M) (1d) Rose crowned
633 IOHN PARTRIDGE 1d 1658 Lion £65
634 IAMES PRENDERGAST 1d

Maynooth (Kildare)
635 RALPH BVLLOCK 1d Man on horseback, POSTMASTER

Milltown Pass (Westmeath)
636 EDMVND DILLON (1d) Family Arms
636A RICHARD DILLON (1d) Family Arms
636B GEORGE DOWDALL 1d Dove with olive branch

Mitchelstown (Cork)
637 THOMAS COOKE (1d) 1661 Fleur-de-lis

Monaghan
638 ROBERT AGNEW 1d Church
639 DAVID CHAMBERS 1d 1663 Haberdashers' Arms
640 GEORGE CVNNINGHAM 1d 1664 (on *rev.*)
640A — CVNINGHAME 1d — (date on *obv.*)

Monasterevin (Kildare)
641 THO BVRROWS 1d Man in armour
642 ROBERT HOBSON (1d)
643 NAT SWAINE 1d 1673 3 buckles with straps, TANNER

Moneymore (Londonderry)
644 DAVID BELL 1d 1671 Bell

645 HENRY HVNTER (1d) 1671 Hunter's horn
645A IOHN M(ET?)RIN 1d 1657 Tree

Mountmellick (Laois)
645B THO CREED 1d Kiln with flames; kiln entrances
646 NATHANIEL DIER (M) 1d 1664
647 — — (M) 1d 1665
648 WILLIAM WILCOCKS 1d 1670 SADLR
649 RICHARD WRIGHT 1d 1656 £60
650 — — 1d 1659

Mountrath (Laois)
651 NICHOLAS RAGGET (1d) Hart £48

Moyne (Tipperary)
652 THOMAS MVRE (1d) Arms; merchant's mark

Mullingar (Westmeath)
653 S.R. (1d) THESE TOKENS ARE FOR MVLLINGAR
654 IOHN DOVGLAS 1d 1659 VINTENER
655 THOMAS GILL 1d Lion; hare
656 THO — ½ — —
657 CHRISTOPHER GILBERT (C) 1d
658 IAMES KENNEDY 1d Family Arms
659 ANTHONI MELAGHLIN 1d Lion
660 CHARLS MELLAGHLIN ½ Lion
661 IAMES MELAGHLIN 1d 1655 Lion £48
661A — — 1d 1665 —
662 IA(ME)S MELLAGHLIN *or* IAMES MELLAGHLEN ½ Lion; 2-headed eagle
663 CRISTOHER PETTIT 1d 1667 Winged horse

Naas (Kildare)
664 RICHARD EVSTAS 1d '68 Wheatsheaf

Navan (Meath)
665 ANT CAMDEN 1d Hand from cloud grasping heart; cross crowned
666 DANIEL LEIGH 1d 1658 Cross

Nenagh (Tipperary)
667 ROB HVTCHINSON (1d) 1658 Man on horse, CLEARK
668 — — (1d) 1659 — —
669 IOSEPH LVCAS 1d 1668 Falcon
670 MAVRICE THOMAS 1d 1666 St. George & dragon

Newcastle (Limerick)
670A WILLIAM BRVDENELL 1d '68 Arms
671 PATRICK CREAGH 1d 166? Tree; castles

Newmarket (Cork)
671A THOMAS (BELL?) 1d 1679 Man on horseback

Newry (Down)
671B HENERY GARDNER (1d) Castle
672 (Probably misreading of 673)
673 ALEX HALL 1d 1668 Hand holding wafer (?)
674 IOHN TERRILL 1d 16?9 Lion
675 IOHN MIDDLETON (1d) Winged horse; tree

Newtownards (Down)
676 IAMES SMARTTS 1d Forearm on crescent; heart
677 IAMES TEMPLETON ½ Gauntlets crossed

Newtown Bagnal (Carlow)
678 WALTER KARNEY (1d) Anchor

(Newtown) Limavady (Londonderry)
679 IOHN HILLHOVSE (1d) Building, NEW HAL; merchant's mark
680 IOHN OLLIVER (1d) Building, NEW HAL; merchant's mark

Phillipstown (now **Daingean**) (Offaly)
681 RICHARD LAMBERT (1d) Paschal lamb; chicken

Portaferry (Down)
682 ROB BELL (1d) 1665 Bell; merchant's mark

Portarlington (Laois)
683 GEORGE COPE (H) (1d) 1673 Blacksmiths' Arms

Raphoe
(See 220)

Rathdrum (Wicklow)
684 IAMES LVCAING 1d Stag

Rathmullen (Donegal)
685 GEORGE HENDERSON 1d Arms

Roscommon
686 VALLENTINE BROWNE 1d 2-headed eagle
687 RICHARD GIRACHT 1d 1657 Castle
688 IOHN HINDS (G) 1d Crown, hind
689 IOHN SLATAR 1d Chequers

Roscrea (Tipperary)
690 IOHN SMITH (E) (1d) Lion

Ross (Wexford)
691 EDWARD DAVIS 1d Lion, V(I *or* E)NTENER
692 RICHARD DELAHYD 1d Arms £65
692A NICHOLAS KEALY 1d 1668 Arms, APOTHECARY
693 IOHN OLLIVER 1d '68 Name in monogram*
694 NATANIEL QVARME 1d 1657 Arms
694A — — 1d 1668 —
695 R.S. 1d 1673 Tree; arm holding sword, THE DILIGE(N)T HAND MAKETH RICH ROS £42

St Albans (now **Lissacoly**) (Longford)
695A TADI FARRELL 1d

Sligo
696 IOHN CONINGHAME (1d) Dove with olive branch; pelican feeding young

* This token also known cmkd I B

697 WILLIAM CRAFORD 1d Harp
697A IOHN CREAN (1d) Ship; heart
698 ARCHIBOLD CVNINGHAM 1d 1678 Merchant's mark £70
699 WILL HVNTER 1d Hunter's horn
700 WAITER LYNCH (1d) 1669 Family Arms
700A MATHEW MAR(CH?) 1d 1656 dolphin
701 IOHN SMITH (1d) Ship; heart

Strabane (Tyrone)
701A IOHN BROWN (1d) Arms; merchant's mark
702 IAMES CONINGHAME (I) (1d) 1664 Merchant's mark
702A IOHN M . . . 1d Merchant Adventurers' Arms
702B CLAVD SCOTT 1d

Strokestown (Roscommon)
703 TADY MAHON 1d Harp, crown

Tallaght (Dublin)
704 T.C. 1d. TALOVGH T.C. cmkd. on no. 355A

Swords (Dublin)
705 C.S. (1d). *Square**

Tanderagee (Armagh)
706 IOHN RICHARDSON 1d Hand holding sword, QVARTER MASTER

Thurles (Tipperary)
707 THOMAS FITZGERALD 1d 1657 Castle £40
708 RICHARD PVRSELL 1d Arms £55

Tipperary
709 R.C. 1d WILL CHANGE THEM AGAN

Toomebridge (Antrim)
710 RICH BODKIN 1d Man in boat, FOR FERRY FORGE AND FISH

Tralee (Kerry)
711 ROWLAND BATEMAN 1d 1671 Arms, crest
712 IAMES CONNOR, MICHAELL FALKINER 1d Castle, falcon

Trim (Meath)
713 PATRICK CLINTON 1d Harp
713A IGNATIVS FRA(YNE?) 1d
714 GEORGE HARRIS (E) 1d 1663 Angel blowing horn
715 GIDEON HAYNE (I) 1d Family Arms, crest £38
716 PATHRICK HELOND 1d Sheaf of barley
717/8 IAMES KELLYE 1d Arrow piercing heart £65
718A T.L. (M) (1d) Bird

Tuam (Galway)
719 IAMES TRESSY 1d 1670 Lynch family Arms

Tullamore (Offaly)
720 ROBERT WORRALL (E) 1d '70 Half boot

* Perhaps not a 17th cent. token

Tullow (Carlow)
721 RICH BVRCHALL (D) (1d) St. George & dragon
721A RICHARD — (1d) 1656 —
722 IOHN GARDINER (H) (1d) Woolpack

Tullow Phelim (Carlow)
723 MATHEW LONG 1d Eagle above hare

Waterford
724 ANDREW RICKARDS (1d) (16)58 Castle; City Arms, MAYOR
725 CORPORATION (1d) 1668 City Arms; castle £40
725A — 1d 1667 City Arms
726 Corporation (1d) (16)59 City Arms b.s. WATERFORDS SAFETY WISHED, PROCEED (AND *or* &) PROSPER £45
727 (Probably misreading of 16)
728 MAR CROSSELEY 1d '79 Crown, dove with olive branch
729 ZACH CLAYTON (1d) '68 Woolpack, initials H^D A
730 PE(E) CRAN(E *or* I)SBROVGH 1d 1671 Lion £32
731 THO EXTON 1d Market square, VINTNER
731A —— 1d — INKEEPER
732 IOHN HEAVEN 1d 1656 City Arms £55
733 WILLIAM IOYE (1d) 1667 Initials H.D.A.
734 THOMAS NOBLE (A) 1d 1656 MERCHT, CITTY
734A —— (A) (1d) — MERCHANT *or* MARCHA
735 —— (A) (1d) n.d. Ship
736 DAVID OWEN 1d '71 Seraph with 6 wings
737 BENIAMIN POWELL (1d) 1673 Monogram of name. Fleur-de-lis cmk.
738 EDMAND RVSSELL 1d '73 Family Arms £35
739 (Probably a worn example of 738)
740 MARY STEPHENS 1d 1667 Mortar and pestle
741 IOHN TYL(ER *or* EY) 1d 1667 Man tending furnace, still above

Westmeath County
742 IOHN LORTE 1d 1658 Dove with olive branch

Wexford
743 PAVL ALFE(RI *or* RY) 1d 1665 CORDWINDER
744 ISACK FREEBORN 1d Commonwealth Arms, INNKEEPER
745 FRANC(IS) HARVEY 1d Family Arms, WHEN YOV PLEASE ILE CHAINGE THES
746 CHARLES HVDDEL (E) (1d) Anchor, rope £65
747 IOHN ILLINGWORTH 1d 1657 Men holding spindle, CLOTHYER
748 THOMAS IONES 1d St. George & dragon
749 MICHAELL KEARNEY 1d Arms, DISTILER £38
750 GEORG LININGTON (M) 1d Sheep, shepherd's crook, MERCER £45
750A GR LI (M) 1d 1654
751 WILLIAM LOVELL 1d

752 THOMAS LOW (M) (1d) 1654 Ship £50
753 —— 1d 1656 Man tending furnace, still above £38
753A —— 1d 1666 ——
754 CONSTANTINE NEAL (1d) Ship £40
755 WILLIAM TREVILL (1d) Family Arms; Town Arms
756 EDWARD VALE (M) (1d) Wheatsheaf
756A PAVL WAKEFIELD 1d 1657 Arms

Wicklow
757 EDW HARTSHORNE (1d) '58 Mercers' Arms
758 IAMES MYTCH (1d) SHOOE MAKR
759 CHRISTOPHER WATKINS (C) (1d) 3 castles

Youghal (Cork)
760/1 P.G. 1d 1658 Town Arms, IF NOT LIKED ILE CHA(I)NG THEM. (Town piece)
762 THOMAS COOKE 1d 1671 Scales. Cmkd. FARTHING
763 IOHN GERALD (I) 1d 1667 Gerard family Arms, crest
764 FLORENCE GILES (1d) Griffin
765 IOHN HANCOCKE (1d) 1666 Family Arms
766 WALLTER HIBBARD (M) (1d) 1668 Family Arms
767 THOMAS IONES (1d) Anchor
768 IOHN LVTHER 1d 1672 Name in monogram. Cmkd. YOVGHAL, and script *I L*
769 As last, *not* cmkd.
770 EDWARD LAWNDEY (1d) Fishmongers' Arms
771 IOHN MERRICK (1d) Arms £60
772 EDWARD PERRY (D) (1d) 1667 Prince of Wales' feathers
773 —— (1d) 1672 Name in monogram; —
774 As last, cmkd. pair of shears
775 IOHN PINNE (1d) 1657
776 THOMAS VAVGH(A *or* O)N (1d) Family Arms £60
777 ABRAHAM VAVGHAN 1d Man on horseback blowing horn, POST MASTER
778 THOMAS WALTERS (1d) Oak-branch
779 ANDREW WANDRIK (1d) 1656 Fleur-de-lis £50

Unknown Locality
779A W.A. (1d) Castle. *Octagonal*
779B F.B., I.C. (1d) Merchant's mark
779C P.B. (1d) Merchant's mark
779D H.C. (1d) Merchant's mark (?)
779E GORGE HACKETT (M), PATERICK HACKETT (M) (1d) 1666
779F I.M. (1d) Merchant's mark

These, with the exception of no. 779E, are probably all from Ulster. They occur struck on French doubles tournois, as do some other tokens from this province.

ISLE OF MAN

See James A. Mackay, *The Pobjoy Encyclopaedia of Isle of Man Coins and Tokens* (2nd edition; Sutton, 1978).

See also C. Clay, *Currency of the Isle of Man* (Douglas, I.o.M., 1869): more background information; and P. Nelson, 'The Coinage of the Isle of Man' (*NC*, 1899).

Minimum price: £800

Douglas

1 IOHN MVRREY 1d 1668 Triskelis
2 (No. 1 with subsequent engraving on *rev.*)

UNCERTAIN TOKENS

New tokens recorded from J. H. Burn, *A Descriptive Catalogue* . . . (see under London); *SNC*, Feb. 1899, Dec. 1908; the Macfadyen collection (sold at Sotheby's, 15 July 1907); J. B. Caldecott and G. C. Yates, 'Leaden Tokens' (*BNJ*, 1907); N. Heywood, 'Further Notes . . .' (see under Cheshire); W. Gilbert, 'Unpublished . . .' (see under Cambridgeshire); H. A. Seaby and P. J. Seaby, *A Catalogue* . . . (see under Dorset); and Michael Mitchiner and Anne Skinner, 'English Tokens, c. 1425 to 1672' (*BNJ*, 1984). See also F. P. Weber, ' "Perkins School-Tokens" of the Seventeenth Century' (*NC*, 1896).

Believed entirely unpublished: 62B, 89A, 89H. Tokens in lead or pewter bearing initials and/or simple devices only – some of which are of as late a period as this – have not been included in this work.

Minimum price for described unvalued tokens: £35

Uncertain Localities

1 (See *Hants.* 172A)
2 (Probably *Yorks.* 250B)
3, 4 (See *Salop* 15A, 15B)
5 (Possibly *London* 969A)
6 (See *Glos.* 152)
7 (See *Lancs.* 114B)
8 (Possibly *Cornwall* 3B)
9 (Possibly *London* 1043, or same issuer)
10 . . . HARTLEY (½?) '70 IN YALLOP. *Octagonal*
11 (Probably *Middx.* 166)
12 THOMAS BVTLER ¼ 1659 P(E *or* O)STE HOVS, clasped book
13 (Same issuer as 88)
14 (See *Oxon.* 1)
15 (See *Som.* 79)
16 (See *Staffs.* 19)
17 (See *Ireland* 695A)
18 (A *duit* of Kampen, Netherlands)
19 (See *Oxon.* 86A)
20 (See *Som.* 183A)
21 (See *Kent* 85)
22 (See *Berks.* 103)
23 (See *Lancs.* 35)
23A IOHN DAVENPORT (R) ½ 1669 IN NELLSVN MERCER
23B MORROW DOBBS ¼ 1660 IN SVCHE, goat's head

Without Names of Localities

24 (A colliery ticket)
25 (Probably same as 26)
26 (See *Som.* 104)
27 IOHN BARHAM ¼ 1666 7 stars
28 (Probably *Yorks.* 103B)
29 (See *Oxon.* 84)
30 *Thomas Bryan* ½ 1667 *Linnen draper*

31 THOMAS BRIAN (H) ¼ 1658 LININ DRAPER
32/3 (See *Som.* 13, 14)
34 W. CLOVGH ½ 1667 Building, walled enclosure in front £20
35 (Probably *London* 2605A)
36 WILLIAM HALL ¼ Orb surmounted by cross; blackamoor's head, PAINES BRINGS GAINES
37 — — ¼ Orb within ornamental double border; 3 crowns, 3 fleurs-de-lis in circle round star
38 — — ¼ Orb; man's head wearing hat
38A — — ¼ — Full-faced crowned bust
39 (See *Bucks.* 34A)
40 STEBVN HEATH ¼ 1666 Dove and olive branch; stars
41 (See *Berks.* 170A)
42 IOHN FEATHERSTON ¼ 1668 AT THE RED, unicorn, INN, 3 plumes of ostrich feathers
43 IAMES HVLLENE ½ 1668 Grocers' Arms
44 (See *Scotland* 1A)
45 (See *Glos.* 179A)
46 *Thomas Hedge* 1d 3 birds
47 RALPH KELLETT (M) ½ 1668 Fruiterers' Arms
48 (Probably misreading of 49)
49 PHINEAS LAMBE, THOMAS HARDWICK ½ 1666 Lamb*
50 (Probably *London* 2522A)
51 CHARLES SCORY ½ 3 tobacco-pipes; name in monogram, TOBACONIST £25
52 (See *Lincs.* 233A)
53 (See *Wales* 92)
54 (Possibly *Suffolk* 197A)
55 ANDREW TVCKER (½?) 1669 Griffin. *Diamond-shape*†
56 (Probably worn or mis-struck example of *Yorks.* 421)
57 (Brockage of unknown token)
58 WILLIAM ADDISON ¼ 1659 THIS PAY**
59 (See *Staffs.* 93A)
60 THOMAS CARTER (F) ¼ 1658
61 (See *Som.* 87)
62 RICHARD CLEMENT ¼ 1663 Man making candles, TALLOW CHANDLER
62A WILLIAM BLACKWELL (R) ¼ AT THE HALF WAY HOVS
62B IOHN BVRNS (?) ¼ Cow. In *pb*††
62C RALPH CORLE (E) ¼ 1650 Unicorn, rose; floral spray In. *pb*§
62D CRISTOPHER FLOWER ¼ Fleur-de-lis; (?Bricklayers) arms. In *pb*
62E FRAN GOWDAMIN ¼ Leopard's head facing. In *pb*‡
62F IOHN HALL (A) ¼ 1656 Bear. In *pb*
62G SAMVEL HALL (E) ¼ KINGS HEAD TAVERNE, bust of Jas. I

* Perhaps of Yorkshire
** Possibly Irish
† A specimen of this token was once found at Hoxton

62H DAVID IAMESON (K) ¼ Chequers. In *pb*
62J A. HAVD MORGAN ¼ HIND In *pb*§
62K MATTHEW NAW ½ AT THE WINDE MILNE HOVSE, horseshoe
62L CHRISTOPHER WARD (F) ¼ AT THE, windmill. In *pb*§

Tokens having only the Initials of Issuers

63 W.B., R.M. (½?) Large I; Salters' Arms, Brewers' Arms
64 W.B., R.M. (½) Large II; — —
65 D.C. ¼ 1664 Bust of Chas. II, TOVCH NOT MINE ANOYNTED; Ironmongers' Arms, FEARE GOD HONOR THE KING
66 P.C. ¼ 4 stars; church, 6 stars around. (St Paul's Church (?)) £22
67 T.F. ¼ Foster family Arms (cf. *Som.* 173) £28
68 T.F. ¼ —. *Square*
69 R.S.G. (½) 1671 Brewers' Arms
70 I.S.L. 1d Wreath; coil of rope, FOR NECESSARY CHAINGE
71 B.A.S. (½?) 1664 Arms of See of London, mitre above
72 I.A.S. ¼ 1659 Woman standing††
73 W.S., I.N. ¼ 1660 Bare-headed bust of Chas. II, TOVCH NOT MINE ANO(I *or* Y)NTED; bible, FEARE GOD HONOR THE KING‡ £30
74 W.M.S. ¼ 1664 — — ; — —
75 I.W., T.B. ¼ 1664 — — ; — — £35
76/7 (Probably private pattern farthings.)
78 S.A., G.C. ¼? 4 large, 5 small roses; 6 large, 4 small roses
79 (See *Worcs.* 44)
80 (½?) 1672 DNE DIE VERBVM; double triangle, letters in angles I A Y I I E
81 (Probably *Ireland* 594A)
82–5 (See *Ireland* 779B *et seq.*)
86 W.E.F. ¼? Lion rampant on shield
87 (See *Worcs.* 45)
88 G.E.H. ¼? Bull's face, (V *or* W)AX CHANDLER IN S.(*or* I.) M.C.L.A.T.C.H.
89 T.T. ¼? Rose, MR H. 9 SEPTEMBER 1670; chequers, NE DECEMBER 25 1670
89A I.C. (M) ¼ THREE STEPS. In *pb*§
89B T.C. ¼ Initials in monogram; heart filling field
89C C.G. (A) ¼ 1651 Dog, IVGGLER. In *pb*§
89D C.H. ½? Merchant's mark between trefoils; shield of arms. *Octagonal* (irregular)
89E W.I. ¼? Cross on shield; boar walking left
89F T.M. (I) ¼ THE OLD ROSE. In *pb*§
89G I.P. (B) ¼ 1659 Anchor
89H R.P. (A) ¼ THE HAND IN HAND. In *pb*§
89J E.S. ¼ Cross botonnée

†† Probably London origin
‡ Probably London (See *London* 745); possibly 74 and 75 also
§ Found by the river Thames in London, so probably originates from here

Tokens without Names of Localities, Issuers, or Initials

90 ¼ Rose crowned between C.R., PRAY FOR THE KING; LORD GIVE THY BLESSING

91 ¼ Arms of Staple-Merchants, THE ARMES OF THE STAPLE; fleece, A STAPLE FARTHING £18

92 ¼ Arms of Staple-Merchants, THE FARTHING OF A MERCHANT; fleece, OF THE STAPLE OF ENGLAND £12

93 ¼ — —; ship —

94 ¼ 1649 Mercers' Arms, THE GROCERS ARMES; 3 cloves, THE MERCES ARMES

95 ¼ Open cross bars, WITH A CROS BARR; *rev.* as *obv.**

* One found at Kingsway, London, so possibly from Holborn Bars or Temple Bar

96 ¼ 1663 Cross potent b.s.

97 (A communion token)

98/9 (Probably counters or jettons)

100/1 (Probably school reward tokens; see *Numismatic Chronicle*, 1896)

102 (Religious jetton)

103 (Gambling token)

104/5 (Probably Scottish colliery checks)

106 (See 100)

107 (As 104/5)

108 (Brockage of unidentified token)

109–14 (See 100)

115 (Probably a counter or jetton)

116 1d Coffee-pot, cups, A COFFEE PENEY FOR; stove, NESESARY CHANGE

Appendices

1. The orders of Charles II concerning tokens

(A) *'By the King. A Proclamation for making currant His Majestie's Farthings and Half-pence of Copper, and forbidding all others to be used.*

'CHARLES R.

'Whereas of late years several Persons and Corporations, upon pretence that there wanted small moneys to be currant in low and ordinary payments amongst the poorer sort, have presumed to cause certain pieces of Brass, Copper, and other Base Metals to be stamped with their private stamps; and then imposed those pieces upon our poor subjects for Pence, Halfpence, or Farthings, as the makers thereof were pleased to call them, whereby our subjects have been greatly defrauded, and our Royal authority and the laws of our kingdom violated: And whereas We, for the prevention of the like abuses for the time to come, did not only direct a severe prosecution of the offenders, but did likewise command the officers of our Mint to cause many thousands of pounds of good sterling silver to be coined into single pence and twopences, that so there might be good money currant among the poorest of our subjects, and fitted for their smaller traffic and commerce; hoping by one or both these means, to have totally suppressed the unlawful practices of these offenders; since which time we have found by experience, that the mischief hath still encreased, partly by having our small silver money bought in and hoarded up, so that there might be a scarcity thereof in common payments: but chiefly for the vast gain and profit which these stampers make to themselves, and for which they choose to run any hazards of law, rather than quit the hopes of their private lucre: we therefore taking the premises into our princely consideration, and believing that our subjects would not easily be wrought upon to accept the Farthings and Halfpence of these private stampers, if there were not some kind of necessity for such small coynes to be made for publique use, which cannot well be done in silver, nor safely in any other metall, unless the intrinsick value of the coyne be equal, or near to that value for which it is made currant; have thought fit, by advice of our Privy Council, to cause certain farthings and halfpence of copper to be stamped at our Mint, according to such form and with such impression as we have directed: and we have given special charge to our officers there, that they cause such halfpence and farthings so to be coyned, to contain as much copper in weight, as shall be the true intrinsick value and worth of a halfpenny or farthing respectively, the charges of coyning and uttering being onely deducted. And we do further by this our Royal Proclamation declare, publish, and authorize the said halfpence and farthings of copper so coyned and to be coyned, to be currant money; and that the same, from and after this instant 16th day of August, shall pass and be received in all payments, bargains, and exchanges to be had or made between our subjects, which shall be under the value of sixpence, and not otherwise, nor in any other manner. And if any person or persons, bodies politique or corporate, shall after the first day of September next, presume to make, vend, or utter any pence, halfpence and farthings, or other pieces of brass, copper, or other base metall, other than the halfpence and farthings by this our Royal Proclamation authorized and allowed, or shall offer to counterfeit any of our halfpence or farthings, we shall hold all such offenders utterly inexcusable, and shall cause their contempt of our laws and government to be chastised with exemplary severity.

'Given at our Court of Whitehall, the 16th day of August, in the 24th year of our reign, 1672.

'GOD SAVE THE KING!'

(B) From the *London Gazette*, 23 February 1673/4.

'Whitehall, February 20th [1673/4]. His Majesty having been informed that divers retailers and shopkeepers, in several cities, towns, and corporations of this Kingdom, do continue to utter, in exchanges and payments, pence, half-pence, and farthings of their own making, in contempt of His Majesties proclamation, and contrary to law, to the great injury and abuse of His Majesties good people; it was ordered by His Majesty in council, that the judges should be acquainted therewith, that they might give the same in charge to the grand juries in the several assizes of the respective counties, that all offenders therein may be severely prosecuted, and punished according to their demerits. And for the better and more speedy furnishing of His Majesty's people with copper farthings and half-pence, His Majesty was further pleased to order, that there should be a daily delivery of them, at the Farthing office in Fenchurch street, London, to all such as shall desire the same.'

(C) *'A Proclamation enjoining the prosecution of all such persons as shall make or utter any farthings, half-pence, or pence of brass, or utter base metals with private stamps.*

'CHARLES R.

'Whereas His Majesty, having by his royal proclamation of the 16th of

August [1672], in the twenty-fourth year of his reign, forbidden the use of all private farthings, did cause sufficient quantities of copper farthings and half-pence, of the intrinsic value, to be coined for the general good and convenience of his subjects: nevertheless, His Majesty has been informed that several persons and corporations remote from London have forborne to call in their private farthings, and do still presume to make use of and utter the same; whereby they continue not only to violate the laws of this Kingdom, and defraud His Majesty's good subjects, but hinder the vending of those half-pence and farthings which were provided for necessary exchange, which would have been ere this time dispersed in those parts, if the said abuses of stamping and uttering of private farthings had been duely suppressed: His Majesty, therefore, to the end that all offenders to the premises, who are now left without excuse, may know the danger they daily incur, and desist from any further proceeding in the like kind, hath thought fit by this his royal proclamation to publish and declare his royal will and pleasure to be, that a strict and severe inquiry shall be made, of all persons that shall, after the 2d day of February [1674/5], next ensuing, stamp, vend, utter, or in any way make use of in payment or exchange, any half-pence, farthings, or other pieces of brass, copper, or other base metals whatsoever, other than the half-pence and farthings of His Majesties royal proclamation authorized and allowed; and whosoever shall be found culpable therein shall be severely punished. And for that purpose, His Majesty doth hereby will and command all his judges, justices of assize, justices of the peace, and all other inferior officers and ministers of justice whatsoever, that they take care at their several and respective courts, assizes, quarter-sessions, and other inferior courts, that have or may have cognizance or punishment of the said offences, that after the 2d day of February they cause all such as shall offend in the premises to be proceeded against, and punished as they deserve.
'Given at our court at Whitehall, the 5th day of December [1674], in the twenty-sixth year of our reign.'

2. Description of a coining press for tokens.

(From *Gentleman's Magazine*, Nov. 1757, pp. 498–9, by Samuel Pegge.)

'The enquiry then is, how this affair of coining was managed and conducted by the private tradesman. At the borough of *Chesterfield* in *Derbyshire*, Mr. *Edward Wood*, and afterwards his son *Richard Wood*, who were both of them apothecaries, coin'd money amongst others; and on the death of the late Mr. *Edward Wood*, son of the said *Richard*, the dies and the press were found in the house, from whence we are enabled to comprehend the whole process, which may be presum'd not to have been very intricate. These *Woods* coined only halfpennies, and there were two sets of dies, one for the father's, and the other for the son's money, who I suppose had a sett of dies made for himself on his father's decease. They were apothecaries, as was mentioned above, and the device was accordingly *Apollo Opifer*. These dies I have seen, and by favour of the gentlemen concern'd, to whom I am greatly oblig'd, one set has fallen into my possession. What I mean by a set is an obverse and reverse; these were cut upon two small pieces of steel, which were afterwards welded upon a larger block of iron, of which the size and the form are expressed in the plate. . . . The press consisted of four pieces of good oak, not less than four inches thick, & very strongly dove-tail'd together. In the upper cross piece was fasten'd an iron box with a female screw, thro' which there passed a stout iron screw of an inch or more diameter, to the bottom of which was fixed one of the dies, whilst the other was received into a square hole made in the bottom cross piece, where it lay very steady as in a proper bed. The screw was wrought by hand, in the manner of a capstan, by means of four handles affixed to the top of it, of about 9 inches long each. And thus, after the copper was reduc'd to a proper thickness, shorn to a size, and commodiously rounded, many hundreds of halfpence might be coined, by two persons, in a very short time, by a man we will suppose to ply the screw, and a woman or boy to put on and take off the pieces. And yet, I assure you, sir, these *Chesterfield* halfpennies were extremely well struck. . . .

S.P.'

Bibliography

I cite here works concerned with the entire series, in chronological order. Important references will also be found at the head of each county or section.

SNELLING, THOMAS. *A View of the Copper Coin and Coinage of England.* London, 1766. Includes a section on tokens, the earliest serious study of them, with many fine drawings.

BOYNE, WILLIAM. *Tokens Issued in the Seventeenth Century.* London, 1858. The original standard work, with 42 plates of line-drawings. Although superseded by Williamson's revision, it contains some information not repeated by him, and a very few tokens missed by mistake.

WILLIAMSON, GEORGE C. (Editor). *Trade Tokens Issued in the Seventeenth Century.* London, 1889–91. A renumbered revision of Boyne's work, in two volumes, 250 copies of each printed, with 23 plates of line-drawings and a number of woodcuts. Full descriptions of tokens, with many background notes for some areas contributed by sub-editors. Particularly valuable are the 12 indexes, for Christian names, surnames, trades of issuers, sundry devices, and armorial bearings in the field, among others, and the introduction. The work was reprinted in three volumes by B. A. Seaby Ltd. in 1967.

JEWITT, LLEWELLYNN. The Young Collector series: *English Coins and Tokens.* London, 1890. Has a good section on tokens of the seventeenth century (later series are almost ignored!) with drawings and a descriptive list of the arms of many of the Incorporated Trade (or City Livery) Companies.

GILBERT, WILLIAM. *Unpublished Seventeenth Century Tokens in the Collection of William Gilbert.* Numismatic Chronicle, 1927. 3 plates.

SPINK & SON LTD. *Seventeenth Century Tokens Unpublished by Williamson.* Spink's Numismatic Circular, between April 1947 and November 1949.

These two major lists of additions to Williamson are referred to separately where appropriate under the county or section headings. The Spink lists are unfortunately full of descriptive errors.

WETTON, J. L. *Seventeenth Century Tradesmen's Tokens.* Newcastle-upon-Tyne, 1969. Excellent introduction to the series by a leading authority. 15 plates.

BERRY, GEORGE. *Discovering Trade Tokens.* Tring, 1969. An introductory booklet with a few plates; interesting section on the seventeenth century series, particularly good general background information about issuers and life at the time. Also many articles by him in the magazines *Coins and Medals* and *Coin and Medal News* in the 1970's and 1980's.

BOON, GEORGE C. (Editor). *Welsh Tokens of the Seventeenth Century.* Cardiff, 1973. The introduction to this book covers the background to the whole series very well indeed.

WHITTET, T. D. *A Survey of Apothecaries' Tokens, Including Some Previously Unrecognized Specimens.* Pharmaceutical Journal, various issues from 26 June 1982. A continuing series of articles, which will eventually cover the country, with much painstakingly researched information.

THOMPSON, R. H. *Sylloge of Coins of the British Isles: The Norweb Collection. Tokens of the British Isles, 1575–1750.* London, 1984 and forthcoming. An important survey of the greatest private collection in modern times. Every variety, including some previously unpublished, illustrated. Analysis of the tokens' weights, die-axes, and metals including differentiation between copper and brass. A new classification of the types will help to identify the same device formerly variously described by different authors. Wide-ranging bibliography. Some tokens likely to belong to a location, but not proven so, are very cautiously consigned to an 'Uncertain' section, yet to appear. Part I (Sylloge vol. 31) covers England: Bedfordshire to Devon only.

PECK, C. WILSON. *English Copper, Tin and Bronze Coins in the British Museum, 1558–1958.* Second edition, London, 1964. Although strictly of only limited value for references to tokens, it is invaluable for an understanding of the regal issues directly before and after the period, and for details of the various attempts at official coinage during the 1640's to 1670's.

PLATE 1

21

28

43A

BEDFORDSHIRE

33

49A

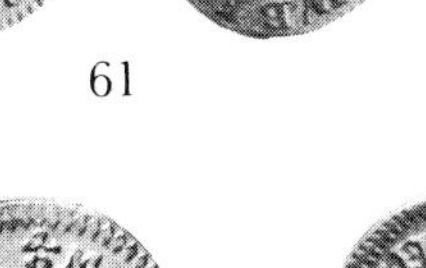

61

86

BERKSHIRE

115

BUCKINGHAMSHIRE

4

51

CHESHIRE

52A

59

CORNWALL

2

CUMBERLAND

4

55

DEVON

32

DORSET

69

209

DORSET

18

DURHAM

351

ESSEX

22A

12

GLOUCESTERSHIRE

PLATE 2

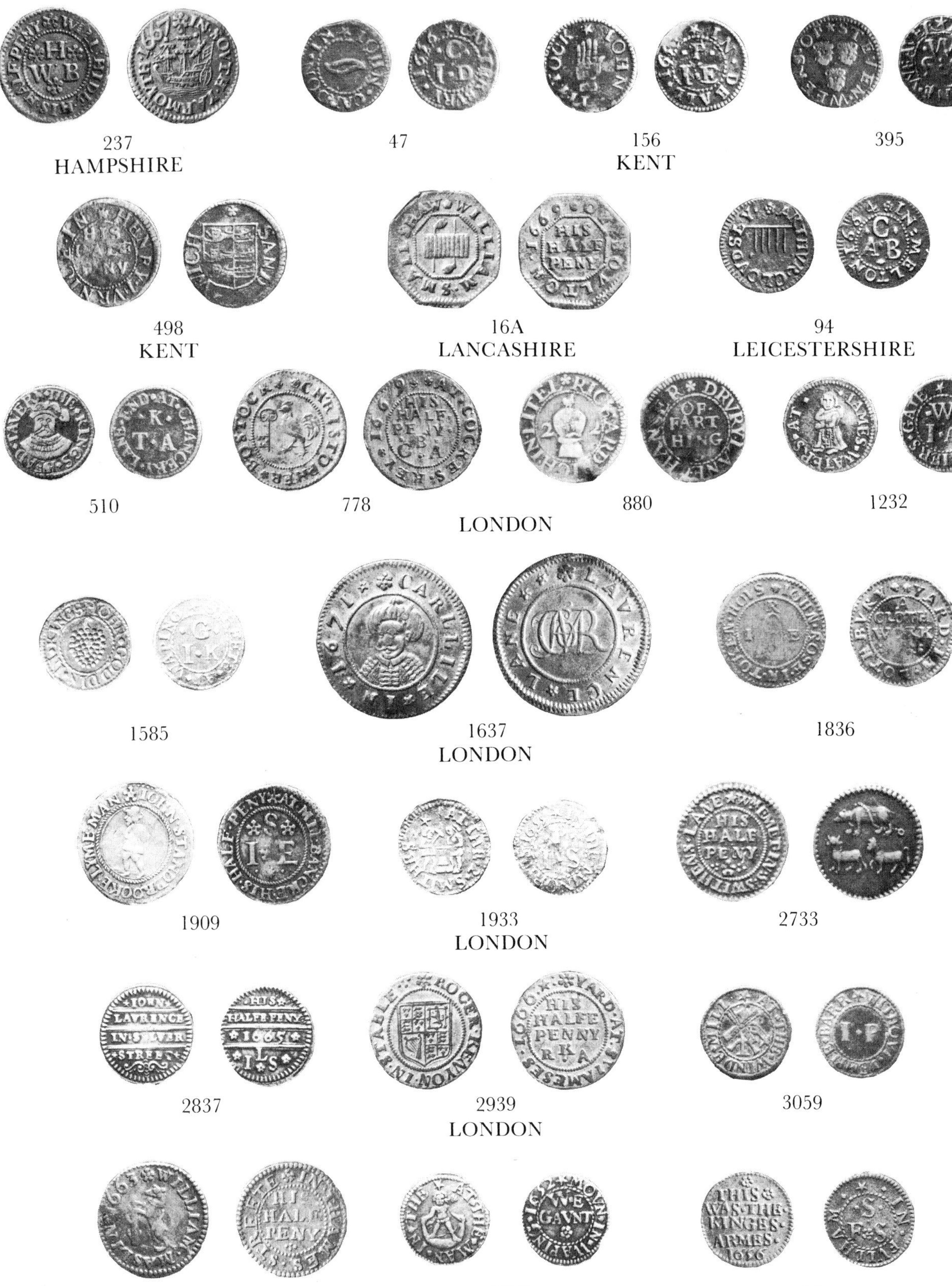

237 HAMPSHIRE · 47 · 156 KENT · 395

498 KENT · 16A LANCASHIRE · 94 LEICESTERSHIRE

510 · 778 · 880 · 1232 LONDON

1585 · 1637 · 1836 LONDON

1909 · 1933 · 2733 LONDON

2837 · 2939 · 3059 LONDON

3109 · 3301 LONDON · 52 MIDDLESEX

PLATE 3

107 137

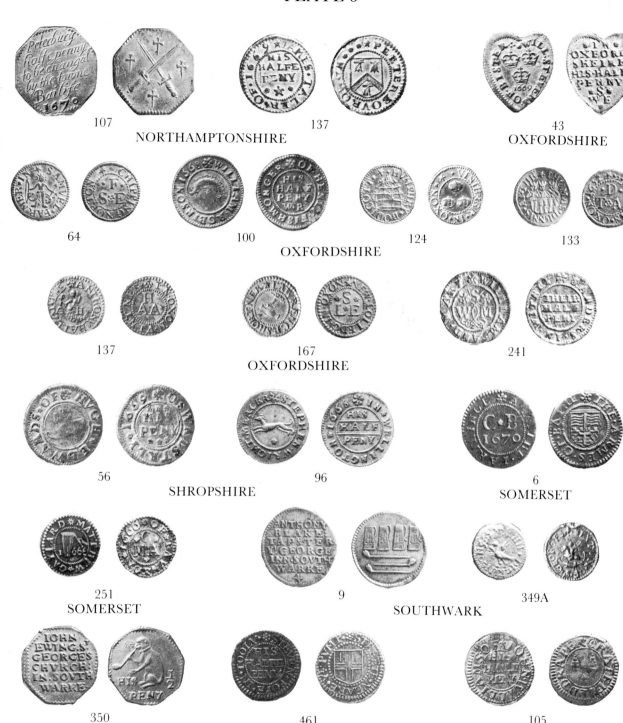

NORTHAMPTONSHIRE

43

OXFORDSHIRE

64 100 124 133

OXFORDSHIRE

137 167 241

OXFORDSHIRE

56 96

SHROPSHIRE

6

SOMERSET

251

SOMERSET

9 349A

SOUTHWARK

350 461

SOUTHWARK

105

SUFFOLK

159 166 188 226

SUFFOLK

PLATE 4

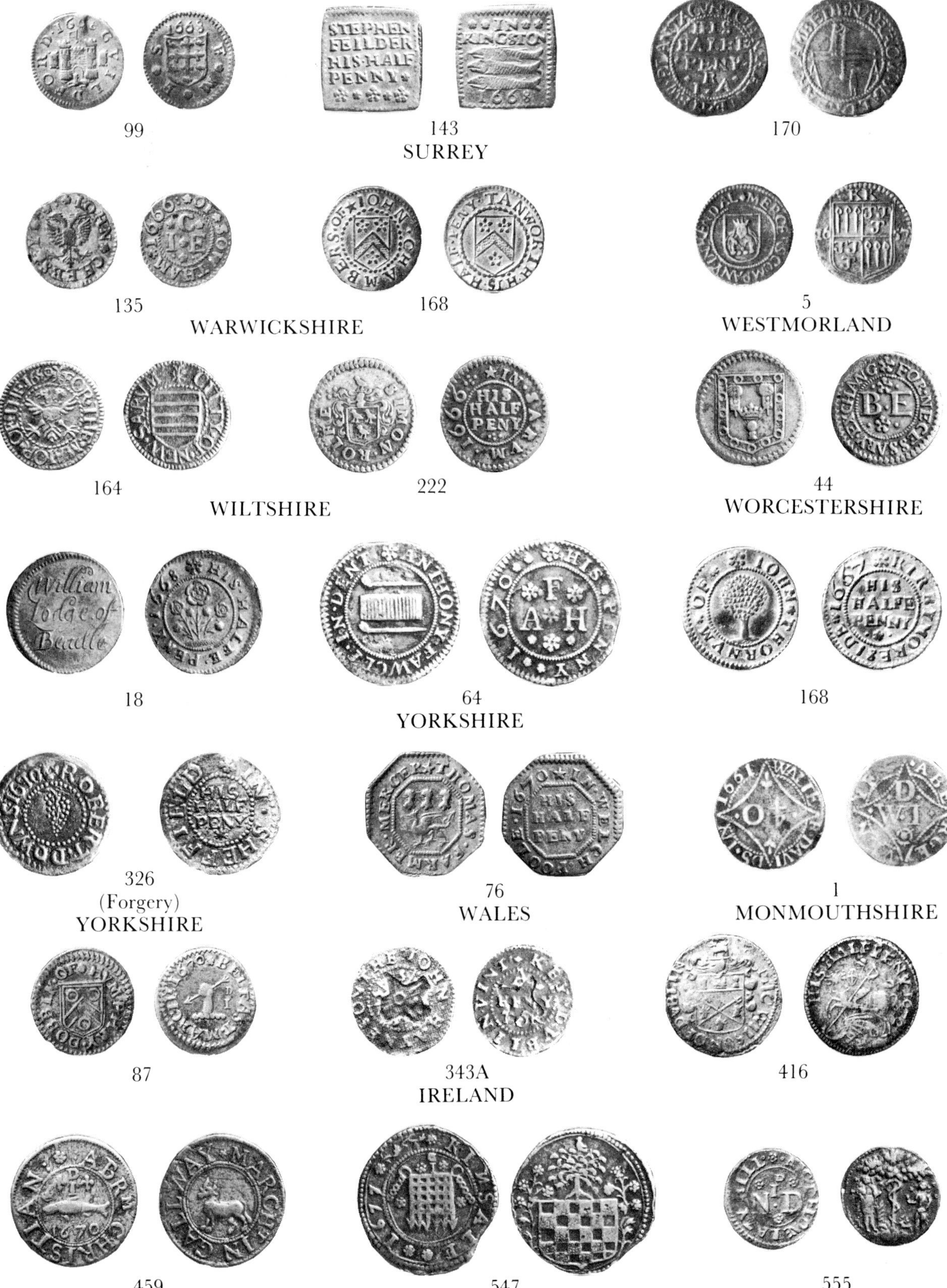

99 — 143 — 170
SURREY

135 — 168
WARWICKSHIRE

5
WESTMORLAND

164 — 222
WILTSHIRE

44
WORCESTERSHIRE

18 — 64 — 168
YORKSHIRE

326
(Forgery)
YORKSHIRE

76
WALES

1
MONMOUTHSHIRE

87 — 343A — 416
IRELAND

459 — 547 — 555
IRELAND

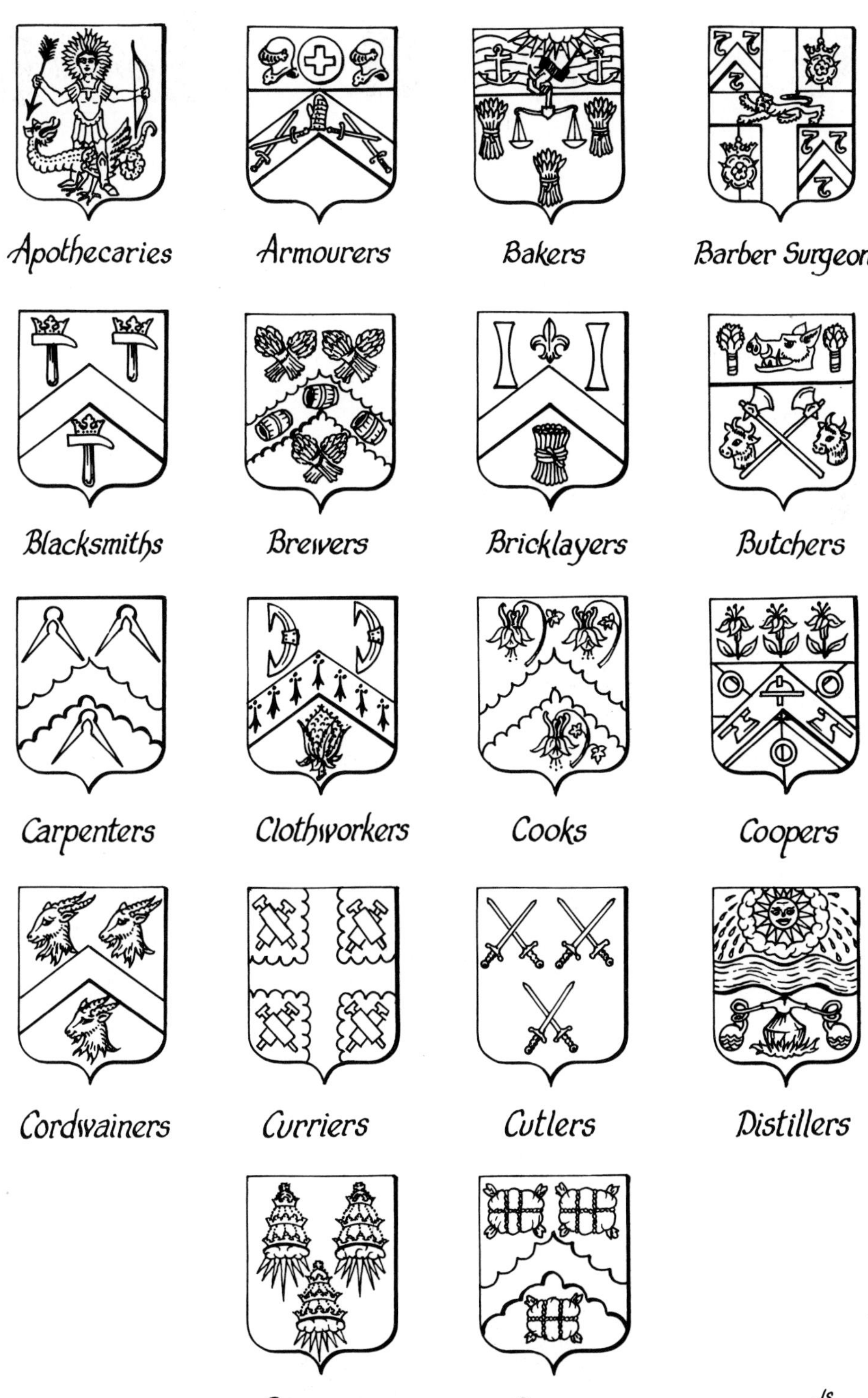
Apothecaries
Armourers
Bakers
Barber Surgeons
Blacksmiths
Brewers
Bricklayers
Butchers
Carpenters
Clothworkers
Cooks
Coopers
Cordwainers
Curriers
Cutlers
Distillers
Drapers
Dyers
JS.

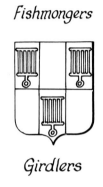

Feltmakers | Fishmongers | Fletchers | Founders

Fruiterers | Girdlers | Glaziers | Glovers

Goldsmiths | Grocers | Haberdashers | Horners

Innholders | Ironmongers | Joiners | Leathersellers

Mercers

Merchant Venturers

JS.

Merchant Taylors

Merchant Staplers

Needlemakers

Pewterers

Pinners

Plasterers

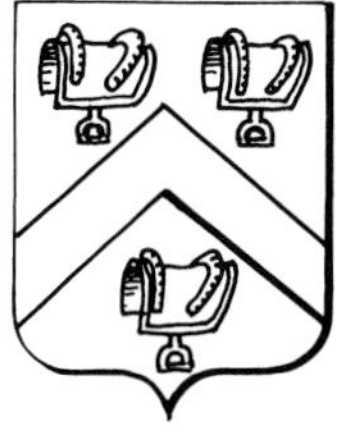
Saddlers

Salters

Shipwrights

Skinners

Soapmakers

Stationers

Tallow Chandlers

Upholders

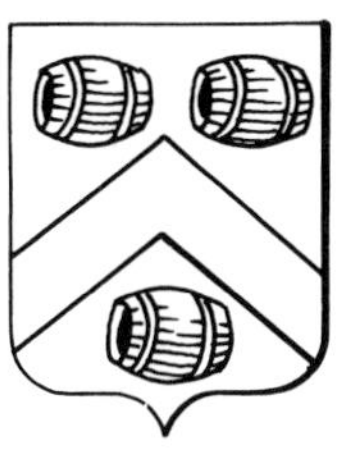
Vintners

Watermen

Weavers

Woodmongers

J.S.

Indexes

1. ALPHABETICAL LIST OF TOKEN-ISSUING LOCALITIES

My aim here has been to include not only the present-day spelling of place-names, but to list as many of the more obscure versions which appear on the tokens themselves as are necessary to enable the user to find the correct location. Many of the seventeenth century spellings listed below are roughly phonetic, but more than a few are quite different and thus very confusing.

The index does not contain by any means all the different spellings and the following must be taken into account:

(1) Similar-sounding vowels are often used, e.g. BERRY for Bury (St Edmunds), WONTAGE for Wantage, PVRTON or PYRTON for Pirton, DARBY for Derby. If two vowels are used together, one should perhaps be dropped to find the correct place, e.g. HOVLBOVRNE is Holborn, AISHTON KEYNES is Ashton Keynes.

(2) Similarly, with consonants, e.g. BAZINGSTOKE for Basingstoke, SKALLDING ALLEY for Scalding Alley.

(3) S on its own is used as well as ST for Saint.

Such minor differences as the above are not usually listed separately.

(4) On all tokens which have legends in capital letters, J is rendered as I, U as V.

Place-names comprising two or more words are usually given here once only, e.g. Sible Hedingham is indexed under H because that is its alphabetical position in its county listing.

2. ALPHABETICAL LIST OF ISSUERS WHOSE TOKENS SHOW NO LOCALITY

This index contains names for whom the place of issue is either known, or supposed; issuers whose location is at present unknown will be found listed in the UNCERTAIN section of the catalogue between nos. 27 and 89.

(A) Full names

(See also note at beginning of this index.)

(B) Initials only